The Measurement and Prediction of
Judgment and Choice

HOLDEN-DAY SERIES IN PSYCHOLOGY
Robert R. Bush, *Editor*

The Measurement and Prediction of Judgment and Choice

R. Darrell Bock
University of Chicago

Lyle V. Jones
University of North Carolina at Chapel Hill

HOLDEN-DAY
San Francisco, Cambridge, London, Amsterdam

In memory of
Louis Leon Thurstone

Preface

This book represents the culmination of more than ten years of research in the area of preference measurement methodology. Work on the project was begun while both authors were at the University of Chicago, and progressed there until 1957 with contract support from the Quartermaster Food and Container Institute for the Armed Forces. Work was continued at the University of North Carolina, supported by annual research contracts awarded from 1957 to 1960 by the Quartermaster General's Office, Environmental Protection Division, in 1961 and 1962 by the U.S. Department of the Army Grant No. DA-QM-19-129-61-62, and from 1964 by PHS Grant M-10006. In addition to support from these sources, we are deeply grateful for the grants awarded to the University of North Carolina by the General Electric Company for research in the area of preference measurement, which also have contributed to this book. A near-final draft was prepared in 1964 and 1965, while Lyle V. Jones was supported by a Special USPH Fellowship grant as a Fellow at the Center for Advanced Study in the Behavioral Sciences.

Our primary aim in this project is to elucidate a class of psychological scaling methods, most of which were suggested, directly or indirectly, by the pioneering work of L. L. Thurstone. In Thurstone's own research, there is little evidence of interest in the statistical bases of the methods which he developed and employed. Typically, his empirical investigations were based upon very large numbers of respondents, and in that context, questions of statistical stability of findings seldom arose. However, in the hands of other workers, in commercial and industrial laboratories as well as in academic settings, Thurstone's methods are often applied to data from only moderate-size samples of judges. Here, the finding of appreciable difference between descriptive statistics does not necessarily imply the validity of inferences which are dependent upon reality of such differences in the population of subjects. In addition, then, to detailed specification of the formal scaling models for the methods of constant stimuli, paired comparisons, rank order, and successive categories, we have attempted to provide corresponding methods for statistical inference.

A serious attempt is made to illustrate all the models presented with detailed examples, typically based upon empirical data. Our aim is not only to illustrate computational steps for each solution, but also to illustrate the essential purposes of the models by way of these examples.

Many colleagues and students, both at the University of Chicago and at the University of North Carolina, have contributed their talents to the project. At Chicago, research assistants participating in the research program included Philip Gradolph, Gerald Gratch, Alan Greenwald, Robert Marston, William Rozeboom, and Karl-Erik Waerneryd. At North Carolina, we are grateful for the active participation of our colleagues Thomas E. Jeffrey and Emir H. Shuford, as well as for the help of research assistants Reid Creech, Edward Johnson, Bishwa Mukherjee, Elizabeth Niehl, Shizuhiko Nishisato, Donald Ross, Douglas Spiegal, and Stephen Zyzanski. Special acknowledgment is due James J. McKeon, whose dissertation " Measurement procedures based on comparative judgment " contributed a number of useful results. The computer programming assistance of Thomas Donnelly at the University of North Carolina is also gratefully acknowledged.

During the fall semester, 1965, this work was used as a text for a course in the Psychometric Laboratory, University of North Carolina. Numerous changes in the exposition were made in response to criticism from students, particularly from Larry Gordon, Jim Kahan, Karen Reinfurt, Nancy Stooksberry, and Edward Youngs, as well as from Dr. John Gilbert, L. L. Thurstone Distinguished Fellow for 1965–1966.

We are grateful to Dr. Joseph Zinnes for his critical reading of the manuscript on behalf of the publisher. His astute comments led to a number of improvements in exposition.

The importance of the talented clerical help we have received could not be underestimated. The task of translating ill-formed " squiggles " into meaningful symbols and preparing the typescript for early drafts of this work was shared by Mrs. Linda Bode and Mr. Samuel Vaughn. The final draft was typed by Mrs. Julie Raventos and Mrs. Jane Patterson. We acknowledge also the skillful editorial assistance of Mrs. Roslyn Foust and Mrs. Katherine Holbrook and the clerical aid of Mrs. Mary Warnock. We express special thanks to Mrs. Patterson for her essential aid in compling the bibliography.

Our greatest debt is to the late Professor L. L. Thurstone, whose research guidance, both by personal contact and through his research papers, served to inspire this project.

R. Darrell Bock

Lyle V. Jones

Chicago and
Chapel Hill
September, 1967

Contents

1 Objectives and Overview

1.1 The Problem of Predicting Choice

Much of human behavior may be viewed as a succession of choices made among more or less well-defined alternatives. The problem we try to solve in this book is how to predict these choices when the alternatives are fixed in advance by the investigator. We use the term *choice behavior* to designate the general domain of our study. Within this domain, we distinguish between two conditions under which choice behavior may be observed. On the one hand, there is the behavior of *given* subjects choosing among fixed alternatives in each of a succession of trials. In this case, our objective is to predict the choices of these same subjects in future trials. On the other hand, we have the behavior of subjects who have been *sampled* from a specified population, each choosing among the alternatives in one or more trials. In this case, our objective is to predict the choice behavior of the subject population.

In either case our objective is limited to statistical prediction; we do not attempt to predict deterministically particular choices of particular subjects. Our goal is merely to state the probability that a specified subject will choose a given alternative on a randomly selected occasion, or that a randomly selected subject from the specified population will choose a given alternative. Thus, we predict a distribution of choices over alternatives, and not the individual choices.

There are many situations in which statistical prediction of choice is of practical importance. As many of the examples in the text will testify, we have been especially concerned with applications in the food processing industry. Observations of choice behavior in both the first and second cases are involved in these applications. An example in the first case is the sensory test performed by an expert judge in order to maintain uniform quality in a processed food or

1

beverage. The judge is qualified for this work by his ability to detect small differences in the concentration of constituents of the food or beverage. Since the judge's sensitivity may be expressed in terms of the probability that he will detect a difference of given magnitude, the selection of judges involves prediction of choice under the first condition.

Examples of the second case appear in studies of consumer preference which are conducted for purposes of developing and improving food products. Such research is carried out by asking subjects in a consumer panel or survey sample to express preferences for alternative products. From these data a prediction is made of the proportion of consumers in the population who will prefer each alternative to all others.

All the examples we present in this book are based on data of this second type. No suitable data representative of the first case could be found in either the literature or other sources available to us. Fortunately, in applications where the first type of data might be encountered (Chapters 2, 3, 4, and 5), the same methods of data analysis apply in both cases and are well enough illustrated by data representative of the second case.

Areas of application other than the food industry are also represented in the examples in the text. These include studies of preference for a variety of consumer products (Examples 7.1.1, 7.1.3, 9.2.1, and 9.2.2), a study of the effects of prices of products upon their purchase (Example 9.1b), and applications in personnel psychology (Examples 7.1.2, 7.3.2, and 7.3.3). All these examples involve the second case of prediction of choice.

In our attempt to solve the problems of predicting choice in these diverse situations, we draw on concepts and methods from the fields of psychology and statistics. In the remainder of this chapter, we discuss the sources of the ideas taken from these two fields and give an overview of their application.

1.2   The Psychological Background

The psychological content of the present work is drawn from the fields of psychophysics and psychological scaling, especially from the work of L. L. Thurstone. Thurstone's contributions to these fields appeared in various psychological journals between 1927 and 1957. These papers are now available in a reprinted collection (Thurstone, 1959, Part II). In them may be found the original formulations of the mathematical models for comparative and categorical judgment which are the main theme of the present work. Thurstone developed these models in order to place the ideas of traditional psychophysics on a more rational footing and to make these ideas applicable to the problems of psychological scaling.

When Thurstone first turned his attention to psychophysics, the field was still struggling with the problem put to it in its early years by Fechner (1860). Fechner posed the question: what is the relationship between the intensity of a continuously varying stimulus and the subjective sensation of the stimulus in the consciousness of the subject? He undoubtedly was assuming that the sensation, although unobservable, was also continuous and that the relation could be described by some well-behaved one-to-one function of the stimulus intensity. On the basis of extensive psychophysical experiments (in which he served as his own subject), Fechner came to the conclusion that the sensation was a logarithmic function of the stimulus intensity. The validity of this proposition, which is known as Fechner's law, has been discussed voluminously, most recently by Stevens (1961) and Luce and Galanter (1963). Its truth or falsity is not of interest for our present purposes. What is of interest is the fact that the concept of a sensory continuum remains an essential part of current psychological theory and, in particular, is the central concept of Thurstonian scaling.

Thurstone avoids this terminology (see Section 2.3), but he invokes an unobservable variable of sensation in order to explain the statistical character of the threshold for the detection of stimulus differences. He has to account for the fact that there is no one magnitude of a stimulus difference above which the subject always detects the difference and below which he does not. Empirical studies of discrimination show, rather, that subjects detect a stimulus difference of given magnitude with some constant probability in a series of trials, and that the probability increases as the magnitude of the difference increases. Prior to Thurstone these findings were explained by the supposition that the detection threshold for a subject varies from one time to another and is distributed normally (the phi-gamma hypothesis). As discussed in the next chapter, Thurstone made this idea precise by assuming that each stimulus gives rise to a momentary subjective value which can be described by a real-valued random variable normally distributed on the sensory continuum. When two stimuli are compared by the subject, the stimulus whose momentary value is greater is the one which seems larger to the subject. The more the two distributions are separated on the continuum (i.e., the less they overlap), the more frequently will the subject correctly identify the larger stimulus.

All the Thurstonian models used in the text assume this unidimensional continuum and have been called "linear" models for that reason (David, 1963, p. 14). In many of the applications to be presented, the model is further simplified by assuming that the distributions of the random variables corresponding to different stimuli have constant variance and differ only in location. When this simplified model is tenable, the problem of predicting the subject's response becomes a matter of determining the means of these distributions. Empirically, the relationships between the means and physical characteristics of the stimuli, such as stimulus intensity, are often found to be expressible in polynomials of low degree. The task of fitting models for predicting judgment and choice on the basis of stimulus characteristics is then considerably simplified.

Traditionally, the concept of a sensory continuum applies to the subject's experience of a continuously variable physical event which is called the *stimulus*. The subject's response in comparing two such stimuli is usually called a *judgment* rather than a *choice*. This implies that the subject has no personal preference towards the outcome of the trial, but is merely an objective observer. This terminology carries into applied work when, for example, we call the expert sensory tester a "judge."

When the subject is required to choose among alternatives on the basis of personal preference, his response is ordinarily called a *choice*. We follow this usage in the text. Because the alternatives of such choices are usually discrete entities rather than continuously variable stimuli, we call the stimuli *stimulus objects*, or *psychological objects*, or often just *objects*.

The distinction between continuous stimuli and discrete objects, and the corresponding distinction between objective judgment and preferential choice, can be relevant in the design of psychological experiments. For statistical reasons, it is important that the responses in an experiment be statistically independent. To assume that the same subject can make repeated independent objective judgments of unidentified and qualitatively similar stimuli may be quite reasonable, but to assume that he can make independent personal choices of well-identified qualitatively distinct objects is not reasonable. Thus, experiments involving choice in this sense cannot ordinarily make use of repeated response of the same subjects to the same objects. Such experiments are limited to the Case 2 condition of choice behavior, with each subject providing a choice on only a single trial.

We should note also that the psychological objects need not be represented by values on any physical continuum. They may not even be material objects, but may be such things as musical selections, political platforms, or life goals. For such objects the concept of *sensory* continuum is hardly appropriate. Although a formally identical concept is employed in the models which predict choice for these objects, there does not seem to be any standard terminology for it. In the food research literature, the term " hedonic " continuum is sometimes used in this connection (Jones, Peryam, and Thurstone, 1955). In classical economics, the term " utility " has the same import (see Thurstone, 1931b). Thurstone uses the term " affective value " to describe the location of objects on this continuum, and we continue this practice in the present work.

The psychological background identifies the work reported in this book most closely with the tradition of psychophysical studies going back more than one hundred years. (See Boring, 1950, pp. 275ff., for some of the history of this field.) The present work differs from that preceding it, however, because it focuses on prediction of judgment and choice as the central problem of the field, because it is more concerned with practical applications, and because it attempts to deal with the statistical problems which are encountered in these applications.

The history of the statistical part of this work is not as lengthy as that of the psychological part. It goes back primarily to work of Fisher and of Neyman in the 1920s and 1930s. The approach to statistical problems as described in the following section is based largely on their work.

1.3 The Statistical Background

Statistical problems arise when we attempt to apply the models for judgment and choice to actual data. The sampling of subjects, or the sampling of responses within given subjects, introduces variability in the data which the choice model does not account for. To describe the data adequately, we must therefore combine the choice model with a suitable statistical model of the sampling variation. This is a straightforward procedure if the sampling aspect of the choice experiment conforms to the assumptions of a standard statistical model. In the present applications, we specify designs for the choice experiments which permit us to assume binomial or multinomial sampling models. Then we can combine the choice model with the sampling model by expressing the parameters of the latter in terms of those of the former. This makes available a number of standard statistical procedures for testing the goodness of fit of the choice model, for estimating any parameters of the models which are to be determined from the data, and for expressing the precision of these estimates.

In outline, these procedures involve the following steps: (1) A model is hypothesized and its undetermined parameters are estimated from data; (2) the estimates are substituted in the model and discrepancies between the data and values predicted by the model (i.e. the residuals) are examined relative to a statistical criterion of goodness of fit; (3) if the residuals appear to be random according to this criterion, we may conclude that the model cannot be further improved on the basis of the data at hand; (4) if so, we proceed with the application of the model and, in most cases, report the estimates of the parameters and the precision of these estimates.

In careful work, we find it a good policy to plot the residuals and examine them visually. Sometimes the residuals will display systematic trends which the statistical criterion fails to detect as nonrandom. Conversely, when the criterion indicates nonrandomness, an examination of the residuals may suggest how the model should be modified to improve fit. (See Anscombe and Tukey, 1963, for a discussion of the analysis of residuals.)

We must also add the qualification that, even when the criterion indicates significant lack of fit, the model may still predict reasonably well in the sense that the residuals are small in magnitude relative to the range of values predicted. Whether to carry on with the model as it stands or to try to improve upon it is then a practical rather than a statistical question. The answer will depend upon the accuracy required in particular applications and on the availability of alternative models.

It is an unfortunate fact that there do not exist at present any completely general statistical methods for comparing the goodness of fit of one model with that of another. If one of the models *contains* the other, i.e. a more complex model is constructed by adding parameters to a simpler model, then the improvement in prediction afforded by the additional parameters can be tested for statistical significance. Or if two models have the same number of parameters and these parameters can be estimated by the same method, then the distributions of residuals from the two models may be compared to determine which models show the better fit. But if the models have different numbers of parameters and one model is not an elaboration of another, there is little statistical basis for their comparison. When the model with fewer parameters shows the better fit, then it is clearly the better model. When the model with the greater number of parameters shows the better fit, however, its superiority may be due to the fitting of additional parameters, and the improvement of fit cannot be tested for statistical significance unless one model is nested in the other. The best we can do, in the case of linear estimation, is to compare unbiased estimates of multiple correlation coefficients and favor the model with the larger coefficient.[1] Or, perhaps preferably, we may compare the goodness of fit of the models when parameter estimates from a previous sample are used to predict the observations in new data.

As a method of statistical estimation, we have relied in this work primarily upon a modified form of least squares estimation called "minimum transform chi-square" by Berkson (1956), but sometimes referred to also as the Neyman linearization technique (Reiersøl, 1961). In some applications, however, we make use of the method of maximum likelihood to obtain estimators. Neither method yields unbiased estimates in this context, but both are consistent and may be justified by their large-sample efficiency. Both are Neyman Best Asymptotic Normal (BAN) estimators. In many cases the minimum transform chi-square method is much simpler computationally and is preferred for that reason. (Compare, for example, the computational procedures for maximum likelihood estimation described in Bock, 1968.)

In addition to model testing, the statistical procedures of the text provide measures of the precision of estimation. To express precision, we use Neyman-

---

[1] A method for calculating the unbiased estimate of a multiple correlation has been provided by Olkin and Pratt (1958).

Pearson confidence bounds obtained by inverting critical ratio tests. According to his theoretical persuasions, an investigator may regard a bound with, say, a .95 confidence coefficient as the sample mean plus or minus two standard errors, as an interval which includes the population parameter with probability of at least .95, or roughly as the .025 and .975 points of the a posteriori distribution of the unknown parameter. In most cases of practical interest, the Neyman-Pearson bounds admit of any of these interpretations (see Schlaifer, 1959, p. 667).

1.4 Parameter Estimation as Measurement

In the psychological literature, the experimental and analytical procedures presented in this work are commonly referred to as "measurement." This usage implies a broad definition of the term, such as that proposed by Stevens (1951): "Measurement is the assignment of numerals to objects or events according to rules." By this definition, all the procedures presented here can be classed as measurement. Applied to the choice behavior of a given subject, they involve the estimation of parameters which characterize, or measure, the subject with respect to particular stimuli. Applied to a sample of subjects, they estimate parameters which characterize a specified population and given stimuli. (In most of the examples in the text, only one population of subjects is involved and the estimates are discussed only in terms of the stimuli they characterize.)

An inclusive definition of measurement such as the above is not very useful, however, unless it is accompanied by a classification of the procedures which qualify as measurement. Since the methods of the present text may be viewed as procedures for parameter estimation as well as measurement, it is possible to base their classification on the major components of the process of parameter estimation. These components are (1) the experimental procedure which produces the data, (2) the model which relates the data to the parameters to be estimated, and (3) the mathematical or statistical procedure which determines values of the parameters from the data. The traditional descriptions of psychophysical methods (as represented, for example, in the texts of Guilford, 1954, and Woodworth, 1938) take the experimental procedures as the major level of classification. Within each procedure, they discuss alternative models for the data and, for each model, alternative solutions of the estimation problem.

With the exception of Chapter 9, which is devoted to applications of a variety of methods, we use the same approach in this text. The major divisions of our discussion correspond to the four experimental procedures which we consider most important in the studies of judgment and choice, namely, the *constant method*, the *method of paired comparisons*, the *ranking method*, and the *method of successive categories* (the *rating-scale method*). For each of these procedures we propose several models and their statistical solutions, generally proceeding from simple to more complex cases.

Other points of view on the classification of measurement procedures may be found in the psychological literature. Coombs (1964), for example, presents a classification based on certain abstract characteristics of data which he identifies. Stevens (1951), on the other hand, classifies the methods according to the "strength of scale" of the resulting measurement: If the value obtained is unique except for an arbitrary unit of scale, the measurement is said to be on a *ratio* scale; if the value is unique except for an arbitrary origin and unit of scale, the measurement is said to be on an *interval* scale; if the values merely order the objects, the measurement is said to be on an *ordinal* scale; finally, if the values specify only the class affiliation of the objects, the measurement is said to be on a *nominal* scale.

Beginning students of the subject of scaling sometimes get the impression that strength of scale is determined by the experimental procedure used in the measurement. Actually, this is not the case. Strength of scale is determined by the model for parameter estimation which is applied to the data from the experiment. This fact has been pointed out by Suppes and Zinnes (1963, Section 5) and is illustrated by examples in this text. Data obtained by the method of paired comparisons when analyzed by the conventional model for comparative judgment give estimates on an interval scale (see Chapter 5). But the same method when applied to experiments that can be analyzed in terms of models for compound or contingent judgment provides estimates on a ratio scale (see Section 9.2).

1.5   The Thurstonian System of Measurement

The brief definition quoted above cannot, of course, comprehend all aspects of measurement which are apparent in scientific applications. It refers only to the operational part of the process and would qualify as measurement any data reduction for an isolated experiment. But measurement as it is ordinarily understood assigns to objects and events numerals which have significance beyond the particular experiment by which they were obtained. If we are concerned with measuring some quantity, it is because that quantity appears as a parameter in models other than the one which provided the measurement. Usually, these other models have predictive value. Thus, for example, we measure the dimensions of a container because we have a formula (model), containing the dimensions as parameters, which enables us to compute (predict) the volume of the container. Or, less directly, we may measure the refractive index of an organic liquid in order to identity it and thus predict other of its properties. In this case the published tables of refractive indices of known compounds play the role of model and the argument of the table is the parameter.

It is a mark of the maturity of a science that the number of parameters with which it deals is small and the number of models large. In such a science, measurement can reach a high level of perfection because, first, there is generally more than one distinct model which can be used to estimate a given parametric value. This provides the possibility for independent measurement by different methods, which serves to confirm the validity of each. Second, the science may include models which make it possible to predict the effect of altered experimental conditions on the measurement procedure. This allows the investigator to correct the measurement to standard conditions. In other words, in a well-developed science, measurement can be made to yield invariant results both over a variety of measurement methods and over a range of experimental conditions for any one method.

It is unfortunate, but nevertheless true, that psychological measurement does not universally enjoy these sources of support from the science of psychology. The literature of the field contains numerous examples of studies which cannot be replicated when the behavior in question is measured by different methods or under slightly different conditions. (For a recent discussion of this problem in the area of personality measurement, see Fiske, 1966.) The only part of psychology that is to some degree an exception in this respect is the area that provides the background of the present work, namely, psychophysics and psychological scaling. Especially in the system of psychological measurement based on the Thurstonian models, we achieve some of the invariance in measurement which is characteristic of other of the sciences.

With respect to invariance over alternative methods, the four experimental procedures which we discuss do, in fact, provide independent methods of measuring the same quantities. This is true because Thurstonian models containing a common set of parameters can be formulated for each. There are examples in the text (Chapter 6) which demonstrate the agreement of estimates obtained by more than one of these methods, and other examples may be found in the literature (Saffir, 1937; Bishop, 1940). Furthermore, in Chapter 9 a number of examples are presented in which estimates obtained by one of the four basic methods are used to predict choice in more complex experiments. Ordinarily, we would think of the examples as demonstrating the larger significance of the measurements made with the basic methods. In most cases, however, the process can be reversed and the results of the more complex experiment used, if need be, to estimate the parameters. Thus these examples also show the invariance with respect to methods of measurement which is provided by the Thurstonian models.

There is evidence also that the methods of the text provide invariant parameter estimates over a considerable range of experimental context. When a choice experiment is repeated there are two ways in which this context may vary. The subjects may, and usually will, be different, and the stimuli may be different. We control the variation from individual differences among subjects merely by insisting that the subjects be sampled randomly from a specified population. We can then calculate from standard statistical results the variance of the estimates which the sampling of subjects can be expected to produce. If the observed variation of the estimates does not significantly exceed this figure, we do not consider it to constitute a failure of invariance. A still stronger invariance with respect to different subjects has been shown empirically for the method of successive categories. Jones (1959c) reports results from large-scale food preference surveys made over a period of years, which demonstrate remarkable stability of parameter estimates associated with a standard form for rating preference (the hedonic scale).

With regard to invariance of findings for different stimuli, the constant method is specifically designed so that the parameter estimates do not depend upon the intensities of the test stimuli, which are arbitrarily chosen. To the extent that the measurement model fits, this sort of invariance is assured. How the estimates depend upon the intensity of the standard stimulus is a question of psychological fact, and it has been intensely studied. For many stimuli the relationship is given by Weber's law, or modifications thereof (see Luce and Galanter, 1963). The present text gives a statistical test of Weber's law and presents data from an experiment in which the law was found to hold (Chapter 5).

The model for the method of paired comparisons also implies that the parameters for given objects are independent of other objects in the experiment. It is a simple linear model of parameters associated with the separate objects and does not assume effects which might be associated with interactions of objects. Thus, the addition of new objects to the set does not alter the values of the parameters for objects already in the set. To the extent that the model holds—and in many applications it does hold—the expected values of the parameter estimates are invariant with respect to the objects in the experiment (Chapters 6, 9).

Much of Chapter 7 is devoted to studies of how the parameters of the model for paired comparisons depend upon characteristics of the objects which are identifiable and possibly physically measurable. When this dependency can be described mathematically and parameters of the relationship estimated, the prediction of choice for objects with different amounts or combinations of these characteristics becomes possible. Generality of the measurement with respect to different stimuli is thus enhanced. Such results are of practical interest, because they make it possible to predict how to modify the objects in order to obtain a desired response from the subjects. This is, of course, the essential problem in the development or improvement of consumer products. In another sense this is also the problem of psychology generally, that of the definition of the stimulus. Stevens (1951) states it thus: "The complete definition of the stimulus to a given response involves the specification of all the transformations of the environment, both internal and external, that leave the response invariant." The models presented in the text, i.e. the Thurstonian models and elaborations thereof, for a certain class of stimuli and responses, provide one possible approach to the solution of this problem.

Indeed, the Thurstonian models are relevant to problems extending well beyond the comparatively narrow field of psychophysics. Formally identical models are employed in psychometrics to represent the relation of a criterion measure to the probability of a favorable or unfavorable response to a psychological test item. This type of response relation is identical with that between the size of a stimulus difference and the probability of correct discrimination in a psychophysical experiment (see Indow et al., 1962). Furthermore, if the item response model is extended to include the relation between a criterion and the responses of a subject to several items jointly, the result is a model formally identical to that for predicting the choice of one object from among several objects, as discussed in Chapter 9. (See Lord, 1952, and Lord and Novick, 1968, for the relevant psychometric theory.) Because the statistical aspects of fitting any of these models is the same in the two areas of application, a basis exists for a unified methodology of psychophysical and psychometric studies of behavior. The student who wishes to master this methodology at one stroke will do well to study the present work in conjunction with the Lord and Novick volume on mental test theory.

1.6 Other Studies of Judgment and Choice

In recent years a number of primarily theoretical studies have appeared on the topics of psychological scaling and choice behavior. Those that have been published in book form are Arrow, 1951; Torgerson, 1958; Luce, 1959; Thurstone, 1959; Gulliksen and Messick, 1960; Restle, 1961; David, 1963; Luce, Bush, and Galanter, 1963; and Coombs, 1964. The reader will find in these texts discussions of many aspects of these topics which are outside the scope of the present work.

2 The Constant Method

2.1 Introduction

The constant method is one of several experimental procedures introduced by nineteenth-century psychologists for determining the "difference limen" and the "point of subjective equality" of stimulus magnitudes. The difference limen, or difference threshold, is the minimum difference in physical magnitude required for a subject to detect that two stimuli are in fact different. The point of subjective equality is that magnitude of some stimulus to which the subject responds as if it were equal to the magnitude of another stimulus, notwithstanding the fact that the physical magnitudes of the two stimuli may differ. For some types of stimuli, such as intensity of light or sound, the experimenter can readily determine these quantities by asking the subject to adjust the magnitude of one stimulus to apparent equality (or inequality) with that of another stimulus. This procedure is called the method of "adjustment" or "reproduction" (see Woodworth, 1938, or Guilford, 1954). With many types of stimuli, however, the experimenter cannot conveniently vary stimulus magnitude during the experiment.

The "constant methods" were developed for psychophysical studies in which the stimulus magnitudes remain at fixed prearranged values during the experiment. The most important of the constant methods was given prominence by Fechner (1860), under the name "method of right and wrong cases." But the psychologist Titchener (1905, p. 275), who was chiefly responsible for introducing Fechner's methods into the United States, attributes the genesis of the method to the physiologist K. Vierordt, and cites a paper of Vierordt's student Hegelmayer (1852) as the first published report of the method. (Hegelmayer studied judges' ability to discriminate length of lines.) Nevertheless, Fechner was the first to elaborate the method theoreti-

12

cally and to utilize it extensively. It is reported that Fechner's empirical work
with this method, applied to lifted weights, during 1855–1859, entailed no less
than 67,072 comparisons!

Fechner's method is now referred to variously as the " method of constant
stimuli," the " classical constant method," or as we prefer, simply the " constant
method." To carry out an experiment by this method, one prepares a set of
stimuli in which the magnitude of the attribute in question proceeds in
regular steps, each step being well below the expected difference threshold.
One then selects a stimulus near the middle of the series to serve as the
"standard" and presents to the subject each other stimulus simultaneously
or successively with the standard. The subject is required to report which
stimulus of the pair has " more of " the specified attribute. Over many repetitions for each pair, a proportion of " right " or " wrong " responses is generated
which constitutes the data produced by the experiment.

In analyzing data of this type, Fechner utilized Gauss's law of error to
determine from the proportions of correct judgments a measure of precision
of discrimination. Somewhat later, Müller (1878) urged the distinction
between the difference limen and the precision of discrimination and suggested modifications of the statistical method to allow estimation of both.
Further modifications have been suggested by Urban (1908), Spearman
(1908), and Woodworth (1938), among others.

Much of the early literature on the constant method is oriented toward
methodological questions of how the method should be carried out and how
the resulting data should be analyzed (see Guilford, 1954). Considerable
controversy was generated over the question of whether or not a " doubtful "
category should be included as a permissible response. Current thinking is
that it should *not* be included, since even when the subject feels he is merely
guessing, his judgments may in fact contain some information about the
stimulus difference (Gridgeman, 1959). Moreover, statistical treatment of
the data is more straightforward when only two alternatives are permitted.
(See, however, the treatment of the three-category response proposed by
Gridgeman, 1959, and by Glenn and David, 1960.)

Controversy over the proper statistical treatment of data obtained by
the constant method has been largely resolved with the recognition that they
can be identified with the so-called " quantal " response data which have been
studied extensively by statisticians (Finney, 1952). Quantal response data
arise when an experiment has two outcomes, the probabilities of which are
determined by a quantitative independent variable. Typical examples of
quantal data are (1) the number of insects in a sample that succumb to a given
dose of insecticide, (2) the number of experimental animals in a sample that
recover from a disease after receiving a given dose of a drug, (3) the number
of children in a sample from a given age group who have acquired certain of

their permanent teeth, (4) the number of children in a sample from a given age group who pass a certain item of an intelligence test, and of course, (5) the number of subjects sampled from a given population who judge one stimulus greater than another when the stimuli differ in intensity by a given magnitude, i.e. data obtained by the constant method. Because of the importance of quantal data in toxicology and pharmacology, considerable effort has been expended to develop efficient and practical methods for their statistical analysis (Finney, 1952; Bliss, 1935; Berkson, 1955; Claringbold, Biggers, and Emmers, 1953). In this chapter and the one following, we discuss the application of some of these methods to the quantal data generated by the constant method.

At the present time, the classical form of the constant method is seen only infrequently in applied studies. Certain variants of the method, however, are widely used, especially in food research and allied fields. Cameron (1947), for example, studied the relative sweetness of sugars and other sweet substances by a ranking variant of the constant method. He determined relative sweetness from the concentrations at which solutions of two different sugars appeared equally sweet to the subjects, i.e. the point of subjective equality. Schutz and Pilgrim (1957), also using a ranking variant of the constant method, studied the differential sensitivity of subjects to various concentrations of substances representative of the " pure " tastes, sweet, sour, salt, and bitter. They used the method to estimate difference limens and the ratio of the difference limen to the concentration of the standard stimulus, the so-called " Weber ratio " (see Chapter 5).

By far the most widely used variant of the constant method is, however, the " triangle " test. In this test, which we describe in more detail in Chapter 4, the subject is presented with three stimuli, of which two are identical standard stimuli, and the third is the test stimulus. The subject is instructed to select the " odd " stimulus. This procedure makes it unnecessary to describe the stimulus attribute to the subject. The method can therefore be used to determine whether given stimuli are detectably different, even when the nature of the difference cannot be specified. For this reason, the triangle test is widely applied in the quality control of products in which taste, odor, texture, etc., all may be important properties. New production lots of a product are tested against previous lots to determine whether any difference in sensory quality is detectable. Other variants of the constant method are also used for this purpose (Peryam, 1958). Triangle tests are also used for determining absolute threshold of a stimulus magnitude (i.e. the least magnitude of a stimulus which is detectable). The difficulties of describing the apparent quality of a stimulus at very small magnitudes are thereby avoided (see Chapter 4).

We give considerable attention to the constant method and allied statistical procedures, because the constant method provides the simplest setting in

which to introduce the Thurstonian judgmental model. Detailed consideration of the method thus serves to lay the groundwork for the more advanced
applications of the Thurstone model to the method of paired comparisons
and the method of successive categories. But this attention also testifies to our
belief that the constant method enjoys several practical advantages. The
judgmental task for the subject is simple to comprehend and perform, and
the appropriate statistical analysis is straightforward. For the class of sensory
problems to which it applies, the constant method continues to have great
practical value.

2.2 The Experimental Procedure

The following formal description of the constant method will serve to
introduce notation which we will use throughout this book.

(a) A set of $n + 1$ stimuli, designated $X_1, X_2, \ldots, X_n$, and X_c, is prepared.
X_c is to serve as the standard stimulus. The stimuli have physical magnitudes
$x_1, x_2, \ldots, x_n$, and x_c on some specified attribute. Common practice is to let
x_c be the centermost magnitude, with the other magnitudes placed in equal
steps above and below x_c. In some cases it is convenient to make these steps
equal with respect to the logarithms of the stimulus magnitudes rather than
the magnitudes themselves (see Chapter 4). Preferably, the greatest and least
magnitudes should not be so extreme as to be correctly identified in all
comparisons with the standard.

(b) With X_c serving as the standard stimulus, a second stimulus, say
X_j, is selected as the "test" stimulus. X_j is paired with X_c and the two stimuli
are presented to the subject simultaneously or successively.

(c) An attribute of the stimuli is described to the subject, and he is
instructed to judge which stimulus of the pair exhibits the greater amount
of that attribute. The judgment of equality is not permitted.

(d) In recording the subject's response, one takes note of the spatial
or temporal order in which the two stimuli were presented. When X_j precedes
X_c (or is "to the left of," or above X_c), the response is scored

$$s_{jci} = 1 \text{ if subject } i \text{ judges } X_j \text{ greater than } X_c,$$
$$s_{jci} = 0 \text{ if subject } i \text{ judges } X_c \text{ greater than } X_j;$$

when X_c precedes X_j

$$s_{cji} = 1 \text{ if subject } i \text{ judges } X_j \text{ greater than } X_c,$$
$$s_{cji} = 0 \text{ if subject } i \text{ judges } X_c \text{ greater than } X_j.$$

The order of presentation should be counterbalanced for each of the n pairs
of stimuli; i.e. each order should be employed an equal number of times.

(e) When planning a constant method experiment, one must distinguish between the following two sampling conditions, the choice of which has implications for the statistical analysis of the data.

    (i) *Single-judgment condition.* Each subject judges only one pair of stimuli. If there are n pairs of stimuli in the experiment and N subjects judge each pair, then nN subjects are required in total. With randomly sampled subjects and no communication between subjects, all judgments are necessarily independent.

    (ii) *Multiple-judgment condition.* Each subject judges all pairs of stimuli in the experiment. If a purpose of the experiment is to investigate the sensory acuity of a particular subject, the subject may also replicate the experiment N times. In other applications, each subject judges all pairs in one replicate only. For N replicates, N subjects are then required. In the multiple-judgment condition, the judgments made by the same subject may or may not be independent. Conditions under which independence might be assumed are discussed in Section 2.7 in connection with the method of paired comparisons. For the multiple-judgment condition not only is order of presentation within pairs of stimuli counterbalanced, but the sequence in which orders appear should be randomized over trials.

Data obtained by the foregoing procedure may be summarized as the number of times X_j is judged greater than X_c in the ordered pair (X_j, X_c). Thus, if N_{jc} subjects make this comparison, this number is

$$r_{jc} = \sum_{i=1}^{N_{jc}} s_{jci}.$$

Assuming these judgments to be random samples from a population of judgments in which the probability is P_{jc} that X_j is judged greater than X_c in the ordered pair (X_j, X_c), we may compute from the binomial probability law the probability that the sum of the response scores takes the value r_{jc}:

$$\text{Prob}(r_{jc}) = \frac{N_{jc}!}{r_{jc}!(N_{jc} - r_{jc})!} P_{jc}^{r_{jc}}(1 - P_{jc})^{(N_{jc} - r_{jc})}. \tag{2.1}$$

These assumptions are undoubtedly justified in the single-judgment case, and may possibly be justified in the multiple-judgment case if the "identity" of the stimuli is withheld from the subject (see Section 6.7). The statistical methods of this and the following three chapters depend upon the assumption of independence but this is relaxed somewhat in the treatment of paired comparisons in Section 6.7.

If the spatial or temporal order of the stimuli has no effect on the judgments, P_{jc} and P_{cj} may be assumed equal. In this case, r_{jc} and r_{cj} may be added together and treated in the statistical analysis as the number of judgments $X_j > X_c$ in a total of $N_{jc} + N_{cj} = N_j$ judgments. On the other hand, if the order in which the stimuli are presented has an effect, the outcomes of the judgments cannot be pooled in this way, and the statistical model for the constant method must be extended to include the order effect (see Section 3.4). In most cases, however, the error incurred by ignoring order effect will be minor if the same number of judgments are made in each order and if the order effect is symmetric. For suppose P_{jc} and P_{cj} are expressed as the sum of an object effect, P_j, and a deviation, $\pm D$, due to order effect:

$$P_{jc} = P_j + D$$

$$P_{cj} = P_j - D \, .$$

If $N/2$ judgments are made in each order, the proportion of judgments $X_j > X_c$ irrespective of order is an unbiased estimate of P_j:

$$\mathscr{E}\left(\frac{r_{jc} + r_{cj}}{N}\right) = \frac{1}{N}\left[(P_j + D)N/2 + (P_j - D)N/2\right]$$

$$= P_j \, .$$

The variance of this estimate is diminished by the square of the order effect:

$$\mathscr{V}\left(\frac{r_{jc} + r_{cj}}{N}\right) = \frac{1}{N^2}\left[(P_j + D)(1 - P_j - D)N/2 + (P_j - D)(1 - P_j + D)N/2\right]$$

$$= \frac{P_j(1 - P_j) - D^2}{N} \, .$$

Unless D is large relative to P_j or $1 - P_j$, this variance will differ but little from the usual variance of a binomial proportion, $P_j(1 - P_j)/N$. In any event the use of the binomial variance for purposes of interval estimation or tests of hypothesis will be conservative.

In the remainder of this chapter and in the first three sections of Chapter 3, we assume the order effect is not present or is negligible. In Section 4 of Chapter 3 we introduce a judgmental model which includes the order effect and extend the statistical methods of the previous sections to apply to it.

2.3 The Judgmental Model: Thurstone's Model for the Discriminal Process

"A term is needed for that process by which the organism identifies, distinguishes, discriminates, or reacts to stimuli, a term which is innocuous and as noncommittal as possible, because we are not now interested in the nature of that process. ... In order to avoid any implications, I shall call the psychological values of psychophysics *discriminal* processes" (Thurstone,

1927b). The discriminal process is not directly observable, but plays a central role in the judgmental model. In current statistical terminology, this model may be specified as follows.[1] The discriminal process associated with a stimulus X_j will be represented as a random variable, v_j. Following Thurstone, we consider a value of v_j for a randomly sampled subject to be composed of a fixed component μ_j common to all judges and a random component ε_j:

$$v_j = \mu_j + \varepsilon_j.$$

Similarly, a value of the discriminal process v_c associated with a standard stimulus X_c may be expressed as

$$v_c = \mu_c + \varepsilon_c.$$

The joint distribution of ε_j and ε_c is assumed to be bivariate normal with means 0 and 0, variances σ_j^2 and σ_c^2, and correlation coefficient ρ_{jc}. Then the distribution of v_j and v_c will be bivariate normal with means μ_j and μ_c, variances σ_j^2 and σ_c^2, and correlation ρ_{jc}. Marginal distributions of v_j and v_c are portrayed in Figure 2.1.

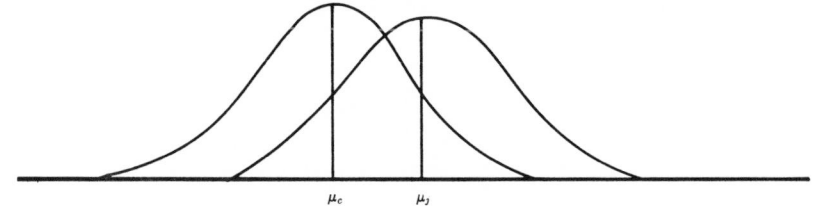

μ_c μ_j

FIG. 2.1. Schematic marginal distributions of v_j and v_c.

The response of subject i is assumed to be determined as follows: The ith subject will judge $X_j > X_c$ whenever $v_{ji} > v_{ci}$, that is, whenever $v_{ji} - v_{ci} > 0$. Similarly, the ith subject will judge $X_c > X_j$ whenever $v_{ci} > v_{ji}$, that is, whenever $v_{ji} - v_{ci} < 0$. (The case of $v_{ji} = v_{ci}$ is assumed to have zero probability.)

Thus, the model can be expressed in terms of the difference between discriminal processes,

$$v_{jc} = v_j - v_c = (\mu_j - \mu_c) + (\varepsilon_j - \varepsilon_c) = \mu_{jc} + \varepsilon_{jc}. \tag{2.2}$$

---

[1] Thurstone specified several "cases" of his model. The development here is essentially Thurstone's Case II. Thurstone's Case I pertains to repeated judgments from a single subject, which differs from the model to be presented in the interpretation of parameters. In Case I, the parameter μ would characterize an individual rather than a population of persons, and the discriminal process would vary over occasions rather than over subjects.

The distribution of v_{jc} is univariate normal: $N(\mu_{jc}, \sigma_{jc}^2)$, where

$$\mu_{jc} = \mu_j - \mu_c$$

and

$$\sigma_{jc}^2 = \sigma_j^2 + \sigma_c^2 - 2\rho_{jc}\sigma_j\sigma_c.$$

Then if $v_{jci} > 0$, subject i responds $X_j > X_c$; if $v_{jci} < 0$, subject i responds $X_c > X_j$.

The distribution of v_{jc} may be represented as in Figure 2.2. The prob-

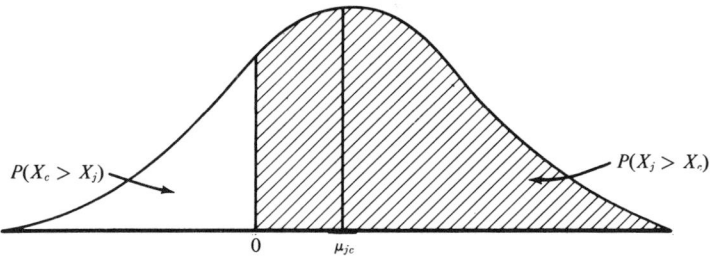

FIG. 2.2. Schematic distribution of v_{jc}.

ability that a randomly selected subject will judge $X_j > X_c$ (the probability represented by the shaded area in Figure 2.2) is given by the integral

$$P_{jc} = \text{Prob}(X_j > X_c) = \frac{1}{\sqrt{2\pi}\sigma_{jc}} \int_0^\infty \exp\left[-\frac{1}{2}\left(\frac{y - \mu_{jc}}{\sigma_{jc}}\right)^2\right] dy.$$

At this point, it proves convenient to introduce the change of variable

$$z = \frac{y - \mu_{jc}}{\sigma_{jc}}. \tag{2.3}$$

Then

$$dz = \frac{1}{\sigma_{jc}} dy,$$

and when

$$y = 0,$$

$$z = -\mu_{jc}/\sigma_{jc}.$$

With this change of variable,

$$P_{jc} = \frac{1}{\sqrt{2\pi}} \int_{-\mu_{jc}/\sigma_{jc}}^{\infty} \exp(-\tfrac{1}{2} .\,^2)\, dz.$$

This expression is the integral of the unit normal density function, with argument μ_{jc}/σ_{jc}. For notational convenience, let the integral be expressed $\Phi(\mu_{jc}/\sigma_{jc})$. Then

$$P_{jc} = \Phi(\mu_{jc}/\sigma_{jc}). \tag{2.4}$$

Equation (2.4) may be referred to as a "response function." It specifies a one-to-one relation between the parameters of the model, on the right of the equation, and an expected proportion of response $X_j > X_c$, on the left. This particular specification represents the normal response function. The entire system of Thurstone scaling is based upon specifying a response function, usually the normal response function.[2]

For known values of μ_{jc} and σ_{jc}, Equation (2.4) for the Thurstone judgmental model determines the probability P_{jc} of the response $X_j > X_c$. However, in applications of the model, the parameters μ_{jc} and σ_{jc} are unknown. From an experiment, there are observed values r_{jc}. Given these observed r_{jc}, the task is one of estimating parameters of the model.

Since μ_{jc}/σ_{jc} is invariant under changes in the unit of measurement for the discriminal processes, the model allows us to establish that unit arbitrarily. A convenient unit is assigned by setting, for some particular j,

$$\sigma_{jc} = 1. \tag{2.5}$$

Then, for that value of j, Equation (2.4) becomes

$$P_{jc} = \frac{1}{\sqrt{2\pi}} \int_{-\mu_{jc}}^{\infty} \exp\left(-\tfrac{1}{2}z^2\right) dz = \Phi(\mu_{jc}). \tag{2.6}$$

Based upon the function (2.6) we could determine, for any known value of the parameter μ_{jc}, a corresponding probability P_{jc}. However, we wish to use the inverse of this function so that, given an estimate of P_{jc}, we may obtain an estimate $\hat{\mu}_{jc}$ of μ_{jc}. The best (i.e. minimum-variance) unbiased estimate of P_{jc} is

$$p_{jc} = r_{jc}/N_{jc}.$$

---

[2] The response function differs in one important respect from the "psychometric function" of classical psychophysics. The response function relates P_{jc} to μ_{jc}/σ_{jc}, defined in terms of the discriminal process; the psychometric function relates P_{jc} directly to the difference between physical stimulus magnitudes $(x_j - x_c)$. The assumption that the psychometric function is accurately described by the integral of the normal distribution has traditionally been called the phi-gamma hypothesis.

Then from the inverse function of (2.6), after substitution of sample estimates for parameters,

$$\hat{\mu}_{jc} = \Phi^{-1}(p_{jc}) = y_{jc}. \tag{2.7}$$

It will be recognized that y_{jc} is simply the unit normal deviate corresponding to a proportion p_{jc} in the upper tail of the normal distribution. For an observed value of p_{jc}, y_{jc} may be read directly from a table of the standard normal distribution function.

It may be shown that y_{jc} is a consistent estimate for μ_{jc}; for as sample size increases without limit, $p_{jc} \rightarrow P_{jc}$ and $y_{jc} \rightarrow \mu_{jc}$. (The consistency of this estimate is shown formally in Section 2.7, using a lemma proposed by Rao.) Now, even for small samples, p_{jc} is an unbiased estimate of P_{jc}. However, y_{jc}, a nonlinear transform of p_{jc}, is not an unbiased estimate of μ_{jc}. The situation may be clarified by representing the observed deviate as a random variable of the form

$$y_{jc} = \mu_{jc} + \delta_{jc} + \xi_{jc}, \tag{2.8}$$

where δ_{jc} represents a component attributable to bias, and ξ_{jc} is a random component of sampling variation.

The degree of bias δ_{jc} will be dependent upon sample size and upon the parameter P_{jc}, and will be particularly sensitive to the strategy adopted when there are encountered observed proportions, p_{jc}, of zero or one. Since, in some procedures for fitting the judgmental model, it is necessary to obtain a finite estimate, y_{jc}, for each variable stimulus X_j, a special convention is required for observed p_{jc} of zero or one, where the corresponding y_{jc}, from (2.7), would be infinite.

A rule often recommended for handling this case when an observed proportion of responses is zero (e.g., Berkson, 1953, 1955a, 1957) is to record $1/2N_{jc}$ rather than zero. The value recorded thus is the median within the interval between zero and the smallest possible nonzero value for p_{jc}, $1/N_{jc}$. In place of an observed p_{jc} of unity, the value $1 - (1/2N_{jc})$ is recorded.

It is possible to evaluate directly the δ_{jc} of (2.8) for selected values of N_{jc} and P_{jc}. Such evaluation is achieved by considering the binomial distribution of r_{jc} associated with parameters N_{jc} and P_{jc}. For each element of the sample set of r_{jc}, a corresponding y_{jc} may be found using (2.7), and the mean $\bar{y}_{jc}$ for the sampling population may be determined. But knowing P_{jc}, the parameter $Y_{jc} = \mu_{jc}$ is found as the normal deviate

$$Y_{jc} = \Phi^{-1}(P_{jc}).$$

Then

$$\delta_{jc} = \bar{y}_{jc} - Y_{jc}.$$

By this method, δ_{jc} is plotted against P_{jc} in Figure 2.3 for $N_{jc} = 5$, 10, 20, and 40. For all p_{jc} of zero or one have been substituted the values of $1/2N_{jc}$ or $1 - (1/2N_{jc})$.[3]

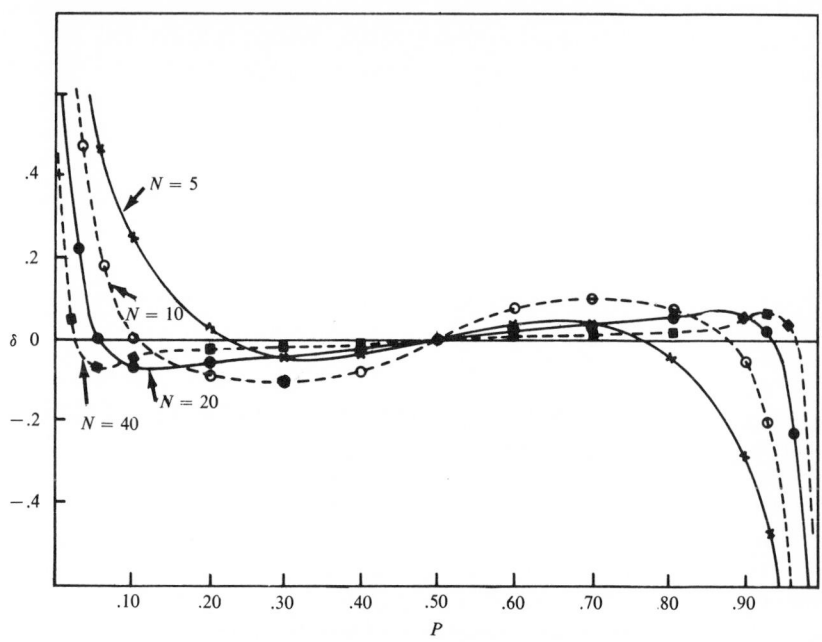

FIG. 2.3. δ_i as a function of P_i and N_i using $1/2N$ rule.

We may note from Figure 2.3 that the bias of y_{jc} as an estimate of μ_{jc} in (2.8) is small for moderate values of P, even with small N. When $NP \geq 1$, $|\delta| < .08$.[4]

---

[3] Bias first was determined by looking up values in tables, then was verified by a computer program written in BALGOL and run on the IBM 7090 at the Stanford University Computation Center. Normal deviates Y and y were determined using the method of Computing Note B of the Appendix. Mean square error was also evaluated by this program, which, in modified form, also served to evaluate the logistic and arc sine response functions introduced in Section 3 of Chapter 3. The authors are grateful to Dr. John P. Gilbert for programming advice.

[4] Several alternatives to the $1/2N$ rule for $p = 0$ have been suggested. Among these are suggestions to substitute for a p of zero (a) $1/4N$, (b) $3/8N$, (c) $2\Phi^{-1}(1/N) - \Phi^{-1}(2/N)$, or (d) the mean deviate in the tail of a normal distribution, given by $h[\Phi^{-1}(1/N)]/(1/N)$. All these have a consistent tendency to reduce bias for extreme values of P_{jc}, but only at the cost of increasing bias for moderate values of P_{jc}. For a well-designed study when it is probable that $N_{jc}P_{jc} > 1$ for all P_{jc}, this cost would be appreciable, since over-all bias would be likely to exceed that which would occur using the $1/2N$ rule.

For any value of N and P, it is also possible to evaluate mean square error of the estimator (2.7) about its parametric value μ_{jc}. For sample size $N = 10$ and 40 the mean square error is plotted as a function of P in Figure 2.4 and compared with $\mathscr{V}(y_{jc})$, determined by Equation (2.22). Clearly, with

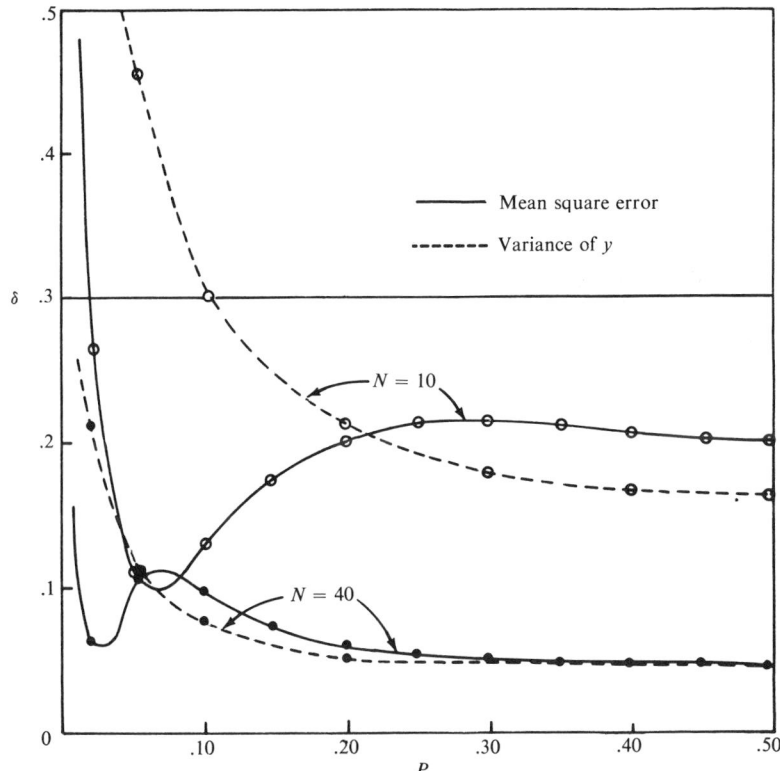

FIG. 2.4. Mean square error and theoretical variance of y_{jc} as an estimate of μ_{jc}, normal response function.

small N and extreme P, the high probability of occurrence of observed p's of zero or one (and the substitution of $1/2N$ or $1 - (1/2N)$ for each) sharply reduces the empirical sampling variance of y compared with its theoretically expected value. Only when $NP \geq 2$ does the mean square error closely approximate $\mathscr{V}(y_{jc})$. Comparison of results portrayed in Figures 2.3 and 2.4 indicates that, except for very extreme parametric P_{jc}, bias in y_{jc} as an estimate of μ_{jc} is small relative to the sampling variability of y_{jc}. Consequently, the bias in (2.8) is seldom of major concern.

We shall return to consideration of effects of bias in Section 2.7, where it will be found that the amount of bias in the estimates of the μ_{jc} will directly influence bias in estimation of β, the slope parameter in the psychophysical model (2.9).

Clearly, Equation (2.7), based upon the normal response function (2.4), together with a rule for treating p_{jc} of zero or one, provides a means of estimating μ_{jc} for some particular variable stimulus j. However, in order to estimate by this method the μ_{jc} for all values of j, Equation (2.5) is extended to become an assumption that the values of σ_{jc} are equal for all values of j:

$$\sigma_{jc} = 1 \qquad \text{for } j = 1, 2, \ldots, n. \tag{2.5a}$$

This assumption is the equivalent of Thurstone's Case V for paired-comparisons data, to be introduced in Chapter 6. The assumption follows from the principle of Fullerton and Cattell (1892) that "equally often noticed differences are equal" (see also Thurstone, 1932). An alternative assumption, in which σ_{jc} is dependent upon μ_{jc}, will be presented in Section 3.3.

Although we may now estimate the μ_{jc}, this is seldom an end point of a psychophysical investigation. Such estimates, in fact, are of relatively little direct interest, but provide intermediate results useful for finding a difference limen or point of subjective equality, or, more generally, for determining a stimulus which is correctly distinguished from the standard stimulus with some specified probability.

It is highly unlikely that any preselected variable stimulus will be just limenally different from the standard, or will be judged different a prespecified proportion of the time. The problem then becomes one of interpolation from values μ_{jc} for the specific stimuli studied so as to find values for other stimuli which will give rise to discriminating judgments with specified probabilities. Solution to this problem demands consideration of physical stimulus magnitudes and introduction of a psychophysical model which specifies the form of relation between discriminal processes and those physical stimulus magnitudes.

2.4   Application of the Judgmental Model to Prediction of Response— The Psychophysical Model

To connect the judgmental model to the physical magnitudes of the stimuli, an additional specification of the idealized stimulus discrimination experiment is required. Let the n selected "variable" stimuli, $X_1, X_2, \ldots, X_n$, have physical magnitudes $x_1, x_2, \ldots, x_n$, respectively, and let X_c have physical magnitude x_c. Define

$$x_{jc} = x_j - x_c.$$

We assume that, within the range of stimuli selected for the experiment, the mean difference between discriminal processes for any stimulus j and stimulus

c is a linear function of the physical stimulus difference,

$$\mu_{jc} = \alpha_c + \beta_c x_{jc}. \tag{2.9}$$

Here α_c and β_c are dimensional constants, subject to change with changes in the measurement unit for x_{jc} or for μ_{jc}. Note that α_c and β_c are assumed invariant over $j = 1, 2, \ldots, n$.

Expression (2.9) may be considered the specification of a *psychophysical model*, relating a psychological variate μ_{jc} to a physical magnitude x_{jc}.

A word in defense of the linear psychophysical model (2.9) may be appropriate here. Most treatments of the psychophysical relation postulate a logarithmic function (see Chapter 5) or a power function (see Stevens, 1957) rather than a direct linear function. These alternative functions, however, typically are presumed to pertain to the relation between μ_j and x_j, the mean discriminal process of a given stimulus and the physical magnitude of that stimulus. Equation (2.9), on the other hand, refers to the relation between μ_{jc} and x_{jc}, where both represent *differences* between stimuli. Furthermore, the stimuli selected for a study of discriminal precision are stimuli for which such differences are small, relative to the absolute magnitude of the stimuli. For any moderately well-behaved monotonic function relating μ_j to x_j, a linear function will be seen to approximate quite accurately the relation between small differences in discriminal processes μ_{jc} and small differences in physical magnitude x_{jc}. (For a discussion of this issue, see Thurstone, 1928.)

The right side of (2.9) may be substituted for μ_{jc} in (2.2), to yield

$$v_{jc} = \alpha_c + \beta_c x_{jc} + \varepsilon_{jc}, \tag{2.10}$$

an expression for the difference between discriminal processes associated with stimuli X_j and X_c for a randomly selected subject. Further, (2.9) may be incorporated into the response function (2.6) to define a psychophysical function relating $\mathrm{Prob}(X_j > X_c)$ to the physical magnitude of the difference between the two stimuli:

$$P_{jc} = \frac{1}{\sqrt{2\pi}} \int_{-\alpha_c - \beta_c x_{jc}}^{\infty} \exp(-\tfrac{1}{2}z^2)\, dz = \Phi(\alpha_c + \beta_c x_{jc}). \tag{2.11}$$

Estimates for μ_{jc} may be obtained from the experimental data using (2.7). Next it is desired to determine estimates of α_c and β_c. Knowledge of these parameters allows the determination of the mean discriminal process for a stimulus not included among the set of n stimuli in the experiment, as well as the determination of the point of subjective equality and the difference limen.

Let X_k be a stimulus not included in the experiment, the physical magnitude of which is x_k. Then, by (2.9), knowledge of α_c and β_c allows computation of μ_{kc}, which yields $\mathrm{Prob}(X_k > X_c)$ from the normal response function (2.6).

Further, when α_c and β_c are known, the point of subjective equality is $x_c + x_{kc}$ where, from (2.9), when $\mu_{kc} = 0$ (and $P_{jc} = .5$),

$$x_{kc} = -\alpha_c/\beta_c. \tag{2.12}$$

Accepting the customary definition for the difference limen, we substitute $P_{kc} = .75$ and $P_{kc} = .25$ in (2.6), and refer to tables of the unit normal distribution to find $\mu_{kc} = \pm.675$. Substituting in (2.9) and solving for x_{kc} yields, for the upper difference limen

$$\mathrm{dl}_U = (.675 - \alpha_c)/\beta_c, \tag{2.13}$$

and, for the lower difference limen

$$\mathrm{dl}_L = (-.675 - \alpha_c)/\beta_c. \tag{2.13a}$$

A single estimate of the difference limen is obtained as the mean of the absolute values of the upper and lower limens.

The parameter β_c is also of interest for other reasons. It is directly interpretable as a measure of discriminal precision, the degree to which subjects are sensitive to differences among stimulus magnitudes. For as the regression line (2.9) approaches the horizontal, i.e. as $\beta_c \to 0$, variable stimuli of any magnitude become indistinguishable from the standard. A steep regression line, with β_c large, reflects either a large physical difference between stimuli or the ability of the subjects to discriminate among the stimuli. If the physical differences among stimuli are known to be small, a large β_c implies a high degree of discriminal precision on the part of the subjects.

2.5   Fitting the Psychophysical Model

From (2.8) and (2.9) it is apparent that

$$\mathscr{E}(y_{jc}) = \alpha_c + \beta_c x_{jc} + \delta_{jc}. \tag{2.14}$$

The data from an experiment provide an observed value y_{jc}, the unit normal deviate corresponding to an observed proportion p_{jc}, for every stimulus X_j. Given observed values y_{jc} for all X_j we wish to estimate α_c and β_c. Such estimates are provided by fitting the psychophysical model to the data. Three solutions for fitting the model will be considered: (1) a graphical method, (2) Urban's method of weighted least squares (and an unweighted modification thereof), and (3) the method of maximum likelihood (Chapter 3). For Urban's method and the maximum likelihood solution, statistical tests of the adequacy of the linear psychophysical model are provided.

In fitting the psychophysical model the practical difficulty encountered when any observed values p_{jc} are zero or one was noted in Section 2.3. In selecting stimuli for the purpose of studying discriminal precision, it is desirable to avoid stimuli X_j so distinct from X_c as to be distinguished 100% of the time. Nevertheless, particularly with small N_j, observed proportions p_{jc} of zero or one sometimes will occur. A direct application of (2.6) then yields no finite solution for the corresponding y_{jc}. But for the purpose of fitting the psychophysical model, the y_{jc} are considered observed data, and a finite estimate of each is required. As will be seen in Section 3.1, such an estimate (y_w) is provided in the method of maximum likelihood even for observed p_{jc} of zero or one. Only for the graphical method and the method of least squares, then, is this a critical problem. The recommended remedial tactic is to employ the $1/2N$ rule (see Section 2.3). If for two (or more) adjacent stimuli X_j at either extreme of physical magnitude x_j, observed proportions are zero or one, the remedial tactic should be employed only for the less extreme stimulus, and the more extreme stimulus (or stimuli) should be ignored for the purpose of analysis.

2.6 The Graphical Solution

In the graphical method one fits "by eye" a straight line to the plot of y_{jc} against x_{jc} to represent the best line of relationship. Estimates $\hat{\alpha}$ and $\hat{\beta}$ for α and β are obtained as the intercept and slope, respectively, of that line of best fit.[5] In terms of these estimates, the normal deviates are represented as

$$y_j = \hat{\alpha} + \hat{\beta} x_j + e_j, \qquad (2.15)$$

where e_j is the difference between y_j and the fitted regression line at the point x_j. In the graphical method one should choose a line which appears to minimize magnitudes of these residual differences, the vertical discrepancies of points from the line.

For many psychophysical studies, the graphical method should prove quite satisfactory as a means for fitting a psychophysical function. In fact, its primary limitation is only that the graphical solution has associated with it no suitable statistical tests on the parameters of the psychophysical model. But the adequacy of the fitted function often is about as good in a graphical solution as in a least squares or maximum likelihood solution.

An interesting adjunct to the method of graphical estimation is the construction of confidence bounds for μ_j (i.e. for the parametric normal deviate Y_j) at each x_j before fitting the line. The method of constructing these bounds is based on the following reasoning. Recall that the judgments in the constant method can be considered Bernoulli trials, i.e. repetitions of a "simple experiment," the outcomes of which take on values $s_j = 1$ or $s_j = 0$ with constant probabilities P_j and $Q_j = 1 - P_j$. In this application $s_j = 1$

---

[5] For convenience, the subscript c is omitted throughout the remainder of this chapter.

represents the judgment $X_j > X_c$. According to the binomial distribution, the probability of observing fewer than r_j values of $s_j = 1$, when there are N_j judgments, is

$$\text{Prob}\left(\sum_i^{N_j} s_{ji} < r_j\right) = \sum_{r=0}^{r_j-1} \binom{N_j}{r} P_j^r Q_j^{N_j-r}.$$

Conversely, the probability of observing a value of r greater than r_j is

$$\text{Prob}\left(\sum_i^{N_j} s_{ji} > r_j\right) = \sum_{r=r_j+1}^{N_j} \binom{N_j}{r} P_j^r Q_j^{N_j-r}.$$

For an observed number of successes, r_j, a confidence bound on P_j with confidence coefficient $1 - \gamma$ is determined by finding values P_{jL} and P_{jU} which satisfy

$$\text{Prob}\left(\sum_i^{N_j} s_{ij} < r_j\right) = \sum_{r=0}^{r_j-1} \binom{N_j}{r} P_{jL}^r Q_{jL}^{N_j-r} = 1 - \frac{\gamma}{2}, \qquad (2.16)$$

$$\text{Prob}\left(\sum_i^{N_j} s_{ij} > r_j\right) = \sum_{r=r_j+1}^{N_j} \binom{N_j}{r} P_{jU}^r Q_{jU}^{N_j-r} = 1 - \frac{\gamma}{2}. \qquad (2.17)$$

The values P_{jL} and P_{jU} may be found in several alternative ways. For $1 < N < 30$ and confidence coefficient $1 - \gamma$ of .90, .95, or .99, these bounds may be read directly from Table A10. For $30 < N < 50$, the values may be determined with the aid of tables of the binomial distribution.[6] For $N \geq 50$ and $.20 \leq p_j \leq .80$ (where $p_j = r_j/N_j$), the normal approximation to the binomial distribution provides satisfactory estimates. Using the normal approximation,

$$P_{jL} \cong p_j - z_{1-(\gamma/2)}\sqrt{\frac{p_j(1 - p_j)}{N_j}}$$

and

$$P_{jU} \cong p_j + z_{1-(\gamma/2)}\sqrt{\frac{p_j(1 - p_j)}{N_j}}$$

where $z_{1-(\gamma/2)}$ is the $1 - (\gamma/2)$ point of the unit normal distribution. For selected values of N_j, nomographs may be used to approximate P_{jL} and P_{jU}.[7]

[6] National Bureau of Standards, *Tables of Binomial Probability Distribution*, Applied Mathematics Series No. 6, U.S. Government Printing Office, Washington, D.C., 1949; reprinted with corrections, 1952.

[7] W. J. Dixon and F. J. Massey, Jr., *Introduction to Statistical Analysis*, McGraw-Hill, New York, 1951, pp. 320–323.

When N_j exceeds 30, so that Table A10 cannot be used, or for larger N_j when p_j lies outside the range .20–.80, then the most convenient determination of P_{jL} and P_{jU} makes use of tables of the F distribution. The relation between F and the binomial distribution depends upon the relation of each to the incomplete beta distribution (see Kendall and Stuart, 1963, p. 151, and Wilks, 1962, pp. 186–187). As a consequence of these relations, we may determine the lower bound on P by

$$P_{jL} = \frac{r_j}{r_j + (N_j - r_j + 1)F_{1 - (\gamma/2)}}, \qquad (2.18)$$

where $F_{1 - (\gamma/2)}$ is the $1 - (\gamma/2)$ point of the F distribution with degrees of freedom $n_1 = 2(N_j - r_j + 1)$ and $n_2 = 2r_j$; the corresponding upper bound, P_{jU}, is obtained from

$$P_{jU} = \frac{(r_j + 1)F_{1 - (\gamma/2)}}{N_j - r_j + (r_j + 1)F_{1 - (\gamma/2)}}, \qquad (2.19)$$

with degrees of freedom $n_1 = 2(r_j + 1)$ and $n_2 = 2(N - r_j)$. Expressions (2.18) and (2.19) are developed by Brownlee (1960, pp. 117–120).

Once the bounding values of P have been determined, the corresponding bounds on population normal deviates Y_j may then be determined using tables of the normal distribution from

$$Y_{jL} = \Phi^{-1}(P_{jL})$$

and

$$Y_{jU} = \Phi^{-1}(P_{jU}).$$

Values of Y_{jL} and Y_{jU} are unit normal deviates corresponding to the areas P_{jL} and P_{jU}, in the upper and lower tail, respectively, under the unit normal curve.

Assuming that the observed deviates corresponding to different values of the variable stimulus are statistically independent, our confidence that the n confidence intervals so constructed will simultaneously include all the true Y_j, $j = 1, 2, \ldots, n$, is, of course, $(1 - \gamma)^n$. This will be called the joint confidence coefficient.[8]

---

[8] The assumption of independence will be fulfilled in the single-judgment condition as defined in Section 2.2. If more than one judgment per pair is taken (as is always the case in the multiple-judgment condition) certain forms of dependence may occur. In these cases, a conservative simultaneous confidence interval can be computed by replacing $(1 - \gamma)^n$ with $(1 - n\gamma)$ in the foregoing argument, then computing the confidence interval in the usual fashion. This second type of interval has the disadvantage of producing very small joint confidence when n is large. (If $n = 20$, $\gamma = .05$, then the simultaneous confidence level is zero.) It does, however, provide a lower bound to the actual level of simultaneous confidence.

The question naturally arises concerning the strategy for choosing an appropriate confidence coefficient for the interval estimates. In this application, the principal aim is not one of simultaneous estimation of all μ_j, but rather one of obtaining guidance for fitting a line to the observed y_j. Were the purpose the simultaneous estimation of the Y_j, it would seem warranted to select a joint confidence coefficient of .90 or .95, say, and determine the value of γ which would provide this joint coefficient. However, for the present purpose, it is more helpful to select a joint confidence coefficient at a lower level, as low as .50, so as to obtain more positive guidance (less broad confidence intervals) for the fit of the line. Then in fitting a line to the plot of y_j vs x_j, some effort should be made to keep the line within the confidence bounds, as well as to keep the e_j of (2.15) generally small. As will be seen in the following example, the width of the confidence interval at each point y_j may provide guidance as to how close to the point the line of fit should pass; the smaller the bound, the closer the line should pass to the observed y_j.

Example 2.6

An experiment was performed to determine the precision of taste discrimination for different concentrations of sodium chloride in distilled water.[9] For the standard stimulus X_c, the concentration of sodium chloride was set at 1 % (1 g/100 ml). Six variable stimuli were prepared, with concentrations of .7, .8, .9, 1.1, 1.2, and 1.3 %.

Fifty adult subjects, some male, some female, were selected as judges. All were volunteers, and all were employees of the Quartermaster Food and Container Institute for the U.S. Armed Forces. Using a multiple-judgment condition, each subject was presented all stimulus pairs (X_j, X_c), $j = 1, 2, 3, 4, 5, 6$. However, to better assure independence of judgments, only one pair was presented during a single experimental sitting. Each subject thus visited the taste laboratory six times during a two-week period, tasting an (X_j, X_c) pair on each visit. Order of presentation of the pairs was randomized over subjects.

On each experimental trial a subject was presented samples of the standard and variable stimulus in small unmarked containers. Each sample consisted of 6 ml of solution at room temperature. The subject was instructed to take first the entire contents of the left-hand container in his mouth, swirl it around, expectorate, and rinse with (charcoal-filtered) distilled water; then to rest 3 seconds, taste the sample in the right-hand container in the same way, and state which sample tasted more salty.

The results of this experiment are given in Table 2.1.

---

[9] Data were collected at the Quartermaster Food and Container Institute for the U.S. Armed Forces. We are grateful to Howard G. Shutz for permission to use it here.

TABLE 2.1. Graphical Solution for the Constant Method*

Concentration, %, x_j	N_j	r_{jc}	p_j	P_{jL}*	P_{jU}*	$y_j = \hat{Y}_{jc}$	Y_{jL}	Y_{jU}
1.3	49	48	.980	.906	.999	2.05	1.32	3.09
1.2	47	38	.809	.688	.897	.87	.49	1.26
1.1	50	31	.620	.493	.737	.31	.02	.63
.9	48	13	.271	.168	.398	− .61	− .96	− .26
.8	48	3	.062	.017	.155	−1.54	−2.12	−1.02
.7	49	2	.041	.007	.124	−1.74	−2.46	−1.16

* Confidence bounds on the P_j are based upon individual confidence coefficients, $1 - \gamma = .90$; P_{jL} and P_{jU} are determined from (2.18) and (2.19), respectively.

For interval estimation of the μ_j, we adopt a confidence coefficient $1 - \gamma$ of .90. This yields a joint confidence coefficient of $(1 - \gamma)^6 = .53$.

For the data of this example, sample sizes are greater than 30, so that confidence bounds on P cannot be read from Table A10. Instead, we use Equations (2.18) and (2.19), and refer to the F distribution, noting that for this problem $F_{1 - (\gamma/2)} = F_{.95}$. To illustrate the solution, consider bounds on P for $j = 4$ in Table 2.1. To utilize (2.18), we require the numbers

$$r_j = 31,$$

$$N_j - r_j + 1 = 20,$$

$$n_1 = 2(N_j - r_j + 1) = 40,$$

$$n_2 = 2r_j = 62.$$

Referring to a table of F, the .95 point of the distribution with 40 and 62 degrees of freedom is found to be $F_{1 - (\gamma/2)} = 1.59$. Substitution of the above values in (2.18) yields

$$P_{jL} = \frac{31}{31 + 20(1.59)} = .493.$$

To find P_{jU} for $j = 4$ we note that, with $n_r = 2(r_j + 1) = 64$ and $n_2 = 2(N - r_j) = 38$, $F_{.95} = 1.66$. Substitution in (2.19) yields

$$P_{jU} = \frac{32(1.66)}{19 + 32(1.66)} = .737.$$

Similarly, other values of P_{jL} and P_{jU} have been found and recorded in Table 2.1.

Values of Y_{jL} and Y_{jU} corresponding to values of P_{jL} and P_{jU} may be read directly (from Table A3) as unit normal deviates corresponding to the P proportion of cases to the left of Y. That is, Y_j is the value of a standard normal deviate which is such that $\text{Prob}(y_j < Y_j) = p_j$. The values Y_{jL} and Y_{jU} are similarly found. These, too, are recorded in Table 2.1.

Finally, in Table 2.1 appear the values p_j, calculated from the data, $p_j = r_j/N_j$. From a table of normal deviates (Table A3) we read that value of y_j to the left of which resides p_j proportion of observation.

Based upon information of Table 2.1 the graphical solution is displayed in Figure 2.5. The six points y_j are plotted; horizontal dashes represent the

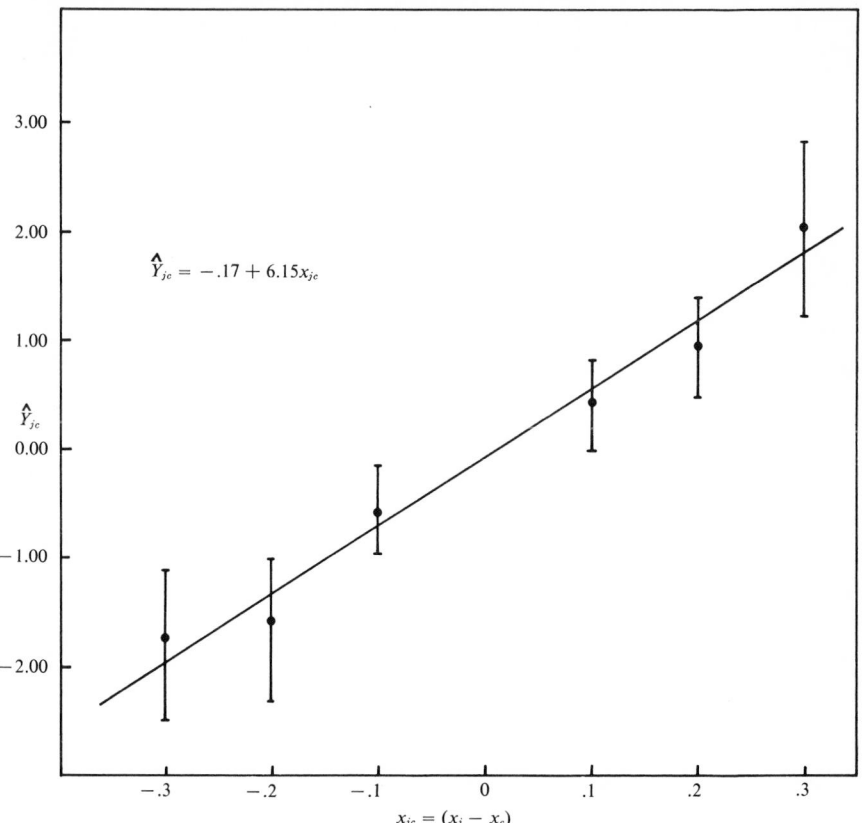

$$\hat{Y}_{jc} = -.17 + 6.15x_{jc}$$

$x_{jc} = (x_j - x_c)$

FIG. 2.5. Plot of graphical solution for the constant method.

pair of values Y_{jL} and Y_{jU} associated with each Y_j. A solid line is fitted (by eye) to the points y_j in such fashion as to fall within each interval (Y_{jU}, Y_{jL}). The relative sizes of these intervals also provide guidance concerning position of the fitted line. The smaller the interval about a particular y_j, the more important it is that the line pass close to that point.

The weighted least squares regression of y_j on x_{jc} (Eq. (2.43)) gives $\hat{\alpha} = -.162$, $\hat{\beta} = 6.011$ or, in equation form,

$$\hat{Y}_{jc} = -.162 + 6.011 x_{jc} \, ;$$

the equation fitted "by eye" from Figure 2.5 gives

$$\hat{Y}_{jc} = -.17 + 6.15 x_{jc} \, ,$$

which is in error by only slightly more than the width of the line, a result which would probably be considered quite satisfactory.

For the data of this example, it is a simple matter to determine the point of subjective equality and the difference limen. For the former, we substitute estimates for α and β in (2.12) to find

$$x_{kc} = .17/6.15 = .028 \, .$$

In physical stimulus units,

$$\text{pse} = x_c + .028 = 1.028 \% \text{ concentration}$$

That is, a stimulus at 1.028% concentration, when paired with the standard stimulus under the condition of this experiment, would be expected to yield $P_{jc} = P_{cj} = 1/2$. Substituting the estimates for α and β in (2.13) and (2.13a), we may find the upper and lower difference limen:

$$\text{dl}_U = \frac{.675 - \alpha}{\beta} = \frac{.675 + .17}{6.15} = .137 \, ;$$

$$\text{dl}_L = \frac{-.675 - \alpha}{\beta} = \frac{-.675 + .17}{6.15} = -.082 \, .$$

It is estimated that a solution of concentration 1.137% or a solution of concentration $.918\%$ would be judged distinct from the standard with probability .75. A single value for the difference limen is obtained as the mean absolute value of the two determinations:

$$\text{dl} = \frac{.137 + .082}{2} = .110 \% \text{ concentration.}$$

2.7 Urban's Solution (Minimum Normit χ^2)

THE PRINCIPLE OF LEAST SQUARES. In the tradition of psychophysics, the standard method of fitting data by the normal response law is that of Urban (1908). His method is an application of the classic principle of least squares (see Computing Note D). According to this principle, estimates of the parameters of a model should be chosen so as to minimize an appropriate linear function of squared residual components. Statistical considerations dictate that this function be a formal goodness-of-fit criterion whose sampling distribution is known and tabulated.

Urban's method depends on the minimization of the "normit" χ^2, to use Berkson's terminology (1955b). (Berkson calls y_j the "normit" of p_j.)

MINIMUM NORMIT χ^2. To formulate the normit χ^2 it is necessary to derive the large-sample distribution of the error component of the observed normal deviates. Assume first that the fundamental random variable from an experiment using the constant method is the Bernoulli variate,

$$s_j = 1 \text{ with probability } P_j,$$

$$s_j = 0 \text{ with probability } Q_j,$$

with expected value

$$\mathscr{E}(s_j) = P$$

and variance

$$\mathscr{V}(s_j) = \mathscr{E}(s_j^2) - \mathscr{E}^2(s_j) = P_j - P_j^2 = P_j Q_j.$$

Then the proportion

$$p_j = \sum_{i=1}^{N_j} s_{ji}/N_j$$

is a random variable with an expected value P_j and, by virtue of the independence of s_j over subjects or trials, with variance $P_j Q_j/N_j$. Hence, the corresponding standardized variable

$$(p_j - P_j)/\sqrt{P_j Q_j/N_j}$$

has zero mean and unit variance. By the well-known DeMoivre theorem (Cramér, 1951, p. 198), its limiting distribution is the unit normal distribution. Thus the limiting distribution of the observed proportions p_j is normal with mean P_j and variance $P_j Q_j/N_j$.

Knowing this limiting distribution of the observed proportions p_j, we obtain the limiting distribution of the corresponding normal deviates y_j by specialization of a lemma on the transformation of statistics given by Rao (1952, p. 207; also 1965, p. 319):

Let the distribution of the statistic t tend to normal form with mean θ and variance σ^2/N. Then if $f(t)$ is any continuous function with continuous first derivatives, the variable

$$u = \sqrt{N}\,[f(t) - f(\theta)]$$

is distributed normally in the limit with mean zero and variance

$$\sigma^2 \left[\frac{\partial f}{\partial \theta}\right]^2.$$

To apply Rao's lemma, we consider the statistic p_j and recall (2.8) that the observed normal deviates

$$y_j = \Phi^{-1}(p_j) = \mu_j + \delta_j + \xi_j.$$

Let us define a random variable

$$u_j = \sqrt{N_j}(\delta_j + \xi_j)$$
$$= \sqrt{N_j}(y_j - \mu_j)$$
$$= \sqrt{N_j}[\Phi^{-1}(p_j) - \Phi^{-1}(P_j)]. \qquad (2.20)$$

Hence, from Rao's lemma, u_j is distributed normally in the limit with mean zero, and the variance of u_j,

$$\mathcal{V}(u_j) = P_j Q_j \left[\frac{\partial \Phi^{-1}}{\partial P_j}\right]^2. \qquad (2.21)$$

Recall that

$$P_j = \frac{1}{\sqrt{2\pi}} \int_{-Y_j}^{\infty} \exp(-\tfrac{1}{2}z^2)\, dz.$$

Thus

$$dP_j = h(Y_j)\, dY_j,$$

where

$$h(Y_j) = \frac{1}{\sqrt{2\pi}} \exp(-\tfrac{1}{2}Y_j^2).$$

That is, $h(Y_j)$ is the ordinate at the point Y_j of a variate distributed $N(0, 1)$.

Now

$$\frac{dY_j}{dP_j} = \frac{\partial \Phi^{-1}}{\partial P_j} = \frac{1}{h(Y_j)}.$$

Substituting in (2.21),

$$\mathcal{V}(u_j) = P_j Q_j / h^2(Y_j) = 1/W_j, \text{ say},$$

where $h(Y_j)$ is the ordinate of the normal curve corresponding to the expected deviate $Y_j = \Phi^{-1}(P_j)$, and $h^2(Y_j)$ is the squared value of that ordinate.
But by (2.20),

$$\mathcal{V}(u_j) = N_j \mathcal{V}(y_j),$$

so that

$$\mathcal{V}(y_j) = 1/N_j W_j. \qquad (2.22)$$

Then the variate

$$(y_j - \mu_j)/\sigma_{y_j} = \sqrt{N_j W_j}\,(y_j - \mu_j)$$

has unit normal distribution in the limit. Assuming the y_j are independent over j, the quantity

$$Q = \sum_{j=1}^{n} \left(\frac{y_j - \mu_j}{\sigma_{y_j}}\right)^2 = \sum_{j=1}^{n} N_j W_j (y_j - \mu_j)^2 \qquad (2.23)$$

is distributed as χ^2 in the limit, with n degrees of freedom when μ_j and σ_{y_j} are known. This is the normit χ^2.

ESTIMATION. Substituting $\mu_j = \alpha + \beta x_j$ in (2.23) according to the linearity assumption of the psychophysical model (2.9) yields

$$Q = \Sigma N_j W_j (y_j - \alpha - \beta x_j)^2. \qquad (2.24)$$

Partially differentiating the right-hand expression in (2.24) with respect to α and β to locate the extrema of the function gives rise to the normal equations

$$\frac{\partial Q}{\partial \alpha} = -2\Sigma N_j W_j (y_j - \hat{\alpha} - \hat{\beta} x_j) = 0,$$

$$\frac{\partial Q}{\partial \beta} = -2\Sigma N_j W_j x_j (y_j - \hat{\alpha} - \hat{\beta} x_j) = 0.$$

Since Q is a positive quadratic form for all values of α and β, it has only one turning point and that point is a minimum.

It is convenient to define the weighted means

$$\bar{x} = \Sigma_j N_j W_j x_j / \Sigma_j N_j W_j,$$

and

$$\bar{y} = \Sigma_j N_j W_j y_j / \Sigma_j N_j W_j.$$

Then the solution of the normal equations for α and β gives the estimators

$$\hat{\beta} = \frac{\Sigma N_j W_j y_j (x_j - \bar{x})}{\Sigma N_j W_j x_j (x_j - \bar{x})} = \frac{S_{xy}}{S_{x^2}}, \text{ say}, \qquad (2.25)$$

and

$$\hat{\alpha} = \bar{y} - \hat{\beta}\bar{x}. \qquad (2.26)$$

Note that $\Sigma NWy(x - \bar{x}) = \Sigma NWx(y - \bar{y}) = \Sigma NW(x - \bar{x})(y - \bar{y}) = S_{xy}$.

The equation of the fitted line is, substituting estimates for the parameters in (2.9),

$$\hat{\mu}_j = \bar{y} - \hat{\beta}\bar{x} + \hat{\beta}x_j$$

or

$$(\hat{\mu}_j - \bar{y}) = \hat{\beta}(x_j - \bar{x}).$$

Since $\hat{\alpha}$ and $\hat{\beta}$ are linear functions of the observed deviates, their expectations and variances are easy to compute. Beginning with $\hat{\beta}$, we have

$$\mathcal{E}(\hat{\beta}) = \frac{1}{S_{x^2}} \{ \Sigma N_j W_j x_j [\alpha + \beta x_j + \delta_j + \mathcal{E}(\xi_j)] - \bar{x}\Sigma N_j W_j$$

$$\times [\alpha + \beta x_j + \delta_j + \mathcal{E}(\xi_j)] \}$$

$$= \frac{1}{S_{x^2}} [\alpha(\Sigma N_j W_j x_j - \bar{x}\Sigma N_j W_j) + \beta(\Sigma N_j W_j x_j^2 - \bar{x}\Sigma N_j W_j x_j)$$

$$+ \Sigma N_j W_j \delta_j(x_j - \bar{x})]$$

$$= \beta + \frac{\Sigma N_j W_j \delta_j(x_j - \bar{x})}{S_{x^2}} \tag{2.27}$$

and

$$\mathcal{E}(\hat{\alpha}) = \mathcal{E}(\bar{y}) - \mathcal{E}(\hat{\beta}\bar{x})$$

$$= \frac{\Sigma N_j W_j[\alpha + \beta x_j + \delta_j + \mathcal{E}(\xi_j)]}{\Sigma N_j W_j} - \bar{x}\mathcal{E}(\hat{\beta})$$

$$= \alpha \frac{\Sigma N_j W_j}{\Sigma N_j W_j} + \beta \frac{\Sigma N_j W_j(x_j - \bar{x})}{\Sigma N_j W_j} + \frac{\Sigma N_j W_j \delta_j}{\Sigma N_j W_j} - \frac{\bar{x}\Sigma N_j W_j \delta_j(x_j - \bar{x})}{S_{x^2}}$$

$$= \alpha + \frac{\Sigma N_j W_j \delta_j}{\Sigma N_j W_j} - \frac{\bar{x}\Sigma N_j W_j \delta_j(x_j - \bar{x})}{S_{x^2}}. \tag{2.28}$$

When the parameters P_j are symmetric about .5, then for each positive δ_j there will be a symmetric negative δ_j identical in absolute value. Under this condition, the second term in (2.28) vanishes. When $\bar{x} = 0$, the third term in (2.28) also vanishes and $\hat{\alpha}$ is an unbiased estimator of α. $\hat{\beta}$ will remain a biased estimator of β, however, even in this special case, since the skew–symmetric pattern of the δ_j (about 0, when $P_j = .50$) is accompanied by a skew–symmetric pattern of the $(x_j - \bar{x})$. Berkson (1957, p. 426) shows that the size of this bias for $N = 10$, $n = 3$, and $P_1 = .3$, $P_2 = .5$, $P_3 = .7$, is less than one-tenth the size of the standard error of $\hat{\beta}$ as an estimate of β. (For observed p_j of zero or one, Berkson recorded values of $1/2N$ and $1 - (1/2N)$, respectively.) In general, if for all variable stimuli X_j the sample size is sufficiently large and/or the parametric proportion of judgment is sufficiently moderate so that $N_{jc}P_{jc} \geq 1$, then the bias in (2.27) should remain inconsequential. Also, under these conditions, the mean square error of $\hat{\beta}$ about β

will be approximated by the variance of $\hat{\beta}$ as given by (2.29). When these conditions fail to be met, serious consideration should be given the angular response function (Section 3.3) which is affected by bias much less than the normal response function.

For $\hat{\beta}$, the variance is[10]

$$\mathcal{V}(\hat{\beta}) = \left(\frac{1}{S_{x^2}}\right)^2 \mathcal{V}[\Sigma N_j W_j y_j (x_j - \bar{x})]$$

$$= \left(\frac{1}{S_{x^2}}\right)^2 [\mathcal{V}(\Sigma N_j W_j x_j y_j) + \mathcal{V}(\bar{x}\Sigma N_j W_j y_j)$$

$$- 2\mathcal{V}(\Sigma N_j W_j x_j y_j, \bar{x}\Sigma N_j W_j y_j)]$$

$$= \left(\frac{1}{S_{x^2}}\right)^2 [\Sigma N_j^2 W_j^2 x_j^2 \, \mathcal{V}(y_j) + \bar{x}^2 \Sigma N_j^2 W_j^2 \, \mathcal{V}(y_j)$$

$$- 2\bar{x}\Sigma N_j^2 W_j^2 x_j \, \mathcal{V}(y_j)]$$

$$= \left(\frac{1}{S_{x^2}}\right)^2 [\Sigma N_j W_j x_j^2 - \bar{x}\Sigma N_j W_j x_j]$$

$$= \frac{1}{S_{x^2}}. \tag{2.29}$$

(The above result makes use of the fact that the variance of the sum of independent variates is the sum of the variances of the separate variates.)

For $\hat{\alpha}$, the variance is

$$\mathcal{V}(\hat{\alpha}) = \mathcal{V}(\bar{y} - \hat{\beta}\bar{x})$$

$$= \mathcal{V}(\bar{y}) + \bar{x}^2 \mathcal{V}(\hat{\beta}) - 2\bar{x}\mathcal{V}(\bar{y}, \hat{\beta})$$

$$= \left(\frac{1}{\Sigma N_j W_j}\right)^2 \mathcal{V}(\Sigma N_j W_j y_j) + \frac{\bar{x}^2}{S_{x^2}}$$

$$= \frac{1}{\Sigma N_j W_j} + \frac{\bar{x}^2}{S_{x^2}} \tag{2.30}$$

since

$$\mathcal{V}(\bar{y}, \hat{\beta}) = \frac{1}{S_{x^2}} \cdot \frac{1}{\Sigma N_j W_j} [\mathcal{V}(\Sigma N_j W_j y_j, \Sigma N_j W_j x_j y_j) - \bar{x}\mathcal{V}(\Sigma N_j W_j y_j)]$$

$$= \frac{1}{S_{x^2}} \left[\frac{\Sigma N_j W_j x_j}{\Sigma N_j W_j} - \bar{x}\right]$$

$$= 0. \tag{2.31}$$

[10] Note: The variance symbol with two variates, e.g., $\mathcal{V}(x, y)$, designates the co-variance of the variates.

In addition, we have

$$\mathscr{V}(\hat{\alpha}, \hat{\beta}) = \mathscr{V}(\bar{y} - \hat{\beta}\bar{x}, \hat{\beta})$$

$$= \mathscr{V}(\bar{y}, \hat{\beta}) - \bar{x}\mathscr{V}(\hat{\beta})$$

$$= -\bar{x}/S_{x^2}. \tag{2.32}$$

Since $\hat{\alpha}$ and $\hat{\beta}$ are linear functions of variates which are normally distributed in the limit, they are in the limit normally distributed with the means and variances given above. We may therefore invert critical ratio tests to determine values for confidence bounds on the parameters α and β as follows:

$$\text{for } \alpha: \qquad \hat{\alpha} \pm z_{1-(\gamma/2)}\sqrt{\frac{1}{\Sigma N_j W_j} + \frac{\bar{x}^2}{S_{x^2}}} \tag{2.33}$$

$$\text{for } \beta: \qquad \hat{\beta} \pm z_{1-(\gamma/2)}\sqrt{1/S_{x^2}}. \tag{2.34}$$

These bounds have confidence coefficient $(1 - \gamma)$, when $z_{1-(\gamma/2)}$ is the critical value of the unit normal deviate which corresponds to a cumulative probability point of $(1 - (\gamma/2))$. A confidence region, jointly on α and β, may be found by the method described by Brownlee (1960, pp. 303–306).

Furthermore, we may construct confidence bounds for each $\mu_j = \alpha = \beta x_j$ from the variance of the ordinate of the fitted line at the point x_j. We have

$$\mathscr{V}(\hat{\mu}_j) = \mathscr{V}[(\hat{\alpha} - \alpha) + (\hat{\beta} - \beta)x_j]$$

$$= \mathscr{V}(\hat{\alpha}) + x_j^2 \mathscr{V}(\hat{\beta}) + 2x_j \mathscr{V}(\hat{\alpha}, \hat{\beta}).$$

With appropriate substitutions from (2.29)–(2.32),

$$\mathscr{V}(\hat{\mu}_j) = \frac{1}{\Sigma N_j W_j} + \frac{\bar{x}^2}{S_{x^2}} + \frac{x_j^2}{S_{x^2}} - \frac{2x_j \bar{x}}{S_{x^2}}$$

$$= \frac{1}{\Sigma N_j W_j} + \frac{(x_j - \bar{x})^2}{S_{x^2}}.$$

Thus values for the $(1 - \gamma)$ confidence bounds may be determined

$$\text{for } \mu_j: \qquad \hat{\mu}_j \pm z_{1-(\gamma/2)}\sqrt{\frac{1}{\Sigma N_j W_j} + \frac{(x_j - \bar{x})^2}{S_{x^2}}}. \tag{2.35}$$

Let us assume that the linear regression model fitted to the ΣN observations remains valid for a further set of N_0 observations which might be taken for some value, x_0, not included in the initial design. We then may estimate μ_0 at that value, using (2.9), (2.25), and (2.26),

$$\hat{\mu}_0 = \bar{y} + \frac{S_{xy}}{S_{x^2}}(x_0 - \bar{x}).$$

The variance of the estimator

$$\mathscr{V}(\hat{\mu}_0) = \frac{1}{\Sigma N_j W_j} + \frac{(x_0 - \bar{x})^2}{S_{x^2}} + \frac{1}{N_0}, \tag{2.36}$$

and the values of the $(1 - \gamma)$ confidence bounds may be determined

for μ_0: $$\hat{\mu}_0 \pm z_{1-(\gamma/2)} \left(\frac{1}{\Sigma N_j W_j} + \frac{x_0 - \bar{x}}{S_{x^2}} + \frac{1}{N_0} \right)^{1/2}. \tag{2.37}$$

(See Kendall and Stuart, 1961, p. 363.)

We also may construct a confidence *band* or confidence region for the regression line, i.e. a region such that the probability is $1 - \gamma$ that the true regression line resides within the region. The method is presented by Kendall and Stuart (1961, pp. 365–369), where it is shown that the form of solution is identical with that of Equation 2.35, the only difference being the substitution for $z_{1-(\gamma/2)}$ the term $(\chi^2_{1-\gamma})^{1/2}$ where $\chi^2_{1-\gamma}$ is the $(1 - \gamma)$ point of the χ^2 distribution with two degrees of freedom. As will be seen in Example 2.7, the loci of confidence bounds from (2.36) trace a hyperbola with the regression line as diameter. For fixed γ, the confidence band upon the regression line is a hyperbola of the same form, with the band at every point μ_j typically (for usual levels of γ) about 25% broader than the loci of (2.35). This solution was originally derived by Working and Hotelling (1929).

Finally, we may establish confidence bounds on the point of subjective equality and on difference limen, using results of this section. Recall, from (2.12), that an estimate of the point of subjective equality (pse) may be expressed

$$\widehat{\text{pse}} = x_c - \hat{\alpha}/\hat{\beta};$$

substituting for $\hat{\alpha}$ from (2.26),

$$\widehat{\text{pse}} = x_c + \bar{x}_{jc} - \bar{y}_{jc}/\hat{\beta}.$$

For a given experiment, both x_c and $\bar{x}$ are constants, only $\bar{y}$ and $\hat{\beta}$ being sample values. To approximate the sampling variance of the estimate of pse, we consider a generalized form of (2.21), noting that for any two-variable function, say $t = \Phi(u, v)$,

$$\mathscr{V}(t) \approx \left(\frac{\partial \phi}{\partial u} \right)^2 \mathscr{V}(u) + \left(\frac{\partial \phi}{\partial v} \right)^2 \mathscr{V}(v) + 2 \frac{\partial \phi}{\partial u} \frac{\partial \phi}{\partial v} \mathscr{V}(u, v)$$

(Kendall, 1948, I, p. 208). In this case we use Equations (2.29)–(2.31) to find

$$\mathscr{V}(\widehat{\text{pse}}) \approx \frac{1}{\hat{\beta}^2} \left(\frac{1}{\Sigma N_j W_j} \right) + \left(\frac{\bar{y}_{jc}}{\hat{\beta}^2} \right)^2 \left(\frac{1}{S_{x^2}} \right)$$

$$\approx \frac{1}{\hat{\beta}^2} \left\{ \frac{1}{\Sigma N_j W_j} + \frac{[\widehat{\text{pse}} - (x_c + \bar{x}_{jc})]^2}{S_{x^2}} \right\}. \tag{2.38}$$

Approximate values of the $(1 - \gamma)$ confidence bounds on the unknown parameter pse can be obtained by inverting a critical ratio test based upon this variance,

$$\text{for pse:} \qquad \widehat{\text{pse}} \pm z_{1-(\gamma/2)} [\mathscr{V}(\text{pse})]^{1/2}, \qquad (2.39)$$

where $z_{1-(\gamma/2)}$ is the normal deviate at the $(1 - (\gamma/2))$ point of the normal distribution.

This method of estimating variance and confidence bounds also applies for the substitution for pse of any percentile of the discriminal response distribution. Thus, for the upper difference limen defined at the 75th percentile, using (2.13)

$$\mathscr{V}(\widehat{\text{dl}}_U) \approx \frac{1}{\hat{\beta}^2} \left[\frac{1}{\Sigma N_j W_j} + \frac{(\widehat{\text{dl}}_U - \bar{x}_{jc})^2}{S_{x^2}} \right], \qquad (2.40)$$

and approximate $(1 - \gamma)$ confidence bounds are

$$\text{for dl}_U: \qquad \widehat{\text{dl}}_U \pm z_{1-(\gamma/2)} [\mathscr{V}(\widehat{\text{dl}}_U)]^{1/2}. \qquad (2.41)$$

Bounds for dl_L are similarly obtained by substituting $\widehat{\text{dl}}_L$ (and dl_L) for $\widehat{\text{dl}}_U$ (and dl_U) in (2.40) and (2.41).

In the preceding results, the weights

$$W_j = h^2(Y_j)/P_j Q_j$$

are assumed known. But since they depend upon the unknown population proportion, P_j, they are in general not known. It can be shown, however, that when weights determined from the *observed* proportions, say $w_j = h^2(y_j)/p_j q_j$, are used in (2.23) in place of the W_j, the limiting distribution of (2.24) remains χ^2; the limiting distributions of $\hat{\alpha}$ and $\hat{\beta}$ remain normal with the indicated means and variances.

In finite data the approximation to the limiting distributions can be improved by using weights determined from a provisional graphic fitting of the line of relationship between the expected deviates Y_j and the physical differences, x_j (actually x_{jc}). The ordinates of this line at the points x provide provisional estimates of the expected deviates, say $y_{j,\text{prov}}$. From tables of the inverse normal distribution and the normal ordinate, provisional expected proportions and ordinates can be obtained in order to compute the provisional weights:

$$W_{j,\text{prov}} = h^2(Y_{j,\text{prov}})/P_{j,\text{prov}}(1 - P_{j,\text{prov}}). \qquad (2.42)$$

Alternatively, the provisional weights may be read from a table of the Müller-Urban weights as a function of $Y_{j,\text{prov}}$ (Table A6).

TESTING GOODNESS OF FIT. The minimum value of the normit χ^2 is attained when, in Equation (2.24), $\hat{\alpha}$ and $\hat{\beta}$ are substituted for α and β, respectively. With this substitution, (2.24) remains a χ^2 statistic, but with $n - 2$ degrees of freedom. In the context of analysis of variance, this minimum value may be viewed as the "sum of squares for error" (SSE). It may be simplified as follows:

$$SSE = \Sigma N_j W_j (y_j - \hat{\alpha} - \hat{\beta} x_j)^2$$
$$= \Sigma N_j W_j [(y_j - \bar{y}) - \hat{\beta}(x_j - \bar{x})]^2$$
$$= \Sigma N_j W_j (y_j - \bar{y})^2 - 2\hat{\beta}\Sigma N_j W_j (x_j - \bar{x})(y_j - \bar{y}) + \hat{\beta}^2 \Sigma N_j W_j (x_j - \bar{x})^2 .$$

Substituting from (2.25) for $\hat{\beta}$, expanding and recombining terms, we obtain, say

$$SSE = \Sigma N_j W_j (y_j - \bar{y})^2 - \hat{\beta}\Sigma N_j W_j (x_j - \bar{x})(y_j - \bar{y})$$
$$= S_{y^2} - \hat{\beta} S_{xy} = SST - SSR .$$

A partition of the total weighted sum of squares implicit in this expression may be presented in the form of a summary table for analysis of variance (Table 2.2).

TABLE 2.2. Summary Table for Analysis of Variance for Testing
Psychophysical Model

Source of variation	Degrees of freedom, d.f.	Sum of squares	Expected sum of squares*
Regression	1	$SSR = \hat{\beta} S_{xy}$	$\sigma^2 + \beta^2 S_{x^2}$
Error	$n - 2$	$SSE = SST - SSR$	$(n - 2)\sigma^2$
Total (corrected to the mean)	$n - 1$	$SST = S_{y^2}$	$(n - 1)\sigma^2 + \beta^2 S_{x^2}$

* $\sigma^2 = \mathscr{V}(y_j \sqrt{N_j W_j}) = 1$.

The interpretation of entries in Table 2.2 depends upon the expected values of the sums of squares. If the bias terms are neglected, these expected values are derived as follows:

$$\mathscr{E}(SST) = \Sigma N_j W_j \mathscr{E}(y_j^2) - \Sigma N_j W_j \mathscr{E}(\bar{y})^2$$
$$= \Sigma N_j W_j \mathscr{E}(\alpha + \beta x_j + \xi_j)^2 - \Sigma N_j W_j \mathscr{E}\left(\alpha + \beta\bar{x} + \frac{\Sigma N_j W_j \xi_j}{\Sigma N_j W_j}\right)^2 .$$

Recalling that $\sigma^2 = \mathscr{V}(\sqrt{N_j W_j} y_j) = 1$, we obtain

$$\mathscr{E}(SST) = \alpha^2 \Sigma N_j W_j + 2\alpha\beta\Sigma N_j W_j x_j + \beta^2 \Sigma N_j W_j x_j^2 + n - \alpha^2 \Sigma N_j W_j$$
$$- 2\alpha\beta\bar{x}\Sigma N_j W_j - \beta^2 \bar{x}^2 \Sigma N_j W_j - 1$$
$$= n - 1 + \beta^2 (\Sigma N_j W_j x_j^2 - \bar{x}\Sigma N_j W_j x_j)$$
$$= n - 1 + \beta^2 S_{x^2} ;$$

$$\mathscr{E}(\text{SSR}) = S_{x^2}\mathscr{E}(\hat{\beta}^2)$$

$$= S_{x^2}(1/S_{x^2} + \beta^2)$$

$$= 1 + \beta^2 S_{x^2} \, ;$$

$$\mathscr{E}(\text{SSE}) = \mathscr{E}(\text{SST}) - \mathscr{E}(\text{SSR})$$

$$= n - 2 \, .$$

For testing goodness of fit to the data of the psychophysical (regression) model and the normal response function, we use the error sum of squares, with expected value $(n - 2)\sigma^2$. We wish to test the hypothesis that the population sum of squares estimated by the error sum of squares has this expectation. Since errors are normally distributed under the model, by definition of the χ^2 statistic, the quantity SSE/σ^2 is a χ^2 statistic with $n - 2$ degrees of freedom. Since $\sigma^2 = 1$, $\text{SSE} = \chi^2_{n-2}$ may be referred directly to the χ^2 table for a test of significance.

Significance of this error χ^2 may be viewed as sufficient evidence that discrepancies between the observations and the model cannot be attributed merely to random variation introduced by the sampling of subjects. In this case we would question either the appropriateness of the normal response function or the linearity of regression specified by the psychophysical model. If we fail to reject the model on the basis of the above goodness of fit test, we may wish to test the hypothesis $\beta = 0$. On this hypothesis, SSR has the χ^2 distribution with one degree of freedom. A significant value of

$$\chi^2 = \text{SSR}$$

at the nominal .10 level leads to rejection of the hypothesis $\beta = 0$ with actual significance level .05. (Note that the actual level may be taken at one-half the nominal value, since the alternative to the hypothesis $\beta = 0$ is, in all psychophysical applications, a one-sided alternative hypothesis, typically $\beta > 0$.)

Since the normit χ^2 is distributed as χ^2 only as $N_j \to \infty$, judgment should be withheld when the error sum of squares is only marginally significant. In this case, a test of $\beta = 0$ is still available by considering

$$F = \frac{\text{SSR}}{\text{SSE}/(n-2)},$$

distributed as F with 1 and $(n - 2)$ degrees of freedom (when SSE does represent random error and not systematic departure from linearity). Here, too, the alternative to $\beta = 0$ is $\beta > 0$, so that the nominal level of significance should be halved to produce the actual significance level associated with the test.

Example 2.7

We will again employ the data of Example 2.6 to illustrate Urban's solution for the constant method. For this purpose, values of N_j, r_j, and p_j are reproduced in Table 2.3, columns 2–4. It is convenient for computation to code values of x_{jc} as shown in column *1*. Coding is accomplished by subtracting a constant k from each raw x_{jc}, then dividing by a constant f. In the present case, $k = 0$, $f = .1$, as noted under column *1* in Table 2.3. The coding is simply a change of origin and unit of x_{jc} to obtain the new variable, $x'_{jc} = (x_{jc} - k)/f$. When the computations are completed, the results are decoded by substituting $(x_{jc} - k)/f$ for x'_{jc} in the coded regression line.

Calculations in Table 2.3 are as follows. From observed values p_j, column *4*, we determine values of corresponding normal deviates y_j, entered in column *5*. (These correspond exactly with the values y_j in Table 2.1.) The graphical solution of Example 2.6 provides an adequate provisional regression line. From that line, we read provisional values of Y (specifically, values of Y_{prov}) corresponding to $x_{jc} = -.3, -.2, -.1, .1, .2$, and $.3$. In other words, the $Y_{j,\text{prov}}$ are obtained (from the graphically fitted regression line) as ordinates of the line at the points $x_{jc} = -.3, -.2$, etc. These provisional values, shown under column *6* of Table 2.3, are estimates of the expected deviates associated with the stimuli, X_j, $j = 1, 2, \ldots, n$.

The values $Y_{j,\text{prov}}$ are used to find corresponding values $W_{j,\text{prov}}$, using Equation (2.42). To reduce tedious computation, the values of $W_{j,\text{prov}}$ corresponding to values of $Y_{j,\text{prov}} = .00$ (.01) 2.99 have been tabulated in Table A6. Thus the values of $Y_{j,\text{prov}}$ in column *6* of Table 2.3 are used to find the corresponding values $W_{j,\text{prov}}$, which are listed under column *7*. Products of entries in columns *2* and *7* provide the values $N_j W_{j,\text{prov}}$ of column *8*. Products of entries in columns *1* and *8* provide the $N_j W_j x'_{jc}$ of column *9*; products of entries in columns *5* and *8* yield the $N_j W_j y_j$ of column *10*.

Intermediate results are obtained in Table 2.3 as follows:

Sum column *8* to obtain $\Sigma N_j W_j$.
Sum column *9* to obtain $\Sigma N_j W_j x'_{jc}$.
Sum column *10* to obtain $\Sigma N_j W_j y_j$.
Sum products of entries in columns *1* and *9*, $\Sigma N_j W_j x'^2_{jc}$.
Sum products of entries in columns *5* and *10*, $\Sigma N_j W_j y^2_j$.
Sum products of entries in columns *1* and *10*, or sum products of entries in columns *5* and *9* to obtain $\Sigma N_j W_j x'_{jc} y_j$.

Then $\bar{x}'$, $\bar{y}$ are found and recorded (see page 36). $S_{x'^2}$, S_{y^2}, and $S_{x'y}$ are determined as shown in Table 2.3. Finally $\hat{\alpha}$ and $\hat{\beta}$ are found, from Equations (2.25) and (2.26), and the equation may be written for the regression of $\hat{Y}_{jc}$ upon the given raw values of x_{jc}:

$$\hat{Y}_{jc} = -.162 + 6.011 x_{jc}. \qquad (2.43)$$

TABLE 2.3. Urban's Solution for the Constant Method

Levels, j	Concentration, %	x_{jc}	1 Coded x_j	2 N_j	3 r_j	4 p_j	5 y_j	6 $Y_{j,\text{prov}}$	7 $W_{j,\text{prov}}$	8 NW	9 NWx	10 NWy
6	1.3	.3	3	49	48	.980	2.05	1.62	.2315	11.344	34.032	23.255
5	1.2	.2	2	47	38	.808	.87	1.02	.4317	20.290	40.580	17.652
4	1.1	.1	1	50	31	.620	.31	.42	.5971	29.855	29.855	9.255
3	.9	−.1	−1	48	13	.271	−.61	−.75	.5173	24.830	−24.830	−15.146
2	.8	−.2	−2	48	3	.062	−1.54	−1.35	.3189	15.307	−30.614	−23.573
1	.7	−.3	−3	49	2	.041	−1.74	−1.95	.1424	6.978	−20.934	−12.142

$k = 0, f = .1$.

Letting x refer to coded values:

$\Sigma NW = 108.604$
$\Sigma NWx = 28.089$
$\Sigma NWy = -.699$
$\Sigma NWx^2 = 361.971$
$\Sigma NWy^2 = 132.568$
$\Sigma NWxy = 213.042$

$\bar{x} = \Sigma NWx / \Sigma NW = .2586$
$\bar{y} = \Sigma NWy / \Sigma NW = -.0064$
$S_{x^2} = \Sigma NWx^2 - \bar{x}\Sigma NWx = 354.7072$
$S_{y^2} = \Sigma NWy^2 - \bar{y}\Sigma NWy = 132.5635$
$S_{xy} = \Sigma NWxy - \bar{x}\Sigma NWy = 213.2228$
$b = S_{xy}/S_{x^2} = .6011$
$\hat{\beta} = b/f = 6.011$
raw $\bar{x} = f(\text{coded } \bar{x}) + k = .0259$
$\hat{\alpha} = \bar{y} - \hat{\beta}\bar{x} = -.1618$

Then, using raw $\bar{x}$,

Expressing $\hat{Y}_{jc}$ as a function of the raw x_j,

$$\hat{Y}_{jc} = \hat{\alpha} + \hat{\beta}x_{jc} = -.162 + 6.011x_{jc}$$

(Note in Table 2.3 the need for conversion from coded x'_{jc} to raw x_{jc} before final values $\hat{\alpha}$ and $\hat{\beta}$ are determined, in order that the resulting regression equation be interpretable in raw-score deviation units.)

An analysis of regression of these results may next be performed. The findings appear in Table 2.4 and are based upon the solution given in Table

TABLE 2.4. Analysis of Regression and Confidence Bounds on μ_j, Least Squares Solution

Source of variation	d.f.	Sum of squares	=	χ^2	Probability
Regression	1	$SSR = bS_{xy}$	=	128.168	$p < .001$
Error	$(n - 2) = 4$	$SSE = SST - SSR$	=	4.396	$.50 > p > .30$
Total	$(n - 1) = 5$	$SST = Sy^2$	=	132.564	

$$SE_{\hat{\alpha}} = \sqrt{\frac{1}{\Sigma N_j W_j} + \frac{\bar{x}^2}{S_{x^2}}} = \sqrt{.0093963} = .0969$$

$$SE_{\beta} = \frac{1}{f}\sqrt{1/S_{x^2}} = 10\sqrt{.0028192} = .513$$

From (2.32), using $z_\gamma = 1.96$ ($\gamma = .05$), the .95 c.i. for α is
$$-3.52 \text{ to } +.028$$

From (2.32), using $z_\gamma = 1.96$, the .95 c.i. for β is
$$5.006 \text{ to } 7.016$$

From (2.33), using $z_\gamma = 1.96$, the .95 c.i. for μ_j at the point x_j is

$$\hat{\mu}_j \geq 1.96 \sqrt{.0092077 + \frac{(x_j - .2586)^2}{354.7072}},$$

where x_j is in coded-score form.

2.3 where the total χ^2 is decomposed into two independent components, one for the variation accounted for by regression, the other for residual variation about the regression line. It will be seen that evaluation of the χ^2 associated with error, with four degrees of freedom, provides insufficient evidence to reject the hypothesis that the psychophysical model fits the data ($.25 < p < .75$). Accepting the model, we then test the regression χ^2, with one degree of freedom, and reject the hypothesis $\beta = 0$ at the significance point $.001$.

Next in Table 2.4 appear determinations of standard errors for $\hat{\alpha}$ and $\hat{\beta}$. These are used, in conjunction with Equations (2.33) and (2.34), to obtain .95 confidence intervals for α and for β. Then from Equation (2.35) we determine values of the .95 confidence bounds for each μ_{jc} on the population regression line (the final entry in Table 2.4) as it applies to the coded form of x_{jc}:

$$\text{c.i. for } \mu_j: \qquad \hat{\mu}_j \pm 1.96\sqrt{.0092077 + \frac{(x'_{jc} - .2586)^2}{354.7072}}. \qquad (2.44)$$

The .95 confidence band on the true regression line, substituting $(\chi^2_{2,1-\gamma})^{1/2}$ for $z_{1-(\gamma/2)}$, is seen to be for $(\alpha + \beta x'_{jc})$: $(\hat{\alpha} + \hat{\beta} x'_{jc}) \pm 2.45 \sqrt{.0092077 + \dfrac{(x'_{jc} - .2586)^2}{354.7072}}$.   (2.45)

TABLE 2.5. Predicted μ_j and Limits Provided by the .95 Confidence Bounds, Least Squares Solution

x_{jc}	y_j	$\hat{\mu}_j$	1.96 SE$_{\hat{\mu}}$	μ_{jL}	μ_{jU}
.3	2.05	1.641	.342	1.30	1.98
.2	.87	1.040	.261	.78	1.30
.1	.31	.439	.203	.24	.64
−.1	− .61	− .763	.229	− .99	− .53
−.2	−1.54	−1.364	.301	−1.66	−1.06
−.3	−1.74	−1.965	.388	−2.35	−1.58

Specific findings now may be summarized in Table 2.5, which serves to provide the values plotted in Figure 2.6. In the table appear the values x_{jc},

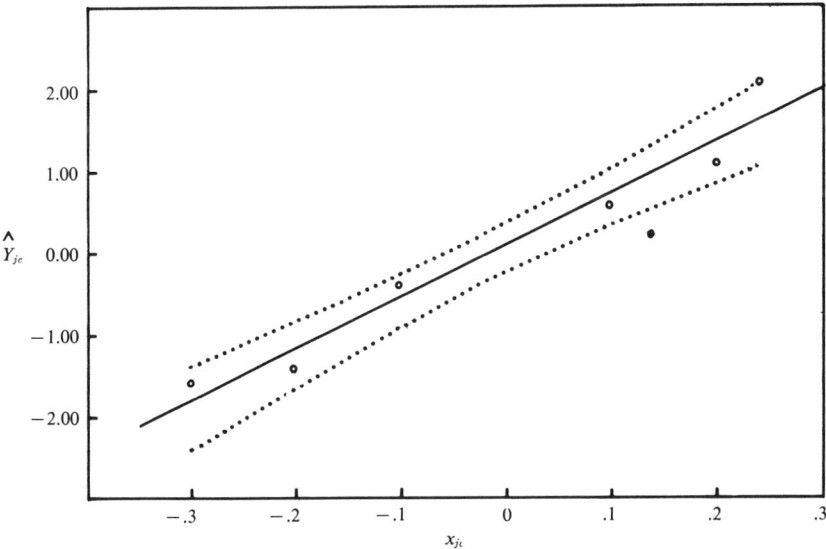

FIG. 2.6. Urban's solution for constant method.

the normal deviates y_j (the deviates associated with the observed p_j; see Table 2.1), and the predicted values μ_{jc}, determined from regression Equation (2.43). Equation (2.44) is used to obtain lower and upper .95 bounds on each μ_{jc}, the μ_{jL} and μ_{jU} of Table 2.5. Figure 2.6 presents this information graphically. Observed y_j appear as points in the figure. The regression line of Equation (2.43) is drawn, falling, of course, through all values $\hat{\mu}_{jc}$. The confidence band about the regression line, determined from (2.45), forms the dotted-line hyperbolas. The interpretation of this confidence band is that, with probability .95, the band includes the population regression line.

It is interesting to convert the regression line of Figure 2.6 into a line for predicting P_j, given x_j. P_j is, it will be remembered, the population proportion of judgments $X_j > X_c$. Conversion is made from tables of the normal distribution (Table A1 in the Appendix) with argument $\hat{\mu}_j$, recalling from (2.6) that

$$\hat{P}_j = \Phi(\hat{\mu}_j).$$

Figure 2.7 displays the results. The ogive represents predicted points, $\hat{P}_j$. The observed points p_j are plotted, and the loci of .95 confidence bounds on

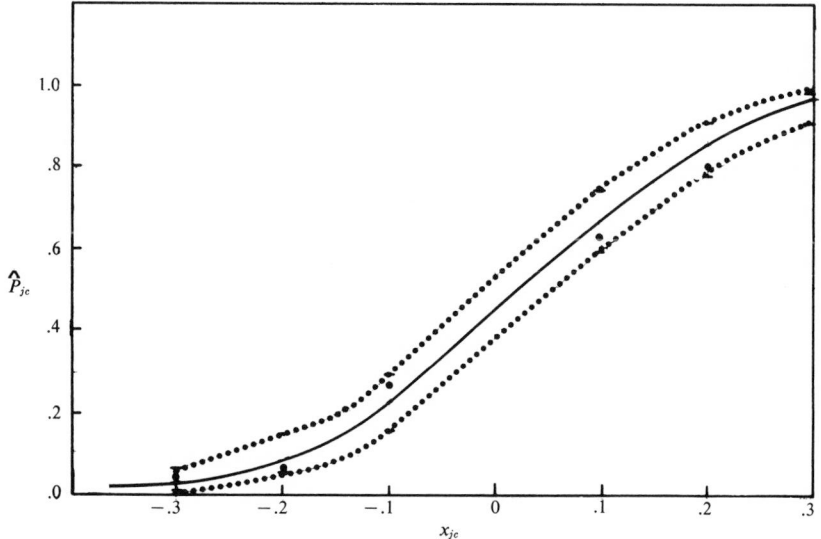

FIG. 2.7.   Predicting P_j from x_j, Urban's solution.

P_j are sketched, located by transforming the μ_{jL} and μ_{jU} of Table 2.5 into corresponding values P_{jL} and P_{jU}.

From Figure 2.7 it is possible to predict, for any value of x_j in the approximate range .7–1.3%, the proportion of subjects in the population that would judge $X_j > X_c$, when $x_c = 1\%$. An approximate .95 confidence interval is provided for each estimated P_j.

A NOTE ON THE ALTERNATIVE BASES FOR CONFIDENCE BOUNDS. Confidence bounds now have been determined on regression parameters by two distinct approaches, and the results are markedly different, as attested by the discrepancies of bounds portrayed in Figures 2.5 and 2.6. In the former case, where bounds on each μ_j are determined for aid in graphical solution for a regression line, .59 joint confidence bounds are even broader than the .53 confidence band from the minimum normit solution. It is instructive to consider the difference between these two approaches to interval estimation.

Recall that, in Section 2.6, a confidence interval was determined separately for each P_j, then was transformed by the inverse normal distribution function $\mu_j = \Phi^{-1}(P_j)$ to be an appropriate interval for μ_j. The basis for establishing the interval, however, was the binomial distribution which was applied separately for each level j. In the graphical solution, then, bounds were determined separately for *six distinct parameters*.

In the minimum normit solution, however, the approach is quite different. A *two-parameter* psychophysical model serves as the basis for determination of confidence bounds for each μ_j and of the confidence band about the population regression line. Clearly, from the same data, joint sampling variation about two parameters is expected to be less than about n parameters when $n > 2$. The difference is so great that, in the present example, the .53 confidence bounds in the six-parameter case are actually broader than the .95 confidence bounds generated by the two-parameter solution.

This difference emphasizes the utility of a psychophysical model for the purpose of statistical prediction. To the extent that the model fits the data, greater precision of prediction is enjoyed. An additional bonus, of course, is that of conceptual clarity; the model provides the means by which a body of knowledge is organized succinctly, systematically, and coherently.

2.8 An Unweighted Minimum Normit Solution

For estimation of parameters of the psychophysical model, a good approximation is achieved by using Urban's solution with equal values of W_j. Sampling experiments by Cramer (1964) have demonstrated that the error mean squares of estimates for α and β, obtained by weighted and unweighted Urban solutions, are essentially identical. Cramer refers to the method based upon equal weights as the unweighted minimum normit method.

The unweighted minimum normit solution is computationally simple. Its chief advantage over a graphical solution is that no subjective judgment is required. It is limited, as is the graphical method, by its failure to provide statistical tests or interval estimates on the parameters of the psychophysical model.

In applying the unweighted minimum normit solution, it is suggested that extreme proportions, $p_j = 0$ and $p_j = 1$, be replaced by $p_j = 1/(2N_j)$ and $p_j = 1 - 1/(2N_j)$, the same advice recommended for the graphical method and for the complete minimum normit solution.

Example 2.8

The form of the unweighted minimum normit solution is illustrated in Table 2.6, where the data of Example 2.6 once again are treated for purpose

TABLE 2.6. Unweighted Minimum Normit Solution for the Constant Method

Levels	Concentration, %	x_{Jc}	Coded x_J	N_J	r_J	p_J	y_J
6	1.3	.3	3	49	48	.980	2.05
5	1.2	.2	2	47	38	.808	.87
4	1.1	.1	1	50	31	.620	.31
3	.9	−.1	−1	48	13	.271	− .61
2	.8	−.2	−2	48	3	.062	−1.54
1	.7	−.3	−3	49	2	.041	−1.74

$k = 0, f = .1.$
Letting x refer to coded values:

$$\Sigma N = 291 \qquad\qquad \bar{x} = \Sigma Nx/\Sigma N = 0$$
$$\Sigma Nx = 0 \qquad\qquad \bar{y} = \Sigma Ny/\Sigma N = -.1086$$
$$\Sigma Ny = -31.62 \qquad S_{x^2} = \Sigma Nx^2 - \bar{x}\Sigma Nx = 1360$$
$$\Sigma Nx^2 = 1360 \qquad S_{y^2} = \Sigma Ny^2 - \bar{y}\Sigma Ny = 522.9179$$
$$\Sigma Ny^2 = 526.3518 \qquad S_{xy} = \Sigma Nxy - \bar{x}\Sigma Ny = 831.53$$
$$\Sigma Nxy = 831.53 \qquad b = S_{xy}/S_{x^2} = .6114$$
$$\hat{\beta} = b/f = 6.114$$
$$\text{raw } \bar{x} = f(\text{coded } \bar{x} + k) = 0$$
$$\text{Using raw } \bar{x},\ \hat{\alpha} = \bar{y} - \hat{\beta}\bar{x} = -.1086$$
$$\hat{Y}_{Jc} = \hat{\alpha} + \hat{\beta}x_{Jc} = -.109 + 6.114x_{Jc}$$

of comparison. Steps in the solution are identical to those of the minimum normit method, shown in Table 2.2, except that all W_j are set equal to unity. A plot of the data points and the regression line resulting from this analysis,

$$\hat{Y}_{jc} = -.109 + 6.114x_{jc},$$

would confirm the adequacy of fit to these data. Estimates of α and β display only trivial differences from those found in Examples 2.6 and 2.7, relative to the standard errors of those estimates given in Table 2.4.

3 Advanced Solutions for the Constant Method

This chapter is devoted to solutions for the constant method whicn are valid under conditions more general than those assumed for the minimum normit solution in Chapter 2. In Section 3.1, a solution utilizing the information in 0 and 100% responses is obtained by the method of maximum likelihood. The example in Chapter 2 is reworked by this method and, in Section 3.2, the results are compared with those of the previous solutions. In Section 3.3 the logistic and angular response functions are introduced as possible alternatives to the normal response function. Minor changes in the computing procedures of the least squares and maximum likelihood solutions required by these response functions are then described. In the remaining sections of the chapter solutions are given for a model for constant-method data which includes a term for the order effect. These solutions are applied to a sample of taste-test data in which an effect of order of tasting is clearly present.

3.1 The Maximum Likelihood Solution

A third approach to estimating the parameters of the psychophysical model makes use of the principle of maximum likelihood. The likelihood function is defined for a random sample of p observations from the frequency distribution $f(y, \theta)$, where θ is an $m \times 1$ vector of parameters. The likelihood function L then has the same form as the *joint* frequency function of the observations:

$$L = f(\mathbf{y}, \theta),$$

where $\mathbf{y}$ is the given $p \times 1$ vector of observations. The vector $\hat{\theta}$, a maximum likelihood estimate of θ, is that vector of the parameters which maximizes the likelihood function for the given observations, when L is considered as a function of θ.

51

Assume $m \leq p$. Then the estimate $\hat{\theta}$ is a solution of the m equations

$$\partial L/\partial\theta = 0 .$$

(This is a symbolic derivative of a scalar with respect to a vector; see Dwyer and MacPhail, 1948). Since the function $\log L = l$, say, is a monotonic transformation on L, it has its maximum at the same point as L, and we may find $\hat{\theta}$ more conveniently from the solution of the so-called *likelihood equations*,

$$\frac{\partial \log L}{\partial\theta} = \frac{\partial l}{\partial\theta} = 0 .$$

The principle of maximum likelihood provides a general method for estimating parameters of probability distribution functions, or of the unknown constants of models which connect the parameters with other variables. Maximum likelihood estimators exist whenever certain regularity conditions on the probability or probability density function are met, as they are for most distributions of practical interest (Rao, 1952; Mood and Graybill, 1963). Although a maximum likelihood estimator is not necessarily unbiased or of minimum variance in small samples, it is "efficient"; that is, its limiting variance attains the theoretical minimum. When several parameters are estimated jointly by maximum likelihood, the respective limiting variances of the estimates are given by the negative of the diagonal elements of the expected inverse of the matrix of second derivatives:

$$\mathscr{V}(\hat{\theta}) = -\mathscr{E}\left[\frac{\partial^2 l}{\partial\theta\partial\theta'}\right]^{-1} .$$

The negative of the expected value of the matrix of second derivatives (not inverted) is called the "information" matrix. It is the matric generalization of the information about the parameters supplied by the observations, as defined by Fisher.

Maximum likelihood estimates are normally distributed in the limit; thus they belong to the class of Best Asymptotic Normal (BAN) estimators (Neyman, 1949). They also yield the *sufficient* estimators of the parameters whenever such estimators exist (see Mood and Graybill, 1963).

The generality of maximum likelihood estimation is to our advantage in obtaining a solution for the constant method. The minimum normit χ^2 solution does not exist, strictly speaking, when 0 or 100% proportions of response are observed. The maximum likelihood solution, on the other hand, exists even in this case. It is obtained as follows.

Under the assumption of independent sampling of subjects, in the single-judgment condition (see Section 2.2), or independence of response in the multiple-judgment condition, the probability of a particular set of observations is the product of binomial probabilities,

$$P(\Sigma s_{1i} = r_{1c}, \Sigma s_{2i} = r_{2c}, \ldots, \Sigma s_{ni} = r_{nc})$$

$$= \prod_{j=1}^{n} \frac{N_{jc}!}{r_{jc}!(N_{jc} - r_{jc})!} \, P_{jc}^{r_{jc}} Q_{jc}^{(N_{jc} - r_{jc})}. \qquad (3.1)$$

Regarded as a function of P_{jc}, expression (3.1) is the likelihood function. For particular observed values of r_{jc}, the maximum likelihood solution for the constant method is obtained by maximizing (3.1) with respect to α and β, which determine P_{jc} and $Q_{jc} = 1 - P_{jc}$, via the response function

$$P_j = \Phi(\alpha + \beta x_{jc}).$$

Φ is, as before, the unit normal distribution function. For purpose of maximization it is convenient to take the logarithm of (3.1) to define the log likelihood

$$l = \Sigma \log \frac{N!}{r!(N - r)!} + \Sigma r \log P + \Sigma(N - r) \log Q, \qquad (3.2)$$

where the j and c subscripts for each symbol on the right are omitted for ease of writing. To determine $\hat{\alpha}$, we set the first derivatives of l with respect to α equal to zero to obtain the likelihood equations

$$\frac{\partial l}{\partial \alpha} = \frac{\partial l}{\partial P} \frac{\partial P}{\partial \alpha}$$

$$= \Sigma \left(\frac{r}{P} - \frac{N - r}{Q} \right) \frac{\partial P}{\partial \alpha}$$

$$= \Sigma \frac{N(p - P)}{PQ} \frac{\partial P}{\partial \alpha} = 0$$

$$= \Sigma \frac{N(p - P)h(Y)}{PQ} = 0 \qquad (3.3)$$

since

$$\frac{\partial P}{\partial \alpha} = \frac{\partial \Phi(\alpha + \beta x)}{\partial \alpha} = h(Y); \qquad (3.4)$$

$h(Y_{jc})$, it will be recalled, is the ordinate of the unit normal curve at the deviate Y_{jc}. Similarly, differentiating l with respect to β,

$$\frac{\partial l}{\partial \beta} = \Sigma \frac{N(p - P)}{PQ} x h(Y) = 0, \qquad (3.5)$$

since

$$\frac{\partial P}{\partial \beta} = xh(Y).\qquad(3.6)$$

Because the likelihood equations are nonlinear implicit functions of the unknowns α and β, they are not solvable in the fashion of the normal equations of the minimum normit χ^2 solution. However, a numerical solution may be readily obtained by the Newton-Raphson method, which we now describe.

Let $f(x)$ be a continuous function with continuous derivatives in the neighborhood of x_0, where x_0 is a root of $f(x) = 0$, and let $f'(x)$ be the first derivative of the function evaluated at the point x. Suppose another point in the neighborhood of x_0 is x_k. Then the value of the function at x_0 is approximated by the first two terms of a Taylor series

$$f(x_0) \approx f(x_k) + \frac{f'(x_k)(x_0 - x_k)}{1!}.$$

If x_k is sufficiently close to x_0, then x_{k+1}, a closer approximation of x_0, is obtained by

$$x_{k+1} = x_k - f(x_k)/f'(x_k).$$

Repeated application of this process will converge to the root (Householder, 1953, p. 122; Henrici, 1964, p. 79; Willers, 1948, p. 219). The process will encounter difficulties if x_0 is a multiple root, for then $f'(x_0) = 0$.

The Newton-Raphson procedure can be extended to n independent functions in n unknowns. Let the $n \times 1$ vector $\mathbf{x}_0$ be the simultaneous solution of

$$f_1(\mathbf{x}) = 0$$
$$f_2(\mathbf{x}) = 0$$
$$\vdots$$
$$f_n(\mathbf{x}) = 0.$$

From an approximate solution $\mathbf{x}_k$ in which each element is sufficiently close to the corresponding element of $\mathbf{x}_0$, an improved approximation can be obtained by

$$\mathbf{x}_{k+1} = \mathbf{x}_k - [f'_1(\mathbf{x}_k), f'_2(\mathbf{x}_k), \ldots, f'_n(\mathbf{x}_k)]^{-1} \begin{bmatrix} f_1(\mathbf{x}_k) \\ f_2(\mathbf{x}_k) \\ \vdots \\ f_n(\mathbf{x}_k) \end{bmatrix},$$

where the derivative of each of the n functions with respect to $\mathbf{x}$ is understood to be an $n \times 1$ vector. These n vectors comprise the $n \times n$ symmetric matrix of first derivatives. Since the inverse of the matrix of first derivatives is required, the procedure will encounter difficulties if this matrix is singular or near singular.

Berkson (1955a), gives some examples of this problem for the case of three equally spaced values of the physical variable. When two of the three sample response proportions are 0 or 1 in this situation, the maximum likelihood solution corresponds to infinite values of the parameters. In more typical applications, however, the matrix of second derivatives is negative definite for all finite values of the parameters. Thus, the likelihood surface is concave downward at all points, and the solution will converge to the unique maximum for any finite values of the parameters.

To use the Newton-Raphson method in the present application we need the first derivatives of the expressions in (3.3) and (3.5), i.e. the second derivatives of the log likelihood function (3.2).

For P as a function of two variables, say u and v in general, we find using the quotient rule,

$$\frac{\partial^2 l}{\partial u \partial v} = \sum \left\{ \frac{NPQ(p-P)\dfrac{\partial^2 P}{\partial u \partial v} - NPQ\dfrac{\partial P}{\partial u}\dfrac{\partial P}{\partial v} - N(p-P)(Q-P)\dfrac{\partial P}{\partial u}\dfrac{\partial P}{\partial v}}{P^2 Q^2} \right\}$$

since

$$\frac{\partial PQ}{\partial P} = \frac{\partial P(1-P)}{\partial P} = 1 - 2P = Q - P.$$

Now, differentiating (3.4) and (3.6), we obtain

$$\frac{\partial^2 P}{\partial \alpha^2} = h'(Y),$$

$$\frac{\partial^2 P}{\partial \alpha \partial \beta} = xh'(Y),$$

and

$$\frac{\partial^2 P}{\partial \beta^2} = x^2 h'(Y).$$

Then

$$\frac{\partial^2 l}{\partial \alpha^2} = \sum \frac{N(p-P)h'(Y)}{PQ} - \sum \frac{Nh^2(Y)}{PQ} - \sum \frac{N(p-P)(Q-P)h^2(Y)}{P^2 Q^2}$$

$$= \sum \frac{Nh(Y)(p-P)}{PQ} \left(\frac{h'(Y)}{h(Y)} - \frac{(Q-P)h(Y)}{PQ} \right) - \sum \frac{Nh^2(Y)}{PQ}.$$

However

$$h'(Y) = \partial\left(\frac{1}{\sqrt{2\pi}}\exp(-\tfrac{1}{2}Y^2)\right)\bigg/\partial\alpha = -Yh(Y)\frac{\partial Y}{\partial\alpha};$$

but $\partial Y/\partial\alpha = 1$, hence

$$\frac{h'(Y)}{h(Y)} = -Y.$$

Thus

$$\frac{\partial^2 l}{\partial\alpha^2} = \sum \frac{Nh(Y)(p-P)}{PQ}\left(-Y - \frac{h(Y)}{P} + \frac{h(Y)}{Q}\right) - \sum \frac{Nh^2(Y)}{PQ}.$$

Similarly,

$$\frac{\partial^2 l}{\partial\alpha\partial\beta} = \sum \frac{Nh(Y)(p-P)}{PQ}\left(-Y - \frac{h(Y)}{P} + \frac{h(Y)}{Q}\right)x - \sum \frac{Nh^2(Y)}{PQ}x,$$

and

$$\frac{\partial^2 l}{\partial\beta^2} = \sum \frac{Nh(Y)(p-P)}{PQ}\left(-Y - \frac{h(Y)}{P} + \frac{h(Y)}{Q}\right)x^2 - \sum \frac{Nh^2(Y)}{PQ}x^2.$$

From any kth stage provisional estimates, say $[\alpha, \beta]_k$, improved estimates may be obtained from

$$\begin{bmatrix}\alpha\\\beta\end{bmatrix}_{k+1} = \begin{bmatrix}\alpha\\\beta\end{bmatrix}_k - \begin{bmatrix}\partial^2 l/\partial\alpha^2 & \partial^2 l/\partial\alpha\partial\beta\\\partial^2 l/\partial\beta\partial\alpha & \partial^2 l/\partial\beta^2\end{bmatrix}_k^{-1}\begin{bmatrix}\partial l/\partial\alpha\\\partial l/\partial\beta\end{bmatrix}_k. \tag{3.7}$$

First-stage provisional values for α and β might conveniently be taken from a graphical solution, or from an unweighted least squares solution.

The quantities in equation (3.7) involve only the provisional α and β, the provisional deviates, ordinates, and areas which they determine, and the observed proportions, p. Since the observed deviates $y = \Phi^{-1}(p)$ are not required, the occurrence of proportions of 0 or 1 typically causes no difficulty.

In machine computation the inverse of the matrix of second derivatives in (3.7) may be obtained numerically or calculated from the formula

$$\frac{1}{(\partial^2 l/\partial\alpha^2)(\partial^2 l/\partial\beta^2) - (\partial^2 l/\partial\alpha\partial\beta)^2}\begin{bmatrix}\partial^2 l/\partial\beta^2 & -\partial^2 l/\partial\beta\partial\alpha\\-\partial^2 l/\partial\alpha\partial\beta & \partial^2 l/\partial\alpha^2\end{bmatrix}.$$

The Newton-Raphson process may be continued until the estimates are stabilized. It is not necessary to recompute the second derivatives each time. This solution was first given by Garwood (1941).

Computation is considerably facilitated by using approximations to the second derivatives. If the observations are replaced by their expected values in the second derivatives, the left-hand terms vanish and the Newton's process reduces to

$$\begin{bmatrix}\alpha\\\beta\end{bmatrix}_{k+1} = \begin{bmatrix}\alpha\\\beta\end{bmatrix}_k + \begin{bmatrix}\Sigma NW & \Sigma NWx\\\Sigma NWx & \Sigma NWx^2\end{bmatrix}_k^{-1}\begin{bmatrix}\Sigma Nh(Y)(p-P)/PQ\\\Sigma Nh(Y)(p-P)x/PQ\end{bmatrix}_k \tag{3.8}$$

where

$$W_k = h^2(Y_k)/P_k Q_k.$$

Now define the "working" deviates

$$y_{wk} = \frac{(r - NP_k)}{Nh(Y_k)} + Y_k = Y_k + \frac{1}{h(Y_k)}(p - P_k). \tag{3.9}$$

(Working deviates are given, for arguments p and Y_k, in Table A8.) Writing the inverse in (3.8) explicitly,

$$\begin{bmatrix} \alpha_{k+1} \\ \beta_{k+1} \end{bmatrix} = \begin{bmatrix} \alpha_k \\ \beta_k \end{bmatrix} + \frac{1}{\Sigma NW_k \Sigma NW_k x^2 - (\Sigma NW_k x)^2} \begin{bmatrix} \Sigma NW_k x^2 & -\Sigma NW_k x \\ -\Sigma NW_k x & \Sigma NW_k \end{bmatrix}$$

$$\cdot \begin{bmatrix} \Sigma NW_k(y_{wk} - Y_k) \\ \Sigma NW_k(y_{wk} - Y_k)x \end{bmatrix}$$

$$\beta_{k+1} = \beta_k - \frac{\Sigma NW_k x \Sigma NW_k(y_{wk} - Y_k) - \Sigma NW_k \Sigma NW_k(y_{wk} - Y_k)x}{\Sigma NW_k \Sigma NW_k x^2 - (\Sigma NW_k x)^2}.$$

Dividing numerator and denominator by ΣNW_k gives

$$\beta_{k+1} = \beta_k - [\bar{x}\Sigma NW_k(y_{wk} - Y_k) - \Sigma NW_k(y_{wk} - Y_k)x]/S_{x_k^2}$$

$$= \beta_k - (\Sigma NW_k Y_k x - \bar{x}\Sigma NW_k)/S_{x^2} + (\Sigma NW_k y_{wk} x - \bar{x}\Sigma NW_k y_{wk})/S_{x_k^2}.$$

But if Y_k and W_k have been determined by a provisional regression line with slope β_k, the first two terms on the right are equal. Hence,

$$\beta_{k+1} = S_{xy_{wk}}/S_{x_k^2}. \tag{3.10}$$

That is, the maximum likelihood estimate of β may be obtained by repeated application of the least squares solution, with the working deviates replacing the observed deviates. Note that unlike the observed deviates, the working deviates are defined for $p = 0$ and $p = 1$. At each repetition, new provisional deviates, weights, and working deviates are obtained and new least squares solutions for α and β computed. The process is continued until stable values are obtained.

Similarly,

$$\alpha_{k+1} = \alpha_k - \frac{\Sigma NW_k x^2 \Sigma NW_k(y_{wk} - Y_k) - \Sigma NW_k x \Sigma NW_k(y_{wk} - Y_k)x}{\Sigma NW_k \Sigma NW_k x^2 - (\Sigma NWx)^2}.$$

Dividing numerator and denominator of the fraction by ΣNW_k gives

$$\alpha_{k+1} = \alpha_k - \frac{\Sigma NW_k x^2(\bar{y}_{wk} - \bar{Y}_k) - \bar{x}\Sigma NW_k(y_{wk} - Y_k)x}{S_{x_k^2}};$$

Adding and subtracting $\bar{Y}_k \bar{x} \Sigma N W_k x$ and $\bar{y}_{wk} \bar{x} \Sigma N W_k x$,

$$\alpha_{k+1} = \alpha_k - \frac{\bar{Y}_k(\Sigma N W_k x^2 - \bar{x}\Sigma N W_k x) - \bar{x}(\Sigma N W_k Y_k x - \bar{Y}_k \Sigma N W_k x)}{S_{x_k^2}}$$

$$+ \frac{\bar{y}_{wk}(\Sigma N W_k x^2 - \bar{x}\Sigma N W_k x) - \bar{x}(\Sigma N W_k y_{wk} x - \bar{y}_{wk} \Sigma N W_k x)}{S_{x_k^2}}$$

$$= \alpha_k - (Y_k - \beta_k \bar{x}) + \bar{y}_{wk} - \beta_{k+1} \bar{x}.$$

If Y_k and W_k have been determined from a provisional regression line with slope β_k and intercept α_k, this reduces to

$$\alpha_{k+1} = \bar{y}_{wk} - \beta_{k+1} \bar{x}. \tag{3.11}$$

Thus the maximum likelihood estimate of α may also be obtained by repeated application of the least squares procedure.

This latter type of maximum likelihood solution was first devised by Fisher (1935) and described in detail by Finney (1952), who terms the procedure "probit" analysis. In most cases, the probit solution converges only slightly more slowly than the complete Newton's solution.

To estimate the limiting variances of the maximum likelihood estimates, we invert the matrix of the second derivatives in the final stage of the probit procedure. After some simplification of the terms in the inverse we find, as before,

$$\mathscr{V}(\hat{\alpha}) = \frac{1}{\Sigma N W^*} + \frac{\bar{x}^2}{\Sigma N W^* x^2 - \bar{x}\Sigma N W^* x}, \tag{3.12}$$

$$\mathscr{V}(\hat{\beta}) = 1/(\Sigma N W^* x^2 - \bar{x}\Sigma N W^* x), \tag{3.13}$$

$$\mathscr{V}(\hat{\alpha}, \hat{\beta}) = -\bar{x}/(\Sigma N W^* x^2 - \bar{x}\Sigma N W^* x), \tag{3.14}$$

$$\mathscr{V}(\hat{\mu}_j) = \frac{1}{\Sigma N W^*} + \frac{(x_j - \bar{x})^2}{\Sigma N W^* x^2 - \bar{x}\Sigma N W^* x}, \tag{3.15}$$

where the W^* are determined from the deviates predicted from the final estimates of α and β. These variances may be used for the construction of confidence bounds as in the minimum normit χ^2 solution.

An analysis of variance in terms of working deviates also applies to the maximum likelihood solution. Let

$$\hat{P}_j = \Phi(\hat{\alpha} + \hat{\beta} x_j).$$

Then the residual sum of squares for this analysis is exactly equal to

$$\sum_{j=1}^{n} \frac{N_j(p_j - \hat{P}_j)^2}{\hat{P}_j \hat{Q}_j},$$

TABLE 3.1. Maximum Likelihood Solution for Constant Method

Levels	x_{jc}	1 Coded x_j	2 N_j	3 r_j	4 p_j	5 y_j	6 $Y_{j,prov}$	7 W_j	8 NW	9 NWx	10 y_w	11 NWy_w	12 $NWxy_w$
6	.3	3	49	48	.980	2.05	1.62	.2315	11.3435	34.0305	1.924	21.8249	65.4747
5	.2	2	47	38	.808	.87	1.02	.4317	20.2899	40.5798	.859	17.4790	34.9580
4	.1	1	50	31	.620	.31	.42	.5971	29.8550	29.8550	.303	9.0461	9.0461
3	−.1	−1	48	13	.271	−.61	−.75	.5173	24.8304	−24.8304	−.601	−14.9231	14.9231
2	−.2	−2	48	3	.062	−1.54	−1.35	.3189	14.3072	−30.6144	−1.514	−21.6611	43.3222
1	−.3	−3	49	2	.041	−1.74	−1.95	.1424	6.9776	−20.9328	−1.688	−11.7782	35.3346

$c = 0, f = .1.$

$\Sigma NW = 107.6063$
$\Sigma NWx = 28.0877$
$\Sigma NWy = -.0124$
$\Sigma NWxy = 203.0587$
$\Sigma NWx^2 = 361.9637$
$\Sigma NWy^2 = 121.3918$

$$\bar{x} = \Sigma NWx/\Sigma NW = .2610$$
$$\bar{y} = \Sigma NWy/\Sigma NW = -.0001$$
$$S_x^2 = \Sigma NWx^2 - \bar{x}\Sigma NWx = 354.6328$$
$$S_y^2 = \Sigma NWy^2 - \bar{y}\Sigma NWy = 121.3918$$
$$S_{xy} = \Sigma NWxy - \bar{y}\Sigma NWx - \bar{x}\Sigma NWy = 203.0619$$
$$b = S_{xy}/S_x^2 = .5726$$
$$\beta = b/f = 5.726$$
$$\text{raw } \bar{x} = f(\text{coded } x) + c = .0261$$

Using raw x,
$$\hat{\alpha} = \bar{y} - \beta\bar{x} = -.1495$$

$$Y_{jc} = \hat{\alpha} + \hat{\beta}x_{jc} = -.1495 + 5.726x_{jc}$$

which is the Pearsonian χ^2 with $n - 2$ degrees of freedom for testing the goodness of fit of the model.

Example 3.1

In Table 3.1 appear results of a first approximation to the maximum likelihood solution for the data on sodium chloride also analyzed in Examples 2.6, 2.7, and 2.8. Columns numbered *1–9* in Table 3.1 are identical to corresponding columns in Table 2.3. The entries y_w of column *10* are obtained from Table A8, using joint arguments p_j and $Y_{j,\text{prov}}$ (where the latter are taken from the graphical solution, Example 2.6). All other features of the solution in Table 3.1 either are self-explanatory, or are directly analogous to steps of the minimum normit χ^2 solution of Table 2.3.

In Table 3.2 is shown an iteration of this solution. We utilize the resulting equation for $\hat{\mu}_j$ (Table 3.2) to determine an improved second-stage set of

TABLE 3.2. Maximum Likelihood Solution for Constant Method (First Iteration)

Coded x_{jc}	x_j	N_j	Y_j, prov	W_j	NW	NWx	y_w	NWy_w	$NWxy_w$
.3	3	49	1.57	.2468	12.0932	36.2796	1.898	22.9529	68.8587
.2	2	47	1.00	.4386	20.6142	41.2884	.863	17.7901	35.5802
.1	1	50	0.42	.5971	29.8550	29.8550	.303	9.0461	9.0461
−.1	−1	48	−0.72	.5261	25.2528	−25.2528	−.605	−15.2779	−15.2779
−.2	−2	48	−1.29	.3394	16.2912	−32.5824	−1.500	−24.4368	48.8736
−.3	−3	49	−1.87	.1619	7.9331	−23.7993	−1.720	−13.6449	40.9347

$c = 0, f = .1.$

$$\Sigma NW = 112.0395 \qquad\qquad \bar{x} = \Sigma NWx/\Sigma NW = .2296$$
$$\Sigma NWx = 25.7285 \qquad\qquad \bar{y} = \Sigma NWy/\Sigma NW = -.0319$$
$$\Sigma NWy = -3.5705 \qquad\qquad S_{x^2} = \Sigma NWx^2 - \bar{x}\Sigma NWx = 377.0588$$
$$\Sigma NWxy = 218.5712 \qquad\qquad S_{y^2} = \Sigma NWy^2 - \bar{y}\Sigma NWy = 130.9121$$
$$\Sigma NWx^2 = 382.9661 \qquad\qquad S_{xy} = \Sigma NWxy - \bar{x}\Sigma NWy = 219.3910$$
$$\Sigma NWy^2 = 131.0260 \qquad\qquad b = S_{xy}/S_{x^2} = 0.5818$$
$$\hat{\beta} = b/f = 5.818$$
$$\text{raw } \bar{x} = f(\text{coded } \bar{x}) + c = .0230$$
$$\text{Then, using raw } \bar{x}$$
$$\hat{\alpha} = \bar{y}\hat{\beta}\bar{x} = -.1657$$
$$\hat{Y}_{jc} = -.1657 + 5.818x_{jc}$$

provisional deviates

$$Y_{j,\text{prov}} = -.150 + 5.726x_{jc}$$

(where x_{jc}, here, represents uncoded concentrations). Using these rather than the graphically determined $Y_{j,\text{prov}}$ of Table 3.1, we determine new W_j and new y_w, in order to iterate the solution.

In Table 3.3 appears a second iteration of the solution, using as provisional deviates those resulting from the first iteration of Table 3.2:

$$Y_{j, \text{prov}} = -.166 + 5.818x_{jc}.$$

On the basis of newly determined W_j and y_w, the resulting regression equation is

$$\hat{Y}_{jc} = -.165 + 5.821x_{jc}.$$

This result is judged sufficiently close to that of the previous iteration to justify its acceptance as a final solution.

Based upon this solution, the regression analysis of Table 3.4 is performed, all computations being based upon the same formulations as those familiar from Example 2.7.

TABLE 3.3. Maximum Likelihood Solution for Constant Method (Second Iteration)

x_{jc}	Coded x_j	N_j	$Y_{j, \text{prov}}$	W_j	NW	NWx	y_w	NWy_w	$NWxy_w$
.3	3	49	1.58	.2435	11.9315	35.7945	1.903	22.7056	68.1168
.2	2	47	1.00	.4386	20.6142	41.2284	.863	17.7901	35.5802
.1	1	50	.42	.5971	29.8550	29.8550	.303	9.0461	9.0461
−.1	−1	48	− .75	.5173	24.8304	−24.8304	− .601	−14.9231	14.9231
−.2	−2	48	−1.33	.3254	15.6192	−31.2384	−1.510	−23.5850	47.1700
−.3	−3	49	−1.91	.1519	7.4431	−22.3293	−1.708	−12.7128	38.1384

$c = 0, f = .1.$

$\Sigma NW \quad = 110.2934$

$\Sigma NWx \quad = 28.4798$

$\Sigma NWy \quad = -1.6791$

$\Sigma NWxy = 212.9746$

$\Sigma NWx^2 = 373.9904$

$\Sigma NWy^2 = 127.5982$

$\bar{x} = \quad .2582$

$\bar{y} = \quad -.0152$

$S_{x^2} = 366.6369$

$S_{y^2} = 127.5727$

$S_{xy} = 213.4081$

$b = \quad .5821$

$\hat{\beta} = \quad 5.821$

raw $\bar{x} = \quad .0258$

$\hat{\alpha} = \quad -.1654$

$\hat{Y}_{jc} = \quad -.1654 + 5.821x_{jc}$

TABLE 3.4. Regression Analysis: Maximum Likelihood Solution for Constant Method

Source of variation	d.f.	Sum of squares	=	χ^2	Probability
Regression	1	$SSR = bS_{xy}$	=	124.2249	$p < .001$
Residual	$(n-2) = 4$	$SSE = SST - SSR$	=	3.3478	$.50 > p > .30$
Total (corrected to the mean)	$(n-1) = 5$	$SST = S_{y^2}$	=	127.5727	

$$SE_{\hat{\alpha}} = \sqrt{1/(\Sigma NW) + \bar{x}^2/S_{x^2}} = .0962$$

$$SE_{\hat{\beta}} = \frac{1}{f}\sqrt{1/S_{x^2}} = .522$$

From (2.35), a $(1 - \gamma)$ confidence band on μ_j is provided by

$$\hat{\mu}_j \pm z_{\bar{\gamma}}\sqrt{1/\Sigma NW + (x_j - \bar{x})^2 S_{x^2}}$$

For $\gamma = .05$, the limits of the band at x are

$$\hat{\mu}_j \pm 1.96\sqrt{.00906672 + .002727\,(x_j - .2582)^2}$$

3.2   Comparison of Graphical, Least Squares, and Maximum Likelihood Solutions

In Examples 2.6, 2.7, 2.8, and 3.1, identical data were treated by graphical, weighted least squares, unweighted least squares, and maximum likelihood methods. From these solutions, the psychophysical equation was estimated to be

$$\hat{\mu}_{jc} = -.17 + 6.15x_{jc},$$

$$\hat{\mu}_{jc} = -.162 + 6.011x_{jc},$$

$$\hat{\mu}_{jc} = -.109 + 6.114x_{jc},$$

or

$$\hat{\mu}_{jc} = -.165 + 5.821x_{jc},$$

respectively. All four solutions are quite similar in this example. (Similarity of solutions provided by the weighted least squares and maximum likelihood methods is further evidenced by the results from the regression analyses; note that differences between the $\hat{\alpha}$ and $\hat{\beta}$ values are substantially smaller than the standard errors of these values, as given in Table 3.4.)

It is noteworthy that the simple graphical solution provides very satisfactory estimates of α and β. Generally this is the case, if the investigator exercises care and good judgment in fitting a line to data points. However, the method is limited if statistical inference is at issue, since no satisfactory interval estimates of the parameters are supplied.

Three studies of the relative value of the minimum normit χ^2 solution and the maximum likelihood solution have been reported in the journal literature (Berkson, 1957; Cramer, 1962, 1964).

By exhausting all possible samples (where $N_j = 10, j = 3$) and computing estimates of various known values of α and β for each, Berkson was able to conclude that "in the experiments presented, the mean square error of the minimum normit χ^2 estimate is smaller than that of the maximum likelihood estimate." Differences between the methods, although systematically favoring minimum normit χ^2, were small. Berkson stresses that "the important finding of the present investigation is not that the minimum normit χ^2 estimator has a smaller error than the maximum likelihood estimator, even if this is accepted in full generality, but rather that the maximum likelihood estimator does *not* have the smaller error in all circumstances." The implication of Berkson's findings is that, since the minimum normit χ^2 solution is the easier to compute, it should be preferred.

Cramer (1962) performed random sampling experiments with $N_j = 10$ and then with $N_j = 20, j = 6$, for four distinct spacings of stimuli, and from each sample obtained estimates for the point of subjective equality and the difference limen. From his results, he concludes that "the maximum likelihood method is the only one which is certain to produce reliable estimates" of these parameters.

Several differences between the conditions of these two studies should be noted. First, Berkson studied only symmetrically placed values of the physical variable (in terms of the expected y_{jc}, i.e. symmetric with respect to $Y_{jc} = 0$). Cramer included asymmetric sets of values, and it was for these cases that the method of maximum likelihood appeared to provide estimators with smaller variance. Second, a difference in strategy was adopted in the minimum χ^2 solution for observed proportions of zero or one. For such proportions, Berkson substituted $1/2N_j$ or $1 - (1/2N_j)$ (.05 or .95), whereas Cramer substituted $1/10N_j$ or $1 - (1/10N_j)$ (.01 or .99 for $N_j = 10$, .005 or .995 for $N_j = 20$). As Cramer suggests, different conventions for handling observed proportions of zero or one will markedly effect the minimum normit χ^2 solution. In particular, if the values inserted for such p_{jc} are close to the parametric values, considerable "favorable" bias would result. Finally, conclusions from the studies of Berkson (1957) and Cramer (1962) pertain to estimates of different parameters, α and β in the one case, pse and dl in the other.

Cramer (1964) provides additional comparisons between maximum likelihood, minimum normit χ^2, and unweighted minimum normit solutions. In this investigation, the sampling experiments were comparable to those used by Berkson (1957). For each method, Cramer determined mean square error of estimates for the known parameters β, pse, and dl.

For estimating pse and dl, when values of the physical variable stimuli were symmetrically placed, as in Berkson's study, the three methods produce almost identical mean square errors. When this condition fails to be met, the maximum likelihood method has smallest variance.

For estimating β, on the other hand, the maximum likelihood method displays larger mean square errors than the weighted or unweighted minimum normit solutions, for which the errors are essentially equivalent. Cramer suggests a major source of this finding to be the substitution in the minimum normit solutions of $1/2N$ and $1 - (1/2N)$ for observed proportions of zero and one.

Both minimum normit χ^2 and maximum likelihood estimates are asymptotically distributed normally and are efficient. It would appear that, when variable stimuli have been selected so as to be roughly symmetric about the constant stimulus and when observed proportions are in a range .05–.95, say, then the methods will also produce in small samples estimates with almost equal sampling variances. However, when the above conditions are not met, maximum likelihood provides the more trustworthy estimates for predicted values, $\hat{Y}$ (and thus for $\hat{P}$), and the minimum normit solution provides better estimation of the parameter β.

3.3   Alternative Response Functions

By relaxing the assumption that the difference processes are normally distributed, a general class of models for sensory discrimination may be obtained. Models in this class assume a response law of the same general form as Equation (2.6), but with an arbitrary probability density function substituted for the normal density. David (1963, p. 14) refers to these as "linear" models, since they require that the discriminal processes be represented as points on a linear scale with arbitrary origin. All these models describe a response probability increasing monotonically to unity with increasing magnitude of the test stimulus. They would not be appropriate for a stimulus which, at some point, ceased to show an increase in apparent intensity as physical intensity increased. Such stimuli are perhaps exceptional but they are not unknown; saccharin, for example, appears to diminish in sweetness at high concentrations because a bitter taste becomes noticeable. Since anomalous response relationships of this type will usually be detected by the test of fit in the least squares or maximum likelihood solution, the investigator is not likely to be led astray if he assumed initially a linear model.

The choice of the integrated normal density function as a response function may be rationalized by the same arguments which justify the assumption that measurement error or biological variation is normally distributed.

When the judgmental model is applied to responses from a number of subjects, we may justify the normal response function on the grounds that the difference thresholds of the subjects are polygenically determined and thus approximate a normal distribution (see Kempthorne, 1957, p. 217). Contrary cases should not be ruled out, however. The bitter taste of phenylthiocarbamide (PTC), for example, is believed to be controlled by a single gene. About one-third of subjects of Indo-European origin have little ability to taste this substance, whereas the remaining two-thirds taste it readily. If the sample of subjects contains both tasters and nontasters, any attempt to fit a psychophysical model to response to PTC will encounter difficulties. The response distribution will be definitely bimodal and inconsistent with an assumed normal response function. (See Sheba, Ashkenazi, and Szeinberg, 1962, for typical data.) Similar effects are common among other compounds containing the thiocyano group, but have not yet been found in compounds outside this class (Kalmus, 1959). Another example is in color vision, where the four common forms of color blindness are analogous effects. Psychophysical studies involving responses which segregate in this manner can be carried out on a population basis only if subjects of different genetic constitution are investigated separately.

Whether we are analyzing judgments from a number of subjects or repeated judgments from a single subject, the discriminal process is assumed to be under the influence of many more or less independent sources of variation. If these sources of variability are independent of the size of the discriminal process, and if they combine additively, then we are assured by the central limit theorem that the distribution of the process, and of the difference processes, will approximate normality.

However, let us assume that the variability of the distribution of discriminal processes is proportional to the mean discriminal process (where the distribution is taken either over a population of subjects, or over a population of occasions for a single judge). This assumption leads to replacement of the Case V specification of equal σ_j for all discriminal processes by

$$\sigma_j = a + b\mu_j, \tag{3.16}$$

and

$$\sigma_c = a + b\mu_c,$$

where a is a positive constant and b has the same sign as μ. Invoking the central limit theorem for this case yields the result that the discriminal processes have the log normal distribution (Cramér, 1951, p. 220), and the corresponding log normal response function is

$$P_{jc} = \frac{1}{\sqrt{2\pi}} \int_{Y_{jc}}^{\infty} \exp(-\tfrac{1}{2}z)^2 \, dz, \tag{3.17}$$

where

$$Y_{jc} = \log \mu_j - \log \mu_c. \tag{3.18}$$

(Proofs are given by Aitchison and Brown, 1957, and by Eisler, 1965, under the condition that (3.16) is replaced by $\sigma = b\mu$. Note that the proof remains valid, starting from (3.16), if we define $\sigma' = \sigma - a$; for then σ', measured from its minimum value a, is proportional to μ. Equation (3.16) is preferred for its greater generality and since it allows for a nonzero σ even when μ is zero.) The log normal response function has been referred to by Stevens (1959, 1966) as Case VI of Thurstone's law of comparative judgment.

In Chapter 2 it was shown that, assuming a normal response function, the normal deviate y_{jc} associated with a proportion p_{jc} provides an estimate of the difference between mean discriminal processes

$$y_{jc} = \hat{\mu}_j - \hat{\mu}_c.$$

Assuming a log normal response function,

$$y_{jc} = \log \hat{\mu}_j - \log \hat{\mu}_c = \log(\hat{\mu}_j/\hat{\mu}_c)$$

is an estimate of the log ratio of the two mean discriminal processes.

Now, the judgment model formulated in terms of a log normal response function is operationally indistinguishable from the model specified by a normal response function. In each case distributions are transformed to normal form, and the model is incapable of detecting whether it serves to determine $\hat{\mu}_j - \hat{\mu}_c$ or $\log(\hat{\mu}_j/\hat{\mu}_c)$. Yet the consequent estimates of μ clearly are distinct under the two response functions. Thus the degree of fit to a postulated linear psychophysical model might be quite different. In fact, empirical evidence is accruing which favors the log normal response function (Stevens, 1966; Eisler, 1965; Ekman, 1956, 1959, 1962; Jones, 1967). However, within the context of the constant method, postulating a log normal response function and a linear psychophysical model is equivalent to postulating a normal response function and a logarithmic psychophysical model, as in Chapter 5. The log normal response function does assume greater importance in paired comparisons, as will be noted in Chapter 6 and Chapter 9.

Another alternative to the normal response function is the "logistic" function

$$P_{jc} = \frac{1}{4} \int_{-\mu_{jc}/\sigma_{jc}}^{\infty} \operatorname{sech}^2 \frac{z}{2}\, dz, \qquad (3.19)$$

where

$$\mu_{jc} = \mu_j - \mu_c.$$

Suppose that the discriminal processes have some actual physical intensity which is always positive, and assume that the subject judges stimulus X_j greater than X_c when the ratio of the respective processes exceeds one, say, $v_j/v_c > 1$. If v_j and v_c are random variables with medians π_j and π_c, the probability that X_j will be judged greater than X_c approaches zero as π_c increases without limit for fixed π_j. If $\pi_j = \pi_c$, the probability is one-half. As π_j increases without limit for fixed π_c, the probability approaches one. A simple function of π_j/π_c which has these properties is

$$P(X_j > X_c) = \frac{\pi_j/\pi_c}{1 + (\pi_j/\pi_c)}. \qquad (3.20)$$

To express the ratio π_j/π_c by a psychophysical model such as Equation (2.9) is not very satisfactory, however, because the value which the equation might assign to the ratio is not necessarily positive. This difficulty may be remedied by an exponential reparameterization of (3.20) such that $\pi_j/\pi_c = \exp(\mu_{jc})$, say. Then

$$P(X_j > X_c) = \frac{\exp(\mu_{jc})}{1 + \exp(\mu_{jc})} = P_{jc}. \qquad (3.21)$$

When $\sigma_{jc} = 1$, this is the definite integral given by (3.19) since

$$P_{jc} = \left[\frac{1}{2}\tanh\frac{z}{2}\right]_{-\mu_{jc}}^{\infty}$$

$$= \frac{1}{2}\left[1 + \frac{\exp(\mu_{jc}/2) - \exp(-\mu_{jc}/2)}{\exp(\mu_{jc}/2) + \exp(-\mu_{jc}/2)}\right]$$

$$= \frac{\exp(\mu_{jc})}{1 + \exp(\mu_{jc})}.$$

The inverse transformation is obtained as follows. Since

$$Q_{jc} = 1 - P_{jc} = \frac{1}{1 + \exp(\mu_{jc})},$$

$$P_{jc}/Q_{jc} = \exp(\mu_{jc}).$$

Hence,

$$\ln(P_{jc}/Q_{jc}) = \mu_{jc}.$$

This transformation applied to the observed proportions yields the observed *logistic* deviates (Berkson uses the term "logits."),

$$y_{jc} = \ln(p_{jc}/q_{jc}). \tag{3.22}$$

Following Berkson (1953), for observed p or q of zero, the value $1/2N$ is substituted; for observed p or q of one, we substitute $1 - (1/2N)$.

According to Rao's lemma (see Section 2.7) the logistic deviates have a limiting normal distribution with mean μ_{jc} and variance

$$\mathscr{V}(y_{jc}) = \mathscr{V}(p_{jc})\left(\frac{\partial \ln P_{jc}/Q_{jc}}{\partial P_{jc}}\right)^2$$

$$= \frac{P_{jc}Q_{jc}}{N_{jc}}\left(\frac{1}{P_{jc}^2 Q_{jc}^2}\right)$$

$$= \frac{1}{N_{jc}P_{jc}Q_{jc}}.$$

For small samples, y_{jc} as defined by (3.22) is a biased estimate of μ_{jc} so that

$$\mathscr{E}(y_{jc}) = \mu_{jc} + \delta_{jc}.$$

Anscombe (1956) stipulates that the bias in y_{jc} as an estimate of μ_{jc} can be largely removed by writing (3.22) as

$$y'_{jc} = \ln\left(\frac{p_{jc} + (1/2N)}{q_{jc} + (1/2N)}\right). \tag{3.22a}$$

The asymptotic sampling variance of (3.22a) remains $1/NPQ$, and the asymptotic mean is μ_{jc}. For small samples,

$$\mathscr{E}(y'_{jc}) = \mu_{jc} + \delta'_{jc}.$$

As in Section 2.3 for the normal response function, we are able to evaluate the bias in (3.22) and in (3.22a), as estimators of μ_{jc}, by exhaustively sampling from the binomial sampling distribution for various values of P_{jc} and N_j, converting each sample p_{jc} to y_{jc} by (3.22) and (3.22a).[1] In assessing (3.22), $1/2N$ or $1 - (1/2N)$ is substituted for an observed proportion of 0 or 1.

For sample sizes of 5, 10, 20, and 40, the bias in (3.22) as an estimator of μ_{jc} is presented in Figure 3.1, as a function of the parameter P_{jc}. Figure 3.2

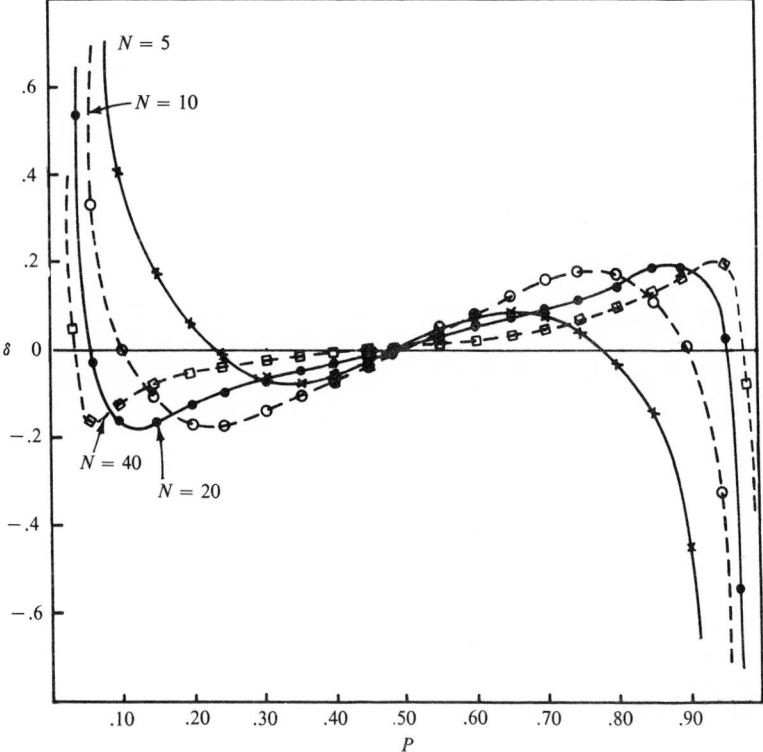

FIG. 3.1. Bias in logistic estimates, Equation (3.22).

[1] The programs for evaluating bias and mean square error of logistic estimates (and of arc sine estimates) were written in BALGOL and run at the Stanford University Computation Center on an IBM 7090. The programming advice of Dr. John P. Gilbert is gratefully acknowledged.

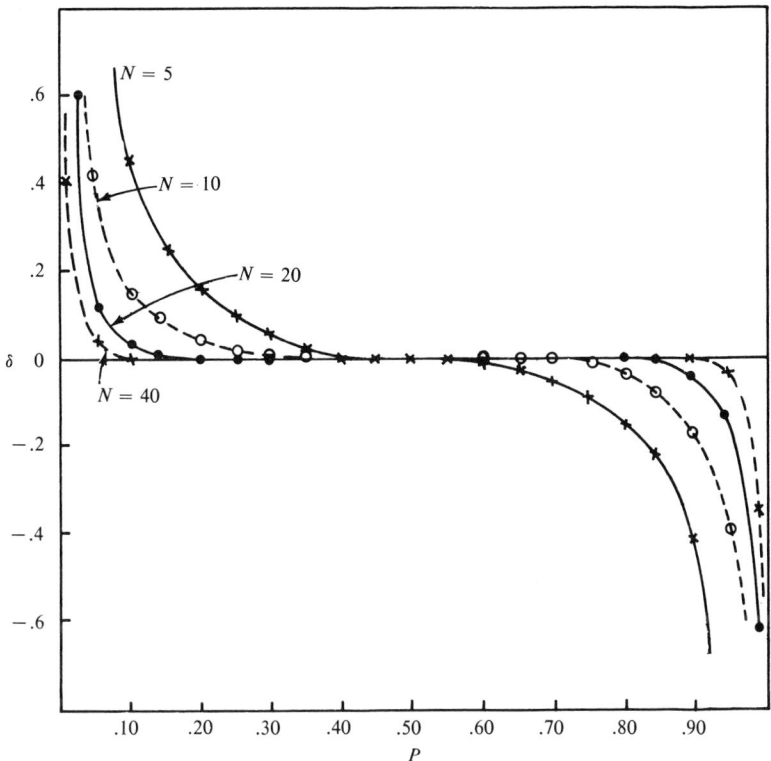

FIG. 3.2. Bias in logistic estimates, Equation (3.22a).

shows comparable results for δ'_{jc}, the bias in (3.22a) as an estimator of μ_{jc}. Anscombe's correction, included in (3.22a) but not in (3.22), does have a salutary effect on bias, particularly for moderate values of P. When $NP \geq 1.5$, bias in (3.22a) is so small as to be inconsequential. In Figure 3.3, mean square error of estimates from (3.22) and (3.22a) are compared with the theoretical sampling variance of y, $1/NPQ$. Mean square error is defined as $\Sigma(y_{jc} - \mu_{jc})^2/N$, and is determined over the entire sampling distribution. It is observed for each value of N that the mean square error of (3.22a) approximates the theoretical variance over a larger range of P than does that of (3.22). (At $P = .50$, the mean square error of (3.22a) is precisely the variance of y, but this fails to be true for (3.22), due to occurrences of sample p's of zero. These occurrences, and the use of the $1/2N$ rule, also account for the more irregular form of M.S. as a function of P, based upon (3.22).) Because bias is smaller and mean square error is closer to $1/NPQ$, (3.22a) is recommended over (3.22). However, it will be noted that unless $NP \geq 1.5$, even (3.22a) is troublesome, exhibiting a mean square error rather far from the expected variance of y.

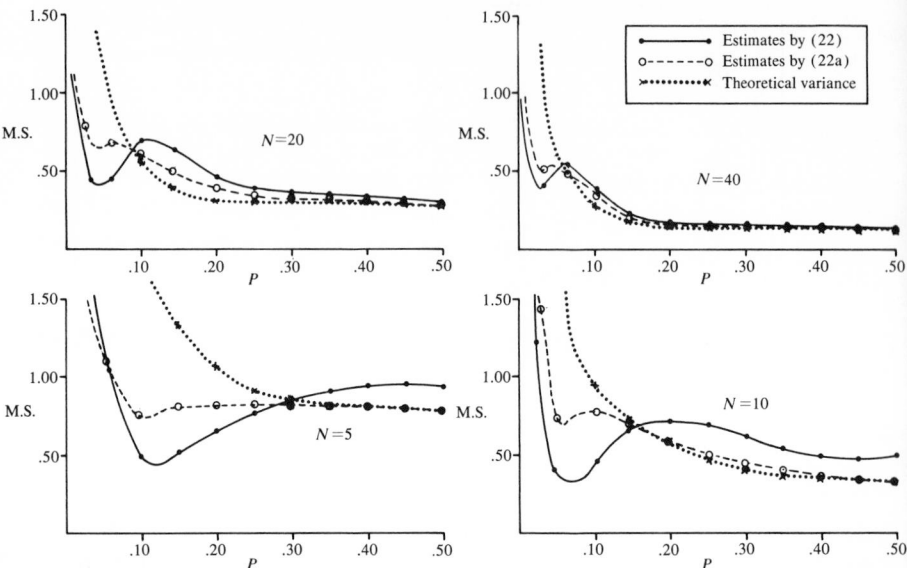

Fig. 3.3. Mean square error and theoretical sampling variance for logistic estimates.

Bias and mean square error also were determined for (3.22a) when that expression was modified by substituting in both numerator and denominator for $1/2N$ the quantities $1/4N$ and $1/10N$. In both cases bias was uniformly more negative at all values of $P < .5$ and more positive for $P > .5$, which made bias more nearly zero for extreme P but further removed from zero for moderate P. Mean square error compared unfavorably with that of the unmodified (3.22a), straying from $\mathscr{V}(y)$ even for moderate P. Thus (3.22a) in its unmodified form is judged superior to these two alternatives.

Finally, there was investigated still another logistic function, logically related to an arc sine transformation proposed by Freeman and Tukey (1950). This formulation, suggested by John Tukey,[2] is

$$y = \left(\ln \frac{1}{2} \frac{r}{N - r + 1} + \ln \frac{r + 1}{N - r} \right).$$

For $r = 0$ (or $r = N$) the values 1/2, 1/4, or 1/10 were tried as replacements for r in the numerator of the first term (or for $N - r$ in the denominator of the second). Replacement by 1/4 resulted in a function practically indistinguishable from that of (3.22a). Use of either 1/2 or 1/10 when $r = 0$ was less satisfactory in terms both of bias and mean square error.

[2] Personal communication.

The logistic density function is slightly leptokurtic to the normal curve, but the difference is so slight that the two functions are indistinguishable in practical work. The choice between them is largely a question of computational convenience, but even in this connection the difference is slight. All the calculations required in the minimum normit χ^2 and maximum likelihood solutions under the normal response function also apply when the logistic function is substituted. The only alterations are the following: (a) The logistic deviates given by (3.22) or (3.22a) replace the normal deviates; (b) the W_{jc} required in the solutions are simply $P_{jc} Q_{jc}$; (c) following Berkson (1953), when using (3.22) for the minimum normit χ^2 solution, if the observed p or q is zero, we substitute the value $1/2N$, and if the observed p or q is one, the value $1 - (1/2N)$ is substituted; (d) since the ordinate of the logistic density function is $P_{jc} Q_{jc}$, the working deviates in the maximum likelihood solution are $y_w = Y + (p - P)/PQ$. In all other respects the two solutions are identical.

The logistic response function also has interesting applications to the method of paired comparisons and prediction of choice, as discussed in Sections 6.5.1 and 9.1.3. These applications make use of a generalized form of logistic deviate suitable for multinomial data. They may be used in the fitting of a multinomial response relation by maximum likelihood methods which are straightforward generalizations of the method discussed above for the binomial case (see Bock, 1968).

Another widely used response function is the so-called "angular" function. From the point of view of convenience in computation, the angular response function is superior to either the normal or the logistic function. Expressed in a form comparable to the other response functions, the angular function is

$$P_{jc} = \frac{1}{2} \int_{-\mu_{jc}}^{\pi/2} \sin\left(-z + \frac{\pi}{2}\right) dz; \qquad -\frac{\pi}{2} \le z \le \frac{\pi}{2}.$$

The definite integral is the closed form

$$P_{jc} = \frac{1}{2}\left[\cos\left(-z + \frac{\pi}{2}\right)\right]_{-\mu_{jc}}^{\pi/2}$$

$$= \frac{1}{2}\left[1 - \cos\left(\mu_{jc} + \frac{\pi}{2}\right)\right]$$

$$= \sin^2\left(\frac{\mu_{jc} + \frac{\pi}{2}}{2}\right)$$

since $1 - \cos 2\alpha = 2 \sin^2\alpha$. The inverse transformation is therefore,

$$\mu_{jc} = 2 \sin^{-1}\sqrt{P_{jc}} - (\pi/2).$$

(A table of this transformation is presented in Table A5.) Applied to the observed proportions this transformation gives the angular deviates

$$y_{jc} = 2 \sin^{-1} \sqrt{p_{jc}} - (\pi/2).$$ (3.23)

The convenience of the angular response function lies in the nearly constant sampling variance of the angular deviates. Carrying the Taylor series expansion of the transformation to the second-order terms and calculating the variance (see Eisenhart, 1947, p. 410),[3] we find

$$\mathscr{V}(y_{jc}) \cong \frac{1}{N_{jc}} - \frac{3}{8N_{jc}^2} \left[\frac{(1 - 2P_{jc})^2}{P_{jc} Q_{jc}} \right].$$

Since the second term tends to zero as $P_{jk} \to 1/2$ or $N_{jc} \to \infty$, the sampling variance of the angular deviates in radian measure is approximately constant at $1/N_{jc}$ in moderate to large samples.

Although (3.23) is asymptotically unbiased as an estimate of μ_{jc}, bias is present in small samples. Anscombe (1954, 1956) has proposed an alternative designed to reduce the bias. Anscombe's formula, in slightly modified form, is

$$y'_{jc} = 2 \sin^{-1} \sqrt{p'_{jc}} - (\pi/2),$$ (3.23a)

where

$$p'_{jc} = (r_{jc} + \tfrac{1}{4})/(N_{jc} + \tfrac{1}{2}).$$

The sampling variance of p'_{jc} remains relatively stable and approximately $1/N_{jc}$. Still another form of the angular transformation, also suggested by Anscombe (1948), is

$$y''_{jc} = 2 \sin^{-1} \sqrt{p''_{jc}} - (\pi/2),$$ (3.23b)

where

$$p''_{jc} = (r_{jc} + \tfrac{3}{8})/(N_{jc} + \tfrac{3}{4}).$$

The relative bias in and the mean square error of (3.23), (3.23a), and (3.23b) as estimators of μ_{jc} were investigated by use of a computer program prepared to exhaustively determine sampling distributions of y_{jc}, y'_{jc}, and y''_{jc} for samples of size 5, 10, 20, and 40 and selected parametric values of P.[4]

---

[3] A misprint in Eisenhart's derivation should be corrected. In the equation at the top of p. 410, the second term on the right-hand side should have the coefficient $-1/4$ instead of $+3/4$.

[4] Also investigated were bias and mean square error in the transformation suggested by Freeman and Tukey (1950) and later tabulated by Mosteller and Youtz (1961). For $p = 0$ or ($p = 1$), the value $1/2N$ (or $1 - (1/2N)$) was substituted. In no case was bias smaller than that of (3.23a). The Freeman-Tukey transformation did provide mean square errors slightly more stable over variations in P asymptotic to $1/(N + .5)$. However, the simpler transformation (3.23a) is still recommended.

Results for (3.23) and (3.23a) are portrayed for bias in Figures 3.4 and 3.5 and for mean square error in Figure 3.6.

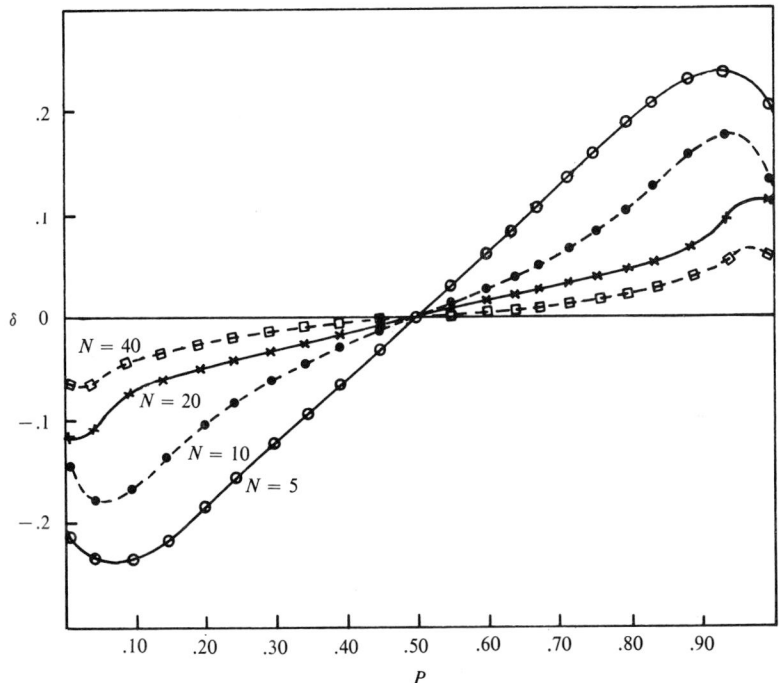

FIG. 3.4. Bias in y_{jc}, Equation (3.23), as an estimate of μ_{jc}.

Bias in (3.23), Figure 3.4, is appreciable as P departs from .50. For $NP \geq 1$, bias in (3.23) may be as great as one-half the standard error of y_{jc}. It is noteworthy that (3.23a) serves to reduce bias to a negligible amount when $NP \geq 1$ (Fig. 3.5), while also reducing the mean square error of y_{jc} as an estimate of μ_{jc}. For (3.23b) mean square error is similar in magnitude to that of (3.23a), being larger than that of (3.23a) for extreme P, slightly smaller for central values of P. Bias in (3.23b), although considerably smaller than that in (3.23), is uniformly greater than that in (3.23a) for all values of N and P. Consequently, (3.23a) is to be preferred when the angular response function is adopted. Table A5 remains useful in connection with (3.23a). The table is entered simply with $(r + 1/4)/(N + 1/2)$ rather than with r/N, as would be required by (3.23).

Since the sampling variance of the angular deviates is essentially independent of P_{jc}, equal weights are employed in the minimum normit χ^2 solution

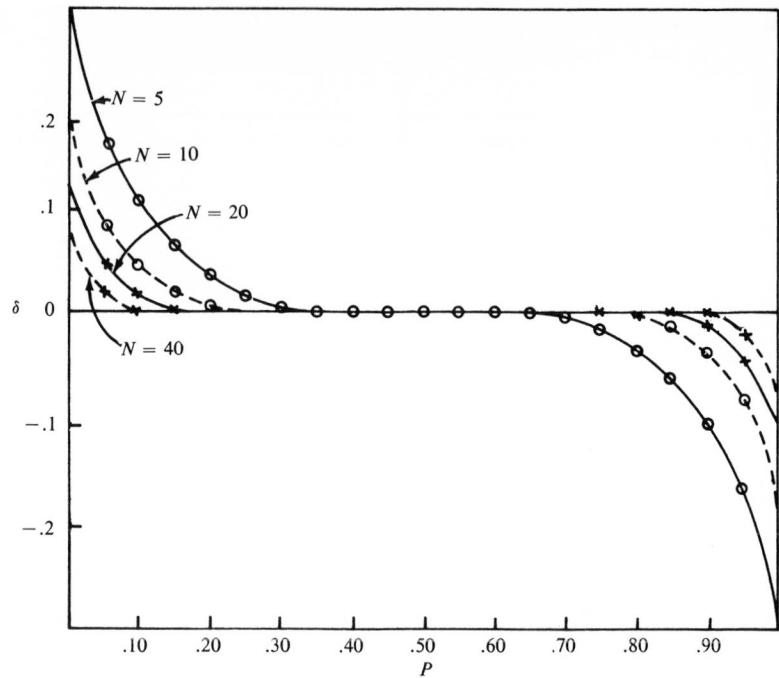

FIG. 3.5. Bias in y'_{jc}, Equations (3.23a) and (3.23b), as an estimate of μ_{jc}.

for the constant method. The solution reduces to a simple regression analysis in which the angular deviates calculated from the observed response proportions serve as data. The angular deviates may be read from Table A5 in terms of p_{jc}, or in machine computation may be calculated by applying a standard subroutine for the arc sine to the square root of p_{jc} (see Hastings, 1955). The remainder of the calculations follow the form of Example 2.7 with all weights $W_{jc} = 1$, so that $N_{jc} W_{jc} = N_{jc}$. Since the ordinate of the angular density function is $\sqrt{PQ}$, the working deviates for the maximum likelihood solution are $y = Y + (p - P)/\sqrt{PQ}$.

The angular response function approximates the normal function reasonably well in the range .05–.95 of the response proportions, but the two yield rather different results outside this range. Indeed, for the angular response function scaled as in (3.23)–(3.23b), the tails terminate at $\pm\pi/2$, at which point the slope of the density function is ± 1. Thus the angular deviates, unlike the normal and logistic deviates, are finite in range. If they are represented by a linear psychophysical function, there may be some values of the physical stimulus difference for which corresponding angular deviates lie outside the interval $\pm\pi/2$. In this case, the response probability for a deviate greater than

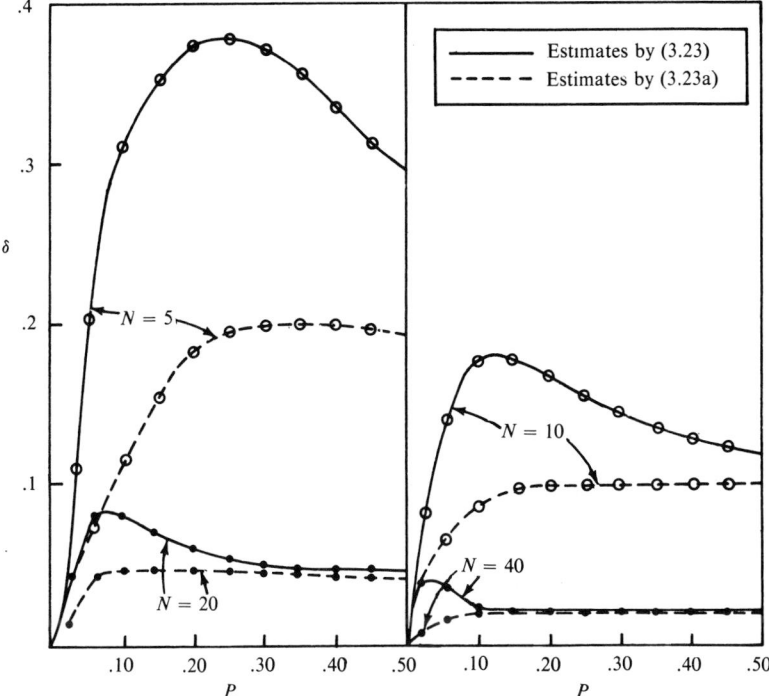

FIG. 3.6. Mean square error in arc sine estimates.

$\pi/2$ may be set equal to 1, and that for a deviate less than $-\pi/2$ may be set equal to 0. In many applications, these limitations of the angular response function are not serious, i.e. whenever the response probabilities actually predicted are not more extreme than .05 or .95.

In practical work the angular response function is quite a satisfactory alternative to the normal function. Other applications of the angular response function are discussed in Chapters 6 and 7.

3.4 An Order-effect Model for the Constant Method

In Section 2.2 we pointed out that for a constant-method experiment in which the order of presentation of the stimuli is balanced, the analysis will not be seriously affected by small spatial or temporal biases in the responses of the subjects. That sensory experiments must be balanced in order to eliminate the average effect of these biases has long been recognized by psychophysicists.

The effect of these biases on the sampling variances of the observed proportions, on the other hand, appears to have been ignored. Actually, the stimuli commonly investigated in the earlier psychophysics—shades of gray, tones of varying pitch, lifted weights, etc.—do not ordinarily produce much order effect. The published numerical results from these studies probably would not be appreciably different by an analysis which takes account of the effect of the bias on the sampling variance.

When gustatory or olfactory stimuli are investigated, however, the effects of order of presentation are more likely to be important in the analysis. The relative slowness with which these stimuli can be cleared from the receptors, and possible effects of the stimulating substance on the sensitivity of the receptor, may cause the second of two stimuli to be judged under quite different conditions than the first. Usually the effect will be to decrease the sensitivity of the receptor, with the result that the subject will tend to judge the second stimulus weaker than the first. If substantial effects of this sort are anticipated, it may be advisable to identify the order of presentation of the stimuli when the responses are recorded. The order effect can then be incorporated in the model and the variances of the observations represented correctly in the analysis.

Let r_{jc} denote the number of judgments $X_j > X_c$ from a total of N_{jc} in which the test stimulus is judged greater than the standard when the test stimulus is presented first (or on the left, say, if a spatial effect is involved). Conversely, let r_{cj} denote the number of judgments $X_j > X_c$ in N_{cj} when the standard stimulus is presented first (or on the left). Then the proportion of judgments $X_j > X_c$ may be represented $p_{jc} = r_{jc}/N_{jc}$ and $p_{cj} = r_{cj}/N_{cj}$.

The simplest model for the order effect, and the only one we will consider, is one in which the order effect is the same for all stimulus pairs. In this case the observed deviates corresponding to these proportions may be assumed to have the following composition (ignoring possible bias in the deviates):

$$y_{jc} = \alpha + \delta + \beta x_{jc} + \xi_{jc}$$
$$y_{cj} = \alpha - \delta + \beta x_{jc} + \xi_{cj}.$$

This assumes that the physical differences $x_{jc} = x_j - x_c$ are the same for both orders of presentation. The order effect δ is assumed to add when the test stimulus is presented first (or on the left) and subtract when it is presented second (or on the right). Solutions for this model for the constant method are only slightly more complicated than the conventional solutions.

3.4.1 The Graphical or Simple Least Squares Solution for the Order-effect Model

For a graphical solution, one merely draws the regression lines separately for deviates corresponding to each order of presentation, but with the restriction that the lines be parallel. Half the difference between the ordinates of the two lines estimates δ.

For a simple unweighted solution when $N_{jc} = N_{cj} = N$, the angular response function may be assumed. The model is reparameterized by setting $\alpha = \alpha' - \beta \bar{x}_c$, where $\bar{x}_c = (1/n)\Sigma_j x_{jc}$. Then the estimators of α', δ, and β are

$$\hat{\alpha}' = \frac{1}{2n}(\Sigma y_{jc} + \Sigma y_{cj}),$$

$$\hat{\delta} = \frac{1}{2n}(\Sigma y_{jc} - \Sigma y_{cj}),$$

$$\hat{\beta} = \frac{\Sigma y_{jc}(x_{jc} - \bar{x}_c) + \Sigma y_{cj}(x_{jc} - \bar{x}_c)}{2\Sigma(x_{jc} - \bar{x}_c)^2},$$

and

$$\hat{\alpha} = \hat{\alpha}' - \hat{\beta}\bar{x}_c.$$

The variances of these estimates are

$$\mathcal{V}(\hat{\alpha}') = 1/2nN$$

$$\mathcal{V}(\hat{\delta}) = 1/2nN$$

$$\mathcal{V}(\hat{\beta}) = 1/[2\Sigma N(x_{jc} - \bar{x}_c)^2]$$

$$\mathcal{V}(\hat{\alpha}) = \frac{1}{2N}\left[\frac{1}{n} + \frac{\bar{x}_c^2}{\Sigma(x_{jc} - \bar{x}_c)^2}\right].$$

The analysis of variance for this solution is shown in Table 3.5.

TABLE 3.5. Analysis of Variance for the Constant Method Assuming an Angular Response Function and an Order-effect Model

Source of variation	d.f.	Sum of squares	Expected sum of squares*
Intercept	1	SSA $= \hat{\alpha}'(\Sigma y_{jc} + \Sigma y_{cj})$	$\sigma^2 + 2n\alpha'^2$
Order effect	1	SSM $= \hat{\delta}(\Sigma y_{jc} - \Sigma y_{cj})$	$\sigma^2 + 2n\delta^2$
Slope	1	SSR $= \hat{\beta}\Sigma(x_{jc} - \bar{x}_c)(y_{jc} + y_{cj})$	$\sigma^2 + 2\beta^2\Sigma(x_{jc} - \bar{x}_c)^2$
Error	$2n - 3$	SSE $=$ SST $-$ SSA $-$ SSM $-$ SSR	$(2n - 3)\sigma^2$
Total	$2n$	SST $= \Sigma y_{jc}^2 + \Sigma y_{cj}^2$	

* $\sigma^2 = 1/N$.

3.4.2 The Minimum Normit χ^2 and Maximum Likelihood Solutions for the Order-effect Model

When using the normal response function, the weights for the minimum normit χ^2 solution of the order-effect model must be computed separately for each order of presentation. Provisional values of Y_{jc} and Y_{cj} for this purpose are read from the graphical solution. Then the weights W_{jc} and W_{cj} are obtained from Table A6.

To derive the solution and to express the estimators, it is helpful to define the following quantities:

$$\Sigma NW = \Sigma N_{jc} W_{jc} + \Sigma N_{cj} W_{cj}$$
$$\Sigma NW^* = \Sigma N_{jc} W_{jc} - \Sigma_{cj} N W_{cj}$$
$$\Sigma NWx = \Sigma N_{jc} W_{jc} x_{jc} + \Sigma N_{cj} W_{cj} x_{jc}$$
$$\Sigma NWx^* = \Sigma N_{jc} W_{jc} x_{jc} - \Sigma N_{cj} W_{cj} x_{jc}$$
$$\Sigma NWy = \Sigma N_{jc} W_{jc} y_{jc} + \Sigma N_{cj} W_{cj} y_{cj}$$
$$\Sigma NWy^* = \Sigma N_{jc} W_{jc} y_{jc} - \Sigma N_{cj} W_{cj} y_{cj}$$
$$\Sigma NWx^2 = \Sigma N_{jc} W_{jc} x_{jc}^2 + \Sigma N_{cj} W_{cj} x_{jc}^2$$
$$\Sigma NWy^2 = \Sigma N_{jc} W_{jc} y_{jc}^2 + \Sigma N_{cj} W_{cj} y_{cj}^2$$
$$\Sigma NWxy = \Sigma N_{jc} W_{jc} x_{jc} y_{jc} + \Sigma N_{cj} W_{cj} x_{jc} y_{cj}$$

The solution of the normal equations is facilitated by a reparameterization which sets

$$\alpha = \alpha' - \delta \bar{w} - \beta \bar{x},$$

where

$$\bar{w} = \Sigma NW^*/\Sigma NW \qquad \text{and} \qquad \bar{x} = \Sigma NWx/\Sigma NW.$$

Then the normal equations are

$$\Sigma NW \hat{\alpha}' - \Sigma NWy = 0$$
$$(\Sigma NW - \bar{w}\Sigma NW^*)\hat{\delta} + (\Sigma NWx^* - \bar{x}\Sigma NW^*)\hat{\beta} - (\Sigma NWy^* - \bar{w}\Sigma NWy) = 0$$
$$(\Sigma NWx^* - \bar{x}\Sigma NW^*)\hat{\delta} + (\Sigma NWx^2 - \bar{x}\Sigma NWx)\hat{\beta} - (\Sigma NWxy - \bar{x}\Sigma NWy) = 0.$$

The normal equations may be written more concisely by introducing special symbols for the coefficients and constant terms and making use of matrix notation:

$$\begin{bmatrix} \Sigma NW & 0 & 0 \\ 0 & S_w & S_{x*} \\ 0 & S_{x*} & S_{x^2} \end{bmatrix} \begin{bmatrix} \hat{\alpha}' \\ \hat{\delta} \\ \hat{\beta} \end{bmatrix} = \begin{bmatrix} S_y \\ S_{y*} \\ S_{xy} \end{bmatrix}.$$

Following the methods of Computing Note D, we construct the inverse of the matrix of coefficients:

$$\begin{bmatrix} 1/\Sigma NW & 0 & 0 \\ 0 & S_{x^2}/d & -S_{x*}/d \\ 0 & -S_{x*}/d & S_w/d \end{bmatrix}$$

where

$$d = S_w S_{x^2} - (S_{x*})^2.$$

Premultiplying the vector of constant terms by the inverse matrix gives the estimates of α', δ, and β, namely,

$$\hat{\alpha}' = S_y/\Sigma NW = \bar{y}, \quad \text{say}.$$

$$\hat{\delta} = \left(S_{y*} - \frac{S_{x*}S_{xy}}{S_{x^2}}\right)\Big/\left[S_w - \frac{(S_{x*})^2}{S_{x^2}}\right];$$

$$\hat{\beta} = \left(S_{xy} - \frac{S_{x*}S_{y*}}{S_w}\right)\Big/\left[S_{x^2} - \frac{(S_{x*})^2}{S_w}\right].$$

Then

$$\hat{\alpha} = \bar{y} - \hat{\delta}\bar{w} - \hat{\beta}\bar{x}.$$

The sampling variances and covariances of the estimates are given by the elements of the inverse matrix. Simplifying these expressions somewhat gives

$$\mathscr{V}(\hat{\alpha}') = 1/\Sigma NW,$$

$$\mathscr{V}(\hat{\delta}) = \frac{1}{S_w - (S_{x*})^2/S_{x^2}},$$

$$\mathscr{V}(\hat{\beta}) = \frac{1}{S_{x^2} - (S_{x*})^2/S_w},$$

and the covariance of $\hat{\delta}$ and $\hat{\beta}$,

$$\mathscr{V}(\hat{\delta}, \hat{\beta}) = - \frac{S_{x*}/S_w}{S_{x^2} - (S_{x*})^2/S_w}.$$

Then the variance of $\hat{\alpha}$ is

$$\mathscr{V}(\hat{\alpha}) = \frac{1}{\Sigma NW} + \frac{\bar{w}^2}{S_w - (S_{x*})^2/S_{x^2}} + \frac{\bar{x}^2}{S_{x^2} - (S_{x*})^2/S_w} - 2\frac{\bar{w}\bar{x}S_{x*}}{S_w S_{x^2} - (S_{x*})^2}.$$

The analysis of variance associated with this solution may be derived by the method of Computing Note D. The triangular matrix which effects the orthogonal reparameterization of the model (i.e. the lower triangular matrix which transforms the matrix of coefficients of the normal equation to upper triangular form) proves to be

$$\begin{bmatrix} 1 & 0 & 0 \\ 0 & 1 & 0 \\ 0 & -S_{x*}/S_w & 1 \end{bmatrix}.$$

Premultiplying both members of the transposed normal equations by this matrix gives

$$\begin{bmatrix} \Sigma NW & 0 & 0 \\ 0 & S_w & S_{x*} \\ 0 & 0 & S_{x^2} - (S_{x*})^2/S_w \end{bmatrix} \begin{bmatrix} \hat{\alpha}' \\ \hat{\delta} \\ \hat{\beta} \end{bmatrix} = \begin{bmatrix} S_y \\ S_{y*} \\ S_{xy} - \dfrac{S_{x*}S_{y*}}{S_w} \end{bmatrix}.$$

Dividing through each equation by the square root of the respective diagonal element of the matrix of coefficients gives the expressions for orthogonal estimates, say

$$u_1 = S_y/\sqrt{\Sigma NW},$$

$$u_2 = S_{y*}/\sqrt{S_w},$$

$$u_3 = \frac{S_{yx} - (S_{x*}S_{y*}/S_w)}{[S_{x^2} - (S_{x*}/S_w)^2]^{1/2}}.$$

These estimates have expectations

$$\mathscr{E}(u_1) = (\alpha + \delta\bar{w} + \beta\bar{x})\sqrt{\Sigma NW},$$

$$\mathscr{E}(u_2) = (\delta + \beta S_{x*})\sqrt{S_w},$$

$$\mathscr{E}(u_3) = \beta\sqrt{S_{x^2} - (S_{x*})^2/S_w}.$$

They are uncorrelated and have unit variances.

In the analysis of variance associated with the minimum normit χ^2 solution the squares of the orthogonal estimates provide the partition of variation accounted for by the fitted model. The sum of squares for residual variation is obtained by subtraction from the total sum of squares as shown in Table 3.6. In addition to the test of the model using SSE as a χ^2 statistic on $2n - 3$ degrees of freedom, the analysis of variance in Table 3.6 is set up in a form which permits a test of the hypothesis $\beta = 0$, independent of the order effect and intercept. This test makes use of the fact that SSR $= \chi^2$ on one degree of freedom on the null hypothesis. If β is not assumed null, the order effect is confounded with slope and cannot be tested in this analysis. If a test of the

TABLE 3.6. Analysis of Variance from the Minimum Normit Solution
for the Order-effect Model

Source of variation	d.f.	Sum of squares	Expected sum of squares*
Intercept	1	SSA $= (S_y)^2/\Sigma NW$	$\sigma^2 + (\alpha + \delta\bar{w} + \beta\bar{x})^2\Sigma NW$
Order effect, eliminating intercept	1	SSD $= (S_{y*})^2/S_w$	$\sigma^2 + (\delta + \beta S_{x*})^2 S_w$
Slope, eliminating order effect and intercept	1	SSR $= \dfrac{\left(S_{xy} - \dfrac{S_{x*}S_{y*}}{S_w}\right)^2}{S_{x^2} - \dfrac{(S_{x*})^2}{S_w}}$	$\sigma^2 + \beta^2\left[S_{x^2} - \dfrac{(S_{x*})^2}{S_w}\right]$
Residual	$2n - 3$	SSE $=$ SST $-$ SSA $-$ SSD $-$ SSR	$(2n - 3)\sigma^2$
Total	$2n$	SST $= \Sigma NWy^2$	

* $\sigma^2 = 1$.

order effect is desired in this case, the positions of δ and β in the transposed normal equations may be interchanged as follows:

$$\begin{bmatrix} \Sigma NW & 0 & 0 \\ 0 & S_{x^2} & S_{x*} \\ 0 & S_{x*} & S_w \end{bmatrix} \begin{bmatrix} \hat{\alpha} \\ \hat{\beta} \\ \hat{\delta} \end{bmatrix} = \begin{bmatrix} S \\ S_{xy} \\ S_{y*} \end{bmatrix}.$$

Then the transformation to orthogonal estimates is carried out once more to provide the partition of variation accounted for by the model. Since $\hat{\delta}$ and $\hat{\beta}$ alone are involved in the reorthogonalization, only the second and third lines of the analysis of variance table are changed. The new lines may be obtained merely by exchanging the roles of S_w and S_{x^2}, of S_{xy} and S_{y*}, and of δ and β:

Slope, eliminating 1 $\text{SSR}' = (S_{xy})^2/S_{x^2}$ $\sigma^2 + (\beta + \delta S_{x*})^2 S_{x^2}$
intercepts

Order effect,
eliminating 1 $\displaystyle \text{SSD}' = \frac{\left(S_{y*} - \dfrac{S_{xy}S_{x*}}{S_{x^2}}\right)^2}{S_w - \dfrac{(S_{x*})^2}{S_{x^2}}}$ $\sigma^2 + \delta^2\left[S_w - \dfrac{(S_{x*})^2}{S_{x^2}}\right]$
intercept and
slope

As is evident from its expected value, SSD', taken as χ^2 on one degree of freedom, may be used to test the hypothesis $\delta = 0$. A significant value of SSD' indicates that the proportion of responses $X_j > X_c$ is influenced by the order in which these two stimuli are presented to the subjects.

Confidence intervals for α, δ, and β may be obtained in the usual manner by adding to, and subtracting from, the respective estimate an appropriate multiple of its standard error (obtained from the variances of $\hat{\alpha}$, $\hat{\delta}$, and $\hat{\beta}$ shown above). The confidence interval for Y_{jc} at x_{jc} is slightly more complicated. The order-effect model yields point estimates of two parallel regression lines which differ in intercept by 2δ. The confidence interval for Y_{jc} and x_{jc}, associated with one of the lines, is

$$Y_{jc}: \qquad \bar{y} + \hat{\delta} + \hat{\beta}(x_{jc} - \bar{x}) \pm z_{1-(\gamma/2)}[\mathscr{V}(\hat{Y}_{jc})]^{1/2}$$

where

$$\mathscr{V}(\hat{Y}_{jc}) = \frac{1}{\Sigma NW} + \frac{1}{S_w - (S_{x*})^2/S_{x^2}} + \frac{(x_{jc} - \bar{x})^2}{S_{x^2} - (S_{x*})^2/S_w} - \frac{2(x_{jc} - \bar{x})S_{x*}}{S_w S_{x^2} - (S_{x*})^2}$$

and $z_{1-(\gamma/2)}$ is the $1 - (\gamma/2)$ point of the normal distribution. The interval for Y_{cj}, associated with the other line, is given by this expression with the sign of $\hat{\delta}$ and of the last term in the expression for the variance reversed.

If the maximum likelihood solution for the order-effect model may be required, it is only necessary to substitute working deviates for observed deviates in the minimum normit χ^2 solution and iterate until stable estimates are obtained. The initial values of the provisional deviates, $Y_{jc,\text{prov}}$ and $Y_{cj,\text{prov}}$, needed to obtain the weights and working deviates for the maximum likelihood (from Tables A6 and A8) may be determined from a preliminary graphical solution. The provisional deviates are the ordinates above the points x_{ij} of the lines fitted to the observed deviates, y_{jc} and y_{cj}, respectively.

Example 3.4.2

To illustrate the minimum normit χ^2 solution for the order-effect model we make use of data which appear in a conventional solution in Table 5.2. The stimuli are four concentrations of sugar (sucrose) solution compared with a standard 3 g/100 ml sugar solution. Since the analysis in Chapter 5 is carried out in terms of log concentrations, we use the logarithmic metric in this example also. Thus the quantities x_{ij} in the solution are the (natural) log stimulus ratios which appear in column 3 of Table 3.7.

All quantities required for estimation and the analysis of variance are shown in Table 3.7. The estimated common slope of the two regression lines is 2.5480 (in natural log measure). This value differs somewhat from $4.764648/2.302585 = 2.069260$, the estimated slope for these data obtained in the conventional solution of Table 5.2. However, it agrees well with the value of 2.606435 for the over-all slope computed in Table 5.2.

Notice that the variance of $\hat{\beta}$ differs from that of the conventional solution only by the term (S_{x*}^2/S_w) in the denominator. This term is always positive and, when subtracted from S_{x^2}, increases the calculated variance of $\hat{\beta}$. However, since S_{x*} is the difference of the sum of weighted x_{jc} values for the different orders it tends to be so small that the effect of this term is negligible.

The analysis of variance for this solution shown in Table 3.8 includes both the partition eliminating order effect from slope, and that eliminating slope from order effect. Each of these effects is clearly significant. The estimate of the order effect in Table 3.6 indicates that it is large, amounting to somewhat more than half a standard deviation. The residual χ^2 falls just short of significance at the .05 level. This is the same level of probability observed in the conventional solution in Table 5.2—another indication that the variance calculated from the pooled data for both orders of presentation is not necessarily in serious error. The rather poor fit of both the conventional and order-effect model to these data appears to be due to the unexpectedly small observed proportion for the level two of the second order of presentation. If we consider the pooled estimate of β from Table 5.2 the correct value, this deviant value affects less the order-effect solution than the conventional solution. This is apparently to be expected since in the order-effect solution it is one of eight observations fitted, rather than one of four in the conventional solution.

TABLE 3.7. Minimum Normit χ^2 Solution for the Order-effect Model

Order	levels	$\ln x_j/x_c$	N_{jc}	r_{jc}	P_{jc}	y_{jc}	$Y_{jc,\text{prov}}$	$W_{jc,\text{prov}}$	$N_{jc}W_{jc}$	$N_{jc}W_{jc}x_{jc}$	$N_{jc}W_{jc}y_{jc}$
1	1	$-.231512$	13	7	.538	.0954	.226	.6248	8.1229	1.8805	.7749
1	2	$-.076161$	11	7	.636	.3478	.620	.5529	6.0819	$-.4632$	2.1153
1	3	.076961	11	10	.909	1.3346	1.009	.4359	4.7949	.3690	6.3993
1	4	.231112	8	8	.938	1.5382	1.400	.3017	2.4136	.5578	3.7126

Order	levels	$\ln x_j/x_c$	N_{cj}	r_{cj}	P_{cj}	y_{cj}	$Y_{cj,\text{prov}}$	$W_{cj,\text{prov}}$	$N_{cj}W_{cj}$	$N_{cj}W_{cj}x_{jc}$	$N_{cj}W_{cj}y_{cj}$
2	1	$-.231512$	11	5	.455	$-.1130$	$-.817$	.4974	5.4714	-1.2667	$-.6183$
2	2	$-.076161$	11	1	.091	-1.3346	$-.423$	.5965	6.5615	$-.4997$	-8.7570
2	3	.076961	11	7	.636	.3478	$-.035$	.6364	7.0004	.5388	2.4347
2	4	.231112	9	5	.556	.1408	.356	.6078	5.4702	1.2642	.7702

$$\Sigma NW = 45.9168$$
$$\Sigma NW^* = -3.0902$$
$$\Sigma NWx = -1.3803$$
$$\Sigma NWx^* = -1.4535$$
$$\Sigma NWy = 6.8317$$
$$\Sigma NWy^* = 19.1725$$
$$\Sigma NWx^2 = 1.2929$$
$$\Sigma NWy^2 = 27.7730$$
$$\Sigma NWxy = 2.1855$$

$$w = \Sigma NW^*/\Sigma NW = -.0673$$
$$\bar{x} = \Sigma NWx/\Sigma NW = -.0301$$
$$\bar{y} = \Sigma NWy/\Sigma NW = .1488$$
$$S_w = \Sigma NW - \bar{w}\Sigma NW^* = 45.7088$$
$$S_{x^*} = \Sigma NWx^* - \bar{x}\Sigma NW^* = -1.5465$$
$$S_{y^*} = \Sigma NWy^* - \bar{x}\Sigma NWy = 19.6323$$
$$S_{x^2} = \Sigma NWx^2 - \bar{x}\Sigma NWx = 1.2514$$
$$S_{xy} = \Sigma NWxy - \bar{x}\Sigma NWy = 2.3911$$

$$\beta = \frac{S_{xy} - (S_{x^*}\cdot S_{y^*}/S_w)}{S_{x^2} - [(S_{x^*})^2/S_w]} = 2.5480$$

$$\delta = \frac{S_{y^*} - (S_{x^*}\cdot S_{xy}/S_{x^2})}{S_{w^*} - [(S_{x^*})^2/S_{x^2}]} = .5157$$

$$\hat{\alpha} = \bar{y} - \delta\bar{w} - \beta\bar{x} = .2602$$

$$Y_{j(1)} = \hat{\alpha} + \hat{\delta} + \beta x_{jc} = .7759 + 2.5480x_{jc}$$

$$Y_{j(2)} = \hat{\alpha} - \hat{\delta} + \beta x_{jc} = -.2555 + 2.5480x_{jc}$$

TABLE 3.8. Analysis of Variance for Example 3.4. 2

Source of variation	d.f.	Sum of squares, χ^2	Probability
Intercept	1	1.0166	
Order effect, eliminating intercept	1	8.4322	
Slope, eliminating order effect and intercept	1	7.7851	$p < .005$
Slope, eliminating intercept	1	4.5687	
Order effect, eliminating intercept and slope	1	11.6487	$p < .001$
Residual	5	10.5391	$p < .10$
Total	8	27.7730	

4 Determination of Absolute Sensory Thresholds by the Constant Method

In Chapter 2 the constant method was presented as a means for determining discriminal precision and point of subjective equality in judgment of stimulus differences. The method also lends itself to the determination of an absolute stimulus threshold—that value of stimulus magnitude which is just noticeably different from zero stimulation. In this chapter we present the statistical analyses for two experimental procedures useful for the determination of absolute thresholds. The first entails comparative judgments of stimuli presented in pairs, whereas the other requires judgments of stimuli presented in triplets. Both least squares and maximum likelihood solutions are presented for each procedure.

4.1 The Two-sample Procedure

A variation of the constant method which is suitable for the determination of absolute thresholds is as follows:

(1) A set of stimuli designated $X_0, X_1, X_2, \ldots, X_n$ is prepared. In stimulus X_0, the attribute in question is absent. In stimuli $X_1, X_2, \ldots, X_n$, the attribute is present in different magnitudes $x_1, x_2, \ldots, x_n$, respectively. A range of magnitudes is chosen in which the attribute is not always noticeable for at least some stimulus.

(2) The stimulus X_0 is paired with a stimulus $X_j, j = 1, 2, \ldots, n$, and presented to subject $i = 1, 2, \ldots, N_j$, selected from a large population of subjects. The spatial or temporal position of X_0 and X_j is random and is balanced.

(3) Subject i is required to state which stimulus in the pair contains the attribute in question. The subject is instructed to guess when in doubt.

(4) The stimuli are assumed to be at such low levels of intensity that little order effect will be present (see Section 3.4). The responses from the two orders of presentation are therefore not distinguished when the responses are recorded as

$$s_{ji} = 1 \text{ when the judgment is correct},$$
$$s_{ji} = 0 \text{ when the judgment is incorrect}.$$

The number of correct responses from a sample of N_j subjects is

$$r_j = \sum_{i=1}^{N_j} s_{ji}.$$

As in the sampling model for the method of constant stimuli in Chapter 2, we may distinguish between the following two conditions.

Single-judgment condition. Subjects are randomly and independently assigned to n experimental groups. Each of the N_j subjects in each group judges one and only one stimulus pair X_j and X_0.

Multiple-judgment condition. Each subject judges each stimulus pair

$$X_j \text{ and } X_0, \qquad j = 1, 2, \dots, n.$$

In the sampling model for the single-judgment condition the population is assumed to consist of two classes of subjects—those who detect the attribute and respond correctly, and those who fail to detect the attribute and guess. In the multiple-judgment condition, the response of the subject is assumed to arise from two populations, one consisting of definite detection of the attribute, and the other consisting of no detection followed by guessing. Suppose a proportion of P_j' is in the class of detection and $1 - P_j'$ is in the class of guesses. Then the probability that in a given judgment a correct response is elicited may be expressed as

$$P_j = P_j' + (1 - P_j')/2.$$

The proportion of P_j' of subjects or responses in the population for which X_j is above threshold (i.e. in which the stimulus is detected) is calculated from the proportion of correct responses by

$$P_j' = 2P_j - 1.$$

Since the subjects are randomly and independently selected, the probability of obtaining r_j correct responses from N_j subjects is

$$\text{Prob}(r_j) = \frac{N_j!}{r_j!(N_j - r_j)!} P_j^{r_j}(1 - P_j)^{N_j - r_j}.$$

In the discriminal model for this procedure, the discriminal process v_j associated with a particular stimulus X_j is assumed normally distributed in the population, with mean μ_j and variance σ_j^2. Since the scale for v_j is arbitrary, we are free to define, as a unit of measurement, $\sigma_j = 1$ for a particular selected value of j. Let us define a transformation of v_j,

$$z_j = v_j - \mu_j.$$

Then the probability than a randomly selected individual will detect the attribute is given by the normal response function

$$P_j' = \frac{1}{\sqrt{2\pi}} \int_{-\mu_j}^{\infty} \exp\left(-\tfrac{1}{2}z^2\right) dz = \Phi(\mu_j), \tag{4.1}$$

and the probability that he will respond *correctly* is, in terms of this response law, implicit in

$$2P_j - 1 = \Phi(\mu_j). \tag{4.2}$$

On the assumption that $\sigma_j = \sigma$ for all j, (4.1) and (4.2) apply to all stimuli, $j = 1, 2, \ldots, n$.

As in Chapter 2, a psychophysical model is postulated. Either of two alternative models might be entertained. One specifies that the mean discriminal process μ_j is a linear function of physical magnitude,

$$\mu_j = Y_j' = \alpha + \beta x_j. \tag{4.3}$$

The other possible model, preferred on a priori grounds (see Chapter 5), specifies that the mean discriminal process is a linear function of the (natural) logarithm of physical magnitude,

$$\mu_j = Y_j' = \alpha + \beta \ln x_j. \tag{4.3a}$$

(Here the α and β are distinct, of course, from those of Equation 4.3.) The remaining development in this section will be written explicitly in terms of the latter model. Illustrative examples which appear later in this section exclusively utilize the logarithmic model.

Using (4.3a), we may rewrite (4.1) and (4.2) as

$$P_j' = 2P_j - 1 = \Phi(\alpha + \beta \ln x_j). \tag{4.4}$$

As in Chapter 2, use of the inverse normal transformation applied to (4.4) facilitates the estimation of its parameters α and β. For this purpose we define the population normal deviate

$$Y_j' = \Phi^{-1}(P_j')$$

and the observed deviate

$$y_j' = \Phi^{-1}(p_j')$$

where $p'_j = 2p_j - 1 = 2r_j/N_j - 1$. That is, the observed deviate is the inverse normal transform of the observed proportion of correct responses, after correction for guessing. If both the normal response function and the logarithmic psychophysical model hold, the plot of y'_j vs $\ln x_j$ will be linear with intercept α and slope β, except for sampling error.

As in Chapter 2, the graphical solution for fitting this line can be aided by constructing confidence bounds on the expected deviates. From the observed values r_j may be obtained binomial bounds on P'_j, (P'_{jL}, P'_{jU}), by the method developed in Section 2.5. Then,

$$Y'_{jL} = \Phi^{-1}(2P_{jL} - 1), \tag{4.5}$$

and

$$Y'_{jU} = \Phi^{-1}(2P_{jU} - 1). \tag{4.6}$$

Entering a table of the normal distribution with P'_{jL} and P'_{jU}, Y'_{jL} and Y'_{jU} are the normal deviates below which fall P'_{jL} and P'_{jU} of the area, respectively (Table A3).

4.2   The Two-sample Minimum Normit χ^2 Solution

The primary object of investigation is the estimation of an absolute stimulus threshold, $\hat{x}_{md}$, say. In order to obtain such an estimate, we first need estimates for α and β of Equation (4.3a). We now turn attention to this estimation problem.

The observed deviates (associated with corrected proportions p'_j) are assumed to be random variables of the form[1]

$$y'_j = \alpha + \beta \ln x_j + \xi'_j.$$

Applying Rao's lemma (see Section 2.7) we find that the errors ξ'_j in the observed deviates are asymptotically normally distributed with mean

$$\mathscr{E}(\xi'_j) = 0$$

and variance

$$\mathscr{V}(\xi'_j) = \left[\frac{\partial Y'_j}{\partial P'_j}\right]^2 \mathscr{V}(P'_j) = 4P_j Q_j/N_j h^2(Y'_j),$$

where $h^2(Y'_j)$ is the square of the ordinate of the normal distribution function at the normal deviate Y'_j. Consequently, to estimate the parameters α and β, we may define the weights

$$W'_j = \frac{1}{N_j \mathscr{V}(\xi'_j)} = h^2(Y'_j)/4P_j Q_j \tag{4.7}$$

---

[1] In this treatment, we ignore a term δ'_j, representing bias in y'_j as an estimate of Y'_j. The degree of bias δ'_j will be a function of N_j and P'_j. For $.50 \le P'_j \le 1.00$, the bias is represented by the right half of Figure 2.3. As for applications of the constant method discussed in Chapter 2, the bias is inconsequential, as long as $N_j P_j \ge 1$ for all j.

and proceed by the minimum normit χ^2 method. Again, the expected deviates Y'_j on which the weights depend may be replaced by provisional deviates $Y'_{j,prov}$ read from a graphical solution. Using $P_{j,prov} = (P_{j,prov} + 1)/2$ and $Q = 1 - P$, the estimated W'_j may be computed. Or, with $Y'_{j,prov}$ in hand, they may be found from Table A7.

Note that neither the observed deviates nor the weights are defined for observed proportions p_j less than or equal to one half. Such proportions should be replaced in the analysis by the proportions $1/2 + 1/4N_j$ and proportions of one should be replaced by $1 - 1/4N_j$.

The values $\hat{\alpha}$ and $\hat{\beta}$ are determined by a simple modification of (2.26) and (2.27). In each case $\ln x$ is substituted for x to accommodate the logarithmic form of the psychophysical model. We have, say,

$$\hat{\alpha} = \bar{y}' - \hat{\beta} \, \overline{\ln x}, \tag{4.8}$$

and

$$\hat{\beta} = \frac{\Sigma N_j W'_j y'_j (\ln x_j - \overline{\ln x})}{\Sigma N_j W'_j \ln x_j (\ln x_j - \overline{\ln x})} = \frac{S_{xy}}{S_{x^2}}. \tag{4.9}$$

In (4.8) and (4.9), y'_j is the normal deviate associated with $p'_j = 2p_j - 1$; W'_j is defined by (4.7);

$$\overline{\ln x} = \Sigma N_j W'_j \ln x_j / \Sigma N_j W'_j; \tag{4.10}$$

and

$$\bar{y}' = \Sigma N_j W'_j y'_j / \Sigma N_j W'_j. \tag{4.11}$$

Equations (4.10) and (4.11) are analogous to the equations defining $\bar{x}$ and $\bar{y}$ in Section 2.7.

The conventional definition of the absolute threshold is the median attribute magnitude, that magnitude which 50% of the population is expected to notice. By this definition, absolute threshold magnitude yields $P' = .50$, $P = .75$. Since at $P' = .50$, $Y' = 0$, the estimated logarithmic threshold, $(\ln \hat{x})_{md}$, is the x-coordinate of the intercept of the fitted regression line with the line $Y' = 0$. Thus,

$$0 = \hat{\alpha} + \hat{\beta} \ln \hat{x}_{md},$$

and

$$(\ln \hat{x})_{md} = -\hat{\alpha}/\hat{\beta}, \tag{4.12}$$

or

$$\hat{x}_{md} = \ln^{-1}(-\hat{\alpha}/\hat{\beta}). \tag{4.13}$$

Substituting in (4.12) for $\hat{\alpha}$ from (4.8),

$$(\ln \hat{x})_{md} = \overline{\ln x} - \bar{y}'/\hat{\beta}. \tag{4.14}$$

To approximate the sampling variance of $\ln \hat{x}_{md}$, we again use the approximation given on page 40 for the variance of a function of two random variables. In this case, using Equations (2.29)–(2.31),

$$\mathscr{V}[(\ln \hat{x})_{md}] \approx \frac{1}{\hat{\beta}^2} \frac{1}{\Sigma N W'} + \left(\frac{\bar{y}'}{\hat{\beta}^2}\right)^2 \frac{1}{S_{x^2}}$$

$$\approx \frac{1}{\hat{\beta}^2} \left\{ \frac{1}{\Sigma N W'} + \frac{[(\ln \hat{x})_{md} - \overline{\ln x}]^2}{S_{x^2}} \right\}. \tag{4.15}$$

Approximate $1 - \gamma$ confidence bounds on the unknown parameter $(\ln x)_{md}$ can be obtained by inverting a critical ratio test based on this variance

$$(\ln x)_{md}: \qquad (\ln \hat{x})_{md} \pm z_{1-(\gamma/2)}[\mathscr{V}(\ln \hat{x})_{md}]^{1/2}, \tag{4.16}$$

where $z_{1-(\gamma/2)}$ is the critical normal deviate.

(This method of estimating variance and confidence bounds also applies for the substitution of any other percentile for $(\ln x)_{md}$.) The antilogarithm (base e) of (4.16) provides a solution in physical stimulus units corresponding to the desired confidence bounds.

The regression analysis based upon the minimum normit χ^2 solution for absolute thresholds proceeds as do those for differential thresholds presented in Chapter 2, as is illustrated in Example 4.2.

Example 4.2

An experiment was performed[2] to determine absolute threshold for detection of sodium benzoate in distilled water solution. We treat the data as if four distinct groups of subjects were employed (single-judgment sampling). Four variable stimuli were used with .005, .01, .02, and .04% concentrations of sodium benzoate. Each subject was presented a pair of stimuli X_j and X_0, where X_0 was undiluted distilled water. Order of presentation was randomly determined and balanced for each subject. On the basis of tasting each stimulus substance of the pair presented to him, the subject judged which solution contained the sodium benzoate.

---

[2] An unpublished experiment by D. R. Peryam, to whom we are grateful for the use of these data.

TABLE 4.1. Least Squares Determination of Absolute Threshold; Two-sample Procedure, Logarithmic Model

Levels, j	Concentration, % x_j	1 $\ln x_j$	2 Coded $\ln x_j$	3 N_j	4 r_j	5 p_j	6 p'_j	7 y'_j	8 $Y_{j,\text{prov}}$	9 W'	10 NW'	11 $NW'x$	12 $NW'y'$
4	.04	-3.2190	3	22	21	.955	.910	1.34	.98	.2030	4.466	13.398	5.984
3	.02	-3.9120	2	33	25	.758	.516	.04	.30	.2354	7.768	15.536	0.311
2	.01	-4.6052	1	35	25	.714	.428	-.18	.36	.1605	5.618	5.618	-1.011
1	.005	-5.2983	0	25	12	.510*	.020	-2.05	-1.02	.0576	1.440	0.0	-2.952

Coded $x = (\ln x + 5.2983)/.6931$, $c = -5.2983$, $f = .6931$.

Letting x refer to coded values:

$\Sigma NW = 19.292$
$\Sigma NWx = 34.552$
$\Sigma NWy = 2.332$
$\Sigma NWx^2 = 76.884$
$\Sigma NWy^2 = 14.265$
$\Sigma NWxy = 17.563$

$$\bar{x} = \Sigma NWx/\Sigma NW = 1.791$$
$$\bar{y} = \Sigma NWy/\Sigma NW = 0.121$$
$$S_{x^2} = \Sigma NWx^2 - \bar{x}\Sigma NWx = 15.001$$
$$S_{y^2} = \Sigma NWy^2 - \bar{y}\Sigma NWy = 13.983$$
$$S_{xy} = \Sigma NWxy - \bar{x}\Sigma NWy = 13.386$$
$$b = S_{xy}/S_{x^2} = .8923$$
$$a = \bar{y} - b\bar{x} = -1.477$$
$$\hat{\beta} = b/f = 1.2874$$

In coded $\ln x$ units, $\hat{Y}_j = a + bx_j = -1.477 + .892x_j$, and $md = -a/b = 1.655$

Expressing $\hat{Y}_j$ as a function of $\ln x_j$

$$\overline{\ln x} = f\bar{x} + c = .6931\bar{x} - 5.2983 = -4.0570$$
$$\hat{\alpha} = \bar{y} - \hat{\beta}\,\overline{\ln x} = +5.3440$$
$$\hat{Y}_j = \hat{\alpha} + \hat{\beta}\ln x_j = 5.3440 + 1.2874 \ln x_j$$
$$(\ln \bar{x})_{md} = -\hat{\alpha}/\hat{\beta} = -4.1510$$
$$\bar{x}_{md} = .0158$$

* Actual p of .480 is replaced by $0.50 + .25/N_j = 0.510$.

In Table 4.1 appear the data from this study and the least squares solution for absolute threshold, assuming a logarithmic psychophysical model, Equation (4.3a). The solution takes the same general form as that for the determination of the difference limen, Example 2.7. However, differences appear as a result of (a) assuming a psychophysical model in which discriminal processes are a linear function of the natural logarithm of stimulus magnitudes, and (b) utilizing observed proportions corrected for guessing as a basis of analysis.

In Table 4.1, the natural logarithms of stimulus magnitudes are recorded in column *1*. Recognizing that for the selected stimuli, differences between adjacent $\ln x_j$ values are constant, a simple integrally coded $\ln x_j$ value is selected, column *2*. Coded values result from subtracting $c = -5.2983$ from each $\ln x_j$, then dividing by $f = .6931$. The numbers c and f are recorded in Table 4.1 for later use.

In columns *3* and *4* appear values of N_j and r_j. The ratio r_j/N_j yields the p_j of column *5*. Column *6* contains entries $p'_j = 2p_j - 1$. In column *7* are the normal deviates y'_j which correspond with p'_j, which may be read from Table A3.

A provisional graphical fit of $\hat{Y}_j$ (to coded $\ln x_j$) appears as the dashed line in Figure 4.1. From this line are read the ordinates $Y'_{j,\text{prov}}$, which are

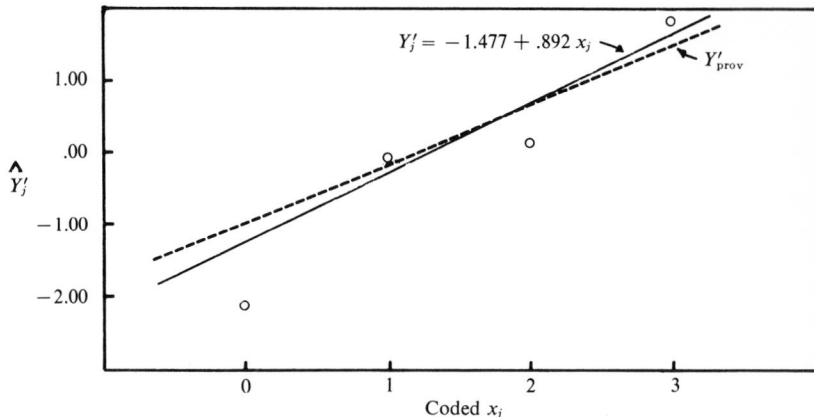

FIG. 4.1. Least squares solution for absolute threshold, logarithmic model.

recorded in column *8*. Entering Table A7 with these values, we obtain provisional weights, recorded in column *9*. In column *10*, we enter products of entries in columns *3* and *9*. In column *11* are products of entries in columns *2* and *10*. Column *12* presents products of entries in columns *7* and *10*.

The intermediate results of Table 4.1 are self-evident. The methods of determination are identical to those presented in Example 2.7. (Note that,

for convenience, coded values of ln x are denoted x, throughout.)
In terms of coded values of x, the fitted model is

$$\hat{Y}_j = a + bx_j = -1.477 + .892\, x_j.$$

To scale the result in terms of ln x_j, we find

$$\hat{\beta}_j = b/f = 1.2874,$$

determine

$$\overline{\ln x} = f\bar{x} + c,$$

and find, from (4.8),

$$\hat{\alpha} = \bar{y}' - \hat{\beta}\,\overline{\ln x} = 5.3440.$$

Then

$$\hat{Y}'_j = 5.3440 + 1.2874 \ln x_j.$$

The absolute threshold is, from (4.12),

$$(\ln \hat{x})_{md} = -\hat{\alpha}/\hat{\beta} = -4.1510.$$

In original stimulus units, from (4.13),

$$\hat{x}_{md} = .0158\,\% \text{ concentration}.$$

The regression line is drawn in Figure 4.1, the solid line of that figure, with reference to the coded values of ln x.

In Table 4.2 an analysis of regression is performed. The detailed justification for the analysis is that presented in Section 2.7. By considering the SSE distributed as χ^2 with two degrees of freedom, it is found that the data provide insufficient evidence for rejection of the psychophysical model. Thus, we may test SSR as χ^2 with one degree of freedom, and find evidence for rejecting the hypothesis $\beta_j = 0$, at the .001 significance point.

The primary aim of this study is one of determining the absolute taste threshold for sodium benzoate. The estimated threshold, found from the analysis presented in Table 4.1, is $(\ln \hat{x}_{md}) = -4.1510$, $\hat{x}_{md} = .0158$. Employing Equation (4.16), .95 confidence bounds on $(\ln x_{md})$ are found (Table 4.2),

$$-4.5019 < (\ln x)_{md} < -3.8005,$$

from which we find corresponding bounds on x_{md},

$$.0111 < x_{md} < .0224.$$

Were it desired also to find interval estimates for α, β, or μ, these could be determined by the identical methods used in Table 2.5.

TABLE 4.2. Analysis of Regression and Confidence Bounds on x_{md},
Logarithmic Model

Source of variation	d.f.	Sum of squares	=	χ^2	Probability
Regression	1	SSR = $bSxy$	=	11.944	$p < .001$
Error	2	SSE = SST − SSR	=	2.039	$.50 > p > .30$
Total	3	SST = $S_y{}^2$	=	13.983	

Letting md refer to the coded $\ln x$ scale, then from (4.15),

$$SE_{md} \approx \sqrt{\frac{1}{b^2}\left(\frac{1}{\Sigma NW} + \frac{(md - \bar{x})^2}{S_x{}^2}\right)}$$

$$\approx \sqrt{\frac{1}{(.8923)^2}\left(\frac{1}{19.292} + \frac{(1.655 - 1.791)^2}{15.001}\right)}$$

$$\approx .258.$$

From (4.16), for approximate .95 confidence bounds on md,

$$md \gtrless 1.655 \pm 1.96\,(0.258)$$

or

$$1.149 < md < 2.161.$$

Since

$$md = \frac{(\ln x)_{md} + 5.2983}{.6931},$$

we find confidence bounds on $(\ln x)_{md}$ to be

$$-4.5019 < (\ln x)_{md} < -3.8005.$$

Taking antilogarithms, we revert to physical stimulus units for bounds on x_{md},

$$.0111 < x_{md} < .0224.$$

The estimated regression parameters $\hat{\alpha}$ and $\hat{\beta}$ may be highly dependent upon the choice of a provisional line in this least squares analysis. However, they tend to vary proportionately, one to the other, so that $\hat{x}_{md} = -\hat{\alpha}/\hat{\beta}$, the estimated absolute stimulus threshold value, remains relatively stable. If the aim of the study is one of predicting proportions of detection for values other than x_{md}, the maximum likelihood solution of Section 4.3 is better suited than this least squares method.

4.3   The Two-sample Maximum Likelihood Solution

The maximum likelihood solution is particularly useful for estimation of thresholds by the two-sample method because it is often difficult to select the range of stimulus magnitudes, on a priori grounds, to assure that the observed proportion of responses p_j is distributed over the range

$$1/2 < p_j < 1.00,$$

as $j = 1, 2, \ldots, n$. Also, in general, this method is less sensitive than the method of least squares to extreme data points, with respect to determination of parameters of the psychophysical model.

Since the proportion p'_j of detections is to be estimated, the derivation of the maximum likelihood solution for threshold differs from that of Chapter 3 in that the log likelihood is differentiated with respect to P'_j where

$$P = (1 + P')/2$$

and P'_j is substituted for P_j; ln x_j is substituted for x_j throughout to accommodate the logarithmic psychophysical model. The differentiation gives the likelihood equations (suppressing the subscript j)

$$\frac{\partial l}{\partial \alpha} = \sum \frac{Nh(Y')(p' - P')}{2PQ} = 0 \,;$$

$$\frac{\partial l}{\partial \beta} = \sum \frac{Nh(Y')(p' - P')\ln x}{2PQ} = 0 \,.$$

The second derivatives for the Newton process have the general form

$$\frac{\partial^2 l}{\partial \alpha^2} = A - B, \qquad \frac{\partial^2 l}{\partial \alpha \partial \beta} = A - B \ln x, \qquad \text{and} \qquad \frac{\partial^2 l}{\partial \beta^2} = A - B(\ln x)^2$$

where

$$A = \Sigma Nh(Y')(p' - P')\left(-Y - \frac{P}{\partial Q} + \frac{Q}{\partial P}\right)$$

and

$$B = \Sigma NW' \,.$$

Again the A term is zero if p is replaced by its expectation and may be neglected in practice. The Newton solution then becomes

$$\begin{bmatrix} \hat{\alpha} \\ \hat{\beta} \end{bmatrix}_{k+1} = \begin{bmatrix} \hat{\alpha} \\ \hat{\beta} \end{bmatrix}_k + \begin{bmatrix} \Sigma NW' & \Sigma NW' \ln x \\ \Sigma NW' \ln x & \Sigma NW'(\ln x)^2 \end{bmatrix}_k^{-1} \begin{bmatrix} \Sigma NW'h(Y')(p' - P')/4PQ \\ \Sigma NW'h(Y')(p' - P')/4PQ \end{bmatrix}_k .$$

If the working deviates are defined as

$$y'_{wk} = Y'_k + \frac{1}{h(Y'_k)}(p' - P'_k)$$

$$= Y'_k + \frac{1}{h(Y'_k)}[2p - (1 + P'_k)] \,,$$

the Newton solution based on the approximate second derivatives is again equivalent to repeated weighted least squares regression of these working deviates on the attribute magnitudes. Values of y'_{wk} may be read from Table A9, with arguments p and Y'_k, interpolating if greater accuracy is desired.

When stable values of $\hat{\alpha}$ and $\hat{\beta}$ are obtained, the median logarithmic stimulus magnitude is calculated by Equation (4.12) as discussed above. The sampling variances, confidence bounds, and analysis of variance are the same as for the minimum normit χ^2 method for absolute thresholds, Section 4.2.

Example 4.3

The two-sample maximum likelihood solution for the absolute threshold is illustrated in Table 4.3. Data pertain to the estimation of gustatory threshold for sodium benzoate, and were collected at the taste testing laboratory of the Quartermaster Food and Container Institute for the U.S. Armed Forces by D. R. Peryam. Responses are those from a single subject, given 14 trials at each of four levels of concentration, .01, .02, .04, and .08 % sodium benzoate in distilled water. Order of levels and order of tasting (X_0 or X_j) were balanced and randomized. It is assumed that responses are experimentally independent over trials. The object of a study such as this one is to establish the gustatory threshold for the particular person serving as a subject.

We use the logarithmic model, and code the natural logarithms of stimulus intensity as shown in Table 4.3. Values of r, p, p', and y' are recorded in the table. Plotting y'_j against coded ln x_j, Figure 4.2, yields a provisional

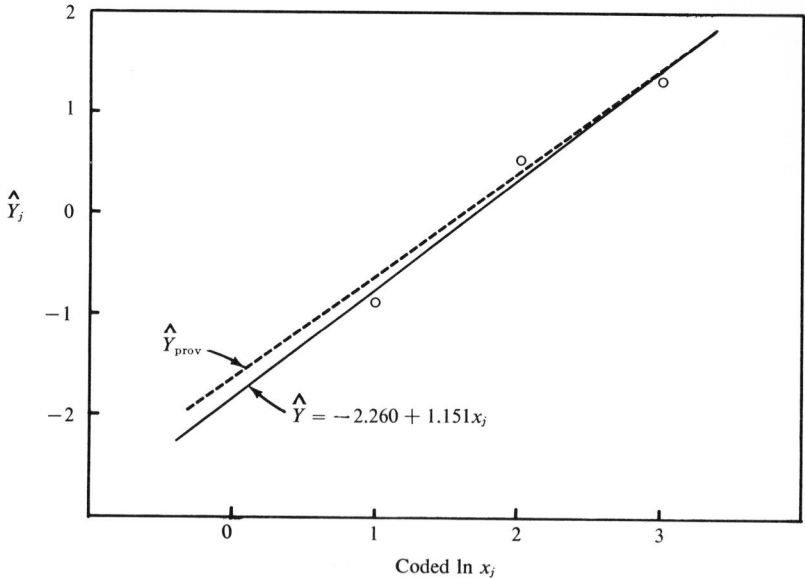

Fig. 4.2. Maximum likelihood two-sample solution for absolute threshold.

TABLE 4.3. Maximum Likelihood Two-sample Solution for Absolute Threshold

Concentration, %	Coded $\ln x$	$\ln x$	r	p	p'^{*}	y'^{*}	$Y'_{j,\mathrm{prov}}$	W'	y'_w	$W'x$	$W'y_w$
.080	3	-2.52573	13	.929	.858	1.07	1.11	.1865	1.070	.5595	.1996
.040	2	-3.21888	11	.786	.572	.18	.14	.2259	.181	.4518	.0409
.020	1	-3.91202	8	.571	.142	-1.07	$-.83$	.0834	-1.046	.0834	$-.0872$
.010	0	-4.60517	6	.429			-1.80	.0062	-4.052	.0000	$-.0251$

$x = (\ln x + 4.60517)/.69315, \quad c = -4.60517, \quad f = .69315, \quad N = 14.$

$\Sigma W = .5020$
$\Sigma Wx = 1.0947$
$\Sigma Wy = .1252$
$\Sigma Wx^2 = 2.6655$
$\Sigma Wy^2 = .4139$
$\Sigma Wxy = .5932$

$$\bar{x} = \Sigma Wx/\Sigma W = 2.1807$$
$$\bar{y} = \Sigma Wy/\Sigma W = .2494$$
$$S_{x^2} = N(\Sigma Wx^2 - \bar{x}\Sigma Wx) = 3.8960$$
$$S_{y^2} = N(\Sigma Wy^2 - \bar{y}\Sigma Wy) = 5.3578$$
$$S_{xy} = N(\Sigma Wxy - \bar{x}\Sigma Wy) = 4.4828$$
$$b = S_{xy}/S_{x^2} = 1.1506$$
$$a = \bar{y} - bx = -2.2597$$

In coded $\ln x$ units, $\hat{Y}_j = a + bx_j = -2.260 + 1.151x_j$
and $md = -a/b = 1.964$

$$\ln x_j = fx + c = .69315\bar{x} - 4.60517 = -3.09362$$
$$\hat{\alpha} = \bar{y} - \hat{\beta}\,\overline{\ln x} = 5.3848$$
$$\hat{\beta} = b/f = 1.6600$$
$$\hat{Y}_j = \hat{\alpha} + \hat{\beta}\ln x_j$$
$$= 5.3848 + 1.6600\ln x_j$$
$$(\ln \bar{x})_{md} = -\hat{\alpha}/\hat{\beta} = -3.2439$$
$$\bar{x}_{md} = \ln^{-1}(-3.2439) = .0390\%$$

* Used in the preliminary graphical solution only.

regression line (the dashed line of Figure 4.2) from which is read values of Y'_{prov}. These values are recorded in Table 4.3, and serve to determine W'_j (from Table A7) and y'_w (interpolating in Table A9).

The solution in Table 4.3 yields, in coded ln x units,

$$\hat{Y}_j = -2.260 + 1.151x_j,$$

a function represented by the solid line, Figure 4.2. (The residual of Table 4.4, shows this solution to be so adequate as to suggest that no iterations would appreciably alter it.) In coded terms

$$md = 1.964,$$

corresponding to

$$(\ln \hat{x})_{md} = -3.2439,$$

or

$$\hat{x}_{md} = .0390\%.$$

The regression analysis of Table 4.4 yields no evidence against the model. The hypothesis $\beta = 0$ is clearly rejected.

TABLE 4.4. Analysis of Regression and Confidence Bounds on Absolute Threshold, from Maximum Likelihood Solution

Source of variation	d.f.	Sum of squares	=	χ^2	Probability
Regression	1	$SSR = bS_{xy}$	=	5.1579	$.025 > p > .01$
Residual	2	$SSE = SST - SSR$	=	.1999	$.95 > p > .90$
Total	3	$SST = S_{y^2}$	=	5.3578	

$$\text{(coded } md) = \bar{x} - \bar{y}/b = 1.9639$$

with $SE_{md} = (1/b)\sqrt{1/N\Sigma W + (md - \bar{x})^2/S_{x^2}} = .3929$

$$(\ln \hat{x})_{md} = f_{(md)} + c = -3.2439$$

$$SE(\ln \hat{x})_{md} = f\ SE_{(md)} = .2723$$

Using .95 confidence bounds, the c.i. for md is

$$1.194\text{---}2.734;$$

for $(\ln x)_{md}$,

$$-3.7776 \text{ to } -2.7101;$$

and, taking antilogarithms, for x_{md},

$$.023\text{---}.066\%.$$

Finally, in Table 4.4, .95 confidence bounds are established for the absolute threshold stimulation. Upon conversion from natural logarithms to percentage concentrations, it is found that the .95 confidence interval for x_{md} is .023—.066%. The relative breadth of this interval is attributable to the small sample N.

4.4 The Three-sample Procedure

In the two-sample procedure for determining absolute thresholds the investigator describes the attribute in question to the subject. For many stimuli, however, it is difficult to characterize verbally the subjective experience of an attribute at near-threshold magnitudes. In this case a three-sample procedure, which requires no such description, may be useful.

(1) A set of stimuli designed $X_0, X_1, X_2, \ldots, X_n$ is prepared. In stimulus X_0, the attribute in question is absent. In stimuli $X_1, X_2, \ldots, X_n$, the attribute is present in different magnitudes $x_1, x_2, \ldots, x_n$, respectively. A range of magnitudes is chosen in which the attribute is not always noticeable for at least some stimuli.

(2) Stimuli are prepared in sets of three, each set comprised of X_0, X_0, and X_j, $j = 1, 2, \ldots, n$. The set is presented to subject i randomly selected from a large population of subjects, $i = 1, 2, \ldots, N_j$. The spatial or temporal position of the odd stimulus X_j in each set is randomly determined.

(3) Subject i is required to state which stimulus in the set is different, i.e. to judge which is the "odd" stimulus. The subject is instructed to guess when in doubt.

(4) The response is scored

$s_{ji} = 1$ when the judgment is correct

$s_{ji} = 0$ when the judgment is incorrect ;

thus the number of correct responses from a sample of N_j subjects is

$$r_j = \sum_{i=1}^{N_j} s_{ji}.$$

As for previous sampling models for the constant method, single-judgment and multiple-judgment conditions should be distinguished.

In the terminology of single-judgment sampling the population is assumed to consist of two classes of subjects, those who distinguish the odd stimulus X_j from the two X_0's, and those who fail to distinguish the difference and guess. Suppose a proportion P_j'' is in the former class and $1 - P_j''$ is in the latter; then the probability that a correct response is elicited from a given subject is

$$P_j = P_j'' + (1 - P_j'')/3 ,$$

and the proportion of subjects in the population for whom X_j is above threshold (i.e. those who distinguish X_j from the X_0's) may be calculated from the proportion of correct responses by

$$P_j'' = (3P_j - 1)/2 .$$

The normal response function is assumed and developed in precisely the same way as for the two-sample procedure of Section 4.1.

$$(3P_j - 1)/2 = \Phi(\alpha + \beta x_j) = \Phi(Y_j'').$$

The expected deviate Y_j'' is therefore estimated by

$$y_j'' = \Phi^{-1}[(3p_j - 1)]/2.$$

The sampling variance of the estimate is

$$\mathscr{V}(y_j'') = 9P_j Q_j / 4N_j h^2(Y_j'').$$

4.5 The Three-sample Minimum Normit χ^2 Solution

The minimum normit χ^2 solution can be carried out in terms of the observed deviates y_j'' and the weights

$$W_j'' = 4h^2(Y_j'')/9P_j Q_j. \tag{4.17}$$

As in previously presented minimum normit χ^2 solutions, weights may be found by substituting $Y_{j,\text{prov}}''$ for Y_j''. From the $Y_{j,\text{prov}}''$ values, $h(Y_{j,\text{prov}}'')$ may be found from Table A2, and P_j'' may be found from Table A1. Then, in (4.17),

$$P_j = P_j'' + (1 - P_j'')/3,$$

and

$$Q_j = (1 - P_j).$$

Since no tables have been constructed for this case, the W_j'' should be determined from (4.17).

In this procedure for an observed $p_j \leq 1/3$, the value of $1/3 + 1/3N_j$ should be recorded; for an observed $p_j = 1$, $1 - (1/3N_j)$ should be recorded.

Example 4.5

This solution is illustrated by applying it to data reported by Lockhart, Tucker, and Merritt (1955). The aim of this study was to determine gustatory threshold for sodium bicarbonate. Solutions were prepared with concentrations of 125, 250, 500, and 1000 parts per million sodium bicarbonate in distilled water. Twenty adult judges were administered the three-sample procedure at each level of the variable stimulus (multiple-judgment condition). They were instructed to taste each solution, served in a 25-ml beaker, and to "select the odd sample." (Half of the samples were of the form X_0, X_0, X_j, and half were of the form X_0, X_j, X_j.)

In Table 4.5 appear the data and the weighted least squares (minimum normit χ^2) solution. Provisional deviates were taken from the dashed line

TABLE 4.5. Three-sample Weighted Least Squares Solution for Absolute Threshold

Levels, j	Concentration, $\% \times 10^6 = x_j$	$\ln x_j$	Coded $\ln x_j$	r_j	p_j	p'_j	y'_j	$Y''_{j,\text{prov}}$	W''	$W''x''$	$W''y''$	$W''x''y''$
4	1000	6.90776	3	15	.75	.625	.32	.27	.3399	1.0197	.1080	.3240
3	500	6.21461	2	11	.55	.325	−.45	−.33	.2604	.5208	−.1172	−.2344
2	250	5.52146	1	9	.45	.175	−.93	−.93	.1203	.1203	−.1119	−.1119
1	125	4.82831	0	8	.40	.100	−1.28	−1.53	.0290	.0000	−.0371	.0000

$x = (\ln x - 4.82831)/.69315$, $\quad c = 4.82831$, $\quad f = .69315$, $\quad N = 20$.

$$\Sigma W = .7496$$
$$\Sigma Wx = 1.6608$$
$$\Sigma Wy = -.1582$$
$$\Sigma Wx^2 = 4.2210$$
$$\Sigma Wy^2 = .2389$$
$$\Sigma Wxy = -.0223$$

$$\bar{x} = \Sigma Wx/\Sigma W = 2.2156$$
$$\bar{y} = \Sigma Wy/\Sigma W = -.2110$$
$$S_{x^2} = N(\Sigma Wx^2 - \bar{x}\Sigma Wx) = 10.8266$$
$$S_{y^2} = N(\Sigma Wy^2 - \bar{y}\Sigma Wy) = 4.1104$$
$$S_{xy} = N(\Sigma Wxy - \bar{x}\Sigma Wy) = 6.5642$$
$$b = S_{xy}/S_{x^2} = .6063$$
$$a = \bar{y} - b\bar{x} = -1.5543$$

In coded form, $Y'_j = a + bx_j = -1.5543 + .6063x_j$
$$md = -a/b = 2.5636$$
$$\beta = b/f = .8747$$
$$\overline{(\ln x)} = (.69315)\bar{x} + 4.82831 = 6.3641$$
$$\hat{\alpha} = \bar{y} - \beta(\overline{\ln x}) = -5.7777$$
$$Y'_j = -5.7777 + .8747 \ln x_j$$
$$(\ln \bar{x})_{md} = -\hat{\alpha}/\beta = 6.6054$$
$$\bar{x}_{md} = 739$$

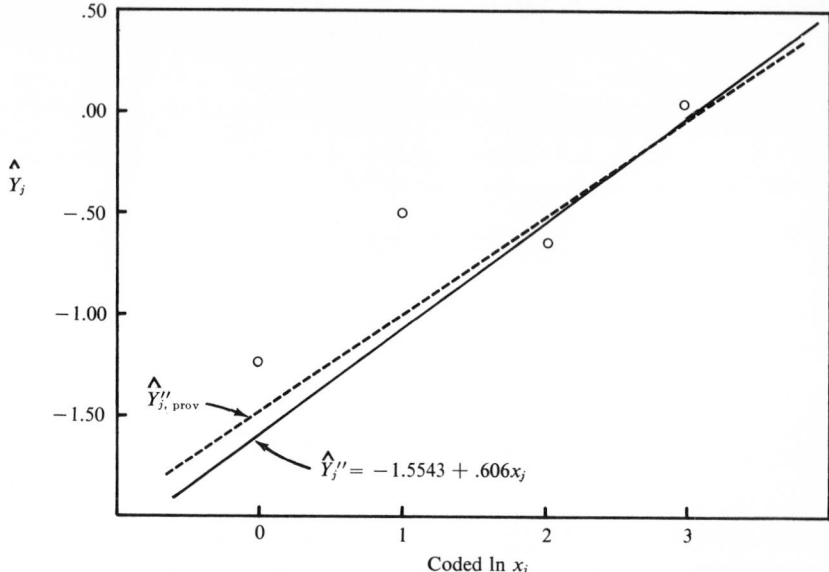

FIG. 4.3. Least squares three-sample solution for absolute threshold.

of Figure 4.3. The solid line of that figure displays the regression function in coded score units. The estimated logarithmic stimulus threshold is 6.6054, corresponding to $\hat{x}_{md} = 739$ parts per million sodium bicarbonate. In Table

TABLE 4.6. Analysis of Regression, Three-sample Least Squares Solution

Source of χ^2	d.f.	Sum of squares	=	χ^2	Probability
Regression	1	$SSR = bS_{xy}$	=	3.9799	$.025 > p > .01$
Residual	2	$SSE = SST - SSR$	=	0.1305	$.98\ > p > .95$
Total	3	$SST = S_{y^2}$	=	4.1104	

$$SE_{md} = \frac{1}{b}\sqrt{\frac{1}{N\Sigma W} + \frac{(md - \bar{x})^2}{NS_{x^2}}} = .4277.$$

An approximate .95 confidence interval for md is given by

$$2.5636 \pm 1.96\,(.4277),$$

or

$$1.7253\text{--}3.4019.$$

For $(\ln x)_{md}$

$$6.0242\text{--}7.1863.$$

For x_{md}

$$413\text{--}1321.$$

4.6 appears the regression analysis for this solution, and determination of the .95 confidence bounds on x_{md}, 413–1321 ppm.

4.6 The Three-sample Maximum Likelihood Solution

In the maximum likelihood solution, the equations for the approximate form of the Newton's procedure are

$$\begin{bmatrix} \alpha \\ \beta \end{bmatrix}_{k+1} = \begin{bmatrix} \alpha \\ \beta \end{bmatrix}_k + \begin{bmatrix} \Sigma N W'' & \Sigma N W'' \ln x \\ \Sigma N W'' \ln x & \Sigma N W''(\ln x)^2 \end{bmatrix}_k^{-1} \begin{bmatrix} (p'' - P'')/4PQ \\ (p'' - P'')/4PQ \end{bmatrix}_k,$$

where the W'' are defined by (4.17).

The working deviates for a solution by repeated regression analysis are therefore

$$y''_{wk} = Y''_k + \frac{1}{h(Y''_k)} (p' - P''_k)$$

$$= Y''_k + \frac{1}{h(Y''_k)} [\tfrac{3}{2}p - (P_k'' - \tfrac{1}{2})].$$

In all other respects the solution is the same as that for the two-sample method.

Example 4.6

Using the same data as are employed in Example 4.5, the maximum likelihood solution is given in Table 4.7. Solution for the absolute stimulus threshold, using a logarithmic psychophysical model, yields $\hat{x}_{md} = 746$ parts per million sodium bicarbonate in distilled water, a threshold very close to that ($\hat{x}_{md} = 739$) given by the weighted least squares solution. The corresponding regression analysis is shown in Table 4.8.

In both Table 4.7 and Table 4.8 the residual sums of squares are unexpectedly small, yielding values of χ^2 so small as to suggest extra-chance goodness of fit of the psychophysical model to the data. The source of this result undoubtedly is to be found in the way in which those particular sample data were selected. These data arose from one of a set of studies reported by Lockhart, Tucker, and Merritt, and were selected from that set because the

TABLE 4.7. Three-sample Maximum Likelihood Solution for Absolute Threshold

Levels, j	Concentration, $\% \times 10^6 = x_j$	x_j	r_j	p_j	$p_j'^*$	$y_j'^*$	$Y_{j,\text{prov}}''$	W''	Y_w''	$W''x''$	$W''y_w''$
4	1000	3	15	.75	.625	.32	.27	.3399	.3184	1.0197	.1082
3	500	2	11	.55	.325	.45	.33	.2604	.4769	.5208	−.1242
2	250	1	9	.45	.175	−.93	−.93	.1203	−.9336	.1203	−.1223
1	125	0	8	.40	.100	−1.28	−1.53	.0290	−1.2284	.0000	−.0356

$$x = \frac{\ln x - 4.82831}{.69315}, \quad c = 4.82831, \quad f = .69315, \quad N = 20.$$

$$\Sigma W = .7496$$
$$\Sigma Wx = 1.6608$$
$$\Sigma Wy = -.1639$$
$$\Sigma Wx^2 = 4.2210$$
$$\Sigma Wy^2 = .2423$$
$$\Sigma Wxy = -.0360$$

$$\bar{x} = \Sigma Wx / \Sigma W = 2.2156$$
$$\bar{y} = \Sigma Wy / \Sigma W = -.2186$$
$$S_{x^2} = N(\Sigma Wx^2 - \bar{x}\Sigma Wx) = 10.8266$$
$$S_{y^2} = N(\Sigma Wy^2 - \bar{y}\Sigma Wy) = 4.1294$$
$$S_{xy} = N(\Sigma Wxy - \bar{x}\Sigma Wy) = 6.5427$$
$$b = S_{xy}/S_{x^2} = .6043$$
$$a = \bar{y} - b\bar{x} = -1.5575$$

In coded score form, $\hat{Y}_j = a + bx_j = -1.5575 + .6043x_j$

$$md = -a/b = 2.5774$$
$$\hat{\beta} = b/f = .8718$$
$$\overline{\ln x} = (.69315)\bar{x} + 4.82831 = 6.3641$$
$$\hat{\alpha} = y - \hat{\beta}(\overline{\ln x}) = -5.7688$$
$$\hat{Y}_j = -5.7688 + .8718 \ln x_j$$
$$(\ln \hat{x})_{md} = -\hat{\alpha}/\hat{\beta} = 6.6148$$
$$\hat{x}_{md} = 746$$

* Used in the preliminary graphical solution only.

results were well-behaved, i.e. the response rate (r_j) was a regular monotonic increasing function of stimulus magnitude (x_j), more regular than is anticipated from an unselected empirical study.

TABLE 4.8. Regression Analysis, Three-sample Maximum Likelihood Solution

Source of χ^2	d.f.	Sum of squares		χ^2	Probability
Regression	1	$SSR = bS_{xy}$	=	3.9538	$.025 > p > .01$
Residual	2	$SSE = SST - SSR$	=	0.1756	$.95\ \ > p > .90$
Total	3	$SST = S_{y^2}$	=	4.1294	

$$SE_{(md)} = \frac{1}{b} \sqrt{1/(N\Sigma W) + (md - \bar{x})^2/S_{x^2}} = .5411$$

An approximate .95 confidence interval for *md* is given by

$$2.5774 \pm 1.96(.5411),$$
$$1.5618\text{–}3.6380.$$

For $(\ln x)_{md}$,

$$5.8745\text{–}7.3448\,;$$

for x_{md}

$$356\text{–}1548\,.$$

5 The Psychophysical Model over a Range of Magnitudes of the Standard Stimulus

In Chapter 2, the discussion of the discriminal model was restricted to only one level of the standard stimulus. The problem attacked was that of fitting the parameters of the psychophysical model at that single level. It was shown how, when the normal response function and the linear psychophysical model are valid, the probability that the variable stimulus is judged greater than the standard stimulus can be predicted for all intensities of the variable stimulus.

Now we consider how this prediction can be extended over a range of intensities of the standard stimulus. For this purpose it is necessary to determine the functional dependence of the parameters of the model upon the intensity of the standard stimulus.

5.1 Functional Dependence of the Psychosphysical Model on the Level of the Standard Stimulus

Assume that the standard and variable stimuli are indistinguishable except for differences in magnitude of the property under study. Then α, the intercept parameter of the linear psychophysical model, is expected to be invariant over variation in levels of the standard stimulus; for we anticipate, when $x_{jc} = 0$, the same Y_{jc} whatever the value of x_c. The slope parameter, β_c, on the other hand, is in general not equal at different levels of the standard. To extend prediction of the mean discriminal difference we wish to specify the function which relates β_c to x_c.

Preliminary to such specification, let us consider again the interpretation of the parameter β_c. The linear psychophysical model, Equation (2.9), is

$$Y_{jc} = \alpha + \beta_c x_{jc}.$$ (5.1)

When experimental conditions have been adequately controlled, and stimulus presentations are randomized, then when $x_{jc} = 0$, we expect $Y_{jc} = 0$. For if the physical magnitudes of X_j and X_c are identical, no systematic difference is expected in responses to those stimuli. But if, when $x_{jc} = 0$, $Y_{jc} = 0$, then $\alpha = 0$.

Let Δx be the difference limen, that particular difference in stimulus magnitudes $x_j - x_c$ for which $Y_{jc} = 1$. (Traditionally the difference limen has been defined as one probable error, associated with $Y_{jc} = .6745$. However, it is more convenient to define the difference limen as one standard deviation, so that the associated $Y_{jc} = 1$.) Then, if $\alpha = 0$, (5.1) may be written

$$1 = \beta_c \Delta x, \tag{5.2}$$

and

$$\beta_c = 1/\Delta x. \tag{5.3}$$

β_c is the reciprocal of the difference limen, and is a measure of the sensitivity of response to stimulus differences. β_c is referred to as the discriminal precision.

We desire the specification of a relation between β_c and the magnitude of the constant stimulus x_c. Such a function

$$\beta_c = f(x_c),$$

will be called the "precision function."

5.2 The Precision Function Based on Weber's Law

Weber's law states that the difference limen Δx is a constant fraction of the intensity of the standard stimulus,

$$\Delta x = k x_c. \tag{5.4}$$

Weber's law is often written in the form

$$\Delta x / x_c = k,$$

where k is the Weber ratio. From Weber's law (5.4) and Equation (5.3), the precision function relating β_c to x_c is seen to be

$$\beta_c = 1/k x_c. \tag{5.5}$$

If Weber's law holds and k is known for some specified range of stimulus intensities, it is clear that the response probabilities for any stimulus difference in that range can be predicted. For, given $\alpha = 0$ and β_c, from (5.5), these probabilities may be found from (5.1) and the normal response function presented in Chapter 2.

The validity of Weber's law could be investigated by comparing the Weber ratio computed from the estimated slope $\hat{\beta}_c$ for various values of the constant stimulus. This approach is not convenient statistically, however, and an alternative method based on a scale transformation is preferable.

5.3 Transformation of the Stimulus Continuum to Stabilize the Difference Limen

Let $Y = f(x)$ be a continuous function of some variable x with continuous derivatives, and consider the result in Y of a change in x.

$$Y + \Delta Y = f(x + \Delta x). \tag{5.6}$$

By Taylor's theorem

$$\Delta Y = \frac{\Delta x}{1!}\frac{df(x)}{dx} + \frac{(\Delta x)^2}{2!}\frac{d^2 f(x)}{dx^2} + \cdots .$$

If Δx is sufficiently small, a good approximation to ΔY is the first term of the series,

$$\Delta Y \approx \Delta x (df(x)/dx). \tag{5.7}$$

Suppose that Δx is a continuous function of x, say $g(x)$, with continuous first derivative. We require an $f(x)$ such that ΔY is some constant, say, unity. In this case, from (5.7), $f(x)$ must satisfy the differential equation

$$1 \approx g(x)(df(x)/dx),$$

or

$$df(x) \approx dx/g(x). \tag{5.8}$$

The solution of this differential equation provides the required function

$$f(x) \approx \int [dx/g(x)] + C . \tag{5.9}$$

In the present application, by Weber's law (5.4)

$$g(x) = kx_c,$$

and, from (5.8)

$$df(x_c) = dx_c/kx_c ;$$

applying (5.9),

$$f(x_c) \approx \frac{1}{k}\ln x_c + C \tag{5.10}$$

is the required function.

Consider once again the difference limen

$$\Delta x = x_j - x_c,$$

for that critical value of x_j such that the corresponding $\Delta Y = 1$. Note then, that, using (5.6),

$$1 = f(x_j^*) - f(x_c) = \frac{1}{k}(\ln x_j^* - \ln x_c)$$

$$= \frac{1}{k}\ln(x_j^*/x_c)$$

or

$$k = \ln(x_j^*/x_c), \tag{5.11}$$

for the critical value x_j^*, one difference limen removed from x_c. Equation (5.11) indicates that the natural logarithm of the difference limen is the constant k, for all values of x_c. Now, consider the expected discriminal difference

$$Y_{jc} = f(x_j) - f(x_c) = \frac{1}{k}\ln(x_j/x_c). \tag{5.12}$$

Equation (5.12) defines a logarithmic psychophysical model. The clear advantage of (5.12) over (5.1) is the invariance of $\beta^* = 1/k$ in (5.12) with changing values of x_c.

Note that the parameter β^* is the reciprocal of the Weber ratio. A statistical test of the equality of all β_c^*, $c = 1, 2, \ldots, r$, therefore is a test of the stability of the Weber ratio (assuming the adequacy of the normal response function).

5.4 A Statistical Test of Weber's Law

Consider a test of the hypothesis

$$\beta_1^* = \beta_2^* = \cdots = \beta_r^* = \beta^*, \text{ say},$$

from data obtained by the constant method with r distinct levels of the standard stimulus. Such a test is identical to a statistical test of the parallelism of r regression lines. An appropriate procedure for this purpose is a weighted analysis of variance, which includes also a test of equality of intercepts. The procedure may be formulated as follows.

Consider a set of standard stimuli X_c, $c = 1, 2, \ldots, r$. Presented together with each standard stimulus is a set of variable stimuli X_j, $j = 1, 2, \ldots, n_c$. Every stimulus X has associated with it a physical measure x.

Let x' represent $\ln x$, and

$$x'_{jc} = \ln x_j - \ln x_c = \ln(x_j/x_c).$$

Data from application of the constant method provide values p_{jc}, the observed proportions of subjects in the sample who judge $X_j > X_c$. Associated with each p_{jc} is a corresponding normal deviate y_{jc}.

For the weighted analysis of variance, it is helpful to define a number of statistics, as follows.

(a) Let the mean deviate be denoted $\bar{y}$. For level c, the mean deviate is

$$\bar{y}_c = \frac{\sum\limits_{j=1}^{n_c} N_{jc} W_{jc} y_{jc}}{\sum\limits_{j=1}^{n_c} N_{jc} W_{jc}}.$$

Summed over all levels,

$$\bar{y}_t = \frac{\sum\limits_{c=1}^{r} \sum\limits_{j=1}^{n_c} N_{jc} W_{jc} y_{jc}}{\sum\limits_{c=1}^{r} \sum\limits_{j=1}^{n_c} N_{jc} W_{jc}}.$$

(b) Consider the mean difference logarithmic stimulus intensity. For level c, let

$$\bar{x}'_c = \frac{\sum\limits_{j} N_{jc} W_{jc} x'_{jc}}{\sum\limits_{j} N_{jc} W_{jc}}.$$

Summed over all levels,

$$\bar{x}'_t = \frac{\sum\limits_{c} \sum\limits_{j} N_{jc} W_{jc} x'_{jc}}{\sum\limits_{c} \sum\limits_{j} N_{jc} W_{jc}}.$$

(c) We define sums of squares and cross products. For levels c,

$$S_{y_c^2} = \sum_j N_{jc} W_{jc} y_{jc}^2 - \bar{y}_c \sum_j N_{jc} W_{jc} y_{jc},$$

$$S_{x_c'^2} = \sum_j N_{jc} W_{jc} x_{jc}'^2 - \bar{x}'_c \sum_j N_{jc} W_{jc} x'_{jc},$$

$$S_{x'y_c} = \sum_j N_{jc} W_{jc} x'_{jc} y_{jc} - \bar{x}'_c \sum_j N_{jc} W_{jc} y_{jc}.$$

Summed over all levels,

$$S_{y_t^2} = \sum_c \sum_j N_{jc} W_{jc} y_{jc}^2 - \bar{y}_t \sum_c \sum_j N_{jc} W_{jc} y_{jc},$$

$$S_{x_t'^2} = \sum_c \sum_j N_{jc} W_{jc} x_{jc}'^2 - \bar{x}'_t \sum_c \sum_j N_{jc} W_{jc} x'_{jc},$$

$$S_{x'y_t} = \sum_c \sum_j N_{jc} W_{jc} x'_{jc} y_{jc} - \bar{x}'_t \sum_c \sum_j N_{jc} W_{jc} y_{jc}.$$

Pooled within levels,

$$S_{y_w^2} = \sum_c S_{y_c^2},$$

$$S_{x_w'^2} = \sum_c S_{x_c'^2},$$

$$S_{x'y_w} = \sum_c S_{x'y_w}.$$

(d) The estimated regression coefficients are as follows: for level c,

$$\hat{\beta}_c^* = S_{x'y_c}/S_{x_c'^2};$$

over all levels,

$$\hat{\beta}_t^* = S_{x'y_t}/S_{x_t'^2};$$

when assumed common within levels,

$$\hat{\beta}_w^* = S_{x'y_w}/S_{x_w'^2}.$$

In terms of the foregoing quantities the total (weighted) sum of squares of all deviates observed at r levels of the standard stimulus may be partitioned as shown in Table 5.1.

TABLE 5.1. Partition of Sums of Squares for a Test of Weber's Law

Source of variation	d.f.	Sums of squares	Expected sums of squares
Over-all regression	1	SSR $= \beta_t^* S_{xy_t}$	
Between means	$r-1$	SSB$_M = (S_{y_t^2} - \beta_t^* S_{xy_t})$ $- (S_{y_w^2} - \beta_w^* S_{xy_w})$	$(r-1)\sigma^2 + [\sum_c(\alpha_c - \alpha)^2 \sum_j W_{jc}$ $+ \Sigma_c(\beta_c^* - \beta^*)^2 S_{x_c^2}]$
Between regressions	$r-1$	SSB$_R = \sum_c^r \beta_c^* S_{xy_c} - \beta_w^* S_{xy_w}$	$(r-1)\sigma^2 + \Sigma_c(\beta_c^* - \beta^*)^2 S_{x_c'^2}$
Residual	$r(n-2)$	SSE $= S_{y_w^2} - \sum_c^r \beta_c^* S_{xy_c}$	$r(n-2)\sigma^2$
Total	$rn-1$	SST $= S_{y_t^2}$	

According to the sampling theory of Chapter 2, $\sigma^2 = 1$ and the residual sum of squares SSE, is distributed as χ^2 with $r(n-2)$ degrees of freedom. If the parameters α_c and β_c^* at each level have been estimated by maximum likelihood, then SSE is a Pearsonian χ^2; if parameters have been estimated by weighted least squares procedures, then SSE is a normit χ^2. Provided the binomial sampling model is valid, significance of this χ^2 at the .05 significance point would be construed as contradicting (5.12), the logarithmic psychophysical model (or the normal response law).

On the assumption that the logarithmic psychophysical model is not rejected, a χ^2 test of parallelism of the r regression lines is provided by SSB_R. When all β_c^* are equal, $(\beta_c^* = \beta_c^*$ for all $c = 1, 2, \ldots, r)$, the expected mean square for SSB_R is $\sigma^2 = 1$. That is, SSB_R is distributed as χ^2 with $r - 1$ degrees of freedom under the hypothesis of parallelism. If parallelism is not rejected the precision function based upon Weber's law is tenable. The regression slope of the psychophysical function is then estimated by $\hat{\beta}_w^*$ with sampling variance $1/S_{x_w^2}$.

Example 5.4

An experiment was performed to test the precision function for predicting responses obtained in gustatory discrimination. Four levels of standard stimulus were prepared, each distinguished by a different concentration of sucrose in distilled water. The standard stimuli selected were 1.5, 3, 8, and 20 grams of sucrose per 100 ml distilled water. At each level of X_c, four variable stimuli X_j were prepared, with concentrations x_j as displayed in Table 5.2.

Subjects were students in elementary psychology laboratory sections at the University of North Carolina. Each subject tasted one and only one pair of stimuli X_j and X_c, and was asked to report which member of the pair was "sweeter." Thus, a single-judgment sampling condition was employed. Six-milliliter solutions were served in one-ounce, plastic-capped, clear plastic vials. Subjects were instructed to hold each solution in the mouth for five seconds, and then, upon signal from the experimenter, expectorate. A twenty-second interval separated administration of the two stimuli of a pair. It will be noted that subjects were naive with respect to taste testing, that no pre-training was given, and that no rinsing of the mouth was provided between the two stimulations. Both the level of constant stimulus and the level of variable stimulus were randomized among the available pool of subjects, as was the order of tasting. Results in terms of r_j and N_j appear in Table 5.2, given for each level of x_j/x_c.

Data were analyzed by the maximum likelihood method described in Chapter 3, using a program for the LGP-30 computer prepared by Richard Lamm, Lederle Laboratories, American Cyanamid Co. Results of the analysis also appear in Table 5.2. Of primary interest is the estimated value β_w^*, the (common) regression parameter.

The computer program utilizes logarithms of stimulus magnitudes to the base 10. The result of computations in Table 5.2, $b_w^* = 6.0010649$, thus is applicable to the equation

$$\hat{Y}_{jc} = b_w^* \log_{10}(x_j/x_c).$$

TABLE 5.2. Maximum Likelihood Solution for Constant Method as Applied to Several Constant Stimuli

	$x_c = 1.5$ g sucrose/100 ml			$x_c = 3.0$ g sucrose/100 ml			$x_c = 8.0$ g sucrose/100 ml			$x_c = 20.0$ g sucrose/100 ml		
	x_j/x_c	r_j	N_j	x_j/x_c	r_j	N_j	x_j/x_c	r_j	N_j	x_j/x_c	r_j	N_j
	.793333	6	23	.793333	12	24	.793750	5	19	.794500	5	21
	.926667	6	21	.926667	8	22	.926250	6	21	.926000	14	19
	1.080000	12	21	1.080000	17	22	1.080000	11	22	1.080000	13	19
	1.260000	15	21	1.260000	13	17	1.258750	18	23	1.259000	14	20

Let $x = \log_{10} x_j - \log_{10} x_c = \log_{10} x_j/x_c$

	$x_c = 1.5$ g	$x_c = 3.0$ g	$x_c = 8.0$ g	$x_c = 20.0$ g
ΣNW	49.94859	50.81194	48.64101	46.59219
ΣNWx	.04235	-.65851	.38992	-.28785
ΣNWy	-5.40970	11.00117	-2.92736	9.01025
$\bar{x}$	-.0008479	-.0129597	.0080162	-.0061781
$\bar{y}$	-.1083054	.2165075	-.0601830	.1933855
S_{x^2}	.2689	.2618	.2467	.2555
S_{y^2}	12.3835	10.6641	14.8520	13.6638
S_{xy}	1.7533	1.2473	1.8108	1.3871
b^*	6.520508	4.764648	7.338867	5.429199

$$b_w^* = 6.0010649, \quad \beta_w^* = 2.606435, \quad \hat{k} = .3837$$

	$x_c = 1.5$ g	$x_c = 3.0$ g	$x_c = 8.0$ g	$x_c = 20.0$ g
Residual χ^2	.9514	4.7212	1.5632	6.1333
d.f.	2	2	2	2
Probability	$.70 > p > .50$	$.10 > p > .05$	$.50 > p > .30$	$.50 > p > .02$

We desire a solution in the form

$$\hat{Y}_{jc} = \hat{\beta}_w^* \ln(x_j/x_c).$$

Converting logarithms from base 10 to base e,

$$\hat{\beta}_w^* = \frac{b_w^*}{2.302585}.$$

For the data of Table 5.2, $\hat{\beta}_w^* = 2.606435$. Correspondingly, $\hat{k} = 1/\hat{\beta}_w^* = .3837$.

In Table 5.3 is given the regression analysis for these results, patterned after Table 5.1. We first test the fit of the psychophysical model to the data by evaluating the residual sum of squares with $r(n - 2) = 8$ degrees of freedom. The moderate p-value yields no evidence for rejecting the model.

Next we test the hypothesis $\beta_c^* = \beta^*$ over the four levels of standard stimuli. The between-regression χ^2, with $r - 1 = 3$ degrees of freedom, fails to reach significance, and the hypothesis of a stable precision function thus remains tenable.

The between-means sum of squares provides a test of equality of α_c in the complete equation

$$Y_{jc} = \alpha_c + \beta_c \ln(x_j/x_c),$$

where $\alpha_c = a_c$, and $a_c = \bar{y} - b_c\bar{x}$. An estimate of α, the assumed constant intercept, is $\hat{\alpha} = \bar{a}_c$; in this example, $\hat{\alpha} = .06808$, not a significant departure from zero (evaluated by determining $SE_{\hat{\alpha}}$, by the method described in Chapter 2, Section 2.7). The between-means sum of squares (Table 5.3) fails to reach significance, so we do not reject the hypothesis $\alpha_c = \alpha$.

TABLE 5.3. Analysis of Regression, Stability of the Precision Function

Source of variation	d.f.	Sums of squares	$= \chi^2$	Probability
Over-all regression	1	SSR	$= 34.48705$	$p < .001$
Between means	3	$SSB_M = (55.75438 - 34.48705)$ $= -(51.56340 - 37.19760) = 6.90153$		$.10 > p > .05$
Between regressions	3	$SSB_R = 38.19541 - 37.19760 \quad = .99781$		$.90 > p > .80$
Residual	8	$SSE = 51.56340 - 38.19541 = 13.36799$		$.50 > p > .30$
Total	15	$SST = 55.75438$		

The over-all regression sum of squares in Table 5.3, on the other hand, is highly significant, allowing the rejection of the hypothesis $\beta_w^* = 0$ in favor of the alternative $\beta_w^* > 0$, with $p < .001$.

Finally, let us determine confidence bounds on β_w^*. The estimate $b_w^* = 6.0010649$ has as standard error

$$SE_{b_w^*} = 1/\sum_c S_{x_c'^2} = 1/1.0329 = .968148.$$

Converting to natural logarithmic units,

$$SE_{\beta_w^*} = \frac{SE_{b_w^*}}{2.302585} = .420461 .$$

Using a .95 confidence coefficient,

$$\beta_w^* \lesseqgtr \hat{\beta}_w^* \pm 1.96 SE_{\beta_w^*} .$$

$$1.782331 < \beta_w^* < 3.430539 .$$

Corresponding bounds on the Weber ratio k are

$$.2915 < k < .5611 ,$$

where $\hat{k} = .3837$.

It will be recalled that our definition of the difference limen Δx is in terms of one standard deviation of Y_{jc} rather than the more traditional definition in terms of one probable error. In these traditional units, the Weber ratio is $.6745k$, and is estimated from this example to be .2598, with lower and upper .95 confidence bounds of .1966 and .3785, respectively. These are not inconsistent with other determinations of Weber's ratio for sucrose solution, typically found to be in the neighborhood of .20. The slightly higher value here would be anticipated because of differences in conditions of this study— the use of naive subjects with no pretraining and no rinsing between administrations. The present study, unlike others which used trained subjects under strict laboratory control, was intended to more nearly approximate conditions under which consumers, in their home environments, judge differences in flavor of food products.

6 The Method of Paired Comparisons

The method of paired comparisons resembles a constant-method experiment in which each stimulus serves both as test stimulus and as standard. Thus, if n stimuli are to be compared, $n(n-1)/2$ pairs of stimuli must be presented if all possible distinct pairs are to be judged. Unlike the constant method, however, the method of paired comparisons is not ordinarily applied to stimuli which vary only in the physical intensity of a single attribute. Instead, the stimuli typically represent discrete entities, which may or may not be material things. We will generally refer to such stimuli as "stimulus objects," or simply "objects." For example, works of art, candidates for public office, moral precepts, social issues, etc., are quite acceptable as stimulus objects for paired comparisons. The only restriction on the stimuli is that the subjects be able to rank one object above another, according to a suitable criterion, in the pairs of objects presented in the experiment.

To Fechner goes the credit for the idea of a psychophysical experiment involving objects that cannot be compared in terms of an obvious physical dimension. From his point of view a dimension of "pleasantness" was altogether as real as a perceived dimension of physical intensity. Thus in his empirical study of aesthetics (1876) he could easily justify having subjects compare pictures, and compare rectangles of varying dimensions, in terms of pleasantness. Fechner did not actually require his subjects to choose the more pleasant of two objects, but he suggested that this procedure would provide the best controlled experiment.

The first use of the modern form of paired comparisons appears to have been that of Cohn (1894), who studied preference for colors of varying hue and brightness. Titchener includes a version of this experiment in his "qualitative" laboratory manual (1905). He instructs each student to analyze his

116

own comparisons by counting the number of times each color is preferred to each of the other twenty-five colors in the experiment. The student is then to relate the proportions of preference to the hue and saturation of the colors by a graphical procedure.

Although the method of paired comparisons had an important early application in the development of Thorndike's (1910) handwriting scale, no rational analysis of the data was available until Thurstone formulated his law of comparative judgment in 1924. Most of the subsequent development of the method of paired comparisons by psychologists has been based on Thurstone's work. The work of Luce (1959), although starting from different assumptions, appears to be closely similar to Thurstone's Case V solution (see Section 6.5.1).

The method of paired comparisons has also aroused the interests of the statisticians and econometricians. An excellent review of contributions from these sources has been published by David (1963).

6.1 Purpose of the Method of Paired Comparisons

The immediate purpose of the paired-comparison experiment is to estimate the probability that a randomly selected subject will rank a particular object above another in all possible pairs from a given set. For any single pair, this probability is best estimated by the proportion of subjects in the sample who give the particular object first rank. For all pairs, however, it is usually more efficient to employ a response model which generates the required probabilities from a smaller number of parameters fitted to the observed proportions. To provide data for estimating these parameters is a further purpose of the method of paired comparisons. Its ultimate purpose, however, is a generalization of that of the constant method, namely, to predict the response probabilities from ancillary information about the objects. This information is not limited to physical measurements, as in the constant method, but may be any independent qualitative or quantitative characterization of the objects. If this information accounts for the response probabilities estimated in the paired-comparison experiment, and is potentially available for all objects in the set from which the experimental stimuli were drawn, it may prove possible to predict response probabilities for all pairs of objects in the larger set. In this way the observations on a limited number of stimuli generalize to a larger domain, much as in the constant method (see Section 7.3).

The statistical solution for the method of paired comparisons, however, is not directly concerned with determining the relations between response probabilities and ancillary information. Rather, it facilitates the study of the relations by subsuming the response probabilities in the parametric values estimated for the objects in the experiment. These parameters are called the "affective values" of the objects. If the model under which the solution is carried out actually holds, prediction of the affective values from ancillary information is tantamount to prediction of the response probabilities for all pairs.

Let us describe in more detail the experimental procedure for paired comparisons before considering how the affective values for the stimuli are estimated.

6.2   The Experimental Procedure

(a) A set of n distinct stimulus objects, designated $X_1, X_2, \ldots, X_n$, is prepared.

(b) On each trial in the experiment a subject is presented two objects from the set, say X_j and X_k. The subject is required to choose the object in this pair which in his judgment exceeds the other according to the criterion prescribed by the experimenter.

The criterion may be verbally described to the subject in terms of the subjective response which the objects are supposed to elicit, e.g., preference, enjoyment, approval, agreement, etc. Accordingly, the subject is instructed to choose the object in the pair which he more prefers, enjoys, approves of, agrees with, etc. The same criterion applies to all pairs in the experiment.

The criterion may also be determined by the experimental arrangement. For example, in studies of the choice of foods by subjects in a cafeteria setting, food preference is the criterion by operational definition.

(c) The objects which make up the pair for each trial in the experiment are specified by the paired-comparison *design*:

  (i) *Complete designs.* All possible pairs of distinct objects are presented, i.e. $j = 1, 2, \ldots, n; \ k = 1, 2, \ldots, n; \ j \neq k$.

  (ii) *Incomplete designs.* Certain pairs are omitted as specified in the incomplete paired-comparison design. If the pair in one order is omitted, e.g., X_j, X_k, the pair in the other order is also omitted, i.e. X_k, X_j (see Section 7.1). The most common form of paired-comparisons experiment, in which only pairs with $j < k$ are presented, is actually a simple type of incomplete design.

(d) Two conditions of response sampling are possible:

  (i) *Single-judgment condition.* Each subject judges only one ordered pair. If N_{jk} subjects judge the j, k pair, $\Sigma_j^n \Sigma_k^n N_{jk}, j \neq k$ subjects are required for an experiment using a complete design on n stimuli. Single-judgment sampling is frequently used in studies of taste preferences for foods (see Examples 6.6 and 7.4).

  (ii) *Multiple-judgment condition.* Each subject judges all pairs specified by the design. If N subjects are used in the experiment,

$n(n - 1)N$ judgments are obtained using a complete design on n objects. Multiple-judgment sampling is typical in laboratory studies employing a small number of trained judges, as well as in "paper-and-pencil" surveys.

(e) Two methods for handling the effect of spatial or temporal order of stimuli within pairs are possible:

(i) Bias due to order effect is eliminated experimentally by obtaining equal numbers of judgments for the pair X_j, X_k and the pair X_k, X_j, but is not treated explicitly in the statistical analysis. Then the response of subject i is recorded without respect to order in the pairs by the score

$$s_{jki} = 1 \text{ for the response } X_j > X_k$$
$$_{j<k}$$
$$s_{jki} = 0 \text{ for the response } X_k > X_j.$$
$$_{j<k}$$

(ii) Order effect is included in the measurement model and is estimated in the statistical analysis of the data. In this case the response must be recorded with respect to the order of the stimuli in the pair:

$$s_{jki} = 1 \text{ when } X_j > X_k \text{ in the pair } X_j, X_k,$$

$$s_{jki} = 0 \text{ when } X_k > X_j \text{ in the pair } X_j, X_k;$$

$$s_{kji} = 1 \text{ when } X_k > X_j \text{ in the pair } X_k, X_j,$$

$$s_{kji} = 0 \text{ when } X_j > X_k \text{ in the pair } X_k, X_j;$$

see Section 6.6.

6.3   The Law of Comparative Judgment

A model for the analysis of paired-comparison data is formulated in Thurstone's fundamental paper "A Law of Comparative Judgment" (1927a). Thurstone assumes the response of a subject to the j, k pair to be determined by the discriminal processes

$$v_j = f(\alpha_j) + \varepsilon_j$$

and

$$v_k = f(\alpha_k) + \varepsilon_k.$$

The terms $f(\alpha_j)$ and $f(\alpha_k)$ represent a single-valued function of parameters α_j and α_k characteristic of the objects participating in the j, k pair. The parameters are called "affective values" of the corresponding objects. The terms

ε_j and ε_k are components of the discriminal processes specific to the randomly selected individual; they are assumed to obey a normal bivariate distribution function

$$\begin{bmatrix} \varepsilon_j \\ \varepsilon_k \end{bmatrix} \sim N\left(\begin{bmatrix} 0 \\ 0 \end{bmatrix}, \begin{bmatrix} \sigma_j^2 & \rho_{jk}\sigma_j\sigma_k \\ \rho_{jk}\sigma_j\sigma_k & \sigma_k^2 \end{bmatrix} \right).$$

Then the difference process $(v_j - v_k)$ is distributed normally with mean $f(\alpha_j) - f(\alpha_k)$ and variance $\sigma_{jk}^2 = \sigma_j^2 + \sigma_k^2 - 2\rho_{jk}\sigma_j\sigma_k$. The subject is supposed to judge $X_j > X_k$ when $(v_j - v_k) > 0$. Thus, the probability that a randomly selected subject will be observed to judge $X_j > X_k$ is

$$\text{Prob}(X_j > X_k) = \frac{1}{\sqrt{2\pi}} \int_{-[f(\alpha_j)-f(\alpha_k)]/\sigma_{jk}}^{\infty} \exp(-z^2/2)\, dz$$

or, say,

$$P_{jk} = \Phi\left[\frac{f(\alpha_j) - f(\alpha_k)}{\sigma_{jk}} \right].$$

This response function, relating the probability of response to the affective values of the objects, may be taken as a statement of the law of comparative judgment.

6.4   Estimates of Affective Values

Various "solutions" for paired-comparisons data based on the law of comparative judgment have been proposed. They differ in the assumptions introduced to deal with the parameter σ_{jk}, which has been called the "comparatal dispersion" (Gulliksen, 1958). We shall consider only two such assumptions: (1) The comparatal dispersions are constant; (2) the discriminal dispersion, from which the comparatal dispersion arises, is a direct monotonic function of the mean (affective value) of the process, e.g.,

$$\sigma_{jk}^2 = g^2(\alpha_j) + g^2(\alpha_k) - 2\rho_{jk}g(\alpha_j)g(\alpha_k).$$

Statistical methods for point and interval estimates of the affective values under these assumptions are presented in this chapter.

6.4.1   Estimates in Thurstone's Case V (or Case VI)

For combinations of n distinct objects taken two at a time, the law of comparative judgment specifies the composition of the $n(n-1)/2$ expected deviates, $Y_{jk}, j < k$, say. To see how the $f(\alpha_j)$ may be recovered from these deviates, set them out in the "row and column" order indexed by their subscripts. Then complete the table, as in Table 6.1, by writing zero in

TABLE 6.1. Composition of Normal Deviates Using the Law of Comparative Judgment

Objects	Objects				
	1	2	3	$\cdots$	n
1	$0 = [f(\alpha_1) - f(\alpha_1)]/\sigma_{11}$	$Y_{12} = [f(\alpha_1) - f(\alpha_2)]/\sigma_{12}$	$Y_{13} = [f(\alpha_1) - f(\alpha_3)]/\sigma_{13}$	$\cdots$	$Y_{1n} = [f(\alpha_1) - f(\alpha_n)]/\sigma_{1n}$
2	$-Y_{12} = [f(\alpha_2) - f(\alpha_1)]/\sigma_{12}$	$0 = [f(\alpha_2) - f(\alpha_2)]/\sigma_{22}$	$Y_{23} = [f(\alpha_2) - f(\alpha_3)]/\sigma_{23}$	$\cdots$	$Y_{2n} = [f(\alpha_2) - f(\alpha_n)]/\sigma_{2n}$
3	$-Y_{13} = [f(\alpha_3) - f(\alpha_1)]/\sigma_{13}$	$-Y_{23} = [f(\alpha_3) - f(\alpha_2)]/\sigma_{23}$	$0 = [f(\alpha_3) - f(\alpha_3)]/\sigma_{33}$	$\cdots$	$Y_{3n} = [f(\alpha_3) - f(\alpha_n)]/\sigma_{3n}$
$\cdot$	$\cdot$	$\cdot$	$\cdot$		$\cdot$
$\cdot$	$\cdot$	$\cdot$	$\cdot$		$\cdot$
n	$-Y_{1n} = [f(\alpha_n) - f(\alpha_1)]/\sigma_{1n}$	$-Y_{2n} = [f(\alpha_n) - f(\alpha_2)]/\sigma_{2n}$	$-Y_{3n} = [f(\alpha_n) - f(\alpha_3)]/\sigma_{3n}$	$\cdots$	$0 = [f(\alpha_n) - f(\alpha_n)]/\sigma_{nn}$

the diagonal and minus the corresponding deviate in symmetrically situated off-diagonal positions.

In Thurstone's Case V solution, it is assumed that $f(\alpha_j) = \alpha_j$. Then if each of the comparatal dispersions is equal, $\sigma_j = \sigma$, the affective values may be recovered from the row sums, except for constants of scale and location; for according to the model, the row sums have the composition

$$\sum_{k=1}^{n} Y_{jk} = \frac{n\alpha_j}{\sigma} - \sum_{k=1}^{n} \frac{\alpha_k}{\sigma}, \qquad j = 1, 2, \ldots, n.$$

Let us set the scale by letting $\sigma = 1$, and set location by letting

$$\sum_{k=1}^{n} \alpha_k = 0.$$

Then we may determine affective values with reference to the selected origin:

$$\alpha_j^0 = \sum_{k=1}^{n} Y_{jk}/n.$$

As in earlier chapters, the estimates of the deviates are the normal transforms of the observed proportions

$$\hat{Y}_{jk} = y_{jk} = \Phi^{-1}(p_{jk});$$

where

$$p_{jk} = \sum_{i=1}^{N_{jk}} s_{jki}/N_{jk}.$$

Estimates of the affective values are simply

$$\hat{\alpha}_j^0 = \sum_{k=1}^{n} y_{jk}/n.$$

This is the so-called "Case V" solution for the method of paired comparisons. It is not efficient, but is useful in many applications. It also provides a provisional solution from which to obtain the efficient minimum normit χ^2 solution, which we take up after considering the assumption that the discriminal dispersions depend on affective value.

Suppose the dispersion of the random component of the discriminal process is a continuous increasing function of affective value with continuous first derivative,

$$\sigma = g(\alpha).$$

More specifically, let σ be a linear function of α,

$$\sigma_j = a + b\alpha$$

for all j, where a is a positive constant and b has the same sign as α. This assumption follows from an argument that, for intensive subjective stimuli (as for intensive physical stimuli), the change on the stimulus dimension required to change mean scale value by a given amount is proportional to the mean scale value of the initial stimulus. The assumption appropriately may be called Weber's law for subjective continua (Eisler, 1965).

To effect a solution, it is convenient (1) to introduce the change of variable $\sigma' = (1/b)(\sigma - a)$, thus measuring discriminal dispersion from an origin at a/b and in units of $1/b$; and (2) to consider a transformation of α, $f(\alpha)$, such that $\sigma[f(\alpha)]$ is constant. Then, by the argument of Section 5.3, if σ' is small relative to the range of the α_j,

$$f(\alpha) = \int \frac{d\alpha}{\sigma'},$$

and, since $\sigma' = \alpha$,

$$f(\alpha) = \int \frac{d\alpha}{\alpha} = \ln \alpha + C.$$

Assume on the scale of transformed affective values $f(\alpha)$ a normal distribution of discriminal differences,

$$y_{jk} = f(\hat{\alpha}_j) - f(\hat{\alpha}_k) = \ln \hat{\alpha}_j - \ln \hat{\alpha}_k.$$

Then the Case V solution would yield

$$\frac{1}{n} \sum_{k=1}^{n} y_{jk} = \ln \hat{\alpha}_j - \frac{1}{n} \sum_{k=1}^{n} \ln \hat{\alpha}_k.$$

Let us set the origin on the transformed scale at

$$\sum_{k=1}^{n} \ln \hat{\alpha}_k = 0.$$

Then,

$$\ln \hat{\alpha}_j = \frac{1}{n} \sum_{k=1}^{n} y_{jk},$$

and desired estimates for α are given by

$$\hat{\alpha}_j = e^{\Sigma y_{jk}/n} = \ln^{-1}(\Sigma y_{jk}/n).$$

This generalization of Case V was introduced by Ekman (1956, 1959), and referred to by Stevens (1959, 1966) as Case VI of the law of comparative judgment. Empirical verification of Case VI has been established for a variety of stimuli in studies performed by Ekman and his associates, reviewed by Stevens (1966) and Eisler (1965). Slightly different proofs that $\hat{\alpha}_j$ has the log normal distribution appear in Aitchison and Brown (1957) and Eisler (1965).

The law of comparative judgment is thus more general than it may first appear. If the statistical test for goodness of fit, which is available in the minimum normit χ^2 solution, does not reject the assumed response function, we may consider the discriminal processes to conform to the law of comparative judgment, possibly with an implicit transformation of the metric of the affective values. There is no way of knowing from the solution itself what this transformation might be. Other empirical relationships such as those investigated in problems of prediction of choice (Section 9.2) are necessary to specify more narrowly the form of the judgmental process.

6.4.2   The Minimum Normit χ^2 Solution under Case V Assumptions

Efficient estimates of affective value may be readily obtained under the following conditions:

(i) The response for each pair, s_{jk}, may be considered an independent Bernoulli process with parameters P_{jk} and N_{jk}. For single-judgment sampling this assumption is entirely justified. For multiple-judgment sampling, it can be justified only when previous judgments of the subject do not influence his later judgments (even though the same objects are appearing repeatedly throughout the trials). The conditions under which multiple-judgment paired comparisons can or cannot be considered independent are discussed in Section 6.7.

(ii) Order effect is of no interest and is eliminated experimentally by counterbalancing. Order of presentation is ignored when recording responses.

(iii) All pairs with $j \neq k$ are presented.

(iv) The generalized Case V model is assumed.

As in Section 6.4.1 we assume the inverse normal transform of the observed proportions

$$y_{jk} = \Phi^{-1}(p_{jk}), \qquad < k,$$

to be a random variable of the form

$$y_{jk} = f(\alpha_j) - f(\alpha_k) + \zeta_{jk}. \tag{6.1}$$

The random sampling error, ζ_{jk}, is the inverse normal transform of the binomial error and as such is distributed in the limit as

$$N[0, \, P_{jk} Q_{jk}/N_{jk} h^2(Y_{jk})] \, .$$

Again $h^2(Y_{jk})$ is the squared normal ordinate at the expected deviate Y_{jk}, and P_{jk}, $Q_{jk} = (1 - P_{jk})$ are areas of the normal density function below and above Y_{jk} (see Section 2.7). Thus in terms of the Müller-Urban weights with argument Y_{jk},

$$W_{jk} = h^2(Y_{jk})/P_{jk} Q_{jk}, \tag{6.2}$$

the variate

$$\sqrt{N_{jk}\,W_{jk}}\{y_{jk} - [f(\alpha_j) - f(\alpha_k)]\}$$

has the limiting unit normal distribution, and

$$Q = \sum_{j<k} N_{jk}\,W_{jk}[y_{jk} - f(\alpha_j) + f(\alpha_k)]^2 \qquad (6.3)$$

is distributed as χ^2 in the limit. To estimate the affective values for the n objects, we minimize the right-hand expression in (6.3) with respect to variation of the parameters. To this end, it is convenient to express (6.1) in matrix notation.[1] (For a resumé of matrix methods in least squares analysis, see Computing Note D.) Let

$$\mathbf{y} = A\boldsymbol{\alpha} + \boldsymbol{\zeta},$$

where $\mathbf{y}$ is the column vector of $n(n-1)/2$ sample deviates in the natural order of their subscripts, namely, $y_{12}, y_{13}, \ldots, y_{1n}, y_{23}, y_{24}, \ldots, y_{2n}$, etc., down to $y_{n-1,n}$; $\boldsymbol{\alpha}$ is the column vector of affective values, $[\alpha_1, \alpha_2, \ldots, \alpha_n]$; A is the $n(n-1)/2$ by n matrix of coefficients in (6.1), and is of the general form (zeros replaced by "$\cdot$")

$$A = \begin{bmatrix}
1 & -1 & \cdot & & \cdot & \cdots & \cdot & & \cdot \\
1 & \cdot & -1 & & \cdot & \cdots & \cdot & & \cdot \\
1 & \cdot & \cdot & -1 & & \cdots & & & \cdot \\
& & & & \vdots & & & & \\
1 & \cdot & \cdot & & \cdot & \cdots & \cdot & -1 \\
\cdot & 1 & -1 & & \cdot & \cdots & & & \cdot \\
& & & & \vdots & & & & \\
\cdot & 1 & \cdot & & \cdot & \cdots & \cdot & -1 \\
\cdot & \cdot & 1 & -1 & & \cdots & & & \cdot \\
& & & & \vdots & & & & \\
\cdot & \cdot & 1 & & \cdot & \cdots & \cdot & -1 \\
& & & & \vdots & & & & \\
& & & & \vdots & & & & \\
\cdot & \cdot & \cdot & & \cdot & \cdots & 1 & -1
\end{bmatrix}
\begin{array}{l}
\left.\rule{0pt}{2.5em}\right\} n-1 \\[1em]
\left.\rule{0pt}{2em}\right\} n-2 \\[1em]
\left.\rule{0pt}{2em}\right\} n-3 \\[1em]
\vdots \\[0.5em]
1
\end{array}$$

Finally, $\boldsymbol{\zeta}$ is the column vector of random sampling error in the corresponding deviates.

---

[1] For notational convenience, let $f(\alpha) = \alpha$, as in conventional Case V. Note that, for Case VI solutions, α would be replaced by ln α.

In terms of the $\frac{1}{2}n(n-1)$-order diagonal matrix of weights,

$$D = \text{diag}[N_{jk} W_{jk}],$$

we can write the normit χ^2

$$Q = (\mathbf{y} - A\boldsymbol{\alpha})'D(\mathbf{y} - A\boldsymbol{\alpha}).$$

Differentiating the expression on the right symbolically with respect to $\boldsymbol{\alpha}$ and equating to zero, we obtain the normal equations, the solution of which provides the minimum variance unbiased estimates of $\boldsymbol{\alpha}$:

or
$$A'D(\mathbf{y} - A\hat{\boldsymbol{\alpha}}) = 0$$

$$A'DA\hat{\boldsymbol{\alpha}} = A'D\mathbf{y}.$$

On evaluation $A'DA$ proves to be of the form

$$
\begin{bmatrix}
\sum_{k=1}^{n} N_{1k} W_{1k} & -N_{12} W_{12} & -N_{13} W_{13} & \cdots & -N_{1n} W_{1n} \\[2ex]
-N_{21} W_{21} & \sum_{k=1}^{n} N_{2k} W_{2k} & -N_{23} W_{23} & \cdots & -N_{2n} W_{2n} \\[2ex]
-N_{31} W_{31} & -N_{32} W_{32} & \sum_{k=1}^{n} N_{3k} W_{3k} & \cdots & -N_{3n} W_{3n} \\[1ex]
& & \vdots & & \\[1ex]
-N_{n1} W_{n1} & -N_{n2} W_{n2} & -N_{n3} W_{n3} & \cdots & \sum_{k=1}^{n} N_{nk} W_{nk}
\end{bmatrix} = W, \quad (6.4)
$$

where $N_{kj} = N_{jk}$, $W_{kj} = W_{jk}$, and $k \neq j$.

The n constant terms, $A'D\mathbf{y}$, are of the form, say

$$\sum_{k=1}^{n} N_{jk} W_{jk} y_{jk} = \mathbf{y}. \; ,$$

where $N_{kj} = N_{jk}$, $W_{kj} = W_{jk}$, and $y_{kj} = -y_{jk}$, $j \neq k$. Then the normal equations may be expressed as

$$W\hat{\boldsymbol{\alpha}} = \mathbf{y}. \; .$$

It is apparent that whereas the sum of any $n-1$ elements in each row or column of W is entirely arbitrary, all n elements sum to zero. Thus any $n-1$ rows or columns are in general linearly independent, whereas all n are linearly dependent. The rank of W is therefore $n-1$ and the system of nonhomogeneous equations has a consistent solution only if $\mathbf{y}.$ is subject to the same linear restriction as W. Because each observed deviate appears twice with the same weight in the elements of $\mathbf{y}.$, once with positive and once with negative sign, $\mathbf{y}.$ is evidently under the same restriction as W. This implies that in general the normal equations have a consistent solution with a one-dimensional solution set; that is, the α_j are estimable up to an arbitrary location constant. "Contrasts" between the affective values of the objects (or in Case VI, between their logarithms)

$$\alpha_j - \alpha_k$$

are absolutely estimable because the arbitrary location constants in the estimated affective values of the two objects subtract out of the difference.

The simplest method for solving the normal equations is to define $\alpha_j^* = \alpha_j - \alpha_n$. For Case V this amounts to setting the affective value for the nth object to zero, since $\alpha_n^* = \alpha_n - \alpha_n = 0$. Then the estimate of the first $n - 1$ values of α_j^* is the simultaneous solution of the first $n - 1$ equations obtained by deleting the last row and column of W and the last row of $\mathbf{y}$.. The reduced matrix of coefficients is in general nonsingular and the $n - 1$ simultaneous equations, say,

$$W^* \hat{\alpha}^* = \mathbf{y}^* \, ,$$

may be solved by a suitable numerical method. For statistical purposes, the preferred method is to compute the $(n - 1) \times (n - 1)$ matrix inverse of W^*, say W^{*-1}. (A method for hand computation of an inverse is given in Computing Note A.) Postmultiplication of the reduced normal equations by W^{*-1} gives

$$W^{*-1} W^* \hat{\alpha}^* = W^{*-1} \mathbf{y}^*$$

$$\hat{\alpha}^* = W^{*-1} \mathbf{y}^*$$

The elements of $\hat{\alpha}^*$ are the estimated affective values of the first $n - 1$ objects relative to that of the last. Before discussing the sampling theory for this solution, we establish the validity of this procedure in a short mathematical digression. (See Browne, 1958, pp. 57ff.)

MATHEMATICAL DIGRESSION. Let A be an $n \times n$ matrix of rank $r < n$. Without loss of generality an $r \times r$ nonsingular submatrix, say A_1, may be brought into leading position to obtain, say

$$A = \begin{bmatrix} A_1 & A_2 \\ B_1 & B_2 \end{bmatrix} \begin{matrix} r \\ n - r \end{matrix}$$
$$\quad\quad r \quad n - r$$

Since A_1 is nonsingular, its inverse exists and the matrix

$$\begin{bmatrix} I & 0 \\ -B_1 A_1^{-1} & I \end{bmatrix} \begin{matrix} r \\ n - r \end{matrix} , \qquad (6.5)$$
$$\quad\quad r \quad n - r$$

when postmultiplied by A, gives

$$\begin{bmatrix} I & 0 \\ -B_1 A_1^{-1} & I \end{bmatrix} \begin{bmatrix} A_1 & A_2 \\ B_1 & B_2 \end{bmatrix} = \begin{bmatrix} A_1 & A_2 \\ 0 & B_2 - B_1 A_1^{-1} A_2 \end{bmatrix} = \begin{bmatrix} A_1 & A_2 \\ 0 & 0 \end{bmatrix},$$

because, if A is of rank r, the rows of B_2 are the same linear compound of the rows of A_2 as the rows of B_1 are those of A_1, in which case $B_2 - B_1 A_1^{-1} A_2 = 0$. Then premultiplying both sides of the nonhomogeneous equations $Ax = h$ by (6.5) yields

$$\begin{bmatrix} A_1 & A_2 \\ 0 & 0 \end{bmatrix} \begin{bmatrix} \mathbf{x}_1 \\ \mathbf{x}_2 \end{bmatrix} = \begin{bmatrix} \mathbf{h}_1 \\ \mathbf{h}_2 - B_1 A_1^{-1} \mathbf{h}_1 \end{bmatrix} = \begin{bmatrix} \mathbf{k}_1 \\ \mathbf{k}_2 \end{bmatrix},$$

say, and the system is consistent if and only if $\mathbf{k}_2 = \mathbf{0}$. In this case a solution is

$$\mathbf{x}_1 = A_1^{-1} \mathbf{k}_1 - A_1^{-1} A_2 \mathbf{x}_2,$$

whence $\mathbf{x}_1$ is determined once $\mathbf{x}_2$ is fixed. The dimension of the solution space is the number of arbitrary elements in $\mathbf{x}_2$.

6.4.3   Sampling Theory

Substituting the estimated affective values in (6.3) we obtain the minimum normit χ^2 and may partition the total χ^2 as in Table 6.2.

TABLE 6.2.   Partition of χ^2 for Minimum Normit χ^2 Solution

Source of χ^2	d.f.	Sums of squares, χ^2	Expected sums of squares
Estimation	$n - 1$	SSR $= \hat{\alpha}^{*\prime} \mathbf{y}^*$	$(n-1)\sigma^2 + \alpha^{*\prime} W^* \alpha^*$
Error	$(n-1)(n-2)/2$	SSE $= \mathbf{y}' D \mathbf{y} - \hat{\alpha}^{*\prime} \mathbf{y}^*$	$(n-1)(n-2)\sigma^2/2$
Total	$n(n-1)/2$	SST $= \mathbf{y}' D \mathbf{y}$	$\frac{1}{2} n(n-1)\sigma^2 + \alpha^{*\prime} W^* \alpha^*$

A statistically significant error χ^2 contradicts the model for comparative judgment under the normal response function . A statistically significant esti-mation χ^2 contradicts the hypothesis,

$$\alpha_1 = \alpha_2 = \cdots = \alpha_n = 0.$$

The expectation of the vector estimate of $\boldsymbol{\alpha}$ is evaluated as follows:

$$\mathscr{E}(\hat{\boldsymbol{\alpha}}^*) = W^{*-1} A^{*\prime} D \mathscr{E}(\mathbf{y})$$

$$= (A^{*\prime} D A^*)^{-1} A^{*\prime} D [A^* \boldsymbol{\alpha}^* + \mathscr{E}(\boldsymbol{\zeta})]$$

$$\cong \boldsymbol{\alpha}^*.$$

This final expression is an approximation due to the bias in y as an estimate of Y, discussed in Section 2.3. In the limiting case $\mathscr{E}(\mathbf{y}) = A^* \boldsymbol{\alpha}^*$. However, for small samples and $P_{jk} \neq .50$, some bias is introduced. The extent of bias, as a function of P_{jk} and N_{jk} is shown in Figure 2.1.

The variance (covariance matrix) of the estimate is

$$\mathscr{V}(\hat{\boldsymbol{\alpha}}^*) = (A^{*\prime}DA^*)^{-1}A^{*\prime}D\mathscr{V}(\mathbf{y})DA^*(A^{*\prime}DA^*)^{-1}$$

$$= (A^{*\prime}DA^*)^{-1}A^{*\prime}DD^{-1}DA^*(A^{*\prime}DA^*)^{-1}$$

$$= (A^{*\prime}DA^*)^{-1}$$

$$= [\sigma_{\hat{\alpha}^*}^{jk}], \quad j = 1, 2, \ldots, n-1, \quad k = 1, 2, \ldots, n-1.$$

That is, the inverse of the diminished matrix of coefficients of the normal equations gives the variances and covariances of the estimated contrasts of the affective values of the first $n - 1$ objects and the last object. The limiting $1 - \gamma$ confidence bounds for the population contrasts are

$$\text{for } (\alpha_j - \alpha_n): \quad \hat{\alpha}_j^* \pm z_{1-(\gamma/2)}\sqrt{\sigma_{\hat{\alpha}^*}^{jj}}$$

when $z_{1-(\gamma/2)}$ is the critical deviate at the $1 - (\gamma/2)$ point of the normal distribution and $\sigma_{\hat{\alpha}^*}^{jj}$ is the jth diagonal element of the inverse of $A^{*\prime}DA^*$.

The variance of estimators of any other contrasts can be computed from the variances and covariances in $(A^{*\prime}DA^*)^{-1}$. For example, the estimate of $\alpha_j - \alpha_k$ is

$$\widehat{(\alpha_j - \alpha_k)} = \widehat{(\alpha_j - \alpha_n)} - \widehat{(\alpha_k - \alpha_n)} = \hat{\alpha}_j^* - \hat{\alpha}_k^*$$

with variance

$$\mathscr{V}(\hat{\alpha}_j^* - \hat{\alpha}_k^*) = \sigma_{\hat{\alpha}^*}^{jj} + \sigma_{\hat{\alpha}^*}^{kk} - 2\sigma_{\hat{\alpha}^*}^{jk}.$$

Throughout this solution we have assumed the weights known when in general they are not. Since minor variation in the weights has little effect on the ultimate solution, any good approximation to them is suitable. For this purpose unbiased estimates from the simple Case V solution can be used to obtain provisional deviates

$$Y_{jk,\text{prov}} = \hat{\alpha}_j^0 - \hat{\alpha}_k^0.$$

Then the weights may be computed from (6.2) or obtained from Table A6.

Example 6.4.3

The minimum normit χ^2 solution for paired comparisons and the single-judgment sampling model are well illustrated by the following " Monte Carlo " experiment. Four objects with affective values $\alpha_1 = 10$, $\alpha_2 = 0.5$, $\alpha_3 = 0.0$, and $\alpha_4 = -0.5$ were assumed. To simulate the difference process for the ith independent judgment of the X_j, X_k pair, a randomly sampled unit normal deviate, ζ_{jki}, say, was added to the difference in affective value of the two objects[2]

$$v_{jki} = \alpha_j - \alpha_k + \zeta_{jki}.$$

A value $v_{jki} > 0$, representing the response $X_j > X_k$, was recorded as $s_{jki} = 1$; the value $v_{jki} \leq 0$, representing $X_j < X_k$, as $s_{jki} = 0$. Sixty random deviates were selected independently for each of the six unordered pairs. The observed proportions p_{jk}, $j < k$, of response $X_j > X_k$ are shown in Table 6.3.

TABLE 6.3. Minimum Normit χ^2 Solution for Paired Comparisons

1. *Observed proportions* ($N = 60$)

Objects	\multicolumn{4}{c}{Objects}

Objects	1	2	3	4
1		.717	.833	.967
2			.767	.883
3				.733
4				

2. *Observed normal deviates, row sums, and provisional estimates of affective value*

Objects	1	2	3	4	Sums	Estimates
1	.0000	.5740	.9661	1.8384	3.3785	.8446
2	− .5740	.0000	.7290	1.1901	1.3451	.3363
3	− .9661	− .7290	.0000	.6219	−1.0732	−.2683
4	−1.8384	−1.1901	−.6219	.0000	−3.6504	−.9126

3. *Matrix of coefficients and weighted row sums*

$$W = \begin{bmatrix} 70.278 & -34.758 & -24.024 & -11.496 \\ -34.758 & 89.358 & -33.396 & -21.204 \\ -24.024 & -33.396 & 90.222 & -32.802 \\ -11.496 & -21.204 & -32.802 & 65.502 \end{bmatrix} ; \mathbf{y} = \begin{bmatrix} 64.2949 \\ 29.6295 \\ -27.1557 \\ -66.7687 \end{bmatrix}$$

4. *Inverse of the first three rows and columns of W; estimated affective values*

$$W^{*-1} = \begin{bmatrix} .025553 & .014486 & .012166 \\ .014486 & .021200 & .011705 \\ .012166 & .011705 & .018656 \end{bmatrix} ; \hat{\alpha}^* = W^{*-1}y^* = \begin{bmatrix} 1.74175 \\ 1.24170 \\ .62242 \\ .00000 \end{bmatrix}$$

In the solution for these data we proceed as if the affective values were unknown. Table A3 is entered to transform the proportions into the normal deviates, y_{jk}, shown in Table 6.3, section 2. Note that deviates y_{kj}, $j < k$ are the negative of the deviates y_{jk}. Provisional estimates of the affective values, $\alpha^0_{j,prov}$, are obtained by summing the rows of Table 6.3, section 2, and dividing by $n = 4$.

[2] Random unit normal deviates were obtained from Herman Wold, *Random Normal Deviates*, Cambridge University Press, Cambridge, 1948.

The weights for the minimum normit χ^2 solution are functions of the provisional deviates,

$$Y_{jk,\text{prov}} = \alpha^0_{j,\text{prov}} - \alpha^0_{k,\text{prov}}$$

and may be read from Table A6. In this instance the provisional deviates and weights are

j, k	$Y_{jk,\text{prov}}$	$W_{jk,\text{prov}}$
1, 2	.5083	.5793
1, 3	1.1129	.4004
1, 4	1.7572	.1916
2, 3	.6046	.5566
2, 4	1.2489	.3534
3, 4	.6443	.5467

From these weights the matrix of coefficients, W, given by (6.4), and the weighted row sums,

$$y_{j\cdot} = \sum_k N_{jk} W_{jk} y_{jk},$$

shown in Table 6.3, section 3, are obtained. Then the inverse of the first three rows and columns of W is computed and multiplied by the vector of weighted row sums to obtain the efficient estimates of affective value, $\hat{\alpha}^*$. The value of $\hat{\alpha}^*_4$ is zero by assumption.

In this artificial experiment the model for comparative judgment and the normal response law hold exactly. The error χ^2 of Table 6.4 testing the goodness

TABLE 6.4. Partition of χ^2 for Example 6.4.3

Source of χ^2	d.f.	Sum of squares	$= \chi^2$	Probability
Estimation	$(n-1) = 3$	$\text{SSR} = \sum_j \hat{\alpha}^*_j \sum_k N_{jk} W_{jk} y_{jk}$	$= 131.87$	$.0005 > p$
Error	$(n-1)(n-2)/2 = 3$	$\text{SSE} = \text{SST} - \text{SSR}$	$= 1.32$	$.80 > p > .70$
Total	$n(n-1)/2 = 6$	$\text{SST} = \sum\sum_{j<k} N_{jk} W_{jk} y^2_{jk}$	$= 133.19$	

Interval estimates of affective value contrasts, using $z_{1-(\gamma/2)} = 1.96$ ($\gamma = .05$):

Contrast	Confidence interval
$\alpha_1 - \alpha_4$	$1.742 \pm 1.96 \sqrt{.025553} = 1.429 - 2.055$
$\alpha_2 - \alpha_4$	$1.242 \pm 1.96 \sqrt{.021200} = .957 - 1.527$
$\alpha_3 - \alpha_4$	$.622 \pm 1.96 \sqrt{.018656} = .354 - .890$

of fit of the model, is not inconsistent with this fact ($.80 > p > .70$). Similarly the χ^2 for estimation rejects the hypothesis that the affective values of the objects are equal, again not inconsistent with the known values. It is of interest to compute the true contrasts from the known affective values of the objects and compare them with the estimated contrasts:

	True	Estimated	Confidence
	value	value	interval
Contrast			
$\alpha_1 - \alpha_4$	1.5	1.742	1.429–2.055
$\alpha_2 - \alpha_4$	1.0	1.242	.957–1.527
$\alpha_3 - \alpha_4$	.5	.622	.354– .890

In each case each .95 confidence interval is found to include the true value.

6.5   Alternative Response Functions

The alternatives to the normal response function which were proposed in Section 3.3 for the constant method may also be applied to paired comparisons. The log normal function already has been discussed, as Case VI of the law of comparative judgment. The logistic response function requires a solution similar in complexity to the normal solution, but is of special interest because of its psychological interpretation. The angular response function is of interest because it permits a solution for paired comparisons which is computationally simple.

6.5.1   The Logistic Response Function

Bradley and Terry (1952) and Luce (1959) have proposed the following model for the probability that X_j is ranked above X_k in the pair X_j, X_k or X_k, X_j:

$$P_{jk} = \frac{\pi_j}{\pi_j + \pi_k}, \qquad j = 1, 2, \ldots, n; k = 1, 2, \ldots, n. \qquad (6.6)$$

π_j and π_k are positive parameters characteristic of objects X_j and X_k, respectively. Bradley and Terry introduce $\pi_j + \pi_k$ in the denominator to normalize π_j, i.e. so that $P_{jk} + P_{kj} = 1$. In Luce's formulation, however, π_j can be interpreted as the probability that X_j will be ranked first among all n objects. The probability that X_j will be ranked first in any subset of objects, and in particular in the subset $\{X_j, X_k\}$, follows from his principle of "independence from irrelevant alternatives." This principle states that the ratio π_j/π_k remains constant regardless of what other objects are in the subset. It may be used to establish (6.6) as follows.

Suppose N subjects judge X_j and X_k in the set $\{X_1, X_2, \ldots, X_j, X_k, \ldots, X_n\}$. Of these N subjects, $N\pi_j$ are expected to judge X_j superior to all others, and will necessarily judge $X_j > X_k$; similarly, $N\pi_k$ are expected to judge $X_k > X_j$. In this subgroup of subjects who give X_j or X_k first rank among all n objects, the proportion who rank X_j above X_k is

$$\frac{N\pi_j}{N\pi_j + N\pi_k}.$$

As for the remainder of the subjects, those who assign first rank to objects other than X_j or X_k, the constancy of the ratio π_j/π_k implies that they too will rank X_j above X_k in the proportion $\pi_j/(\pi_j + \pi_k)$. Then the expected proportion of subjects judging $X_j > X_k$ is

$$P_{jk} = \pi_j + \frac{\pi_j}{\pi_j + \pi_k}\,[1 - (\pi_j + \pi_k)]$$

$$= \pi_j + \frac{\pi_j}{\pi_j + \pi_k} - \pi_j$$

$$= \frac{\pi_j}{\pi_j + \pi_k} = \frac{\pi_j/\pi_k}{\pi_j/\pi_k + 1}.$$

In the manner of Section 3.3, this model may be transformed into the logistic response function by setting $\pi_j/\pi_k = \exp(\alpha_j - \alpha_k)$. Thus, estimates of $\ln \pi_j/\pi_k$ may be obtained by a minimum logit χ^2 solution, a solution of the same form as the minimum normit χ^2 solution, but employing logistic deviates $y_{jk} = \ln p_{jk}/(1 - p_{jk})$, and weights $W_{jk} = P_{jk}(1 - P_{jk})$ (see Section 3.3.1). The ratios π_j/π_k may be recovered if desired from the antilogs of $\alpha_j - \alpha_k$. Alternatively, they may be estimated directly by the maximum likelihood solution given by Bradley and Terry (1952) (see Example 6.5.2).

After exponential transformation of parameters, the Bradley-Terry-Luce model becomes equivalent to Thurstone's Case V model, except that the logistic density replaces the Gaussian density of the Case V response function (see Section 2.3). Indeed, the principle of independence from irrelevant alternatives has the same effect as constant correlation of discriminal processes for all pairs of stimuli. For, if the correlations are constant and the discriminal dispersions equal, the difference processes for pairs of objects not sharing an object in common are uncorrelated. This implies that the conditional probability of a subject's choice between any two objects, given his choice between any other two objects, is equal to the unconditional probability. It is doubtful that the principle is strictly true in practice, since personal preferences for given objects usually extend to similar objects. (A person who likes turnips will probably also like rutabaga and may even have a taste for parsnips.) Nevertheless, the assumptions of Luce's model and Thurstone's Case V appear to be well enough approximated in many applications to allow reasonably accurate predictions of choice. Luce's model is particularly valuable in this connection because it generalizes easily to prediction of the proportion of first choices received by objects when chosen from among n objects. It is, in fact, equivalent to substituting a readily integrable multivariate logistic distribution for the multivariate normal distribution of difference processes (see Section 9.1.1).

6.5.2   The Angular Response Function

When the sample size is constant for all pairs, we avoid the weights in the least squares solution by using angular rather than normal deviates. Since no weights are required, the observed proportions are transformed to angular deviates using formula (3.23) or (3.23a and b) of Section 3.3 to obtain the $n(n-1)/2 \times 1$ vector $\mathbf{y}$ of observed deviates. The normal equations become

$$(A'A)\boldsymbol{\alpha} = A'\mathbf{y}, \tag{6.7}$$

where A is the matrix of coefficients as defined in Section 6.4.2. The matrix product of A' and its transpose shows a very special structure:

$$A'A = \begin{bmatrix} (n-1) & -1 & -1 & \cdots & -1 \\ -1 & (n-1) & -1 & \cdots & -1 \\ -1 & -1 & (n-1) & \cdots & -1 \\ & & \vdots & & \\ -1 & -1 & -1 & \cdots & (n-1) \end{bmatrix}$$

Let each element in this matrix be divided by n to obtain, say

$$\frac{1}{n} A'A = I - \mathbf{1}\mathbf{1}'/n = \Delta. \tag{6.8}$$

The matrix Δ is the projection operator for an $(n-1)$-dimensional subspace in an n-space. (See Stoll, 1952, pp. 153–154.) Let $\mathbf{x} = [x_1, x_2, \ldots, x_n]$ be a vector in the n-space. Then it is projected into the subspace as, say,

$$\mathbf{x}^0 = \Delta\mathbf{x}$$

where it is subject to the restriction

$$\mathbf{x}^{0\prime}\mathbf{1} = \sum_{i=1}^{n} x_i = 0,$$

as can be seen by evaluating $\mathbf{x}'\Delta\mathbf{1}$. A vector already in the subspace is unchanged when operated on by Δ. This implies and is implied by the so-called "idempotence" of projection operators; e.g.,

$$\Delta\Delta = \Delta^2 = \Delta.$$

If the normal equations (6.7) are multiplied on both sides by $1/n$, we have

$$\frac{1}{n}(A'A)\boldsymbol{\alpha} = \Delta\boldsymbol{\alpha} = \frac{1}{n}A'\mathbf{y}.$$

Thus a solution of the normal equations is simply

$$\hat{\boldsymbol{\alpha}}^0 = \frac{1}{n}A'\mathbf{y}.$$

This is evidently just the Case V solution of Section 6.4.2, except that y is understood to be a vector of angular deviates rather than normal deviates. The partition of χ^2 for this model is shown in Table 6.5.

TABLE 6.5. Partition of χ^2 under the Angular Response Law

Source of variation	d.f.	Sum of squares	χ^2	Expected sum of squares
Estimation	$n-1$	$SSR = \hat{\alpha}^{0\prime} A' y$	$N \cdot SSR$	$n - 1 + \alpha' \Delta \alpha$
Error	$(n-1)(n-2)/2$	$SSE = SST - SSR$	$N \cdot SSE$	$(n-1)(n-2)/2$
Total	$n(n-1)/2$	$SST = y' y$		

The expectation and variance of the vector of the estimated affective values are

$$\mathscr{E}(\hat{\alpha}^0) = \frac{1}{n} A' \mathscr{E}(y) \cong \frac{1}{n} A' A \alpha \cong \Delta \alpha = \alpha^0 ; \qquad (6.9)$$

$$\mathscr{V}(\hat{\alpha}^0) = A' \mathscr{V}(y) A / n^2 = A' A / N n^2 = \Delta / N n . \qquad (6.10)$$

Thus the variance of an estimated contrast is

$$\mathscr{V}(\hat{\alpha}_j^0 - \hat{\alpha}_k^0) = (n-1)/n^2 N + (n-1)/n^2 N + 2/n^2 N = 2/nN$$

and the limiting confidence bounds are

$$(\hat{\alpha}_j^0 - \hat{\alpha}_k^0): \qquad \hat{\alpha}_j^0 - \hat{\alpha}_k^0 \pm z_{1-(\gamma/2)} \sqrt{2/nN} .$$

The simplicity of the angular solution recommends it in applications where the data do not contradict the angular response function.

Example 6.5.2a

To show the effect of substituting the angular response function for the normal, we reanalyze the data of Example 6.4.2. The angular deviates from Table A5, the row sums, and the estimated affective values are found to be the following:

Objects	Angular deviates				Sums	Estimates
	1	2	3	4		
1	.0000	.4489	.7288	1.2055	2.3832	.59580
2	−.4489	.0000	.5633	.8726	.9870	.24675
3	− 7288	−.5633	.0000	.4848	−.8073	−.20183
4	−1.2055	−.8726	−.4848	.0000	−2.5629	−.64073

The partition of χ^2 associated with this solution is as follows:

Source of χ^2	Degrees of freedom	Sum of squares = χ^2/N	χ^2	Probability
Estimation	$(n-1) = 3$	$SSR = n\sum_j (\alpha_j^0)^2 = 3.4685$	208.11	$.0005 > p$
Error	$(n-1)(n-2)/2 = 3$	$SSE = SST - SSR = .0312$	1.87	$.70 > p > .60$
Total	$n(n-1)/2 = 6$	$SST = \sum_{j<k} \sum y_{jk}^2 = 3.4997$		

Although these data were generated from random normal deviates, the solution based on angular deviates does not contradict the model. This is true in spite of the extreme observed proportion (.967), which falls in the region where the angular function poorly approximates the normal. Results of this sort are typical for empirical comparisons of the two. They illustrate the fact that very large samples are required to demonstrate a significantly better fit for one or the other of them.

Example 6.5.2b

This example is based on data presented by Bradley (1954) to illustrate an analysis under the response function specified by (3.21). An experiment was performed to determine differences in the flavor of fresh pork roasts prepared from pigs fed on rations consisting of three different proportions of corn and peanuts. Each of five subjects made the three unordered paired comparisons on each of ten occasions. The proportions of judgments $X_j < X_k$, $j > k$, for each subject are shown in Table 6.6, section 1. We assume independence of all judgments. To transform to angular deviates (section 2), we use Anscombe's correction (Equation 3.23a), especially desirable because of the small sample size. The estimates of the affective values of the three rations computed separately for each subject by the angular solution are shown in section 3 of the table. In section 4 the results of the partition of χ^2 associated with the estimated affective values for each subject are put in a form comparable to Bradley's results: i.e. probabilities for the hypothesis of no difference in rations (estimation), and the error χ^2 for the tests of goodness of fit.

Note that the angular and logistic models give essentially the same result, and the conclusions are the same. There is no evidence of departure from the model or that the rations have any differential effect on flavor.

In this application it is useful to obtain if possible an estimate of affective value common to all subjects. A best estimate of the common value is the mean over subjects for each ration shown in section 3 of Table 6.6. To test the hypothesis that departures of the estimated values for individual subjects are attributable to sampling error in the deviates, we perform the analysis of variance shown in section 5. Let the estimated affective value for the jth object and ith subject be $\hat{\alpha}_{ji}$, and the mean for the jth object be $\hat{\alpha}_{j.} = \sum_i^m \hat{\alpha}_{ji}/m$, where m is the number of subjects. Then the between-object sum of squares is

$$\text{SSB} = \sum_j^n \hat{\alpha}_{j.} \sum_i^m \hat{\alpha}_{ji} = m \sum_j^m \hat{\alpha}_{j.}^2 \ ;$$

the total sum of squares is $\text{SST} = \sum_j \sum_i \hat{\alpha}_{ji}^2$, and the subject $\times$ object interaction sum of squares is $\text{SSI} = \text{SST} - \text{SSB}$. The sums of squares for the

TABLE 6.6. Comparison of the Angular and Logistic Solutions for Paired Comparisons

1. Observed proportions ($N = 10$)

Pair	Subject				
j, k	1	2	3	4	5
1, 2	.7	.3	.5	.3	.4
1, 3	.5	.4	.3	.4	.4
2, 3	.6	.5	.5	.5	.8

2. Angular deviates using Anscombe's formula

Pair	Subject				
j, k	1	2	3	4	5
1, 2	.3812	−.3812	.0000	−.3812	−.1871
1, 3	.0000	−.1871	−.3812	−.1871	−.1871
2, 3	.1871	.0000	.0000	.0000	.5920

3. Estimated affective values and mean affective values

Object	Subject					Sum	Mean ($\hat{\alpha}_{j.}$)
	1	2	3	4	5		
1	.1271	−.1894	−.1271	−.1894	−.1247	−.5035	−.10070
2	−.0647	.1271	.0000	.1271	.2597	.4492	.08984
3	−.0624	.0624	.1271	.0624	−.1350	.0545	.01090

4. Comparison of tests of significance

Subject	Estimation (probabilities)		Error χ^2	
	Angular model	Logistic model	Angular model	Logistic model
1	.6–.7	.78	1.13	1.24
2	.4–.5	.50	.13	.15
3	.7–.8	.63	.51	.57
4	.4–.5	.50	.15	.15
5	.2–.3	.25	1.23	1.37

5. Analysis of variance of affective values

Source of variation	d.f.	Sum of squares $= \dfrac{(n-1)\chi^2}{Nn^2}$	χ^2	Probability
General mean	1	identically zero		
Between subjects	$(m-1) = 4$	identically zero		
Between objects	$(n-1) = 2$	$SSB = m\Sigma \hat{\alpha}_{j.}^2 = .09165$	4.12	$.10 < p < .20$
Subjects × objects	$(m-1)(n-1) = 8$	$SSI = SST - SSB = .17795$	8.01	$.40 < p < .50$
Total	$mn = 15$	$SST = \underset{j \ i}{\Sigma\Sigma} \hat{\alpha}_{ji}^2 = .26960$		

general mean (correction term) and for subjects are identically zero because of the restriction $\sum_j \hat{\alpha}_{ji} = 0$.

From (6.10) we know the sampling variance of the estimated affective values to be $(n - 1)/Nn^2$, provided the paired-comparison model is not contradicted. Thus under the hypothesis of no individual differences in affective value, $[Nn^2/(n-1)]$SSI is distributed as χ^2 on $(n-1)(m-1)$ degrees of freedom. Significance of this χ^2 contradicts the assumption that each object has a common affective value among all subjects. (In the example we see that the interactive effect is not significant, $.40 < p < .50$.)

If the interaction is assumed not significant, differences between the affective values of the objects can be tested using $[Nn^2/(n-1)]$ SSB as χ^2 on $n-1$ degrees of freedom. Again in the example the hypothesis of no difference between rations is not rejected. If interaction is assumed present, on the other hand, a variance ratio test of differences between objects using $F = (m-1)$ SSB/SSI as an F statistic on $n-1$ and $(m-1)(n-1)$ degrees of freedom is available on the assumption that the subjects are randomly sampled. In this case SSI reflects variation due to sampling subjects as well as the measurement error from the paired-comparisons procedure.

6.6   An Order-effect Model: Single-judgment Sampling, Complete Design, Angular Response Function

Ordinarily the spatial or temporal position of particular objects in the pair is considered a source of bias to be eliminated by counterbalancing position, and thereafter ignored. But in some applications the effect of order of presentation may be large enough to affect the sampling variance of the proportions, or may be of interest in its own right; a model for the estimation of order effect will now be considered.

We represent the observed deviate for the pair X_j, X_k by the statistical model

$$y_{jk} = \mu + \alpha_j - \alpha_k + \zeta_{jk}, \qquad j \neq k$$

and that for the pair X_k, X_j by

$$y_{kj} = \mu + \alpha_k - \alpha_j + \zeta_{kj}, \qquad j \neq k.$$

That is, the order effect μ is positive in the direction of the first, or left-hand, member of the pair.

This model has a very simple solution when y_{jk} and y_{kj} are understood to be angular deviates. In matrix notation the model is

$$\mathbf{y} = [\mathbf{1}, B]\begin{bmatrix} \mu \\ \boldsymbol{\alpha} \end{bmatrix} + \boldsymbol{\zeta}$$

where $\mathbf{y}$ is the $n(n-1) \times 1$ vector of angular deviates in the natural order of their subscripts,

$\begin{bmatrix} \mu \\ \boldsymbol{\alpha} \end{bmatrix}$ is the $(n+1) \times 1$ vector of the order effect and the affective values of the objects,

1 is the $n(n-1) \times 1$ vector of unities,
B is an $n(n-1) \times n$ matrix of the general form (zeros omitted)

$$
B = \begin{bmatrix}
1 & -1 & & & \cdots & \\
1 & & -1 & & \cdots & \\
1 & & & -1 & \cdots & \\
& & & \vdots & & \\
1 & & & & \cdots & -1 \\
-1 & 1 & & & \cdots & \\
& 1 & -1 & & \cdots & \\
& 1 & & -1 & \cdots & \\
& & & \vdots & & \\
& 1 & & & & -1 \\
-1 & & 1 & & \cdots & \\
& -1 & 1 & & \cdots & \\
& & 1 & -1 & \cdots & \\
& & & \vdots & & \\
& & 1 & & \cdots & -1 \\
& & & \vdots & & \\
& & & \vdots & & \\
-1 & & & & \cdots & 1 \\
& -1 & & & \cdots & 1 \\
& & -1 & & \cdots & 1 \\
& & & \vdots & & \\
& & & \cdots & -1 & 1
\end{bmatrix}
\left.\begin{matrix}
\\ \\ \\ \\ \\
\end{matrix}\right\} n-1
\left.\begin{matrix}
\\ \\ \\ \\ \\
\end{matrix}\right\} n-1
\left.\begin{matrix}
\\ \\ \\ \\ \\
\end{matrix}\right\} n-1
\left.\begin{matrix}
\\ \\ \\ \\ \\
\end{matrix}\right\} n-1
$$

and finally

ζ is the $n(n-1) \times 1$ vector of angular errors distributed in the limit as $N(\mathbf{0}, (1/N)I)$.

The normal equations for the estimation of $\begin{bmatrix} \mu \\ \alpha \end{bmatrix}$ are

$$
\begin{bmatrix} n(n-1) & 0 \\ 0 & B'B \end{bmatrix} \begin{bmatrix} \hat{\mu} \\ \hat{\alpha} \end{bmatrix} = [\mathbf{1}, B]'\mathbf{y}
$$

since $\mathbf{1}'B = 0$. Their solution provides the estimate of μ,

$$
\hat{\mu} = \mathbf{1}'\mathbf{y}/n(n-1) = \sum_j \sum_k y_{jk}/n(n-1), \qquad j \neq k,
$$

which is just the mean of the deviates. Since

$$\frac{1}{n} B'B\hat{\alpha} = \frac{1}{n} B'\mathbf{y},$$

$$2\Delta\hat{\alpha} = \frac{1}{n} B'\mathbf{y},$$

the estimate of α^0 is

$$\hat{\alpha}^0 = B'\mathbf{y}/2n,$$

or

$$\hat{\alpha}_j^0 = \left(\sum_h y_{jh} - \sum_h y_{hj}\right)/2n.$$

In other words, the estimated affective value of the jth object is simply the sum of the jth row of deviates minus the sum of the jth column, all divided by $2n$.

The corresponding analysis of variance is shown in Table 6.7. As in

TABLE 6.7. Analysis of Variance for Testing Order Effect

Source of variation	d.f.	Sums of squares	χ^2	Expected sums of squares
Order effect	1	SSM $= \hat{\mu}\mathbf{1}'\mathbf{y}$	$N \cdot$ SSM	$1 + \mu^2 n(n-1)$
Affective values	$(n-1)$	SSR $= \hat{\alpha}^{0\prime}B\mathbf{y}/n$	$N \cdot$ SSR	$(n-1) + 2n\alpha'\Delta\alpha$
Error	$(n-1)^2 - 1$	SSE $=$ SST $-$ SSR $-$ SSM	$N \cdot$ SSE	$(n-1)^2 - 1$
Total	$n(n-1)$	SST $= \mathbf{y}'\mathbf{y}$		

Sections 6.4 and 6.5, statistical significance of the error χ^2 on $(n-1)^2 - 1$ degrees of freedom contradicts the model. The null hypotheses of no order effect and no differences in affective value are independently testable. Significant χ^2 for order effect on one degree of freedom contradicts the former; significance of the χ^2 for affective values on $n-1$ degrees of freedom contradicts the latter.

Expectations and variances of the estimates are

$$\mathscr{E}(\hat{\mu}) = \frac{1}{n(n-1)} \mathbf{1}'\mathscr{E}(\mathbf{y}) = \frac{1}{n(n-1)} (\mu\mathbf{1}'\mathbf{1} + \mathbf{1}'B\alpha) = \mu;$$

$$\mathscr{V}(\hat{\mu}) = \mathbf{1}'\mathscr{V}(\mathbf{y})\mathbf{1}/n^2(n-1)^2 = \mathbf{1}'I\mathbf{1}/Nn^2(n-1)^2 = \frac{1}{Nn(n-1)}.$$

$$\mathscr{E}(\hat{\alpha}^0) = \frac{1}{2n} B'\mathscr{E}(\mathbf{y}) = \frac{1}{2n} B'B\alpha = \frac{1}{2} 2\Delta\alpha = \alpha^0;$$

$$\mathscr{V}(\hat{\alpha}^0) = \frac{1}{4n^2} B'\mathscr{V}(\mathbf{y})B = \frac{1}{4Nn^2} B'IB = \frac{1}{4Nn} 2\Delta = \frac{1}{2Nn} \Delta.$$

Confidence bounds on contrasts of affective values can be computed in the manner of Example 6.5.2 using these variances.

A minimum normit χ^2 solution is also possible but is more complicated. The generally unequal weights required in this solution confound the affective values of the objects with the order effect. A nonorthogonal analysis is required similar to that in Section 3.4. We will not attempt to describe this solution here.

Example 6.6

An experiment to determine optimal concentrations of salt and sugar in brine used in canning green beans has been reported by Buck and Weckel (1956).[3] Twenty-five samples, each containing one combination of five levels of salt and sugar (0, 1, 2, 3, 4 g/100 ml) were subjected to paired-comparison preference tests under the single-response condition. The trials were carried out in grocery stores in Madison, Wisconsin. Two samples of warmed green beans were served to customers, who tasted the samples and expressed their preference for one of them. Twenty-five different subjects judged each pair in each order.

The arc-sine transforms of the observed proportions for comparisons of 16 of the 25 possible combinations of salt and sugar levels are shown in Table 6.8 (the zero levels are omitted to save space). Each combination represents an object and is designated by a pair of numbers giving the salt and sugar level respectively. The row and column sums, and the affective values estimated from them, are shown in the table, as is the grand sum and the estimated order effect. The partition of χ^2 for the solution is shown in Table 6.9. We observe that the error χ^2 is statistically significant, rejecting the order-effect model or the angular response function. It is hard to say what is causing this inflated error variation. The observed proportions are not so extreme as to question the suitability of the angular response function. Furthermore, if the data from the two orders of presentation are pooled and analyzed by the conventional normal solution, the error χ^2 is still found significant. This suggests either that the original judgments did not obey the law of comparative judgment, or that the sampling variation of the observed proportions, although random, is greater than expected from independent binomial variates. If the latter is the case, variance ratio tests of the order and object effect are justified using the F statistic

$$F = [(n-1)^2 - 1]SSM/SSE$$

on 1 and $(n-1)^2 - 1$ degrees of freedom, and

$$F = [(n-1)^2 - 1]SSR/(n-1)SSE$$

[3] We are indebted to Professor Buck for use of his original data.

TABLE 6.8. Solution for the Order-effect Paired-Comparison Model; Observed Angular Deviates* $(N = 25)$

Objects	Objects															
	11	12	13	14	21	22	23	24	31	32	33	34	41	42	43	44
11		−284	341	040	−368	−748	−313	−368	−284	−644	−644	−456	−644	368	−284	−547
12	456		313	863	284	−547	−120	−038	−248	−456	−284	368	120	−120	−547	120
13	−568	−040		155	−664	−568	−394	−368	−368	−341	−040	−201	−456	−201	−368	−547
14	120	−040	167		−284	−644	−201	−040	−068	−748	−644	−997	−201	−863	−456	−456
21	−284	748	590	284		120	368	−201	155	−368	−368	084	456	644	−253	−309
22	−040	547	394	748	313		076	456	−120	−120	368	040	040	313	084	−078
23	201	748	253	748	456	201		110	−284	456	−201	284	368	456	040	−368
24	120	263	480	284	368	−040	−201		−341	−624	−284	201	284	−040	201	000
31	394	038	644	702	368	−078	547	456		−284	368	547	167	863	547	−040
32	456	644	524	748	456	284	201	201	201		368	201	368	201	547	644
33	284	284	547	748	547	456	110	547	040	000		284	368	284	000	120
34	456	456	284	456	456	644	−232	644	−456	−368	120		284	−284	040	−368
41	−040	201	284	547	456	201	201	456	201	201	167	781		−524	368	−040
42	201	368	120	644	040	−120	284	547	−120	078	201	644	863		568	568
43	644	568	368	284	442	368	368	284	456	456	253	547	−341	120		232
44	442	748	863	368	047	120	120	040	547	120	−078	456	040	040	201	
Col. sum	−4.835	.164	−4.969	−5.355	1.666	3.021	3.468	.671	5.239	6.044	4.619	2.132	3.460	4.886	5.049	4.074
Row sum	2.842	5.249	6.172	7.619	2.917	−.351	.814	2.726	−.689	−2.642	−.698	2.783	1.716	1.257	.688	−1.069
α_j	−.240	−.159	−.349	−.405	−.039	.105	.083	−.064	.185	.271	.166	−.020	.055	.113	.136	.161

Grand total = 29.3340 $\hat{\mu} = .12223$

* All figures rounded from four decimal places.

TABLE 6.9. Statistical Tests for the Order-effect Model

Source of χ^2	d.f.	Sum of squares	$= \chi^2/N$	χ^2	Probability
Order effect	1	$\text{SSM} = \hat{\mu}\Sigma\Sigma y_{jk}$	$= 3.5853$	89.63	$p < .0005$
Object effect	$n - 1 = 15$	$\text{SSR} = 2n\Sigma(\alpha_j^0)^2$	$= 18.8184$	470.46	$p < .0005$
Error	$(n - 1)^2 - 1 = 224$	$\text{SSE} = \text{SST} - \text{SSR} - \text{SSM} = 17.2656$		431.64	$p < .0005$
Total	$n(n - 1) = 240$	$\text{SST} = \underset{j \ne k}{\Sigma\Sigma} y_{jk}^2$	$= 39.6694$		

on $n - 1$ and $(n - 1)^2 - 1$ degrees of freedom, respectively. Both the order and object effects are significant by these criteria. The estimated order effect is positive, indicating a tendency for the first presented object to be preferred, and appears large when compared with the estimated affective values of the samples. That the estimated affective values contain useful information in spite of the failure of the order-effect model will be seen when the response surface for this experiment is fitted in Chapter 7. A consumer preference study in which the fit of the angular response function was found acceptable is described in Example 7.4.

6.7 Multiple-judgment Sampling: Complete Design, Order-effect not of Interest

Under the multiple-judgment condition each subject judges all pairs. For a complete experiment in which position is counterbalanced but not recorded, the response observed for the ith subject may be represented in the $1 \times n(n - 1)/2$ vector

$$\mathbf{s}_i = [s_{jki}]; \qquad j < k,$$

where $s_{jki} = 1$ if the ith subject responds $X_j > X_k$ and $s_{jki} = 0$ otherwise.

The analyses in Sections 6.1–6.6 assume the mutual statistical independence of all responses observed in the experiment. In single-judgment sampling this assumption is met by randomly selecting a subject from a large population for each response. In the multiple-judgment case it is not always possible to assume complete independence. If the subjects are selected randomly, the responses of different subjects will be independent, but the $n(n - 1)/2$ responses obtained from a given subject may or may not be independent.

If the subject is prevented from identifying the objects, it may be possible to repeat the paired comparisons a number of times with the same subject. The result will be a sample from the conceptual population of replications within the subject. Affective values estimated for this population characterize the particular subject and can be used, for example, to qualify him as an expert judge of the objects in question. The sampling error in his responses under these conditions should be due only to temporal variation in judgment. We will refer to this variation as "response error." It should be possible to suppress correlation from this source simply by randomizing the order of the pairs within replicates. If so, the statistical analysis can proceed under the assumptions of single-judgment sampling.

The more common application, however, takes the subject, rather than the replicate within subjects, as the sampling unit; its objective is to estimate affective values of the objects in the population of subjects. In this case the subject who strongly favors object X_1, say, is more likely to rank it first in the pairs X_1, X_2; X_1, X_3; etc.; whereas the subject who disfavors X_1 is more likely to rank it second in these pairs. These consistent individual differences in preference will necessarily introduce correlation in the responses and in the sample proportions for judgments of pairs containing common objects. If this correlation is ignored when analyzing data from multiple-judgment sampling, the common tests of significance and goodness of fit for paired-comparisons solutions (Mosteller, 1951; Bradley, 1954) may be grossly biased. For unbiased tests a more general form of analysis is required. It begins from a generalization of the law of comparative judgment.

6.7.1   A Three-component Model for Comparative Judgment

A description of the discriminal process under multiple-judgment sampling must include two random components, one, $\mathbf{v}_j$, representing an individual difference in preference in all judgments of a randomly selected subject which involve the jth object, and another, say ε_{jt}, attributable to response error in the tth judgment, independent from trial to trial.

Then the discriminal process of a random subject for object X_j is

$$v_{jt} = \mu_j + v_j + \varepsilon_{jt},$$

and the difference process for the pair X_j, X_k is

$$v_{jk} = \mu_j - \mu_k + v_j - v_k + \varepsilon_{jt} - \varepsilon_{kt},$$

the subscript jk being sufficient to identify the trial without specifying t. Proceeding under the generalized Case V assumptions, we assume the random components independently distributed in bivariate form:

$$(v_j, v_k) \sim N(0, 0, \sigma_v^2, \sigma_v^2, \rho)$$

$$(\varepsilon_{jt}, \varepsilon_{kt}) \sim N(0, 0, \sigma_\varepsilon^2, \sigma_\varepsilon^2, 0).$$

Hence, v_{jk} is normally distributed with

$$\mathscr{E}(v_{jk}) = \mu_j - \mu_k$$

and

$$\mathscr{V}(v_{jk}) = 2\sigma_v^2(1 - \rho) + 2\sigma_\varepsilon^2.$$

For two comparisons sharing a common object on the same side of each pair $\mathscr{V}(v_{jk}, v_{jl}) = \sigma_v^2(1 - \rho)$, and for comparisons sharing a common object on opposite sides of each pair $\mathscr{V}(v_{jk}, v_{lj}) = -\sigma_v^2(1 - \rho)$, whereas for two comparisons not sharing a common object, $\mathscr{V}(v_{hk}, v_{jl}) = 0$.

Computing the correlation of two difference processes which share a common object from the covariance and variances, we find, say

$$\rho_v = \frac{\sigma_v^2(1 - \rho)}{2\sigma_v^2(1 - \rho) + 2\sigma_\varepsilon^2}. \tag{6.11}$$

If r is the ratio of response error variance to the variance of individual differences in affective value,

$$r = \sigma_\varepsilon^2/\sigma_v^2(1 - \rho)$$

and (6.11) may be expressed as

$$\rho_v = \frac{1}{2 + 2r}. \tag{6.12}$$

We observe that when subjects differ in their preference for the objects but are perfectly accurate in their responses, difference processes involving a common object take on the maximum correlation with absolute value 1/2. When the subjects are in perfect concordance except for response error, the correlation takes on the minimum value of zero.

The difference processes are not observable, of course. In the forced choice imposed by the method of paired comparisons they are considered to be degraded into the dichotomous variates, s_{jk}, which represent responses of the subjects. With random sampling of subjects, two such variates are distributed in bivariate Bernoulli form with mean, variances, and covariance

$$\mathscr{E}(s_{jk}) = P_{jk}$$

$$\mathscr{V}(s_{jk}) = P_{jk}Q_{jk}$$

$$\mathscr{V}(s_{jk}, s_{jl}) = P_{jk,jl} - P_{jk}P_{jl}$$

where $P_{jk} = \text{Prob}(X_j > X_k)$ and $P_{jk,jl} = \text{Prob}[(X_j > X_k) \text{ and } (X_j > X_l)]$. The corresponding observed proportions for samples of size N are $p_{jk} = \sum_i^N s_{jki}/N$. Then

$$\mathscr{E}(p_{jk}) = P_{jk}$$

$$\mathscr{V}(p_{jk}) = P_{jk}Q_{jk}/N$$

$$\mathscr{V}(p_{jk}, p_{jl}) = (P_{jk,jl} - P_{jk}P_{jl})/N.$$

The population value of the product-moment correlation of the sample proportions for pairs with common objects is then

$$\rho_{jk,jl} = \frac{P_{jk,jl} - P_{jk}P_{jl}}{(P_{jk}Q_{jk}P_{jl}Q_{jl})^{1/2}}. \tag{6.13}$$

This quantity is familiar as the "phi coefficient" for a twofold dichotomous classification.

It is of some interest to determine the value of (6.13) as a function of the parameters of the three-component discriminal model under Case V assumptions. The bivariate normal distribution of the standardized discriminal processes v_{jk} and v_{jl} have mean $Y_{jk} = (\mu_j - \mu_k)/\sigma$ and $Y_{jl} = (\mu_j - \mu_l)/\sigma$, respectively, unit standard deviations, and correlation ρ_v. To evaluate (6.13) in terms of these parameters, we enter the table of the normal distribution with Y_{jk} and Y_{jl} to obtain P_{jk}, Q_{jk}, P_{jl}, and Q_{jl}. To obtain $P_{jk,jl}$, we enter a table of the bivariate normal distribution with Y_{jk}, Y_{jl}, and ρ_v.[4] Values of (6.7) for $\rho_v = 1/2$ and various Y_{jk} and Y_{jl} have been computed and are shown in Figure 6.1. We note that the correlation of the dichotomous variates attains

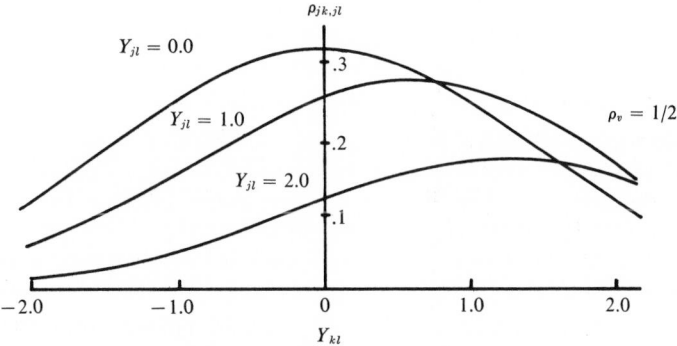

FIG. 6.1.   Evaluation of Equation (6.13) for $\rho_v = 1/2$.

its maximum of $1/3$ when $Y_{jk} = Y_{jl} = 0$. Elsewhere, especially when Y_{jk} and Y_{jl} differ greatly, the correlation of the discriminal processes is considerably attenuated in the dichotomous scoring of responses.

Holding fixed Y_{jk} and Y_{jl} and allowing ρ to vary, we find the values $\rho_{jk,jl}$ shown in Figure 6.2. They prove to be nearly proportional to ρ_v. We shall make use of this fact later to derive a general solution for the multiple-judgment case. In preparation for this solution, we review in the following statistical digression the theory of linear estimation and tests of hypotheses when the observations are correlated.

6.7.2   Statistical Digression

Let the p-variate observation from a random experiment be specified by

$$\mathbf{y} = A\boldsymbol{\alpha} + \boldsymbol{\zeta},$$

[4]National Bureau of Standards, *Tables of the Bivariate Normal Distribution Function and Related Functions*, Applied Math Series No. 50, U.S. Government Printing Office, Washington, D.C., 1956.

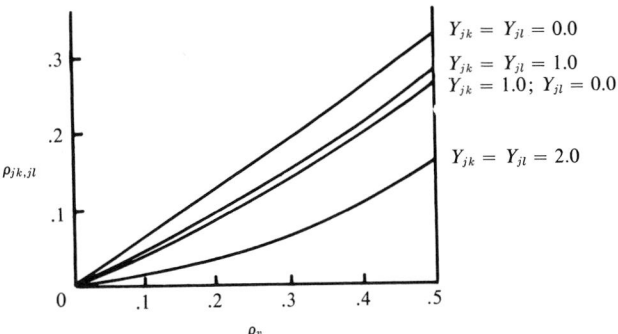

FIG. 6.2. Evaluation of Equation (6.13) for selected fixed values of y_{jk} and y_{jl}.

where α is an $m \times 1$ vector of unknown parameters; A is a $p \times m$ matrix of rank $l \leq m$ which specifies the parametric composition of the observation; and ζ is a $1 \times p$ vector of sampling errors distributed as $N(0, \Sigma)$. We are interested in the case where α is overdetermined by the observation, i.e. $l < p$.

If Σ is known, the observations can be transformed so that the error is uncorrelated. A conventional analysis is then possible: Let T be a factorization of Σ such that $TT' = \Sigma$. The triangular Cholesky factorization has this property (see Computing Note A), as does the matrix $X' \Lambda^{1/2} X$, where X is the orthogonal matrix of latent vectors of Σ, and Λ is the diagonal matrix of corresponding latent roots. But since Σ is nonsingular, T is nonsingular and has the inverse T^{-1}; so

$$T^{-1}\Sigma(T^{-1})' = T^{-1}TT'(T^{-1})' = I.$$

Thus the transformed variate $T^{-1}\mathbf{y}$ has expectation and variance

$$\mathscr{E}(T^{-1}\mathbf{y}) = T^{-1}A\alpha;$$

$$\mathscr{V}(T^{-1}\mathbf{y}) = (T^{-1})\mathscr{V}(\mathbf{y})(T^{-1})' = T^{-1}\Sigma(T^{-1})' = I.$$

Since a linear transform of multivariate normal variates is multivariate normal, the transformed error is distributed

$$T^{-1}\zeta \sim N(0, I).$$

Estimation of α by minimization of the sum of squares of the transformed error proceeds as with independent variates. We have already seen, however, that when the matrix A is of deficient rank (less than m), each parameter in α is not separately estimable. For the paired-comparison model this difficulty can be avoided simply by arbitrarily assigning the value zero to one of the parameters. It is instructive, however, to consider a more general solution.

Let the rank of A now be $l \leq p$. Then l independent linear functions of the parameters α are estimable if (and only if) the coefficients of these functions

L, say, are linearly dependent on A. This condition for estimability is met if the matrix A augmented by L is of the same rank as A:

$$\text{rank} \begin{bmatrix} A \\ L \end{bmatrix} = \text{rank } A = l.$$

(See Roy and Gnanadesiken, 1959.)

The matrix A then may be factored as

$$\underset{p \times m}{A} = \underset{p \times l}{K} \underset{l \times m}{L},$$

say, where

$$K = AL'(LL')^{-1}$$

is also of rank l. The original model may be reparameterized as

$$\mathbf{y} = KL\boldsymbol{\alpha} + \boldsymbol{\zeta} = K\boldsymbol{\alpha}^* + \boldsymbol{\zeta}$$

(see Bock, 1963).

The new parameters $\boldsymbol{\alpha}^*$ may be estimated in a straightforward manner by minimization of the quadratic form in the uncorrelated residuals

$$Q = (\mathbf{y} - K\boldsymbol{\alpha}^*)'(T^{-1})'T^{-1}(\mathbf{y} - K\boldsymbol{\alpha}^*)$$

or, since the inverse of a matrix product is the product of the inverses in the reverse order,

$$Q = (\mathbf{y} - K\boldsymbol{\alpha}^*)\Sigma^{-1}(\mathbf{y} - K\boldsymbol{\alpha}^*).$$

Minimizing this expression with respect to variation in $\boldsymbol{\alpha}^*$, we obtain the normal equations

$$K'\Sigma^{-1}K\hat{\boldsymbol{\alpha}}^* = K'\Sigma^{-1}\mathbf{y}. \tag{6.14}$$

Since the $l \times l$ matrix $K'\Sigma^{-1}K$ is of rank l, its inverse exists, and the estimate of $\boldsymbol{\alpha}^*$ is

$$\hat{\boldsymbol{\alpha}}^* = (K'\Sigma^{-1}K)^{-1}K'\Sigma^{-1}\mathbf{y}.$$

Evaluating the expectation and variance of $\hat{\boldsymbol{\alpha}}^*$, we obtain, as shown in Computing Note D, $\mathscr{E}(\hat{\boldsymbol{\alpha}}^*) = \boldsymbol{\alpha}^*$ and $\mathscr{V}(\hat{\boldsymbol{\alpha}}^*) = K'\Sigma^{-1}K = [\sigma_{\hat{\alpha}*}^{ij}]$, say.

The minimum of the quadratic form may be evaluated in terms of $\hat{\boldsymbol{\alpha}}^*$ and the total sum of squares of the transformed variates partition as in Table 6.10. Note that only Σ^{-1} is required in the calculations. T^{-1} does not appear explicitly.

TABLE 6.10. Analysis of Variance with Correlated Observations

Source of variation	d.f.	Sums of squares	Expected sums of squares
Estimation	l	$SSR = \hat{\alpha}^{*\prime}K'\Sigma^{-1}y$	$l + \alpha^{*\prime}K'\Sigma^{-1}K\alpha^{*}$
Error	$p - l$	$SSE = SST - SSR$	$p - l$
Total	p	$SST = y'\Sigma^{-1}y$	

Since the transformed errors are uncorrelated unit normal deviates, SSE in Table 6.10 may be used as a χ^2 statistic on $p - l$ degrees of freedom. Statistical significance of this χ^2 contradicts the assumed model. Similarly, SSR is a central χ^2 variate if and only if $\alpha^* = 0$. Statistical significance of this χ^2 contradicts the hypothesis $\alpha^* = 0$.

In applying these results to paired comparisons we must first choose L and determine K. Again let us estimate contrasts between the first $n - 1$ affective values and the last. Then L is of the form

$$
L = \begin{bmatrix}
1 & \cdot & \cdot & \cdots & -1 \\
\cdot & 1 & \cdot & \cdots & -1 \\
\cdot & \cdot & 1 & \cdots & -1 \\
& & \vdots & & \\
& & \vdots & & \\
\cdot & \cdot & \cdot & \cdots & -1
\end{bmatrix}
$$

Since these are just the $(n-1)$th, $(n-1+n-2)$th, $(n-1+n-2+n-3)$th, etc., rows of A, L is certainly linearly dependent on A and $L\alpha$ is estimable. Evaluating $K = AL'(LL')^{-1}$, we find that K is simply A with the last column struck out. As we would expect this is just the A^* of Section 6.4.3, as can be seen directly by evaluating $A^*L = A$.

6.7.3 A Solution for the Multiple-judgment Case Assuming the Angular Response Function and Constant Correlation of Angular Deviates

We have seen that under multiple-judgment sampling and Case V assumptions, the observed proportions in a paired-comparison experiment are correlated to an extent which depends upon the parameters of the discriminal model. In the special case of comparisons among objects with equal affective values, all deviates have expected values of zero and the theoretical correlations of the observed proportions are constant. That this " null case" has a simple solution when the angular response function is assumed has been shown by Bock (1958a). To establish this fact we obtain first the limiting form of the sampling covariance of the angular deviates. The general form of Rao's lemma on transformed statistics is required for this purpose (see Section 2.7):

Let the distribution of a $1 \times p$ vector statistic $\mathbf{t}$ tend to multi-variate normal form with mean vector $\boldsymbol{\theta}$, of order $1 \times p$, and co-variance matrix $(1/N)\Sigma$, of order $p \times p$. Then if any q functions $F(\mathbf{t})$ are continuous with continuous first partial derivatives, the $1 \times q$ vector variable

$$\mathbf{u} = \sqrt{N}[F(\mathbf{t}) - F(\boldsymbol{\theta})], \qquad q \leq p$$

is distributed in multivariate normal form in the limit with zero mean vector, and covariance matrix

$$\underset{q \times p}{\left[\frac{\partial F}{\partial \boldsymbol{\theta}}\right]} \underset{p \times p}{\Sigma} \underset{p \times q}{\left[\frac{\partial F}{\partial \boldsymbol{\theta'}}\right]}.$$

Applying Rao's lemma to the arc-sine transformation of each component in the vector of observed proportions, we find that the matrix of first derivatives is diagonal with elements $(1/N)(P_{jk} Q_{jk})^{1/2}$. Thus, the sampling covariance of angular deviates corresponding to comparisons with common objects is in the limit,

$$\mathscr{V}(y_{jk}, y_{jl}) = \frac{P_{jk,jl} - P_{jk} P_{jl}}{N(P_{jk} Q_{jk} P_{jl} Q_{jl})^{1/2}}.$$

But the limiting variance of the observed angular deviates is $1/N$; hence the correlation is in the limit

$$\rho_{jk,jl} = \frac{P_{jk,jl} - P_{jk} P_{jl}}{(P_{jk} Q_{jk} P_{jl} Q_{jl})^{1/2}},$$

which is the same as the correlation matrix of the observed proportions.

Let us now assume the null case and let the correlation of the angular deviates be

$$\rho_{jk,jl} = \rho_y,$$

$$\rho_{jk,lj} = -\rho_y,$$

$$\rho_{jk,hl} = 0,$$

for distinct h, j, k, l. The covariance matrix of the angular deviates is then of the same form as that for the difference processes which we have deduced from the three-component model. It has the property that its inverse can be expressed algebraically, making possible explicit formulas for estimates and sums of squares in the correlated case as developed in Section 6.7.2.

In matrix notation the three-component model is

$$\mathbf{y} = A\boldsymbol{\alpha} + A\mathbf{v} + \boldsymbol{\zeta}.$$

Then the expectation and variance in the population of subjects are

$$\mathscr{E}(\mathbf{y}) = A\boldsymbol{\alpha},$$

$$\mathscr{V}(\mathbf{y}) = \sigma_v^2 AA' + \sigma_\varepsilon^2 I = \Sigma.$$

Since $A'A/n = \Delta = \Delta^2$, from (6.8), it is easy to verify that

$$\Sigma^{-1} = \left[\frac{1}{\sigma_\varepsilon^2}I - \frac{\sigma_v^2}{\sigma_\varepsilon^2(n\sigma_v^2 + \sigma_\varepsilon^2)}AA'\right] = aI - bAA'.$$

Substituting for Σ^{-1} in the normal Equations (6.14) gives

$$A'(aI - bAA')A\hat{\boldsymbol{\alpha}} = A'(aI - bAA')\mathbf{y}$$

$$n(a - bn)\Delta\hat{\boldsymbol{\alpha}} = (a - bn)A'\mathbf{y}$$

$$\Delta\hat{\boldsymbol{\alpha}} = \frac{1}{n}A'\mathbf{y} = \hat{\boldsymbol{\alpha}}^0$$

showing that the estimate of $\boldsymbol{\alpha}_0$ is the same as in the uncorrelated case. This result depends again on the special property of the matrix of coefficients of the complete paired-comparison model, namely, $A'A = n\Delta$.

The sums of squares in the analysis of variance are not the same, however. The difference is brought out most clearly by expressing σ_v^2 in terms of the variance of the angular deviates,

$$\sigma_y^2 = 2\sigma_v^2 + \sigma_\varepsilon^2 = 1/N$$

and the constant correlation which in the null case, is

$$\rho_y = \sigma_v^2/\sigma_y^2.$$

Then $\sigma_v^2 = \rho_y\sigma_y^2$ and $\sigma_\varepsilon^2 = (1 - 2\rho_y)\sigma_y^2$; whence $a = 1/(1 - 2\rho_y)\sigma_y^2$ and $b = \rho_y/(1 - 2\rho_y)[1 + (n - 2)\rho_y]\sigma_y^2$.

Let us evaluate the sums of squares of Table 6.10 in these terms and compare them with the sums of squares for the uncorrelated case. The result is shown in Table 6.11.

We have seen that the correlation of the deviates can range from $\rho_y = 0$ to $\rho_y = 1/3$; thus, the denominator of SSE (correlated) is generally fractional and the residual $\chi^2 = N \cdot \text{SSE}$ is increased in the correlated case. If SSE (uncorrelated) is erroneously used in its place, the residual χ^2 is biased downward and will frequently fail to detect departure of the data from the paired-comparison model. Conversely, SSR (correlated) is diminished in the correlated case, and to ignore this effect in testing the estimation $\chi^2 = N\,\text{SSR}$ will frequently reject the null hypothesis erroneously.

The expressions for the theoretical sums of squares in the null case provide useful bounds for the analysis of multiple-judgment data. For example if ρ_y

TABLE 6.11. Sums of Squares for Correlated vs Uncorrelated Observations

Correlated case (multiple judgment)	Uncorrelated case (single judgment)
$SSR = \mathbf{y}'AA'(aI - bAA')\mathbf{y}$	$SSR = N\mathbf{y}'\dfrac{AA'}{n}\mathbf{y}$
$\quad = (a - nb)\mathbf{y}'\dfrac{AA'}{n}\mathbf{y}$	
$\quad = N\mathbf{y}'\dfrac{AA'}{n}\mathbf{y}/[1 + (n - 2)\rho_y]$	
$SST = \mathbf{y}'(aI - bAA')\mathbf{y}$	$SST = N\mathbf{y}'\mathbf{y}$
$SSE = SST - SSR$	$SSE = SST - SSR$
$\quad = \mathbf{y}'(aI - bAA')\mathbf{y} - (a - nb)\mathbf{y}'\dfrac{AA'}{n}\mathbf{y}$	$\quad = N\mathbf{y}'\left(I - \dfrac{AA'}{n}\right)\mathbf{y}$
$\quad = a\mathbf{y}'\left(I - \dfrac{AA'}{n}\right)\mathbf{y}$	
$\quad = N\mathbf{y}'\left(I - \dfrac{AA'}{n}\right)\mathbf{y}/(1 - 2\rho_y)$	

is assumed to take on its maximum value, 1/3, the residual χ^2 for the correlated case can be computed by multiplying the ordinary SSE by $3N$ (rather than by N). If this χ^2 is not significant, we can be confident that there is no evidence for departure from the model. Conversely, if ρ_y is assumed equal to zero and the usual residual χ^2 is significant, there is evidence of departure. For intermediate cases the general solution of Table 6.11 is necessary.

Similarly, if the χ^2 for estimation is significant when computed by dividing the ordinary SSR by $[1 + (n - 2)/3]/N$ there is evidence of significant difference between the affective values of the objects. Conversely, if this χ^2 is not significant when computed under the assumption $\rho_y = 0$ there is no evidence of differences. Intermediate results require the general solution.

Finally, it should be satisfactory in many applications to obtain maximal $(1 - \gamma)$ confidence bounds for differences between affective values by assuming $\rho_y = 1/3$ and using the formula,

$$\text{for } (\alpha_j - \alpha_k)\text{:}\quad \hat{\alpha}_j^0 - \hat{\alpha}_k^0 \pm z_{1-(\gamma/2)}\sqrt{2[1 + (n - 2)/3]nN}\,.$$

Example 6.7.3

A paired-comparison experiment was performed to investigate the preferences of U.S. Army enlisted men for seven well-known "ready-to-eat" breakfast cereals. The subjects did not actually taste each cereal, but simply indicated their preferences when presented with a pair of the standard one-ounce cartons of the cereals. Each of fifty subjects made the twenty-one comparative judgments of a complete design. The resulting observed proportions, angular deviates, row sums, estimated affective values, and the associated partition of χ^2 are shown in Table 6.12. Note that the uncorrected residual χ^2 is

TABLE 6.12. Analysis of Paired-Comparison Data Obtained from Multiple Judgments

1. Observed proportions ($N = 30$)

Objects	1	2	3	4	5	6	7	Sum	$\hat{\alpha}_j^o$
1		.46	.48	.32	.40	.64	.48		
2	.54		.46	.42	.26	.70	.52		
3	.52	.54		.48	.38	.62	.50		
4	.68	.58	.52		.52	.78	.56		
5	.60	.74	.62	.48		.74	.56		
6	.36	.30	.38	.22	.26		.36		
7	.52	.48	.50	.44	.44	.64			

2. Angular deviates, row sums, and estimates

Objects	1	2	3	4	5	6	7	Sum	$\hat{\alpha}_j^o$
1	.0000	-.0801	-.0400	-.3683	-.2014	.2838	-.0400	-.4460	-.0637
2	.0801	.0000	-.0801	-.1607	-.5007	.4115	.0400	-.2099	-.0300
3	.0400	.0801	.0000	-.0400	-.2424	.2424	.0000	.0801	.0115
4	.3683	.1607	.0400	.0000	.0400	.5944	.1203	1.3237	.1891
5	.2014	.5007	.2424	-.0400	.0000	.5007	.1203	1.5254	.2179
6	-.2838	-.4115	-.2424	-.5944	-.5007	.0000	-.2838	-2.3165	-.3309
7	.0400	-.0400	.0000	-.1203	-.1203	.2838	.0000	.0432	.0062

3. Partition of χ^2

Source of χ^2	d.f.	Sum of squares	χ^2	Probability
Estimation	$n - 1 = 6$	$SSR = \sum_j \hat{\alpha}_j^o \sum_k y_{jk} = 1.3851$	$N \cdot SSR = 69.26$	$p < .0005$
Error	$(n-1)(n-2)/2 = 15$	$SSE = SST - SSR = .1692$	$N \cdot SSE = 8.46$	$.95 > p > .90$
Total	$n(n-1)/2 = 21$	$SST = \sum\sum_{j<k} y_{jk}^2 = 1.5543$		

NOTE: Some fractional discrepancies are due to the truncation of values by the computer.

Corrected χ^2 assuming $\rho_y = 1/3$:

$$\chi^2_{\tilde{R}} = N \cdot SSR/[1 + (n-2)\rho_y] = 25.97 \qquad p < .0005$$
$$\chi^2_{\tilde{E}} = N \cdot [SSE/(1 - 2\rho_y)] = 25.38 \qquad p \cong .05$$

At least .95 confidence interval for $\alpha_j - \alpha_k$, assuming $\rho_y = 1/3$:

$$\hat{\alpha}_j - \hat{\alpha}_k \pm 1.96\sqrt{2[1 + (7-2)/3]/(7 \times 50)}$$

or

$$\hat{\alpha}_j - \hat{\alpha}_k \pm .2419$$

considerably below expectation as predicted by the three-component model $(.95 > p > .90)$. If we take ρ_y equal to its upper bound of $1/3$ the corrected value of the residual χ^2 becomes 25.38 on 15 degrees of freedom. The probability of this value under the model is slightly less than .05. Since this is an upper bound of the actual value of the residual χ^2, the model is not rejected. The χ^2 for estimation, on the other hand, remains significant after correction and contradicts the hypothesis of equal preference values for the cereals. The confidence bound on the estimated contrasts, with coefficient not less than .95, computed assuming $\rho_y = 1/3$, is also shown. Differences in preference for cereals 1, 2, 3, and 7 are evidently not detected in this experiment.

6.7.4   Solution of the Multiple-judgment Case Assuming the Normal Response Function and Non-constant Correlation of the Normal Deviates

The method of Section 6.7.2 can also be used to obtain a minimum normit χ^2 solution for the multiple-judgment case. Again the limiting form of the sampling covariance of the observed normal deviates is obtained by application of Rao's lemma. We recall that the derivative of the inverse normal transformation at the point Y is the reciprocal of the ordinate $h(Y)$. Thus the covariance of deviates corresponding to comparisons sharing a common object is

$$\mathscr{V}(y_{jk}, y_{jl}) = (P_{jk,jl} - P_{jk} P_{jl})/Nh(Y_{jk})h(Y_{jl}). \qquad (6.15)$$

In the null case, i.e. where $Y_{jk} = Y_{jl} = 0$, the maximal value of the covariance can be directly computed by (6.15) since all parameters are known. In this case, however, the normal solution tends to proportionality with the simpler angular solution as N increases, and thus is of little interest.

A more general approach is to use provisional deviates from a preliminary solution to evaluate (6.15), just as the weights for the solution of the single-judgment case are computed as functions of provisional deviates. The simple unbiased estimates of Section 6.4.1 are suitable for this purpose. In addition to the normal areas and ordinates determined by the provisional deviates, the joint proportions $P_{jk,jl}$ may be determined by assuming that the correlation of the difference processes takes on its maximal value of $1/2$, implied by (6.12). Then we could enter a table of the bivariate normal distribution with provisional deviates $Y_{jk,\text{prov}}$ and $Y_{jl,\text{prov}}$ and the correlation coefficient of $1/2$ to read directly $P_{jk,jl}$, from which $\mathscr{V}(y_{jk}, y_{jl})$ is determined by (6.15).

Alternatively the table of phi coefficients for various partitions of a bivariate normal surface with correlation one half, Table A4, can be used for this purpose. Let an entry in this table with arguments Y_{jk} and Y_{jl} be designated $\rho_{jk,jl}$. Then

$$\mathscr{V}(y_{jk}, y_{jl}) = \rho_{jk,jl}\sqrt{P_{jk} Q_{jk} P_{jl} Q_{jl}}/Nh(Y_{jk})h(Y_{jl}). \qquad (6.16)$$

The quantities $\sqrt{P_{jk}Q_{jk}}$ are given in the margin of the table and the ordinates appear in Table A2. Taking $\mathscr{V}(y_{jk}, y_{lj})$ as $-\mathscr{V}(y_{jk}, y_{jl})$ and $\mathscr{V}(y_{jk}, y_{hl}) = 0$, the covariance matrix of the observed deviates may be constructed. The solution of Section 6.7.2 can then proceed, resulting in a bounding minimum normit χ^2 solution analogous to the angular solution of the previous section. Since this solution requires the inversion of a matrix of order $n(n-1)/2$, machine computation will generally be necessary.

The foregoing result assumes that the response error in the data is negligible, so that the correlation of the difference processes is essentially at its maximum of one half. A more general assumption is that this correlation of difference processes is constant for all pairs with common objects, but is arbitrary in the interval zero to one-half, say

$$\rho = c/2, \qquad 0 \le c \le 1.$$

Since the correlation of the observed proportions is nearly proportional to ρ_v (see Figure 6.2), a practical approximation to the covariance of the correlated deviates is

$$v(y_{jk}, y_{jl}) = c\rho_{jk,jl}\sqrt{P_{jk}Q_{jk}P_{jl}Q_{jl}}/Nh(Y_{jk})h(Y_{jl}). \qquad (6.17)$$

A minimum normit χ^2 solution using (6.17) is possible in this case if c can be determined.

One method of determining c is by maximum likelihood estimation, using the observed covariance matrix of the response variates, s_{jki} (see Section 6.7.1). Let this matrix be S, with general element

$$s_{jk,hl} = \frac{1}{N}\sum_i s_{jki}s_{hli} - P_{jk,\text{prov}}P_{hl,\text{prov}}$$

$$= p_{jk,hl} - P_{jk,\text{prov}}P_{hl,\text{prov}}.$$

According to the three-component model, the expected value of S is V, say, with general element

$$v_{jk,hl} = P_{jk,hl} - P_{jk}P_{hl}$$

$$= c\rho_{jk,hl}\sqrt{P_{jk}Q_{jk}P_{hl}Q_{hl}}; \qquad j = h, k \neq l$$

$$= -c\rho_{jk,hl}\sqrt{P_{jk}Q_{jk}P_{hl}Q_{hl}}; \qquad j = l, k \neq h$$

$$= 0; \qquad h \neq j \neq l, h \neq k \neq l$$

or, in matrix notation

$$V = D[I + c(R_0 - I)]D, \qquad (6.18)$$

where $D = \sqrt{P_{jk}Q_{jk}}$ and R_0 is the matrix of phi coefficients computed from Y_{jk}, Y_{jl} when $\rho = 1/2$ as given in Table A4.

The general approach to the maximum likelihood estimation of parameters which determine the covariance of normal observations is as follows. (See Anderson, 1958, pp. 44ff.)

Let x_i, $i = 1, 2, \ldots, N$, be an independent random observation from a p-variate normal population $N[\ \underset{p \times 1}{\theta}\ ,\ \underset{p \times p}{\Sigma(\alpha)}]$ where $\Sigma(\alpha)$ denotes the covariance matrix of the population as a function of α. Then the likelihood of the parameter is defined as

$$L = \prod_{i=1}^{N} \frac{|\Sigma^{-1}(\alpha)|^{1/2}}{(2\pi)^{p/2}} \exp\{-[(\mathbf{x}_i - \boldsymbol{\theta})'\Sigma^{-1}(\alpha)(\mathbf{x}_i - \boldsymbol{\theta})]/2\}.$$

To facilitate the maximizing of the likelihood with respect to variation in α, we transform to log likelihood and express the exponent as a trace of the matrix product $\Sigma^{-1}(\alpha)S$:

$$l = \log L = -\frac{Np}{2}\log(2\pi) + \frac{N}{2}\log|\Sigma^{-1}(\alpha)| - \frac{N}{2}\operatorname{tr}(\Sigma^{-1}(\alpha)S),$$

where

$$S = \frac{1}{N}\left(\sum_{i=1}^{N}\mathbf{x}_i\mathbf{x}_i' - \boldsymbol{\theta}\boldsymbol{\theta}'\right).$$

Then the first partial derivative of log L set equal to zero gives the likelihood equation

$$\frac{\partial l}{\partial \alpha} = \frac{N}{2|\Sigma^{-1}(\alpha)|}\operatorname{tr}\frac{\partial(\Sigma^{-1}(\alpha))}{\partial \alpha} - \frac{N}{2}\operatorname{tr}\frac{\partial(\Sigma^{-1}(\alpha))}{\partial \alpha}S = 0. \tag{6.19}$$

If the elements in the inverse of Σ can be expressed explicitly as differentiable functions of α, this equation can usually be solved to obtain the value of α for which the log likelihood is a maximum.

In the present application $\Sigma(\alpha) = V$, and the inverse of V may be expressed in terms of c and the latent roots and vectors of R_0. Let the $p \times p$ diagonal matrix of latent roots of R_0 be Λ and the corresponding latent vectors, the rows of Z. Then the matrix $[I + c(R_0 - I)]$ has the same latent vectors as R_0, but its latent roots are the elements of the $p \times p$ diagonal matrix

$$\Omega = I + c(\Lambda - I).$$

The inverse of V is therefore

$$\underset{p \times p}{V^{-1}} = D^{-1}Z\Omega^{-1}Z'D^{-1}. \tag{6.20}$$

The desired equation may be obtained by substitution of V^{-1} for $\Sigma^{-1}(\alpha)$ in (6.19). However, given the special form of V^{-1}, a simpler solution is obtained by substituting V^{-1} for $\Sigma^{-1}(\alpha)$ in the expression for l, differentiating l with respect to c, and setting the derivative equal to zero.

Let $Q = ZD^{-1}SD^{-1}Z$. Then

$$\frac{\partial l}{\partial c} = -\sum_{i=1}^{p} \frac{\lambda_i - 1}{1 + \hat{c}(\lambda_i - 1)} + \sum_{i=1}^{p} \frac{(\lambda_i - 1)q_{ii}}{[1 + \hat{c}(\lambda_i - 1)]^2} = 0 \qquad (6.21)$$

where λ_i is the ith element of Λ and q_{ii} is the ith diagonal element of Q. Since $\hat{c}$ is in the interval zero to one, a solution to any desired degree of approximation may be obtained by the method of false position (Willers, 1948, p. 205).

When $\hat{c}$ is determined, the inverse covariance matrix, Σ^{-1} required for the solution of Section 6.7.2 can be constructed. It is obtained from V^{-1} of Equation (6.20) by re-scaling with a diagonal matrix consisting of the terms in the denominator of (6.17), say, $G = \text{diag}[\sqrt{N}\,h(Y_{jk})]$. Then

$$\Sigma^{-1} = GV^{-1}G = GD^{-1}Z'[I + \hat{c}(\Lambda - I)]^{-1}ZD^{-1}G.$$

When the observed deviates are uncorrelated, $c = 0$ and $\Sigma^{-1} = GD^{-2}G$, which is just the diagonal matrix of Müller-Urban weights as in the solution for the single-judgment case. When $c = 1, \Sigma^{-1} = GD^{-1}R_0^{-1}D^{-1}G$, which is the inverse of the covariance matrix when maximal correlation is assumed as in (6.16).

The sequence of computations for the solution of this section is clarified in Example 6.7.4.

Example 6.7.4

In order to compare the angular and normal solutions in the correlated case, we reanalyze the data of Example 6.7.3. Machine computation is required and may be carried out in the following steps.[5]

(1) The cross products of the dichotomously scored responses are accumulated over individuals and divided by N. The diagonal elements of this matrix, which are the observed p_{jk}, are extracted and transformed to observed normal deviates, y_{jk}, by the method of Computing Note C. If it is of interest to examine the extent of correlation in the data, phi coefficients for any two comparisons may be computed from the cross products in this matrix. For the data in this example the observed phi coefficients are shown in Table 6.13. We observe that the correlations have more or less the expected pattern and are sufficiently large to suggest that the correlation effect is near its theoretical maximum.

(2) Provisional estimates of the affective values of the objects are obtained in the computer by Gulliksen's (1956) solution. This provides for the possibility that the design is incomplete. In the complete case these estimates

[5] This example was prepared on a Univac 1105 at the University of North Carolina.

TABLE 6.13. Observed Phi Coefficients for the Data of Example 6.7.3

Object pair					Object pair					
	1, 2	1, 3	1, 4	1, 5	1, 6	1, 7	2, 3	2, 4	2, 5	2, 6	2, 7

Object pair	1, 2	1, 3	1, 4	1, 5	1, 6	1, 7	2, 3	2, 4	2, 5	2, 6	2, 7
1, 2	1.000						(Symmetric)				
1, 3	.639	1.000									
1, 4	.055	.457	1.000								
1, 5	.639	.441	.140	1.000							
1, 6	.358	.470	.157	.527	1.000						
1, 7	.398	.519	.371	.360	.304	1.000					
2, 3	-.288	-.003	.141	-.262	-.144	-.003	1.000				
2, 4	-.623	-.250	.285	-.447	-.290	-.331	.272	1.000			
2, 5	-.181	-.296	-.211	.168	.160	-.113	-.090	.235	1.000		
2, 6	-.534	-.419	.075	-.356	-.127	.245	-.254	.469	.090	1.000	
2, 7	-.318	-.199	-.027	-.196	-.053	.122	.084	.412	.296	.245	1.000
3, 4	-.405	-.282	.285	-.212	-.113	-.202	-.003	.723	.252	.542	.362
3, 5	.104	-.092	.081	.454	.158	.155	-.309	-.082	.569	-.207	.175
3, 6	-.187	-.320	.007	-.034	.014	-.238	-.187	.249	.088	.477	.073
3, 7	-.201	-.320	-.171	-.082	-.167	.160	-.201	.122	.319	.044	.721
4, 5	.485	.282	-.113	.703	.364	.362	-.157	-.480	.296	-.367	-.202
4, 6	.006	.027	-.360	.138	.306	-.070	.103	-.233	.315	.074	-.124
4, 7	.414	.368	.003	.230	.259	.529	-.152	-.552	-.118	-.317	-.045
5, 6	-.276	-.161	-.082	-.540	-.160	-.161	-.002	.042	-.480	.308	-.204
5, 7	-.314	-.116	.003	-.510	-.329	-.126	.252	.101	-.393	.123	.277
6, 7	.062	.113	.214	-.017	-.219	.447	-.234	-.132	-.065	-.327	.387

Object pair	3, 4	3, 5	3, 6	3, 7	4, 5	4, 6	4, 7	5, 6	5, 7	6, 7
3, 4	1.000				(Symmetric)					
3, 5	.073	1.000								
3, 6	.505	-.066	1.000							
3, 7	.240	.288	.041	1.000						
4, 5	-.439	.505	-.257	-.080	1.000					
4, 6	-.263	.018	.082	-.048	.263	1.000				
4, 7	-.519	.030	-.279	.161	.277	.210	1.000			
5, 6	.113	-.569	.287	-.228	-.478	.015	-.066	1.000		
5, 7	.045	-.385	-.030	.322	-.529	-.179	.188	.393	1.000	
6, 7	-.137	.185	-.443	.500	-.030	-.306	.329	-.125	.413	1.000

are the same as the simple unbiased estimates with their origin adjusted so that the value of the nth object is zero (see Table 6.15 below).

(3) The provisional deviates are subtracted pairwise to obtain the provisional deviates, $Y_{jk,\text{prov}}$, corresponding to pairs of objects in the design. These deviates are converted to provisional proportions, $P_{jk,\text{prov}}$, by the normal transformation. (See Computing Note B.) The cross products of the provisional proportions are subtracted from cross products obtained in step1 to obtain the estimated covariance matrix S.

(4) The elements of the diagonal matrix D of weights $(P_{jk,\text{prov}}\,Q_{jk,\text{prov}})^{1/2}$ are computed and from them the scaled covariance matrix $D^{-1}SD^{-1}$.

(5) From the provisional deviates rounded to the nearest tenth, the matrix of expected phi coefficients is obtained from Table A4.

(6) For purposes of estimating the constant of proportionality c in (6.21), the latent roots Λ and latent vectors Z are computed (by the Jacobi method in this example; see Bodewig, 1959). The obtained roots are shown in Table 6.14.

TABLE 6.14. Values of λ_i and q_{ii} for Example 6.7.4

λ_i	q_{ii}
2.62317	3.40391
.33428	.32082
.34575	.48069
.37536	.58521
.34657	.06667
.33367	.25307
2.62055	1.23617
.34134	.36286
.34352	.27221
.37951	.34563
.33458	.53356
2.64401	2.09247
2.55362	3.47169
2.50045	2.11289
2.58052	2.78216
.33671	.46719
.45791	.47300
.34093	.47438
.44595	.48425
.35374	.41945
.40785	.29548

(7) The scaled covariance matrix from step 4 is then transfoimed by Z to obtain

$$Q = ZD^{-1}SD^{-1}Z'.$$

The diagonal elements, q_{ii}, extracted from Q are shown in Table 6.14.

(8) Evaluating (6.21) with trial values of $\hat{c}$, we find one sign change in the interval $0 \leq \hat{c} \leq 1$ corresponding to $\hat{c} = .955$. Our impression that the correlation effect is near its maximum is therefore confirmed.

(9) With this estimate of c, the expected inverse covariance matrix, V^{-1}, of (6.20) and the re-scaled inverse, Σ^{-1}, can be computed.

(10) The analysis then proceeds as in Section 6.7.2. The matrix K^* is constructed and the estimated affective value contrasts obtained from

$$\hat{\boldsymbol{\alpha}}^* = (K^{*\prime}\Sigma^{-1}K^*)^{-1}K^{*\prime}\Sigma^{-1}\mathbf{y}.$$

The partition of χ^2 is computed from

$$SSR = \hat{\boldsymbol{\alpha}}^{*\prime}K^*\Sigma^{-1}\mathbf{y},$$

$$SST = \mathbf{y}'\Sigma^{-1}\mathbf{y},$$

and

$$SSE = SST - SSR.$$

The results of these computations are shown in Tables 6.15 and 6.16. As expected, the error χ^2 in Table 6.16 is considerably larger than the biased

TABLE 6.15. Analysis of Paired-Comparison Data Obtained from Multiple Judgments: Normal Response Function

1. Normal deviates and provisional estimates

Objects	Objects 1	2	3	4	5	6	7	$\alpha_{j,\text{prov}}$
1	.0000	−.1006	−.0502	−.4679	−.2536	.3587	−.0502	−.0886
2	.1006	.0000	−.1006	−.2021	−.6433	.5246	.0502	−.0467
3	.0502	.1006	.0000	−.0502	−.3058	.3058	.0000	.0063
4	.4679	.2021	.0502	.0000	.0502	.7721	.1512	.2339
5	.2536	.6433	.3058	−.0502	.0000	.6434	.1512	.2701
6	−.3587	−.5246	−.3058	−.7721	−.6434	.0000	−.3587	−.4314
7	.0502	−.0502	.0000	−.1512	−.1512	.3587	.0000	.0000

2. Minimum normit χ^2 estimate and contrast covariance matrix

	Estimates	Covariance matrix $\times N$ (where $N = 50$)					
j	$\hat{\alpha}_j^* = \widehat{\alpha_j - \alpha_n}$	1	2	3	j 4	5	6
1	−.0877	1.1686					
2	−.0444	.5854	1.1671				
3	.0067	.5850	.5854	1.1666			
4	.2300	.5842	.5855	.5862	1.1679		
5	.2684	.5842	.5838	.5847	.5864	1.1668	
6	−.4308	.5796	.5800	.5784	.5781	.5755	1.1805

value in Table 6.12, but not quite as large as the corrected value which assumes $\rho_y = 1/3$ in the null case. Again the model for comparative judgment is not

TABLE 6.16. Partition of χ^2 for the General Solution in the Multiple-judgment Case

Source of χ^2	d.f.	χ^2		Probability
Estimation	$n - 1 = 6$	$SSR = \hat{\boldsymbol{\alpha}}^{*\prime} K^* \Sigma^{-1} \mathbf{y}$	$= 26.64$	$p < .0005$
Error	$(n - 1)(n - 2)/2 = 15$	$SSE = SST - SSR$	$= 21.94$	$.20 > p > .10$
Total	$n(n - 1)/2 = 21$	$SST = \mathbf{y}' \Sigma^{-1} \mathbf{y}$	$= 48.57$	

The .95 confidence interval for the contrast $\alpha_1 - \alpha_n$ is found to be

$$-.0877 \pm 1.96 \sqrt{1.1686/50}$$

or

$$-.0877 \pm .2995$$

rejected. We observe also that whereas the error χ^2 is heavily influenced by the correlation effect, the estimated affective-value contrasts are not. The minimum normit χ^2 estimates in Table 6.12 differ from the simple unbiased estimates only in the third decimal place. This reflects the fact that the expected proportions for most of the pairs are not far removed from one-half. The weights are fairly uniform and the weighted solution does not differ greatly from an unweighted solution.

6.8 Ranking as Comparative Judgment

Consider the case where the unidimensional preference model implied by the law of comparative judgment is valid, and stimulus objects are identified and familiar. Then, a subject's paired comparisons may result from a mere recitation of the relative positions of affective values well established in the personal preferences of the subject. Thus, when his affective values for the objects are strongly ordered, the subject is producing the same information in the paired comparisons which he could supply, with less labor, by directly ranking the objects in order of preference. It is a simple matter to check whether a subject's judgments in paired comparisons are completely determined by a rank ordering of the objects. One merely records the responses of each subject in a paired-comparison table using the formal variates " 1 " or " 0," as described in Section 6.7. The sum of each row of the table then gives the number of times the corresponding object is preferred to every other object. If these numbers include all integers 0 through $n - 1$, the paired-comparison judgments effectively rank order the objects without ties. The original judgments can then be reproduced, since in any comparison of distinct objects, the subject will have preferred the object with the higher rank order, i.e. the object with the greater row sum. If the judgments can be reproduced in this manner, all the subject's choices are said to be transitive. That is, if X_j, X_k, X_l are any three of the objects, the choices $X_j > X_k$ and $X_k > X_l$ imply $X_j > X_l$. On the other hand, if some of the choices are intransitive, then some of the row sums are equal and the objects fail to be strongly ordered by the row sums. The comparisons cannot then be entirely reproduced. (See David, 1963, pp. 21ff.)

As an example of this procedure, consider the experiment of Example 6.7.3.[6] The responses of the first subject in Example 6.7.3, recorded in the nominal order of the objects, are as follows.

Objects	Objects							Number of times preferred
	1	2	3	4	5	6	7	
1		1	1	0	0	1	1	4
2	0		0	0	0	0	1	1
3	0	1		0	0	0	1	2
4	1	1	1		0	1	1	5
5	1	1	1	1		1	1	6
6	0	1	1	0	0		1	3
7	0	0	0	0	0	0		0

By rearranging the objects in rank order of the total number of choices received, the data are determined completely by the marginal sums.

Objects	Objects							Number of times preferred	Rank order of preference
	5	4	1	6	3	2	7		
5		1	1	1	1	1	1	6	1
4	0		1	1	1	1	1	5	2
1	0	0		1	1	1	1	4	3
6	0	0	0		1	1	1	3	4
3	0	0	0	0		1	1	2	5
2	0	0	0	0	0		1	1	6
7	0	0	0	0	0	0		0	7

Were we to begin with data obtained by the method of rank order (see Guilford, 1954), we could reverse the process and produce for each subject the matrix of "1's" and "0's" for his hypothetical paired-comparison judgments. For a group of subjects, we could then count the "1's" for each pair of objects and divide by the number of subjects to obtain the set of "observed" proportions for a multiple-judgment paired-comparison solution. If an efficient solution is required, the methods of Section 6.7 should be used, since the rank-order judgments are assumed equivalent to the multiple-judgment case of paired comparisons. The magnitude of the theoretical correlation of correlated deviates can be considered $1/2$, since the intransitivity of response which diminishes this correlation is not present. Table A4 can therefore be used directly for computing the expected covariance matrix of the deviates for the multiple-judgment solution.

---

[6] Only 12 of the 50 subjects in this experiment failed to give completely transitive judgments. For a similar example of highly transitive judgments in paired comparisons see the data on preference for color of automobiles reported by Sadacca (1962).

If the number of subjects in a rank-order experiment is large, it will be advisable to prepare the paired-comparison table by computer methods. Suppose each subject ranks the n objects from 1 to n, where " 1 " indicates the highest ranking. Then, to obtain the paired-comparison table, one may subtract all possible pairs of the rank numbers of each subject and test the sign of the differences. Where a difference is negative, add 1 to the tally for the corresponding pair of objects. After the N subjects in the sample are processed in this way, divide the cumulative tallies by N to obtain the sample proportions.

If a computer is not available, an excellent approximation to the paired-comparison proportions can be obtained by a method developed by Thurstone (1931a). In this method the total number of times that each object is assigned to each rank position is recorded in an "objects $\times$ ranks" table. Each frequency in this table is divided by N to obtain the corresponding sample proportions. This table may be represented as follows:

Objects	*Rank*					
	1	2	$\cdots$	k	$\cdots$	n
1	p_{11}	p_{12}	$\cdots$	p_{1k}	$\cdots$	p_{1n}
2	p_{21}	p_{22}	$\cdots$	p_{2k}	$\cdots$	p_{2n}
$\vdots$			$\vdots$			
j	p_{j1}	p_{j2}	$\cdots$	p_{jk}	$\cdots$	p_{jn}
$\vdots$			$\vdots$			
n	p_{n1}	p_{n2}	$\cdots$	p_{nk}	$\cdots$	p_{nn}

The observed proportions are not statistically independent, but the degree of correlation is unimportant if n is not too small. We therefore follow Thurstone in assuming that the probability that a randomly selected subject will assign object X_j to a rank position prior to k, say,

$$P_{j\uparrow k} = P_{j,k-1} + P_{j,k-2} + \cdots + P_{j2} + P_{j1},$$

where the terms on the right are the expected values of the corresponding sample proportions. Then

$$P_{hk} P_{j\uparrow k}$$

is the probability that a randomly selected subject will place X_h in rank k and X_j in a prior rank position.

Similarly, the probability that a randomly selected subject will assign both objects to rank k, if this were possible, is $P_{hk} P_{jk}$. Since ties are not permitted, we assume in this case that the subject breaks ties randomly so that the probability that object X_h will be ranked before X_j will be $P_{hk} P_{jk}/2$.

Summing over all ranks, we obtain the probability that X_h will be judged greater than X_j in a paired comparison

$$P(X_h > X_j) = \sum_{k=1}^{n} [P_{hk}P_{j\uparrow h} + (P_{hk}P_{jk}/2)] . \tag{6.22}$$

This probability can be estimated for each pair of objects by substituting sample estimates of the corresponding proportions in (6.22). Thurstone's empirical check of this method, as well as a more recent one by McKeon (1961), shows excellent agreement with the proportions obtained by direct comparison of the ranks of individual subjects. The use of this formula is illustrated in the following example.

Example 6.8

As part of the study of breakfast cereal presented in Example 6.7.3 the 50 subjects ranked the cereals by order of preference. The rank proportions obtained are shown in Table 6.17. Applying Equation (6.22) to these data, we obtain the paired-comparison proportions shown in part A of Table 6.18. By direct comparison of each subject's ranks, we obtain the proportions in part B. Finally, the proportions obtained by the method of paired comparisons in connection with Example 6.7.3 are shown to indicate the correspondence between data obtained by the method of rank order and the method of paired comparisons. In view of the fact that the data are based on a sample of only 50 subjects, so that discrepancy in the judgment of one subject changes the observed proportions by .02, the mutual consistency of these three sets of proportions is excellent. The maximum discrepancy between the proportions in parts A and B is .11, and the average absolute deviation is .035. On the whole, the proportions in B correspond better than those in A with the proportions in C obtained by the method of paired comparisons. The maximum deviation for B vs C is .10 and the average absolute deviation is .021. As a general rule it may be preferable to obtain paired-comparison proportions from ranks by direct enumeration as in B whenever it is convenient to do so.

TABLE 6.17. Rank Proportions for Seven Ready-to-eat Breakfast Cereals

Objects	Rank						
	1	2	3	4	5	6	7
1	.14	.08	.22	.06	.10	.20	.20
2	.10	.16	.14	.16	.20	.20	.04
3	.14	.06	.20	.12	.22	.18	.08
4	.22	.18	.22	.10	.10	.08	.10
5	.32	.14	.04	.20	.12	.10	.08
6	.02	.08	.08	.16	.20	.16	.30
7	.06	.30	.10	.20	.06	.08	.20

TABLE 6.18. Paired-Comparison Proportions Obtained (*A*) from Ranks by Thurstone's Formula, (*B*) by Direct Enumeration, and (*C*) by the Method of Paired Comparisons (*N* = 50)

	Objects						
Objects	1	2	3	4	5	6	7
A. Thurstone's formula for ranks							
1		.44	.46	.37	.36	.61	.45
2			.52	.40	.39	.68	.49
3				.38	.39	.66	.47
4					.49	.75	.59
5						.75	.60
6							.33
7							
B. Direct enumeration of ranks							
1		.44	.42	.38	.42	.66	.38
2			.52	.40	.28	.72	.56
3				.42	.36	.58	.50
4					.54	.78	.56
5						.74	.58
6							.36
7							
C. Method of paired comparisons							
1		.46	.48	.32	.40	.64	.48
2			.46	.42	.26	.70	.52
3				.48	.38	.62	.50
4					.52	.78	.56
5						.74	.56
6							.36
7							

7 Advanced Applications of the Method of Paired Comparisons

The formulation in Chapter 6 of a measurement model and statistical methods for the method of paired comparisons prepares the way for applications of the method in realistic settings. Perhaps the most important class of these applications consists of studies in which the investigator attempts to predict choice for given objects on the basis of his knowledge of characteristics of the objects or of the population of subjects making the choices. Studies of this type are particularly relevant in market research and product development, since they give some indication of how changes of product characteristics or changes in the composition of the market may affect acceptance of a consumer product.

Broadly speaking, our approach in this class of applications is to estimate affective values for the objects, then to estimate parameters of a psychophysical model which best accounts for the affective values in terms of characteristics of the objects. Such models may be viewed as multifactor generalizations of the psychophysical model introduced in Chapter 2. We also consider the possibility that a common psychophysical model may not hold in various subgroups of subjects and introduce methods for determining whether a model should be fitted separately in each subgroup. In either case, the use of these models is motivated by the expectation that, if they hold for objects of given characteristics, they will also hold for objects with different combinations or amounts of these characteristics. If so, the predicted affective values of objects not included in the original experiment may be employed in the various predictions of choice which the law of comparative judgment makes possible (see Chapter 9).

Before discussing these models, however, let us consider devices for making less laborious the method of paired comparisons when the number of objects to be compared is large. Since most realistic applications of the method involve moderately large numbers of objects, some economy in the number of comparisons is required if the method is to have practical value. The incomplete paired-comparison designs described in Section 7.1 are useful in this connection.

7.1 Incomplete Paired-comparison Designs

However easy the judgments may be, it is seldom feasible to require of a subject more than about 50 judgments in a multiple-judgment paired-comparison experiment. Even this number may not be attainable if the subject is poorly motivated. This means that the number of objects in a complete multiple-judgment design cannot ordinarily exceed nine or ten. If taste or smell are involved in the judgments, even fewer objects can be successfully studied because of sensory fatigue.

Considerations of the subject's motivation or fatigue place no similar restriction on the single-judgment case, of course. In Example 6.6, we have seen a complete paired-comparison study with 25 objects. In studies of this type, however, the cost of preparing many different sample pairs may be a consideration, and the total number of subjects required may become prohibitively large. If so, even a complete single-judgment experiment may be impractical.

The problem of excessive numbers of pairs is eased by the use of incomplete paired-comparison designs in which certain pairs are omitted entirely. Designs of this type have been proposed by Gulliksen (1956), Jones and Bock (1957), McKeon (1960, 1961), and others (e.g., Uhrbrock and Richardson, 1933). In this section we present the general solution for incomplete designs and discuss three special types of incomplete designs with simple solutions.

Another type of incomplete design, in which not all subjects make all comparisons, has been considered by Bose (1956) and McKeon (1961). These designs yield complete tables of proportions which may be handled in the manner of Section 6.4.1 for an approximate solution by unweighted analysis. An exact analysis, taking into account the correlation of the observed proportions, is complex for these designs and will not be discussed here.

7.1.1 Arbitrary Incomplete Designs

A general solution for incomplete paired-comparison designs is implicit in the minimum normit χ^2 solution of Section 6.4.2. Recall in that solution the diagonal matrix of weights,

$$D = \text{diag}[N_{jk}W_{jk}], \qquad (7.1)$$

where N_{jk} is the number of subjects judging the j, k pair and W_{jk} is the Müller-Urban weight for the pair as calculated (or determined, using Table A6) from a provisional solution. Since W_{jk} is always positive, all diagonal elements of D are positive or zero. If the j, k pair is not judged by any subject, $N_{jk} = 0$ and the corresponding diagonal element of D is zero. This does not necessarily preclude a solution, however. The necessary and sufficient condition for a solution which yields $n - 1$ estimated contrasts of affective value is that the matrix of coefficients in the normal equations

$$A'DA\alpha = A'Dy \qquad (7.2)$$

is of rank $n - 1$. Since the rank of a matrix product cannot exceed the rank of any of its factors, a necessary condition for a solution of (7.2) is that the number of nonzero N_{jk} (i.e. of pairs retained) be not less than $n - 1$. This is not sufficient, however, since if n is greater than three it is possible to find $n - 1$ pairs which exclude one or more of the objects entirely. A sufficient condition is that each object be connected to every other through pairs with objects in common. This ensures that there is only one linear restriction on the rows of $A'D$, i.e. rank $(A'D) = n - 1$. Then, since $A'DA$ can be expressed as the product of the matrix $A'D^{1/2}$ and its transpose, its rank is equal to that of $A'D$.

Although $n - 1$ comparisons can satisfy this condition, it is desirable to have more than this minimal number in an incomplete design so as to over-determine the parameters and have degrees of freedom available for testing the model. If the experimenter has free choice of the pairs for the incomplete design, he can use established designs which prescribe the pairs to be retained. In particular, the designs of Section 7.1.2 have good properties from the point of view of calculation in any unweighted analysis. In some applications, however, certain pairs may be excluded in an irregular way by the experimental conditions. The general normit χ^2 solution is then necessary and the methods of Section 6.4.2 may be applied. The provisional estimates which determine the Müller-Urban weights may be obtained by Gulliksen's (1956) unweighted solution. For this solution the matrix of provisional weights is simply

$$D = \text{diag}[n_{jk}],$$

where

$$n_{jk} = 1 \text{ if the } j, k \text{ pair is retained}$$

$$n_{jk} = 0 \text{ if the } j, k \text{ pair is omitted.}$$

Evaluating the normal equations (7.2) in terms of this weight matrix, we obtain the system

$$\hat{\alpha}_j \sum_k n_{jk} - \sum_k n_{jk} \hat{\alpha}_k = \sum_k n_{jk} y_{jk}.$$

Setting $\hat{\alpha}_n = 0$, we may solve the first $n - 1$ equations to obtain the required provisional estimates of the affective-value contrasts of the first $n - 1$ objects with the last object. These contrasts determine the weights for the minimum normit χ^2 solution in the manner illustrated in the following example.

Example 7.1.1

In an experimental study to determine a rational origin for affective values, Thurstone and Jones (1957) obtained paired-comparison judgments from 194 male college students. The stimulus objects were five birthday gifts and ten distinct pairs of gifts made up from these five. The subjects were required to make three types of choices: those between one gift and another (single-single), those between one gift and a pair of gifts (single-double), and those between two pairs of gifts (double-double). Since it was not considered desirable to present the subject with choices in which the same gift appeared in both alternatives (e.g., A vs A and B), this type of comparison was eliminated from the design. The observed normal deviates for the resulting incomplete design are shown in Table 7.1. These deviates are the conventional normal transforms of the observed proportions, $y_{jk} = \Phi^{-1}(p_{jk})$, with the assumed composition

$$y_{jk} = \frac{\alpha_j - \alpha_k}{\sigma_{jk}} + \xi_{jk}.$$

Thurstone and Jones assume that the discriminal dispersions, σ_{jk}, are not homogeneous, but stand in the ratio $\sqrt{2} : \sqrt{3} : 2$ for the single-single, single-double, and double-double comparisons, respectively. These figures follow from the assumption that each object in the comparison contributes an equal component of random variation to the discriminal variance. In terms of the "stretching" factors, δ_{lm} for the three classes of comparisons, say

$$\delta_{11} = \sqrt{2}, \qquad \delta_{12} = \sqrt{3}, \qquad \delta_{22} = \sqrt{4} = 2,$$

we define the adjusted deviates $y'_{jk} = \delta_{lm} y_{jk}$ with the assumed composition $y'_{jk} = \alpha_j - \alpha_k + \delta_{lm} \xi_{jk}$. The common discriminal dispersion of the adjusted deviates is set to unity as in previous solutions.

Provisional estimates, $\hat{\alpha}_{j,\text{prov}}$, may be obtained by applying Gulliksen's (1956) solution to the adjusted deviates. (Alternatively, we may use the approximate solution in Thurstone and Jones, 1957.) From the provisional solution, the deviates $Y'_{jk,\text{prov}} = \hat{\alpha}_{j,\text{prov}} - \hat{\alpha}_{k,\text{prov}}$ are obtained and the stretching factors removed to obtain the provisional deviates

$$Y_{jk,\text{prov}} = Y'_{jk,\text{prov}}/\delta_{lm}.$$

TABLE 7.1. Observed Normal Deviates: Thurstone-Jones Study

Objects	A	B	C	D	E	AB	AC	AD	AE	BC	BD	BE	CD	CE	DE
									Objects						
A		.10	-1.34	-.47	-.64					-1.75	-.95	-1.04	-2.05	-1.88	-1.34
B	-.10		-1.23	-.58	-.88		-1.55	-1.04	-1.28				-1.75	-1.88	-1.41
C	1.34	1.23		1.23	.58	.58		.74	.47		.61	.61			.50
D	.47	.58	-1.23		-.47	-.15	-1.41		-.67	-1.48		-.52		-1.34	
E	.64	.88	-.58	.47		.08	-1.28	-.44		-1.13	-.03		-1.41		
AB			-.58	.15	-.08								-1.48	-1.48	-.71
AC		1.55		1.41	1.28						1.04	.88			.71
AD		1.04	-.74		.44					-.84		-.05		-1.41	
AE		1.28	-.47	.67						-.61	.39		-1.04		
BC	1.75			1.48	1.13			.84	.61						.52
BD	.95		-.61		.03		-1.04		-.39					-1.48	
BE	1.04		-.61	.52			-.88	.05					-.95		
CD	2.05	1.75			1.41	1.48			1.04			.95			
CE	1.88	1.88		1.34		1.48		1.41			1.48				
DE	1.34	1.41	-.50			.71	-.71			.52					

TABLE 7.2. Estimated Affective Value Contrasts and their Covariance Matrix $\times N$ (where $N = 194$) Thurstone-Jones Study

				Objects				
	A	B	C	D	E	AB	AC	AD
						(Symmetric)		
A	1.6925							
B	1.1629	1.7041						
C	1.0592	0.0577	1.5379					
D	1.1952	1.1946	1.1264	1.6955				
E	1.1798	1.1789	1.1326	1.2349	1.1667			
AB	.9774	.9767	1.0291	1.1308	1.1259	2.0618		
AC	.9378	.9574	.8977	1.0313	1.0428	.8405	2.3489	
Objects AD	1.1300	1.2081	1.1802	1.1887	1.2652	1.0426	.9774	2.2919
AE	1.1295	1.1928	1.1831	1.2555	1.1879	1.0407	.9676	1.1867
BC	.9681	.9455	.9107	1.0401	1.0523	.8505	.7911	1.1473
BD	1.2191	1.1291	1.1776	1.1882	1.2697	1.0415	1.1314	1.1914
BE	1.2040	1.1298	1.1804	1.2631	1.1882	1.0403	1.1486	1.3360
CD	1.1830	1.1817	1.1253	1.2219	1.2730	1.2154	.9980	1.2083
CE	1.1895	1.1898	1.1194	1.2651	1.2191	1.2352	.9885	1.4220
$\alpha_j^* = \alpha_j - \alpha_n$	-2.3807	-2.4790	-.03300	-1.7582	-1.2975	-1.4185	.2870	-.95098

	AE	BC	BD	BE	CD	CE	DE
AE	2.3103						
BC	1.1684	2.2854					
Objects BD	1.3342	.9913	2.3156				
BE	1.1898	.9829	1.1871	2.3019			
CD	1.4296	1.0152	1.2130	1.4044	3.2797		
CE	1.1982	1.0044	1.4003	1.2047	1.2085	3.5560	
$\alpha_j^* = \alpha_j - \alpha_n$	-.59255	.76430	-1.2398	-.92203	1.2090	1.3551	0.0000

In terms of $Y_{jk,\text{prov}}$ the variance of the corresponding observed deviate y_{jk} is $\mathscr{V}(y_{jk}) = P_{jk} Q_{jk}/N_{jk} h^2(Y_{jk,\text{prov}})$. The variance of the adjusted deviate is

$$\mathscr{V}(y'_{jk}) = \delta^2_{lm} \mathscr{V}(y_{jk}).$$

Thus the weight matrix for the minimum normit χ^2 solution for the adjusted deviates is

$$D = \text{diag}[N_{jk} W_{jk}/\delta^2_{lm}],$$

where W_{jk} is the Müller-Urban weight obtained from Table A6.

In this example $N_{jk} = 194$ where the j, k comparison is retained, and 0 elsewhere. The estimated affective values obtained by Thurstone and Jones were used to compute the provisional deviates which determine the W_{jk}. Proceeding with the solution in Section 6.4.2, we obtain the inverse of the first 14 rows and columns of the matrix of coefficients of the normal equations (Table 7.2). The inverse matrix times the row sums of the weighted adjusted deviates gives the estimated affective values which are shown at the bottom of Table 7.2. The partition of χ^2 associated with this solution is shown in Table 7.3.

TABLE 7.3. Partition of χ^2: Thurstone-Jones Study

Source of χ^2	d.f.	χ^2	p
Estimation	14	3781.2	<.0005
Error	41	247.8	<.0005
Total	55		

The partition of χ^2 shows significant departure of the data from the assumed judgmental model, even though the data were obtained by multiple judgments and the error χ^2 is possibly underestimated. Nevertheless, a preponderant part of the variation in the observed deviates is accounted for by the model and contrasts of affective value between objects are determined with good precision. The contrast of object A with DE, for example, is -2.3807. Under the model, the error variance is unity, and the variance of this contrast estimate may be obtained from the variances and covariances of Table 7.2:

$$\mathscr{V}(\alpha_A - \alpha_{DE}) = \mathscr{V}(\hat{\alpha}^*_A) = 1.6925/194.$$

If the departure from the model is considered random variation, the error χ^2 suggests that it is of the order of six times expectation. This would indicate a standard error of the order $[6(1.6925)/194]^{1/2} = .2288$, which is small relative to the magnitude of the contrast. In Chapter 9 these estimated contrasts are used to estimate a rational origin for the affective continuum on which the objects have been measured in the paired-comparison solution.

7.1.2 Balanced and Partially Balanced Incomplete Paired-comparison Designs

By suitable choice of the comparisons to be retained it is possible to construct incomplete paired-comparison designs with simple solutions in any unweighted analysis. Except when the number of objects to be compared is prime, convenient designs can be derived from the so-called "group divisible" partially balanced incomplete block (PBIB) designs developed for agricultural research by Bose et al. (1954).

These designs have two classes of pairs called "first associates" and "second associates." Any two objects are either first associates or second associates, but not both. To assign the pairs to the association classes of a group divisible design, one writes the object designations in a $p \times q$ rectangular array by columns. This array is called an "association scheme." Pairs of objects in the same row are first associates, and those in different rows, second associates. An association scheme for six objects with $p = 2$ and $q = 3$ is, for example,

$$
\begin{array}{ccc}
1 & 3 & 5 \\
2 & 4 & 6.
\end{array}
$$

McKeon (1961) has shown that an easily solved incomplete paired-comparison design can be obtained from the association scheme of a PBIB design by comparing objects which are ith associates ($i = 1, 2$). For the group divisible designs, one compares second associates only. (Comparison of first associates produces two unconnected sets of pairs and a solution for the design does not exist.) Thus, the incomplete paired-comparison design developed from the preceding association scheme is as follows:

	Design					Diagram				
								k		
j	k				j	1	2	3	4	5	6
1	2	4	6		1		x		x		x
2	1	3	5		2	x		x		x	
3	2	4	6		3		x		x		x
4	1	3	5		4	x		x		x	
5	2	4	6		5		x		x		x
6	1	3	5		6	x		x		x	

All partially balanced incomplete paired-comparison (PBIPC) designs generated by comparison of ith associates have the following properties:

(1) Each of the n objects in the design is compared with the same number of other objects, say r_i (and $i = 2$ for group divisible designs).

(2) Each object has exactly n_j jth associates, $j = 1, 2$.

(3) The number of times that two objects which are jth associates are paired with a common object is the same for all jth associates and is equal to λ_{ij}, say, $j = 1, 2$.

(4) The design is symmetric; i.e. if the j, k pair appears, the k, j pair also appears.

The n, r_i, n_i, and λ_{ij} are called the parameters of the design. For PBIPC designs in general, the parameters evidently satisfy

$$r_i = n_i,$$

$$n_i + n_j = n - 1,$$

where $j = 3 - i$. For comparison of second associates of a group divisible design, we have also

$$n_1 = q - 1, \qquad n_2 = (p - 1)q,$$

$$\lambda_{22} = 0, \qquad \lambda_{21} = (p - 1)q.$$

PBIPC designs have simple solutions in terms of these parameters when uniform weights are used. The solutions are exact when the comparisons have been made in single judgments by the same number of subjects and the angular response function is assumed. The weights in (7.1) are then simply $N_{jk} = N$ wherever the j, k pair is retained, and zero elsewhere. Specializing (7.2) in this way, we find that the normal equations for the minimum χ^2 solution take the general form

$$\hat{\alpha}_j \sum_k n_{jk} - \sum_k n_{jk} \hat{\alpha}_k = \sum_k n_{jk} y_{jk} \qquad (y_{jk} = -y_{kj})$$

or, say

$$n_i \hat{\alpha}_j - \Sigma n_{jk} \hat{\alpha}_k = y_{j\,.} . \tag{7.3}$$

The quantities n_{jk} specify the weight matrix

$$D = \text{diag}[n_{jk} N]$$

where

$$n_{jk} = 1 \qquad \text{if the } j, k \text{ pair is present,}$$

$$n_{jk} = 0 \qquad \text{if the } j, k \text{ pair is absent.}$$

The n_{jk} are called the incidence numbers of the design. The factor N in D appears on both sides of (7.3) and cancels.

By defining the $n \times n$ incidence matrix for a design comparing ith associates

$$N_i = [n_{jk}]_i, \qquad j = 1, 2, \ldots, n; \qquad k = 1, 2, \ldots, n,$$

we may write (7.3) in matrix notation,

$$(r_i I - N_i)\hat{\boldsymbol{\alpha}} = \mathbf{y}., \qquad \text{say.}$$

We verify below that the matrix product $(a_i I + b_i N_i)(r_i I - N_i)$ yields $(I - \mathbf{11}'/n) = \Delta$, the idempotent matrix introduced in Section 6.5.2, where

$$a_i = \frac{1}{r_i}\left[1 + (r_i - \lambda_{ij})/n\lambda_{ij}\right],$$

$$b_i = 1/n\lambda_{ij}, \qquad j \neq i.$$

(7.4)

As shown in Section 6.5.2, $\Delta\hat{\boldsymbol{\alpha}} = \hat{\boldsymbol{\alpha}}^0$, the estimator of the affective values, restricted to sum to zero. Then $\hat{\boldsymbol{\alpha}}^0 = (a_i I + b_i N_i)\mathbf{y}.$ or, in scalar notation,

$$\hat{\alpha}_j^0 = a_i \sum_k (n_{jk})_i y_{jk} + b_i \sum_h (n_{hj})_i \sum_k (n_{hk})_i y_{hk} = a_i y_{j.} + b_i \sum_h (n_{hj})_i y_{h.}.\quad(7.5)$$

Thus the estimated affective value of the jth object, in deviation form, is a_i times the sum of the jth row of arc sine deviates plus b_i times the sum of the rows corresponding to objects with which the jth object is compared. (See Example 7.1.2.) These estimates are approximately unbiased (since $\mathscr{E}(\mathbf{y}) \cong A\boldsymbol{\alpha}$)

$$\mathscr{E}(\hat{\boldsymbol{\alpha}}^0) = (a_i I + b_i N_i)A'D\mathscr{E}(\mathbf{y})$$

$$\cong (a_i I + b_i N_i)A'DA\boldsymbol{\alpha}$$

$$\cong (a_i I + b_i N_i)(r_i I - N_i)\boldsymbol{\alpha}$$

$$\cong \Delta\boldsymbol{\alpha}.$$

Their sampling variance is

$$\mathscr{V}(\hat{\boldsymbol{\alpha}}^0) = (a_i I + b_i N_i)\mathscr{V}(\mathbf{y}.)(a_i I + b_i N_i)$$

$$= (a_i I + b_i N_i)A'D\mathscr{V}(\mathbf{y})DA(a_i I + b_i N_i)$$

$$\cong (a_i I + b_i N_i)(r_i I - N_i)(a_i I + b_i N_i)\sigma^2$$

$$\cong \Delta(a_i I + b_i N_i)\sigma^2.$$

For group divisible designs, $i = 2$, diagonal elements of this matrix give

$$\mathscr{V}(\hat{\alpha}_j^0) = \frac{1}{n}[(n-1)a_2 - r_2 b_2]\sigma^2.$$

Covariances for first associates are

$$\mathscr{V}(\hat{\alpha}_j^0, \hat{\alpha}_k^0) = \frac{1}{n}(-a_2 - r_2 b_2)\sigma^2, \qquad \text{when } n_{jk} = 0,$$

and covariances for second associates are

$$\mathscr{V}(\hat{a}_j^0, \hat{a}_k^0) = \frac{1}{n}[-a_2 + (n - r_2)b_2]\sigma^2, \qquad \text{when } n_{jk} = 1.$$

Contrasts between first associates therefore have variance $2a_i\sigma^2$, and between second associates, $2(a_i - b_i)\sigma^2$, where $\sigma^2 = 1/N$ if angular deviates are used. The partition of χ^2 associated with this solution is shown in Table 7.4.

TABLE 7.4. Partition of χ^2 for Group Divisible Designs

Source of χ^2	d.f.	Sum of squares	χ^2	Expected sum of squares
Estimation	$n - 1$	SSR $= \Sigma\hat{a}_j^0 y_j.$	$N \cdot$SSR	$n - 1 + \boldsymbol{\alpha}^{0\prime}\Delta\boldsymbol{\alpha}^0$
Error	$\dfrac{n_i n}{2} - n + 1$	SSE $=$ SST $-$ SSR	$N \cdot$SSE	$\dfrac{n_i n}{2} - n + 1$
Total	$\dfrac{n_i n}{2}$	SST $= \Sigma\Sigma(n_{jk})_i y_{jk}^2$		

The simple form of the unweighted solution for PBIPC designs is a consequence of properties 1 and 2 above. They imply that the product of the incidence matrix with itself is of the form

$$N_i N_i = r_i I + \lambda_{ii} N_i + \lambda_{ij}(\mathbf{1}\mathbf{1}' - I - N_i).$$

Also implied is the following identity in the parameters of the design:

$$(\mathbf{1}'N_i')(N_i\mathbf{1}) = \mathbf{1}'(N_i'N_i)\mathbf{1}$$

$$nr_i^2 = nr_i + \lambda_{ii}nr_i + \lambda_{ij}(n^2 - n - nr_i)$$

$$r_i(r_i - 1) = \lambda_{ii}r_i + \lambda_{ij}(n - r_i - 1)$$

$$= \lambda_{ii}n_i + \lambda_{ij}n_j. \tag{7.6}$$

With these results we are prepared to verify the expression which precedes (7.4) by evaluating

$$(a_i I + b_i N_i)(r_i I - N_i) = [1 + (r_i - \lambda_{ij})/n\lambda_{ij}]I + (r_i/n\lambda_{ij})N_i$$

$$- \frac{1}{r_i}[1 + (r_i - \lambda_{ij})/n\lambda_{ij}]N_i - (r_i/n\lambda_{ij})I$$

$$- (\lambda_{ii}/n\lambda_{ij})N_i - \frac{1}{n}(\mathbf{1}\mathbf{1}' + I + N_i)$$

$$= I - \mathbf{1}\mathbf{1}'/n - \frac{1}{r_i n\lambda_{ij}}[r_i(r_i - 1)$$

$$- (n - r_i - 1)\lambda_{ij} - r_i\lambda_{ii}]N_i$$

$$= I - \mathbf{1}\mathbf{1}'/n$$

$$= \Delta,$$

since by (7.6) the coefficient of N_i vanishes. For details see McKeon (1961, pp. 27–31).

When the number of objects is prime, so that group divisible PBIPC designs do not exist, we may resort to certain balanced incomplete (BIB) designs and other types of partially balanced incomplete designs. For moderate numbers of objects the following designs exist and have been tabulated, together with the parameters required for their solution, in Table A11. (A useful BIB for $n = 16$ is also shown.)

Design	Type	n
1	BIB	7
2	BIB	11
3	BIB	13
4	BIB	15
5	BIB	16
6	C(yclic)PBIB	17
7	S(imple)PBIB	19
8	BIB	21

BIB designs are a subset of PBIB designs in which $\lambda_{ii} = \lambda_{ij} = \lambda_i$. As a result (7.6) specializes to

$$r_i(r_i - 1) = (n - 1)\lambda_i,$$

and (7.5) to

$$\hat{\alpha}_j^0 = \frac{r_i}{n\lambda_i}\left(y_j. + \sum_h n_{hj}\, y_{h.}/r_i\right), \tag{7.5a}$$

where $i = 1$ refers to the design as shown in Table A11 and $i = 2$ to its complement.

The solution of the balanced incomplete paired comparison (BIPC) designs is therefore even simpler than that of the PBIPC designs. (See the numerical example in Section 7.2.2.) With the exception of BIB 16, however, the incidence matrix of BIB designs have some nonzero elements in the diagonal. They correspond formally to the pairing of an object with itself, although such pairs are not usually presented experimentally. Since the incidence matrix of an incomplete paired-comparison design determines the form of the estimated covariance matrix, the variances of estimated contrasts are more irregular than those for the PBIPC designs (except for BIPC 16).

Unfortunately, computational convenience of the PBIPC and BIPC designs is lost when a weighted analysis is performed. The solution of Section 6.7.1 continues to apply, however, as does the solution for the multiple-judgment case using normal deviates, described in 6.7.4. Although they have no computational advantage in these cases, BIPC and PBIPC designs tend to have smaller and more uniform contrast variances than arbitrary designs and should be preferred for this reason. A basis for choosing among possible designs is provided by the relative size of the respective sampling variances of the contrasts they estimate. The ratio of estimated variances for a particular contrast is an index of the relative efficiency of the designs with respect to the contrast. If one of the designs requires more judgments than the other, the ratio of the numbers of judgments required by each may be incorporated to obtain the relative efficiency of the designs per judgment.

Example 7.1.2[1]

This example is drawn from an unpublished study of the preferences of salaried employees for various plans for an increase in compensation. The subjects were 143 male salaried employees of an electrical equipment manufacturer in a large northern city. The plans for increased compensation differed with respect to amount of salary, length of vacation, and the amount of the company's contribution to each employee's retirement benefit, expressed as a percentage of salary. The composition of each planned increase is shown in Table 7.5.

TABLE 7.5. Alternative Plans for Increased Compensation

Plan	Additional annual salary, $	Additional annual vacation, days	Addition to retirement fund, %
A	600		
B	450		
C		12	
D		9	
E			6
F			4.5
G	300	6	
H	300		3
I		6	3

Preferences for the nine plans in Table 7.5 were obtained in a multiple-judgment paired-comparison experiment. To reduce the number of pairs judged by each subject, a group divisible PBIPC design was used. Plans that are second associates in the following scheme were paired in the experiment:

$$\begin{array}{ccc} 1 & 2 & 7 \\ 3 & 4 & 8 \\ 5 & 6 & 9 \end{array}$$

[1] We are indebted to Dr. J. Stacy Adams for data used in the example.

That is, each plan in each row was compared with each of the plans in the other rows. The angular deviates corresponding to comparisons retained in this design are shown in Table 7.6. (These deviates have been obtained by interpolating in Table A5.)

For the solution of this design the sums of the rows of the table, and sums of rows corresponding to comparisons retained in each column of the table are required. These quantities are also shown in Table 7.6. The parameters of this group divisible design are $n = 9$, $r_2 = 6$, $\lambda_{21} = 2 \times 3 = 6$. Thus coefficients in (7.4) are $a_2 = 1/6$, and $b_2 = 1/54$. Applying (7.5) to the data in Table 7.6, we obtain the estimated affective values shown at the bottom of Table 7.6. These estimates will be used later in this chapter to illustrate a multifactor model for the prediction of preferences for the plans (see Section 7.3.3).

The analysis of variance for this solution is shown in Table 7.7. Since the data were obtained in a multiple-judgment design, the estimate of error in Table 7.7 is biased downward somewhat. Nevertheless the error χ^2, although less than 4% of total, is significant and indicates that the Case V model does not hold exactly for these data. Since three of the observed proportions exceed .90 and one exceeds .95, some of the departure from the model may be due to failure of the angular response function at extreme proportions.

7.1.3 Designs with Incomplete Multiple Judgments

When an incomplete design in which each of n objects appears in $r < (n - 1)$ comparisons is used in place of a complete design in a single-judgment experiment, the number of subjects required is reduced from $Nn(n - 1)/2$ to $Nnr/2$. If n is moderately large, even the latter number may be prohibitive, especially in applications where the subjects require lengthy training or experience. For these applications, some means of retaining the advantage of single-judgment sampling (i.e., independent sampling error) while economizing on subjects is obviously desirable.

Incomplete paired-comparison designs which serve this purpose have been devised by Linhart (1966). In these designs, g groups of N subjects are required. Subjects within each group are assigned a subset of the $n(n - 1)/2$ possible pairs in which a given object appears at most *once*. Thus, in the multiple judgments of a given subject there are no comparisons involving a common object, and the problem of correlated errors does not arise. Pairs are assigned to the separate groups of subjects in such a manner that all pairs are connected when the data are brought together in the table of frequencies. The $n - 1$ contrasts of affective value among the objects can therefore be estimated, and differences between objects, as well as goodness of fit of the paired-comparison model, may be tested by means of analysis of variance.

Table 7.6. Observed Angular Deviates ($N = 143$)

	A	B	C	D	E	F	G	H	I
A			.6898	.9343	.2763	.8453		−.0771	.4720
B			.3646	.6540	−.5686	.1191		−.8041	−.2764
C	−.6898	−.3646			−.6718	−.3646	−.9111		−.8041
D	−.9343	−.6540			−.8453	−.6192	−1.1944		−1.0088
E	−.2763	−.5684	−.6718	.8453			.0771	−.5036	
F	−.8453	−.1191	.3646	.6192			.5520	−.9831	
G			.9111	1.1944	−.0771	.5520		−.3797	.1332
H	.0771	.8041			.5036	.9831	.3797		.5036
I	−.4720	.2704	.8041	1.0088			−.1332	−.5036	
$y_{i\cdot}$	3.1406	−.5114	−3.8060	−5.2560	1.3829	−1.5157	2.3339	3.2512	.9805
$\sum_h n_h Y_h.$	−4.9631	−4.9631	5.8108	5.8108	−.8477	−.8477	−4.9631	5.8108	−.8477
$\hat{\alpha}_j^0$	.4315	−.1771	−.5267	−.7684	.2149	−.2682	.2971	.6495	.1478

TABLE 7.7. Partition of χ^2 for the PBIPC Design

Source of χ^2	d.f.	Sum of squares	χ^2	p
Estimation	$n - 1 = 8$	SSR $= \Sigma \hat{\alpha}_j^0 y.$ $= 11.1428$	$N \cdot$ SSR $= 1593.4$	$p < .0005$
Error	$\dfrac{rn}{2} - n + 1 = 19$	SSE $=$ SST $-$ SSR $= .396$	$N \cdot$ SSE $= \quad 56.6$	$p < .0005$
Total	$rn/2 = 27$	SST $= \Sigma\Sigma(n_{jk})_i y_{jk}^2$ $= 11.5389$		

The designs constructed by Linhart are given in Table A12. The sets of pairs to be assigned to each group of subjects appear between semicolons in each row of the table. The designs in Table A12 are cyclic in structure. This means that the coefficients of the normal equations in the least squares solution take the form of a circulant matrix. Each row of the matrix can be obtained from the row above by displacing the elements one column to the right, with end-around carry of the last element. Because the inverse of a circulant is also a circulant, the solution for the design can be specified merely be exhibiting the first row of the inverse. Furthermore, the requirement that a paired-comparison design be symmetric means that the $n - 1$ off-diagonal elements in the first row of the inverse are symmetric. Thus, it is only necessary to tabulate the first $n/2 + 1$ elements of this row if n is even and the first $(n + 1)/2$ if n is odd. Linhart's solutions for the designs in Table A12 are presented in this form in Table A13. The use of Table A13 is explained in connection with Example 7.1.3.

David (1967) has considered the general problem of constructing cyclic designs in which objects are paired in sets in which each object appears exactly once. Such designs are called *resolvable*. Resolvable cyclic designs may be used in incomplete multiple-judgment paired comparisons in the same manner as Linhart's designs. David shows how to construct many resolvable designs which are distinct in the sense that one cannot be obtained from another merely by renaming the objects. He does not give the solutions for these designs but they can always be constructed by standard methods of inverting circulant matrices (see McKeon, 1960) or by computer methods.

Example 7.1.3

Linhart (1966) reports an experiment in which wool samples washed in different detergents were compared for "touch" by expert judges. Seven synthetic detergents and a soap were used in the study. Design 9 of Table A12 was used. Each sample was paired with $r = 3$ other samples and each

TABLE 7.8. Angular Deviates Corresponding to Proportion of Comparisons in which Row Sample is Judged Better than Column Sample

Sample	Sample 1	2	3	4	5	6	7	8	Sum	Estimate
1				−.1445	.4423	.1445			.4423	.006287
2					.4423	.1445	.1445		.7313	.077395
3						.1445	.1445	−.1445	.1445	.100268
4	.1445						−.1445	.1445	.1445	.130091
5	−.4423	−.4423						−.7952	−1.6798	−.470349
6	−.1445	−.1995	−.1445						−.4335	−.083183
7		−.1445	−.1445	.1445					−.1445	−.054418
8			.1445	−.1445	.7952				.7952	−.185070
								Check	.0000	.000001

TABLE 7.9. Partition of χ^2 for Table 7.8

Source	d.f.	Sum of squares*	χ^2
Objects	7	1.058123	7.40686
Error	5	.153401	1.0738
Total	12	1.211524	

*$\sigma^2 = 1/N = .142857$.

pair was judged by $N = 7$ judges. The arc sine deviates corresponding to the observed proportion of judgments of "better touch" are shown in Table 7.8.

The inverse matrix for obtaining the estimated affective values is developed from the figures for design 9 given in Table A12:

$$(A'A)^{-1} = \frac{1}{448} \begin{bmatrix} 141 & -23 & -35 & 9 & 13 & 9 & -35 & -23 \\ -23 & 141 & -23 & -35 & 9 & 13 & 9 & -35 \\ -35 & -23 & 141 & -23 & -35 & 9 & 13 & 9 \\ 9 & -35 & -23 & 141 & -23 & -35 & 9 & 13 \\ 13 & 9 & -35 & -23 & 141 & -23 & -35 & 9 \\ 9 & 13 & 9 & -35 & -23 & 141 & -23 & -35 \\ -35 & 9 & 13 & 9 & -35 & -23 & 141 & -23 \\ -23 & -35 & 9 & 13 & 9 & -35 & -23 & 141 \end{bmatrix}$$

Call the row sums in Table 7.8 y_h. and the elements of the inverse matrix b_{jh}. Then the estimated value of the jth sample on the scale of "touch" is

$$\hat{\alpha}_j^0 = \sum_{h=1}^{n} b_{jh} y_h. \ .$$

These values are shown in the right-hand column of Table 7.8. For the associated partition of χ^2, the sum of squares of the deviates y_{jk} for $j < k$ provides the total, and $\sum_j \hat{\alpha}_j^0 y_j$. the sum of squares for objects. The difference is the error sum of squares. Since the theoretical error variance is $1/N$, the χ^2 values in this case are seven times the corresponding sums of squares. The results show no significant lack of fit nor any significance of differences among objects. This conclusion differs from that of Linhart, who used the ratio of the object mean square to the error mean square to test the object effects.

To obtain the variance-covariance matrix of the estimates, the inverse matrix shown above must be restricted so that its rows and columns sum to zero. This may be done by subtracting $1/n$ times the constant row sum from each element of the matrix. In this case the rows sum to $1/n$ and one subtracts $1/n^2$. The restricted inverse matrix times the theoretical error $1/N$ is the variance-covariance matrix of the estimates. Thus, the variance of an estimated contrast between object j and object k is

$$\mathscr{V}(\hat{\alpha}_j^0 - \hat{\alpha}_k^0) = 2\left[\left(b_{jj} - \frac{1}{n^2}\right) - \left(b_{jk} - \frac{1}{n^2}\right)\right]/N$$

$$= 2(b_{jj} - b_{jk})/N.$$

For example, the estimated difference between the scale value for the sample washed in soap (8) and that washed in the highest-ranking synthetic detergent (4) is .04496. The standard error of this estimate is

$$\sqrt{2(141 - 13)/(448 \times 7)} = .27375.$$

7.2 Incomplete Ranking Designs

In Section 6.8 it was shown that under fairly general conditions paired-comparison judgments may be generated from subjects' rank orderings of a set of stimulus objects. Particularly as the number of objects increases, the rank-order design is more economical and practical than the paired-comparisons design. However, if the subject is required at each stage of the ranking to compare carefully each object with every other object, it may not be feasible to ask him to rank more than about 20 objects.

A possible approach for obtaining rankings of a greater number of objects is to ask the subject to sort the objects initially into, say, three gross categories of "high," "middle," and "low" rank. He can then order the objects within each category to produce a complete ordering. Because two different types of judgment are used in this procedure, however, it must be expected that the precision of an estimated difference of affective value will vary depending on the objects being contrasted. Objects that tend to appear in the same group in the initial sort will probably be estimated with better precision than those that tend to appear in different groups. The extent of this difference in precision will be unknown.

An approach to partial rankings which avoids this difficulty makes use of incomplete ranking designs. The objects are divided into subsets, not mutually exclusive, which systematically include common objects. Subjects rank only within these subsets and the complete ranking is inferred from the positions of the common objects in the sub-rankings. Certain balanced incomplete block (BIB) designs are particularly convenient for this type of ranking design (Gulliksen and Tucker, 1961). The treatments and blocks of the BIB design correspond, respectively, to objects and subsets in the incomplete ranking design. For example, Design 11.7 from Cochran and Cox (1957) provides the following balanced incomplete ranking design:

Subsets (blocks)	Objects (treatments)			
1	1	2	4	$n = 7$
2	2	3	5	$k = 3$
3	3	4	6	$r = 3$
4	4	5	7	$b = 7$
5	5	6	1	$\lambda = 1$
6	6	7	2	
7	7	1	3	

Other useful BIB designs from Cochran and Cox (1957) are 11.22, 10.2, 11.34, 10.3, 11.40, and 11.44. The corresponding incomplete ranking designs have the following properties:

(a) Each of b subsets contains the same number of objects, k.

(b) Each of n objects appears in the same number of subsets, r.

(c) Each pair of objects appears together in the same number of subsets, λ.

Because the BIB designs listed above have $\lambda = 1$, they are especially convenient as incomplete ranking designs. Rank-order judgments obtained with their aid are analyzed as follows. (1) The object judged greater in each of the $n(n - 1)/2$ pairs of distinct objects is determined from the sub-rankings of each subject. (2) Results of these judgments are enumerated over all subjects to obtain the sample proportions of a complete paired-comparison design. (3) The proportions serve as data for an analysis by one of the solutions for the multiple-judgment case of Section 6.7.

As is the case for incomplete paired-comparison designs, a wider class of incomplete ranking designs can be derived from partially balanced incomplete block (PBIB) designs. Considering only PBIB designs with two associate classes, we observe that the following properties are relevant to their use as incomplete ranking designs.

(1) Each of b subsets contains the same number of objects, k.

(2) Each of n objects appears in the same number of subsets, r.

(3) Any two objects are exclusively first associates or second associates. Each object has n_1 first associates and n_2 second associates.

(4) Any two objects which are first associates occur together in exactly the same number of subsets, κ_1; those which are second associates appear together in exactly κ_2 subsets.

(5) Given any two objects which are jth associates, the number of ith associates common to the respective subsets of the two given objects is λ_{ij}.

PIB designs which are useful as incomplete ranking designs have $\kappa_1 = 1$, $\kappa_2 = 0$, or $\kappa_1 = 0$, $\kappa_2 = 1$. Comparison of ranks in the former produces a partially balanced incomplete paired-comparison design corresponding to comparison of first associates. The latter produces the complementary design corresponding to comparison of second associates. These paired-comparison designs can be solved exactly by the general solution for incomplete designs in Section 7.1. In most applications where incomplete rankings are necessary, however, the number of objects will be large and the exact solution will involve heavy computation. The unweighted solution of Section 7.1.2 may then be substituted. The parameters r_i and λ_{ij}, $i \neq j$, required in the solution are listed in Table 7.10 for certain partially balanced incomplete block designs selected from Bose, Clatworthy, and Shrikhande (1954). The values of n, b, k, n_1, n_2, κ_1, and κ_2 are also given in Table 7.10. The form of the unweighted solution for one of these designs is shown in Example 7.2.

Another type of approximate solution for balanced and partially balanced incomplete rankings is also available. The paired-comparison proportions which are obtained from each of the sub-rankings can be used to estimate affective values for the objects in the corresponding subset. Within-subset contrasts of these estimates may then be employed as observations for a conventional analysis of an incomplete block design. This approach will yield an efficient solution if the sampling variances of the estimates are homogeneous. The angular solution for paired comparisons in the multiple-judgment case will tend to provide this homogeneity.

The analysis for balanced incomplete block designs may be found in Cochran and Cox (1957, Chapter 9), and that for partially balanced incomplete block designs in Bose et al. (1954). An application of this latter type of solution for a partially balanced incomplete ranking design is discussed in Chapter 9 (Section 9.2.4).

Example 7.2

A partially balanced incomplete ranking design based on PBIB design T1 from Bose et al. (1954) is as follows.

Subsets	Objects					
1	1	2	3	4	$n = 10,$	$r = 9$
2	5	6	7	1	$k = 4,$	$b = 5$
3	8	9	2	5	$n_1 = 6,$	$n_2 = 3$
4	10	3	6	8	$\kappa_1 = 1,$	$\kappa_2 = 0$
5	4	7	9	10	$r_1 = 6,$	$\lambda_{12} = 4$

TABLE 7.10. Partially Balanced Incomplete Block Designs
Suitable as Incomplete Ranking Designs*

Design	n	r	k	b	n_1	n_2	κ_1	κ_{2j}	r_i	λ_{ij}
SR1	6	2	3	4	1	4	0	1	4	4
R5	8	3	3	8	1	6	0	1	6	6
SR12	9	3	3	9	2	6	0	1	6	6
T1	10	2	4	5	6	3	1	0	6	4
T6	10	3	3	10	6	3	1	0	6	4
SR20	12	3	4	9	2	9	0	1	9	9
SR21	12	4	3	16	3	8	0	1	8	8
C1	13	3	3	13	6	6	1	0	6	3
R24	14	4	4	14	1	12	0	1	12	12
T20	15	2	5	6	8	6	1	0	8	4
T23	15	4	3	20	8	6	1	0	8	4
T28	15	3	3	15	8	6	0	1	6	3
SR40	16	4	4	16	3	12	0	1	12	12
LS14	16	3	3	16	9	6	0	1	6	2
S1.1	19	3	3	19	6	12	1	0	6	2
SR51	20	4	5	16	3	12	0	1	12	12
SR52	20	5	4	25	4	15	0	1	15	15
T31	21	2	6	7	10	10	1	0	10	4
R25	14	6	3	28	1	12	0	1	12	12
SR64	25	5	5	25	4	20	0	1	20	20
S1.4	26	3	6	13	15	10	1	0	15	9
T32	28	2	7	8	12	15	1	0	12	4
SR70	30	5	6	25	4	25	0	1	25	25
S1.9	35	3	7	15	18	16	1	0	18	9
T33	36	2	8	9	14	21	1	0	14	4
LS17	36	5	5	36	15	20	0	1	20	12
S1.12	40	4	4	40	12	27	1	0	12	4
T35	45	2	9	10	16	28	1	0	16	4
S1.14	45	3	5	27	12	32	1	0	12	3
LS18	49	6	6	47	18	30	0	1	30	20
SR83	49	7	7	49	6	42	0	1	42	42
S1.17	50	4	8	25	28	21	1	0	28	16
T36	55	2	10	11	18	36	1	0	18	4
SR85	56	7	8	49	6	49	0	1	49	49
S1.18	57	3	9	19	24	32	1	0	24	9

* Adapted from McKeon (1961, p. 22).

This design generates a paired-comparison table of the form

					Objects					
Objects	1	2	3	4	5	6	7	8	9	10
1		X	X	X	X	X	X			
2	X		X	X	X			X	X	
3	X	X		X		X		X		X
4	X	X	X				X		X	X
5	X	X				X	X	X	X	
6	X		X		X		X	X		X
7	X			X	X	X			X	X
8		X	X		X	X			X	X
9		X		X	X		X	X		X
10			X	X		X	X	X	X	

Coefficients for the solution of this paired-comparison design by formula (7.5) are

$$a_1 = \frac{1}{6}\left[1 + (6 - 4)/(10)(4)\right] = 7/40, \qquad b_1 = 1/(10)(4) = 1/40.$$

Since the solution based on formula (7.5) assumes homogeneity of variance of the transformed proportions, the angular transformation is to be preferred for this analysis.

7.3 Multifactor Models for Comparative Judgment

In Section 6.1, we suggested that the method of paired comparisons has an important role in studies which attempt to account for the choices of subjects for given objects in terms of objective characteristics of those objects. In this section we review some statistical methods which are useful in such studies. These methods are based on various multifactor models for comparative judgment.

In current statistical practice, two general types of multifactor models are now in general use. One is the so-called "response-surface" model, which is employed when the relevant characteristics of the objects are quantitative (Hotelling, 1941; Box and Wilson, 1951). The other is the familiar "factorial" model which applies when the characteristics are qualitative (Anderson and Bancroft, 1952; Kempthorne, 1952). Models incorporating both quantitative and qualitative information are also possible (see Section 7.3.3). All these models are linear in their parameters and may be incorporated in the model for comparative judgment in a straightforward manner as follows.

Let the response of a random subject to the j, k pair be determined by a discriminal process linear in m factors:

$$v_j = \beta_0 + \sum_{h=1}^{m} \beta_h x_{hj} + \varepsilon_j$$

and

$$v_k = \beta_0 + \sum_{h=1}^{m} \beta_h x_{hk} + \varepsilon_k.$$

In vector notation,

$$v_j = \beta_0 + \mathbf{x}_j' \boldsymbol{\beta} + \varepsilon_j$$

and

$$v_k = \beta_0 + \mathbf{x}_k' \boldsymbol{\beta} + \varepsilon_k.$$

The x_{hj} and x_{hk} are measurements of known properties of the objects, and the β_h ($h = 0, 1, \ldots, m$) are parameters of the equations describing the discriminal processes as functions of these measures. The β_h are assumed unknown, but identical for all subjects. As in Section 6.3, the random components ε_j and ε_k are assumed bivariate normal so that the difference process,

$$v_j - v_k = (\mathbf{x}_j - \mathbf{x}_k)'\boldsymbol{\beta} + \varepsilon_j - \varepsilon_k,$$

is distributed as $N[(\mathbf{x}_j - \mathbf{x}_k)'\boldsymbol{\beta}, \sigma_{jk}]$ in the population of subjects. Again we accept the generalized Case V assumptions and consider the σ_{jk} constant and equal to unity. According to the response function assumed, the observed proportion p_{jk} of judgments $X_j > X_k$ may be transformed to normal, angular, or logistic deviates. In any event, we assume that the resulting deviates have approximate expectation

$$\mathscr{E}(y_{jk}) \cong (\mathbf{x}_j - \mathbf{x}_k)'\boldsymbol{\beta}.$$

If there are n objects and p deviates, $p > n - 1 > m$ in all cases of interest.

Estimating $\boldsymbol{\beta}$ and testing the goodness of fit of this model is the same in every important respect as fitting the model for comparative judgment by the methods of Chapter 4. Instead of proceeding in this manner, however, there is merit in performing the solution in two stages—first, estimating the $n - 1$ contrasts of affective value by an appropriate paired-comparison solution, then fitting the multifactor model to these contrasts. It may be shown that, provided the multifactor model is linearly dependent on the paired-comparison model, the parameters estimated by either method will be numerically identical. The advantage of the second method is that error variation in the data is partitioned between that attributable to departure from the model for comparative judgment, and that attributable to departure from the multifactor model as such. If a multifactor model does not fit the data, it will not be worthwhile to entertain an alternative model if the discrepancy can be attributed to failure of the comparative judgment model. In this section we consider only the second method, first formulating the solution under the most general assumptions, then specializing to simpler cases more convenient in practical applications.

Suppose the observed deviates from a paired-comparison experiment (complete or incomplete, single- or multiple-judgment) have $\mathscr{E}(\mathbf{y}) = A\boldsymbol{\alpha}$ and $\mathscr{V}(\mathbf{y}) = \Sigma$, where A is the model for comparative judgment. Then from Section 6.7.2, the minimum χ^2 estimates of the affective value contrasts are

$$\hat{\boldsymbol{\alpha}}^\dagger = (A^{\dagger\prime}\Sigma^{-1}A^\dagger)^{-1}A^{\dagger\prime}\Sigma^{-1}\mathbf{y}.$$

Now let $X^\dagger$ be an $(n - 1) \times m$ matrix containing the same contrasts of the known coefficients of the multifactor model as have been estimated in $\hat{\boldsymbol{\alpha}}^\dagger$. For example, if $\hat{\alpha}_j^\dagger = \hat{\alpha}_j^* = \widehat{\alpha_j - \alpha_n}$, then the jth row of the $(n-1) \times n$ matrix X^* is $(\mathbf{x}_j - \mathbf{x}_n)'$. Then

$$\mathscr{E}(\hat{\alpha}^*) = X^* \boldsymbol{\beta}$$

and

$$\mathscr{V}(\hat{\alpha}^*) = (A^{*'} \Sigma^{-1} A^*)^{-1} = \Psi, \qquad \text{say.}$$

If X^* is of rank m, the minimum χ^2 estimates of the parameters of the multifactor model are

$$\hat{\boldsymbol{\beta}} = (X^{*'} \Psi^{-1} X^*)^{-1} X^{*'} \Psi^{-1} \hat{\alpha}^* \tag{7.7}$$

with

$$\mathscr{E}(\hat{\boldsymbol{\beta}}) = \boldsymbol{\beta}$$

and

$$\mathscr{V}(\hat{\boldsymbol{\beta}}) = (X^{*'} \Psi^{-1} X^*)^{-1}.$$

Note that $\Psi^{-1} = A^{*'} \Sigma^{-1} A^*$ and may be obtained without additional computation from the matrix of coefficients in the normal equations for estimating α_j^*. (If the affective values are estimated under the linear restriction in Section 6.5.2, $A^{\dagger'} \Sigma^{-1} A^\dagger$ is of size $n \times n$ and is singular. In this case $X^\dagger$ is of size $n \times m$ and Ψ^{-1} represents an inverse in a restricted space; i.e. $\Psi \Psi^{-1} = \Delta$, which is the identity transformation of this particular subspace.)

If X^* is of rank $l < m$, we take the approach of Section 6.7.2 and estimate l linearly independent linear functions of $\boldsymbol{\beta}$, say $L\boldsymbol{\beta}$. L must be linearly dependent on X^* so that X^* may be factored as $X^* = K^* L$, say. Then

$$\widehat{L\boldsymbol{\beta}} = (K^{*'} \Psi^{-1} K^*)^{-1} K^{*'} \Psi^{-1} \mathbf{y}, \tag{7.8}$$

with

$$\mathscr{E}(\widehat{L\boldsymbol{\beta}}) = L\boldsymbol{\beta}$$

and

$$\mathscr{V}(\widehat{L\boldsymbol{\beta}}) = (K^{*'} \Psi^{-1} K^*)^{-1}.$$

This solution will be necessary for the factorial model discussed in Section 7.3.2. Note that if $l = m$, we may take $L = I$ and $X^* = K^* I = K^*$; that is, the latter formulation includes the former as a special case. We may therefore represent the partition of χ^2 for the general solution in the form of Table 7.11.

TABLE 7.11. Partition of χ^2 for the General Solution of the Multifactor Model

Source of χ^2	d.f.	Sum of squares $= \chi^2/N$	Expected sum of squares
Multifactor model	l	$\text{SSM} = (\widehat{L\beta})'K^{*\prime}\Psi^{-1}\hat{\alpha}$	$l + (L\beta)'K^{*\prime}\Psi^{-1}K^{*}L\beta$
Departure from multifactor model	$n - 1 - l$	$\text{SSE}_2 = \text{SSR} - \text{SSM}$	$n - 1 - l$
Paired-comparison model	$n - 1$	$\text{SSR} = \hat{\alpha}^{*\prime}\Psi^{-1}\hat{\alpha}^{*}$ $= \hat{\alpha}^{*\prime}A^{*\prime}\Sigma^{-1}y$	$n - 1 + (L\beta)'$ $\times K^{*\prime}\Psi^{-1}K^{*}L\beta$
Departure from paired-comparison model	$p - (n - 1)$	$\text{SSE}_1 = \text{SST} - \text{SSR}$	$p - n + 1$
Total	p	$\text{SST} = y'\Sigma^{-1}y$	

This general solution is greatly simplified when the affective values are obtained from a complete single-judgment paired-comparison experiment analyzed under the angular response function. In this case the covariance matrix of the estimated affective values is proportional to the Δ of Section 6.5.2. The response-surface analysis then reduces to a conventional regression analysis, and the factorial analysis to a conventional analysis of variance. An example of response-surface analysis in this case appears in Section 7.3.1.

If the covariance matrix of the estimates is irregular, as when the paired-comparison design is incomplete, the general solution given above is usually required. Exceptions are certain balanced and partially balanced incomplete designs, which give simple solutions with certain factorial models. An example of the latter appears in Section 7.3.2.

7.3.1 A Response-surface Model

The problem of determining experimentally the point of maximum response in a system influenced by several independent variables is common in many fields of applied research. Example 6.6, from a study conducted by Buck and Weckel to determine the most preferred salt and sugar levels for canned green beans, is an illustration drawn from the field of food research. The statistical problems of determining maxima in such applications have been studied extensively by Box and his colleagues. In this section we apply their methods to paired comparisons and present a numerical example based on the data from Example 6.6. For ease of writing we discuss the case of two independent variables. Extension of the methods to three or more variables is straightforward.

Following Box (1954), we assume that the affective value of the jth object depends on the values of the independent variables x_1 and x_2 through the quadratic function

$$\alpha_j = \beta_{00} + \beta_{10}x_{1j} + \beta_{01}x_{2j} + \beta_{20}x_{1j}^2 + \beta_{02}x_{2j}^2 + \beta_{11}x_{1j}x_{2j}.$$

To put the dependent variable in estimable form, let us subtract the mean on each side to obtain

$$\alpha_j^0 = \beta_{10}(x_{1j} - \bar{x}_1) + \beta_{01}(x_{2j} - \bar{x}_2) + \beta_{20}(x_{1j}^2 - \overline{x_1^2})$$
$$+ \beta_{02}(x_{2j}^2 - \overline{x_2^2}) + \beta_{11}(x_{1j}x_{2j} - \overline{x_1 x_2}).$$

In matrix notation $\alpha^0 = X^0 \beta$, say. (Note that $\overline{x_1^2}$ and $\overline{x_2^2}$ are the means of squares, not the squares of means. Similarly, $\overline{x_1 x_2}$ is the mean of cross products.)

Suppose α_j^0 is estimated from angular deviates obtained in a complete single-judgment experiment. Then Ψ^{-1} is $nN\Delta$ and (7.7) becomes

$$\hat{\beta} = (X^{0\prime}\Delta X^0)^{-1} X^{0\prime} \Delta \hat{\alpha}^0 = (X^{0\prime} X^0)^{-1} X^{0\prime} \hat{\alpha}^0.$$

$X^{0\prime} X^0$ is just the matrix of corrected sums of squares and cross products of the independent variables, and $X^{0\prime} \hat{\alpha}^0$ is the vector of corrected cross products between the dependent variable and the independent variables. $\hat{\beta}$ is therefore the vector of estimated regression coefficients from a conventional regression analysis (Anderson and Bancroft, 1952, Chapter 14). Call this vector of estimates $\mathbf{b} = \hat{\beta}$. Then the equation of the fitted response surface is, say,

$$z = b_{10}(x_1 - \overline{x_1}) + b_{01}(x_2 - \overline{x_2}) + b_{20}(x_1^2 - \overline{x_1^2})$$
$$+ b_{02}(x_2^2 - \overline{x_2^2}) + b_{11}(x_1 x_2 - \overline{x_1 x_2}).$$

Collecting the constant terms in C we have the general relation

$$z = b_{10}x_1 + b_{01}x_2 + b_{20}x_1^2 + b_{02}x_2^2 + b_{11}x_1 x_2 + C. \qquad (7.9)$$

To determine the maximum of this surface, we set to zero the derivative of (7.9) with respect to x_1 and x_2, and obtain the stationary equations

$$\partial z / \partial x_1 = b_{10} + 2b_{20} x_1 + b_{11} x_2 = 0,$$
$$\partial z / \partial x_2 = b_{01} + b_{11} x_1 + 2b_{02} x_2 = 0. \qquad (7.10)$$

If these equations have a simultaneous solution, the surface has a point which is stationary in both directions. Since the variates are non-negative, the point is the required maximum if both b_{20} and b_{02} are negative, i.e. if the second derivatives are negative at the stationary point. The solution of (7.10) is therefore an estimate of the values of the independent variables which produce a maximum response, if a maximum exists.

Some care must be exercised in interpreting this estimate, however, since its precision may be poor if the sampling variance of the coefficients in (7.10) is excessive, or equivalently, if the surface is extremely flat in the neighborhood of the maximum (Box and Hunter, 1954). One method of characterizing the precision of multivariate estimates is to construct a confidence region in the space of the independent variables which includes the true point with assigned probability. In the present case, an implicit form of the equation describing the confidence region for the maximum is given by the χ^2 statistic for testing the hypothesis that the derivatives of the surface are zero at a given point. To compute this statistic, let d_1 and d_2 be the values of $\partial z/\partial x_1$ and $\partial z/\partial x_2$, respectively. Given x_1 and x_2, d_1 and d_2 are linear functions of the estimated parameters of the response surface. If $\Psi^{-1} = nN\Delta$, these estimates have limiting multivariate normal distribution with covariance matrix $(1/nN)(X^{0\prime}X^0)^{-1}$, and the covariance matrix of d_1 and d_2 is easy to compute. Let σ_i^2 be the variances and $\sigma_{i,j}$ the covariances from $(1/nN)(X^{0\prime}X^0)^{-1}$. Then the covariance matrix of d_1 and d_2, say $\mathscr{V}(d)$, has the elements

$$\mathscr{V}(d_1) = \sigma_{10}^2 + 4x_1^2\sigma_{20}^2 + x_2^2\sigma_{11}^2 + 4x_1\sigma_{10,20} + 2x_2\sigma_{10,11}$$
$$+ 4x_1 x_2 \sigma_{20,01}$$

$$\mathscr{V}(d_2) = \sigma_{01}^2 + x_1^2\sigma_{11}^2 + 4x_2^2\sigma_{02}^2 + 2x_1\sigma_{01,11} + 4x_2\sigma_{01,02}$$
$$+ 4x_1 x_2 \sigma_{11,02}$$

$$\mathscr{V}(d_1, d_2) = \sigma_{10,01} + x_1(\sigma_{10,11} + 2\sigma_{20,01}) + x_2(2\sigma_{10,02} + \sigma_{11,01})$$
$$+ 2x_1^2\sigma_{20,11} + 2x_2^2\sigma_{11,02} + x_1 x_2(\sigma_{11}^2 + 4\sigma_{20,02}). \quad (7.11)$$

As shown in Section 6.7.2, a quadratic form such as

$$Q = \mathbf{d}[\mathscr{V}^{-1}(\mathbf{d})]\mathbf{d}', \quad (7.12)$$

which is a function of x_1 and x_2, is distributed as a central χ^2 with two degrees of freedom on the hypothesis that the population values of d_1 and d_2 are zero. This is equivalent to the hypothesis that the point x_1, x_2 is the maximum. A .95 confidence region for the maximum is therefore represented by all points x_1, x_2 for which $Q \leq \chi^2_{2,.05}$. Although it is difficult to put this equation in a form explicit in x_1 or x_2, it is relatively easy to obtain points on the boundary of the confidence region by numerical methods. This may be done by choosing values of x_1, say, in the neighborhood of the maximum and determining the value of x_2 which satisfies (7.11), if it exists, by the method of false position (Willers, 1948, p. 205).

In many cases it may suffice to resolve questions of precision by testing specific hypotheses on the location of the maximum. This only requires computing $\mathscr{V}(\mathbf{d})$ for the hypothesized values of x_1 and x_2, inverting to obtain $\mathscr{V}^{-1}(d)$, computing (7.12), and referring the result to the χ^2 distribution. (See also Wallace, 1958, for methods of approximating the confidence region.)

Example 7.3.1

Buck and Weckel's study of preferred salt and sugar concentrations in canned green beans, reported in Example 6.6, is well suited to response-surface analysis. Since the data were obtained by single judgments in a complete paired-comparison experiment, the affective values estimated from angular deviates, assuming an order-effect model, have sampling covariance matrix $\Delta/2nN$. The response surface can therefore be fitted in a conventional multiple regression analysis. The data for fitting a quadratic surface take the form of Table 7.12. The parameters of the surface estimated in the regression

TABLE 7.12. Affective Values and Ancillary Information for
Buck and Weckel's Study $(N = 25)$

Sample	Dependent variable $\hat{\alpha}_j^0$	x_1	x_2	x_1^2	x_2^2	$x_1 x_2$
11	−.240	1	1	1	1	1
12	−.159	1	2	1	4	2
13	−.349	1	3	1	9	3
14	−.405	1	4	1	16	4
21	−.039	2	1	4	1	2
22	.105	2	2	4	4	4
23	.083	2	3	4	9	6
24	−.064	2	4	4	16	8
31	.185	3	1	9	1	3
32	.271	3	2	9	4	6
33	.166	3	3	9	9	9
34	−.020	3	4	9	16	12
41	.055	4	1	16	1	4
42	.113	4	2	16	4	8
43	.136	4	3	16	9	12
44	.161	4	4	16	16	16
Mean	.000	2.5	2.5	7.5	7.5	6.5

* x_1 = gram percent salt; x_2 = gram percent sugar.

analysis are shown with their covariance matrix in Table 7.13. After collecting the constant terms (by applying the b's in Table 7.13 to the means of Table 7.12), we obtain the following equation for the fitted response surface.

$$z = .500275x_1 + .136350x_2 - .085625x_1^2$$
$$- .045500x_2^2 + .024800x_1 x_2 - .763125. \quad (7.13)$$

Partition of χ^2 for the analysis following Table 7.11 is shown in Table 7.14.

TABLE 7.13. Fitted Parameters of the Quadratic Response Surface
and their Covariance Matrix

	Estimated parameters	Covariance matrix $\times$ $2nN$ (where $n = 16$ and $N = 25$)				
		b_{10}	b_{01}	b_{20}	b_{02}	b_{11}
b_{10}	.500275	1.8625				
b_{01}	.136350	.2500	1.8625			
b_{20}	−.085625	−.3125	.0000	.0625		
b_{02}	−.045500	.0000	−.3125	.0000	.0625	
b_{11}	.024800	−.1000	−.1000	.0000	.0000	.0400

TABLE 7.14. Partition of χ^2 for the Response-surface Problem

Source of χ^2	d.f.	Sum of squares $=\chi^2/N$	χ^2	Probability
Response-surface model	5	SSM $= 17.3672$	434.18	
Departure from response-surface model	10	SSE$_2 = 1.4512$	36.28	$p < .0005$
Paired-comparison model	15	SSR $= 18.8184$	470.46	
Departure from paired-comparison model	224	SSE$_1 = 17.2656$	431.64	$p < .0005$
Total		SST $= 36.0841$		

Table 7.14 indicates significant departure of the data from the quadratic model. However, the χ^2 for departure from the paired-comparison model is also significant. If the discrepancy from the paired-comparison model is considered random, the hypothesis that both error estimates could be obtained from the same population may be tested by the F statistic,

$$\frac{36.28/10}{431.64/224} = 1.88 .$$

The .05 point of the F distribution with 10 and 224 degrees of freedom also is 1.88. Lacking more decisive evidence against the hypothesis, no attempt to fit a more refined model seems warranted. A graphic indication of the goodness of fit is provided by the plot of the observed affective values against those predicted by (7.13) which is shown in Figure 7.1.

The coefficients of (7.13) indicate that the fitted surface is concave downward, is tilted slightly, and changes more rapidly with respect to salt than with respect to sugar. These characteristics are also revealed by the contours of the surface shown in Figure 7.2.

To locate the maximum, we differentiate (7.13) with respect to x_1 and x_2 and, equating to zero, obtain the stationary equations

$$.500275 - 2(.085625x_1) + .024800x_2 = 0,$$
$$.13635 + .024800x_1 - 2(.045500x_2) = 0 . \tag{7.14}$$

Their solution yields the most preferred salt and sugar concentrations:

$$x_1 = 3.27 \text{ gram percent salt, and}$$
$$x_2 = 2.39 \text{ gram percent sugar.}$$

Since the fitted surface changes relatively slowly with sugar concentration, it is of interest to test the hypothesis that the maximum of the true surface can be obtained at $x_1 = 3.267$ gram percent salt and $x_2 = 0$, i.e. no sugar at all.

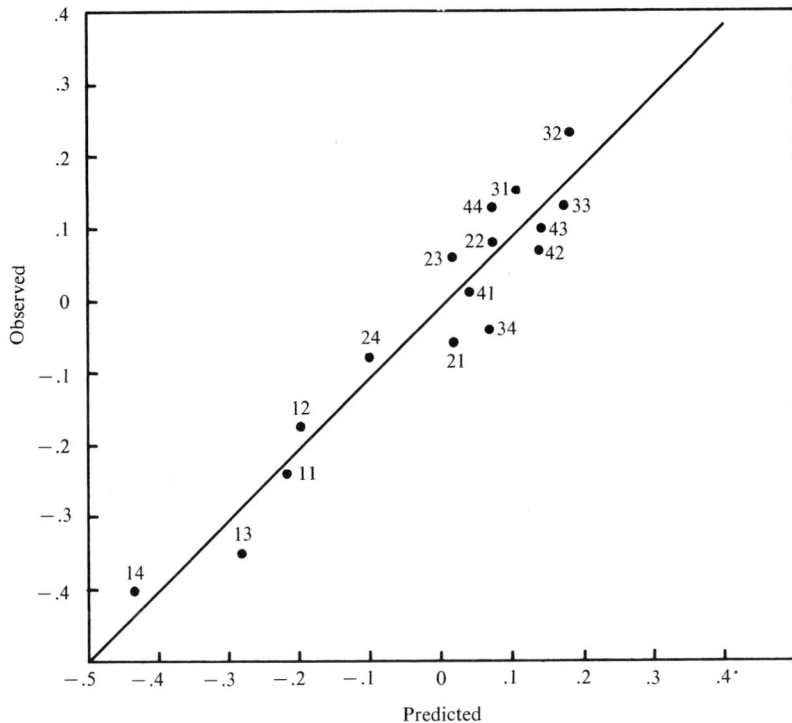

FIG. 7.1. Response surface study: observed vs predicted affective values.

The values of the derivatives (7.14) at this point are $-.059199$ and $.217372$, respectively. Their covariance matrix, computed by (7.11) from the variances and covariances in Table 7.13, is

$$\mathscr{V}(d) = \frac{1}{800}\begin{bmatrix} .447072 & -.076700 \\ -.076700 & 1.636032 \end{bmatrix},$$

with the inverse

$$\mathscr{V}(\mathbf{d})^{-1} = 800\begin{bmatrix} 2.255279 & .105733 \\ .105733 & .616204 \end{bmatrix}.$$

Then the statistic Q is

$$Q = 800[(-.059199)^2(2.255279) - 2(.059199)(.217372)(.105733) \\ + (.217372)^2(.616204)] = 27.43.$$

Since the $\chi^2_{2,.05} = 5.99$ the hypothesis is rejected; the point is well outside the .95 confidence region. On the other hand, the point $x_1 = 3.267$ and $x_2 = 2.0$ has $Q = 7.48$ ($.025 > p > .01$), which shows that it is near the margin of the region.

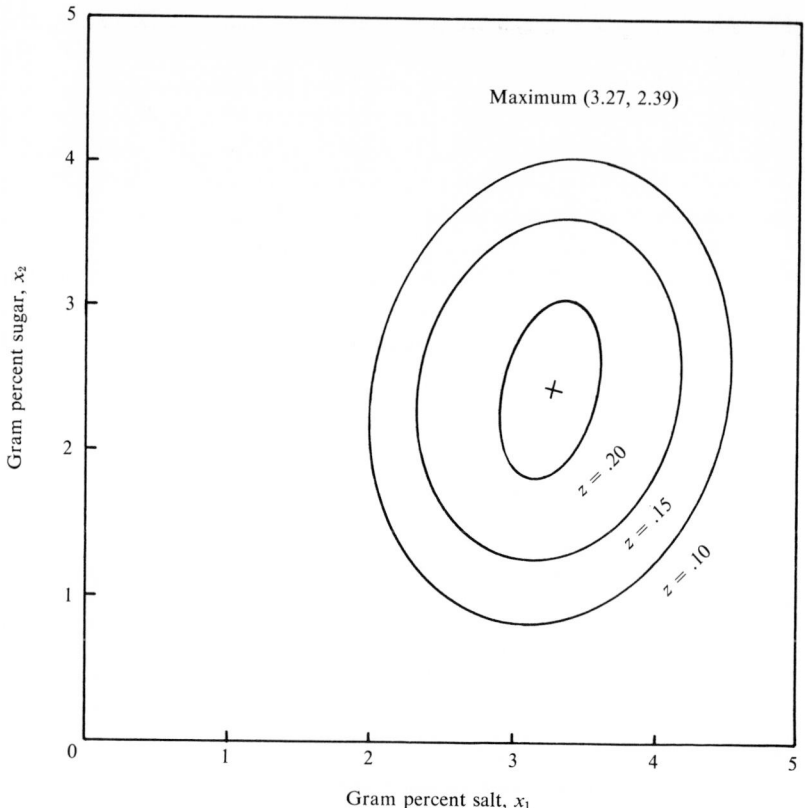

FIG. 7.2. Response surface of Equation (7.13).

We are assuming here that the error variance is $1/(2nN)$. However, if we assume random departure from the model and pool the sums of squares for departure from the response-surface and paired-comparison models, we find that the estimated error is 1.9267 times the theoretical error. If this value for the error is assumed in computing Q, the value of Q above should be divided by 1.9267. $Q/2$ will then be an F statistic with 2 and $p - 1$ degrees of freedom. In particular, the point $x_1 = 3.267$ and $x_2 = 0$ has $F = 7.12$ ($p < .005$) and is still outside the .95 confidence region. The point $x_1 = 3.267$ and $x_2 = 2.0$, however, has $F = 1.94$ ($p > .05$), and is within the region.

7.3.2   A Factorial Model

To investigate the effect of purely qualitative independent variables on judgmental response, we may adapt well established methods for the design and analysis of factorial experiments. These methods have been intensively studied and are the subject of a voluminous literature (Anderson and Bancroft, 1952; Kempthorne, 1952; Graybill, 1961). Nothing approaching a comprehensive review of them is intended here, but a brief discussion connecting the comparative-judgment model and the two-way factorial model will indicate how the factorial paired-comparison model is set up. Examples from the field of industrial psychology illustrating a solution for this model when the paired-comparison design is incomplete will also be presented.

We assume a paired-comparisons experiment in which certain qualitative attributes of the objects identify them with the subclasses of a two-way classification. Let there be b and c classes in the B and C ways of classification, respectively, and denote the objects in the subclasses as follows:

	C			
B	1	2	$\cdots$	c
1	X_{11}	X_{12}	$\cdots$	X_{1c}
2	X_{21}	X_{22}	$\cdots$	X_{2c}
	.			
	.			
b	X_{b1}	X_{b2}	$\cdots$	X_{bc}

We assume that the effect of class membership on the deviate corresponding to the comparison of two objects, X_{hj}, X_{kl}, is additive:

$$\mathcal{E}(Y_{hj,kl}) = \alpha_{hj} - \alpha_{kl} = \beta_h - \beta_k + \gamma_j - \gamma_l.$$

If the data show nonadditivity, this model can be enlarged to include interactive effects, say

$$(\beta\gamma)_{hj} - (\beta\gamma)_{kl}.$$

In terms of the additive model, estimated deviation contrasts of the affective values have expectation

$$\mathcal{E}(\hat{\alpha}_{hj}^0) = \beta_h - \frac{\Sigma\beta_k}{b} + \gamma_j - \frac{\Sigma\gamma_l}{c} = \beta_h^0 + \gamma_j^0.$$

In matrix notation

$$\mathcal{E}(\hat{\alpha}^0) = A\xi^0 = K'L\xi^0, \qquad \text{say.}$$

This will be recognized as the model for a complete two-way analysis of variance design after the data are corrected to the grand mean, i.e. after the general effect is eliminated and the parameters are restricted to sum to zero. At this stage the data are effectively deviations from the sample mean and have covariance matrix proportional to Δ. This is precisely the form in which estimates of affective value are obtained when complete single-judgment paired-comparison data are analyzed under the angular response function. A conventional analysis of variance therefore applies to the factorial model since the covariance matrix of the estimated affective values is $nN\Delta$. In this case, the sums of squares may be multiplied by nN to obtain χ^2 statistics for the tests of hypothesis. The degrees of freedom of these χ^2's are the degrees of freedom for the respective effects. If the interactive effects are zero, the simple additive model may be retained. Its parameters are estimated by the mean affective values for the corresponding way of classification.

When numerous factors are to be studied in one experiment, some form of incomplete design may be necessary to hold the comparisons to a reasonable number. Incomplete (fractional replicate) factorial designs are available for this purpose (Cochran and Cox, 1957, Chapter 6A). It is also possible to use incomplete paired-comparison designs to obtain the estimated affective values, although the conventional analysis of variance solution will no longer hold. With certain incomplete designs, however, only minor adjustments in the conventional solution are needed to obtain a correct analysis. The adjusted solution is illustrated in the following example, which is based on a study of compensation plans similar to that of Example 7.1.2.

Example 7.3.2

Jones and Jeffrey (1964) made use of a 2^4 factorial paired-comparison design to study employee preferences for various compensation plans. Skilled and semiskilled employees in an electrical equipment plant ($N = 194$) were asked to choose between alternative compensation plans which incorporated features which may be briefly described as follows:

Classifi-cation	Classes	
	1	2
A	Hourly wage	Weekly wage
B	No merit incentive	Merit incentive
C	No piecework incentive	Piecework incentive
D	Lower pay class	Higher pay class

To avoid comparisons between plans which differed only in factor D and to reduce the total number of comparisons required, an incomplete paired-comparison design was necessary. The balanced incomplete paired-comparison design for sixteen objects (see Section 7.1.2) proved especially convenient for this purpose.

The exact provisions of each plan were described in some detail to the subjects before the comparative judgments of the sixteen compensation plans were obtained. Each subject made all 48 comparisons in the incomplete design.

The angular deviates transformed from the observed proportions are shown in Table 7.15. Since the incomplete design is balanced with parameters $n = 16$, $r = 6$, $\lambda = 2$, affective values for the plans are estimated by (7.5a) of Section 7.1.2:

$$\hat{\alpha}_j^0 = \frac{6}{(16)(2)} \left[y_{j.} + \frac{\sum_h n_{hj} \, y_{h.}}{6} \right].$$

The values of $y_{j.}$ and $\hat{\alpha}_j^0$ are shown in the final rows of Table 7.15, and partition

TABLE 7.15. Angular Deviates Observed in the Compensation Plan Study and Estimated Affective Values ($N = 194$)

Factors ABCD	1111	1112	1121	1122	1211	1212	1221	1222
1111				−.7615	−.4137			
1112			−.0520					−.7208
1121		.0520					−.3152	
1122	.7615					.0520		
1211	.4137							−.8361
1212				−.0520			.0620	
1221			.3152			−.0620		
1222		.7208			.8361			
2111				−.3576		−.3683	−.4028	−.5539
2112			−.0420		.1344	−.0420	−.2280	
2121		.0921			.1973	−.0420		−.3920
2122	.5167				.3152		.4028	.0100
2211		.1243	.0200	−.1445				−.3683
2212	.5305	.3920	.3363				.1143	
2221	.5305	.2713		−.0520		.0921		
2222	.7076		.4713	.4713	.6041			
$y_{j.}$	−3.4605	−1.6525	−1.0488	.8963	−1.6734	.3702	.3669	2.8611
$\hat{\alpha}_j^0$	−.4088	−.2224	−.1278	.1022	−.1839	.0109	.0462	.3660

Factors ABCD	2111	2112	2121	2122	2211	2212	2221	2222
1111				−.5167		−.5305	−.5305	−.7076
1112			−.0921		−.1243	−.3920	−.2713	
1121		.0420			−.0200	−.3363		−.4713
1122	.3576				.1445		.0520	−.4713
1211		−.1344	−.1973	−.3152				−.6041
1212	.3683	.0420	.0420				−.0921	
1221	.4028	.2280		−.4028		−.1143		
1222	.5539		.3920	−.0100	.3683			
2111					−.9340	−.3257		
2112			.0921					−.6410
2121		−.0921					−.3026	
2122	.9340					.0821		
2211	.3257							−.8664
2212				−.0821			.0721	
2221			.3026			−.0721		
2222		.6410			.8664			
$y_{j.}$	−2.9423	−.7265	−.5393	2.2608	−.9092	1.3631	1.0724	3.7617
$\hat{\alpha}_j^0$	−.3690	−.0976	−.0933	.3150	−.1119	.1787	.1066	.4890

TABLE 7.16. Partition of χ^2 for the Paired-comparison Solution: Compensation Plan Study

Source of variation	d.f.	Sum of squares	χ^2	Probability
Estimation	15	SSR $= \Sigma \hat{\alpha}_j^0 y_{j.} = 7.60189210$	1474.77	$p < .0005$
Error	33	SSE $=$ SST $-$ SSR $= .67571206$	131.09	$p < .0005$
Total	48	SST $= \Sigma\Sigma n_{jk} y_{jk}^2 = 8.27760416$		

of χ^2 for the solution is shown in Table 7.16. Although the proportion of the total variance which is attributable to error is small, it is statistically significant and indicates some departure from the model for comparative judgment. It does not affect appreciably the subsequent analysis of the factorial model.

In fitting the factorial model, we make use of the general method described at the end of Section 7.3.1. From Section 7.1.2, we know that the matrix of coefficients in normal equations for the incomplete paired-comparison design is of the form $(r_i I - N_i)$. It can also be shown (Cochran and Cox, 1957; Bock, 1963) that a factorization of the model matrix of a 2^4 design for the purpose of estimating main and first-order interactive contrasts is a matrix K' of the following form:

$$
\begin{array}{r}
A \\ B \\ C \\ D \\ AB \\ AC \\ AD \\ BC \\ BD \\ CD
\end{array}
\left[
\begin{array}{rrrrrrrrrrrrrrrr}
-1 & -1 & -1 & -1 & -1 & -1 & -1 & -1 & 1 & 1 & 1 & 1 & 1 & 1 & 1 & 1 \\
-1 & -1 & -1 & -1 & 1 & 1 & 1 & 1 & -1 & -1 & -1 & -1 & 1 & 1 & 1 & 1 \\
-1 & -1 & 1 & 1 & -1 & -1 & 1 & 1 & -1 & -1 & 1 & 1 & -1 & -1 & 1 & 1 \\
-1 & 1 & -1 & 1 & -1 & 1 & -1 & 1 & -1 & 1 & -1 & 1 & -1 & 1 & -1 & 1 \\
1 & 1 & 1 & 1 & -1 & -1 & -1 & -1 & -1 & -1 & -1 & -1 & 1 & 1 & 1 & 1 \\
1 & 1 & -1 & -1 & 1 & 1 & -1 & -1 & -1 & -1 & 1 & 1 & -1 & -1 & 1 & 1 \\
1 & -1 & 1 & -1 & 1 & -1 & 1 & -1 & -1 & 1 & -1 & 1 & -1 & 1 & -1 & 1 \\
1 & 1 & -1 & -1 & -1 & -1 & 1 & 1 & 1 & 1 & -1 & -1 & -1 & -1 & 1 & 1 \\
1 & -1 & 1 & -1 & -1 & 1 & -1 & 1 & 1 & -1 & 1 & -1 & -1 & 1 & -1 & 1 \\
1 & -1 & -1 & 1 & 1 & -1 & -1 & 1 & 1 & -1 & -1 & 1 & 1 & -1 & -1 & 1
\end{array}
\right]
$$

Each row of K' corresponds to one degree of freedom in the analysis of variance for the factorial model. The effects associated with each degree of freedom are shown at the left.

In terms of this factorization, the normal equations for the fitting of the factorial model are

$$[K'(r_i I - N_i)K]\widehat{L\xi}^0 = K'(r_i I - N_i)\hat{\alpha}^0. \tag{7.15}$$

Because of the balance in the incidence matrix of the incomplete design, the ten rows and columns of $[K'(r_i I - N_i)K]$ form a diagonal matrix. This means that the first ten effects, which include the main class effects and first-order interactions are unconfounded. (There is, however, some confounding of the second-order interactions with lower-order effects.) The result is that the estimates of the parametric functions $L\xi^0$ obtained by solving (7.15) are those for the conventional solution of a complete 2^4 factorial design and the sums of squares for the first 10 effects differ only by simple constants of proportionality from the conventional values. The correct pooled sum of squares for the remaining five degrees of freedom can be obtained by subtraction from the sum of squares for the paired-comparisons model. The relationship between the conventional and the adjusted solution for this particular design is shown in the analysis of variance in Table 7.17.

TABLE 7.17. Partition of χ^2 for the Factorial Model

Source of variation	d.f.	Conventional sum of squares	Adjustment	χ^2	Probability
A	1	.043587	$\times 8$	67.65	$p < .0005$
B	1	.203243	$\times 8$	315.43	$p < .0005$
C	1	.362374	$\times 8$	562.40	$p < .0005$
D	1	.325954	$\times 8$	505.88	$p < .0005$
AB	1	.000008	$\times 4$	.01	$.95 > p > .90$
AC	1	.000134	$\times 6$	.15	$.90 > p > .80$
AD	1	.011114	$\times 4$	8.63	$.005 > p > .001$
BC	1	.002023	$\times 8$	3.14	$.10 > p > .05$
BD	1	.000523	$\times 8$	.81	$.40 > p > .30$
CD	1	.009865	$\times 4$	7.66	$.010 > p > .005$
Residual	5	.01547		3.00	$p = .70$
Paired-comparison model	15	7.60189		1474.77	
Error	33	.67571		131.09	$p < .0005$
Total	48	8.27760			

With a sampling variance of $1/N$ assumed for the angular deviates, the χ^2 for hypothesis shown in Table 7.17 is the conventional sums of squares multiplied by N times the adjustment factors. By this criterion, only two of the interactive effects show statistical significance. On the other hand, if an error variance is estimated by pooling the sums of squares for residual and departure from the paired-comparison model, the F statistic for the AD interaction is

$$F = \frac{4(.011114)}{(.67571 + .01547)/38} = \frac{.044456}{.018189} = 2.44, \qquad \text{d.f.} = 1, 38;$$

and for the BC interaction is

$$F = 8(.002023)/.018189 = .89, \qquad \text{d.f.} = 1, 38.$$

Since neither of these F statistics is significant, the reality of the interactions is doubtful.

We therefore assume the additive model and estimate contrasts of main-class effects by (7.15). Because of the balance of the paired-comparison design with respect to those contrasts, the solution of (7.15) is identical with the conventional estimates from main-class means. The resulting estimates are shown in the form of deviation contrasts in Table 7.18, and represent the effect of the

TABLE 7.18. Estimated Main-effect Contrasts

	Effect: Class 1 vs Class 2	Deviation contrasts*	Adjusted contrasts
A:	Hourly wage vs weekly salary	.0522	.3657
B:	No merit incentive vs merit incentive	.1127	.7896
C:	No piecework incentive vs piecework incentive	.1505	1.0544
D:	Lower pay class vs higher pay class	.1427	1.0000

* For standard errors, see text.

second class minus the mean of the effects of the two classes. (The estimated deviation contrast for the first class is the negative of that of the second.) Predicted affective values for the additive model may be computed by adding the deviation contrasts corresponding to the classes of the four factors which appear in the compensation plans. Observed vs predicted values are shown in Figure 7.3.

The constants of proportionality used to adjust the sums of squares in Table 7.17 also appear in the standard errors of contrasts. For the main-effect deviation contrasts, the standard errors are $\sigma/4\sqrt{8}$. If the theoretical error is assumed, then $\sigma = 1/\sqrt{N_2} = .07179$, in this case; if an estimated error is used, then $\sigma = \sqrt{.018189} = .13487$ in this case. In terms of the latter, the term to be added to and subtracted from the main-effect contrasts to obtain the .95 confidence interval is $t_{38,.05}(.13487/4\sqrt{8}) = .02408$.

The interpretation of the main-class contrast is greatly facilitated by the way in which the compensation plans were constructed. For each of the classifications A, B, and C, the benefits in the second class—salary, merit incentive, and piecework incentive—were designed to have the same cost to the company as corresponding benefits in the first class—hourly wage, no merit incentive, and no piecework incentive, respectively. It is of interest to compare preference for these less direct benefits which entail no added company costs with preference for the pay increase, an increase of pay (and cost) of 2.5%. For this purpose the contrasts have been scaled in the last column of Table 7.18 so that the pay-class contrast is unity. The affective value of the change from hourly wage to weekly salary is about 36% of that of the pay increase, although the cost to the company of a weekly salary pay basis is no more than that of hourly wage. The apparent worth of the merit incentive (based on foremen's ratings) is some 79% of that of a pay increase. That of the piecework incentive is greater than that of a pay increase. Hence, in each case, preference is shown for the innovation of indirect compensation, even though the innovation was

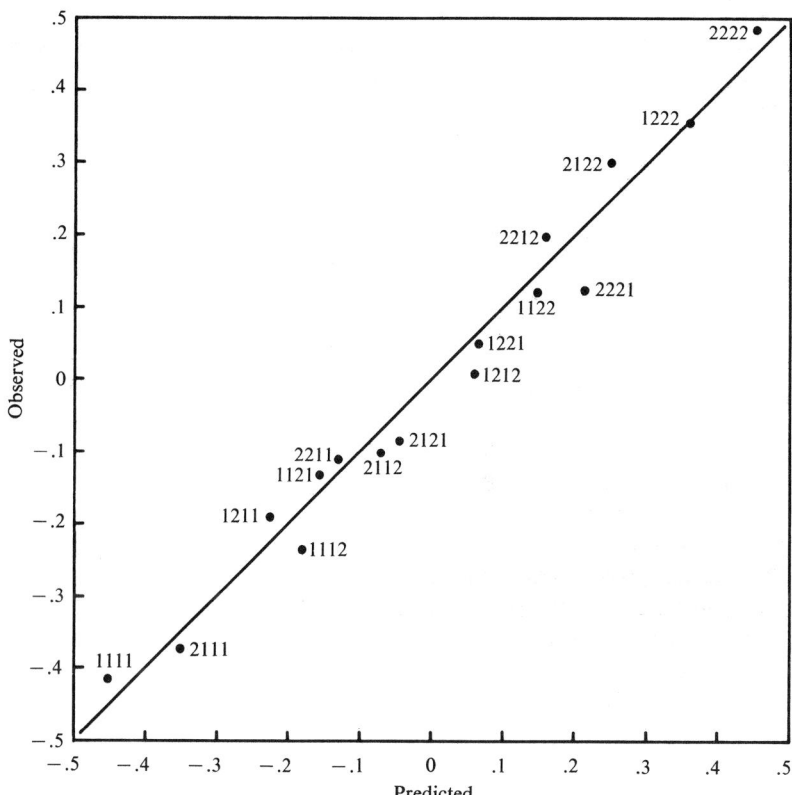

FIG. 7.3. Compensation plan study: observed vs predicted affective values.

designed to maintain present cost to the company. The piecework-incentive condition was preferred even to a 2.5% wage increase.

7.3.3 The General Multifactor Model

When the multifactor model contains both quantitative and qualitative terms, the general solution of Section 7.3 must be used in fitting the model to the data. This solution also allows the covariance matrix of the estimated affective values to be arbitrary. An application of a multifactor model in which both these features of the general solution is required is illustrated in the following example. Data for the example are drawn from the study of increased compensation of salaried workers described in Example 7.1.2.

Example 7.3.3

Several models which are plausible for the data in Example 7.1.2 might be proposed. The simplest model assumes the affective values of the model to be a linear function of the nominal values of the options in the plans. Call this model I. According to model I the expected composition of the affective values is, say,

$$\begin{bmatrix} \alpha_1 \\ \alpha_2 \\ . \\ \\ \\ . \\ \\ \\ \alpha_9 \end{bmatrix} = \begin{bmatrix} 600 & 0 & 0 \\ 450 & 0 & 0 \\ 0 & 12 & 0 \\ 0 & 9 & 0 \\ 0 & 0 & 6 \\ 0 & 0 & 4.5 \\ 300 & 6 & 0 \\ 300 & 0 & 3 \\ 0 & 6 & 3 \end{bmatrix} \cdot \begin{bmatrix} \beta_1 \\ \beta_2 \\ \beta_3 \end{bmatrix}$$

or, briefly, $\alpha = A_I \beta$.

The matrix A_I is of full rank and does not require reparameterization of the model for purposes of least squares estimation. Note also that the model does not include a constant term because the estimated affective values which are to be fitted already sum to zero.

Since the affective values have been estimated in a partially balanced paired-comparison experiment, their covariance matrix has the structure described in Section 7.1.2:

$$\Sigma = \Delta(a_i + b_i N_i)\sigma^2.$$

Although Σ is singular with rank $n - 1$ it has an inverse with respect to Δ in the sense that

$$(a_i I + b_i N_i)(r_i I - N_i) = \Delta,$$

where $(r_i I - N_i) = \Sigma^*$ is the matrix of coefficients in the normal equations of the PBIPC solution. The construction of this matrix is described in Section 7.1.2; r_i is the number of objects with which each object is compared, and N_i is the incidence matrix of the design.

In the present instance the design is group divisible, and the incidence matrix is determined by the association scheme shown in Example 7.1.2. In the matrix of coefficients, the diagonal elements are $r_i = 6$, the off-diagonal elements corresponding to comparisons included in the design are -1, and all other elements are zero. Thus,

$$\Sigma^* = \begin{bmatrix}
6 & 0 & -1 & -1 & -1 & -1 & 0 & -1 & -1 \\
0 & 6 & -1 & -1 & -1 & -1 & 0 & -1 & -1 \\
-1 & -1 & 6 & 0 & -1 & -1 & -1 & 0 & -1 \\
-1 & -1 & 0 & 6 & -1 & -1 & -1 & 0 & -1 \\
-1 & -1 & -1 & -1 & 6 & 0 & -1 & -1 & 0 \\
-1 & -1 & -1 & -1 & 0 & 6 & -1 & -1 & 0 \\
0 & 0 & -1 & -1 & -1 & -1 & 6 & -1 & -1 \\
-1 & -1 & 0 & 0 & -1 & -1 & -1 & 6 & -1 \\
-1 & -1 & -1 & -1 & 0 & 0 & -1 & -1 & 6
\end{bmatrix}.$$

The matrix Σ^* enters the least squares equations wherever Σ^{-1} appears in the general solution. Thus, the estimator of $\hat{\beta}_I$ is of the form

$$\hat{\beta}_I = (A_I' \Sigma^* A_I)^{-1} A_I \Sigma^* \hat{\alpha}^0 .$$

The covariance matrix of these estimates is $\sigma^2 (A_I' \Sigma^* A_I)^{-1}$.

In the present example, the estimated parameters for model I prove to be $\hat{\beta}_1^I = .0046$, $\hat{\beta}_2^I = .1574$, and $\hat{\beta}_3^I = .4328$. The partition of χ^2 for this model is shown in Table 7.19, the sum of squares attributable to the affective values having been taken from Table 7.7.

TABLE 7.19. Partition of χ^2 for Model I and Paired-comparison Model

Source of χ^2	d.f.	Sum of squares	χ^2	p
Model I	3	SSM $= \hat{\beta}_I' A_I \Sigma^* \hat{\alpha}^0 = 10.1494$	$N \cdot$ SSM $= 1451.3$	$p < .0005$
Departure from model I	5	SSE$_2$ = SSR $-$ SSM $= .9934$	$N \cdot$ SSE$_2$ $= 142.1$	$p < .0005$
Paired-comparison model	8	SSR $= \hat{\alpha}' \Sigma^* \hat{\alpha} = 11.1428$	$N \cdot$ SSR $= 1593.4$	
Departure from P.C. model	19	SSE$_1$ = SST $-$ SSR $= .3961$	$N \cdot$ SSE$_1$ $= 56.6$	$p < .0005$
Total	27	SST $=$ y'y $= 11.5389$		

The χ^2 for departure from model I, calculated using the theoretical variance of the angular deviates, is highly significant. However, as we have seen in Table 7.7 the departure from the paired-comparison model was also significant. If we consider the latter random variation, we may compute the variance ratio for the sources of departure:

$$F = \frac{.9934/5}{.3961/19} = 9.54; \qquad \text{d.f.} = 5, 19.$$

This value of F has probability less than .0005 and contradicts the hypothesis that departure from the multifactor model is due to departure from the paired-comparison model. Some improvement of the multifactor model seems possible.

A plausible alternative model is suggested by the theory that the marginal utility of increased income (or other benefit) is inversely proportional to present income or benefit. This implies that the affective values of the plans, considered as measures of utility, should be linear in the logarithms of the nominal values of the options. The fit of the logarithmic model proves to be slightly worse than that of the linear model, however, and does not encourage this line of reasoning.

A more rewarding idea is that the subjects have a preference for diversity of options, that is, that plans 7, 8, and 9, each containing two options, enjoy an additional component of affective value not attributable to the nominal values of the options. If so, the multifactor model for plans 3, 8, and 9 should contain an additional term, say β_4. This term may be introduced into the model by augmenting the matrix of model I by a column with elements $(0, 0, 0, 0, 0, 0, 1, 1, 1)$ and adding β_4 to the parameter vector. Call this model II. With these changes, the parameters of model II are estimated in the same manner as those of model I.

TABLE 7.20.   Partition of χ^2 for Model II

Source of χ^2	d.f.	Sum of squares		χ^2		p
Model II	4	SSM $= \hat{\beta}_{II}A'_{II}\Sigma^*\hat{\alpha}^0$	$= 11.0994$	$N \cdot$ SSM $=$	1587.2	$p < .0005$
Departure from model II	4	SSE$_2 =$ SSR $-$ SSM $=$	.0434	$N \cdot$ SSE$_2 =$	6.2	$p < .10$
Paired-comparison model	8	SSR $= \hat{\alpha}'\Sigma^*\hat{\alpha}$	$= 11.1428$			

The corresponding partition of χ^2 is shown in Table 7.20. The error χ^2, although computed from the theoretical error and possibly overestimated, is clearly not significant. No further improvement of the models appears to be possible. We still need to verify, however, that the improvement of fit due to the inclusion of β_4 in the model is significant. The χ^2 statistic on one degree of freedom for this purpose is the difference between the residuals for the two models:

$$\chi^2 = 56.6 - 6.2 = 50.4; \quad p < .0005.$$

This χ^2 indicates a significant improvement in fit. Similarly, the corresponding F statistic on 1 and 19 degrees of freedom, based on the empirical error estimate provided by departure from the paired-comparison model, is significant:

$$F = \frac{(.9934 - .0434)/1}{.3961/19} = 45.5; \quad p < .0005.$$

The parameter estimates for model II are

$$\hat{\beta}_1^{II} = .00358, \qquad \hat{\beta}_3^{II} = .32453,$$
$$\hat{\beta}_2^{II} = .10328, \qquad \hat{\beta}_4^{II} = .32490.$$

The variances and covariances of these estimates are given by σ^2 times the following matrix:

$$\begin{bmatrix}
.56626 \times 10^{-5} & .24319 \times 10^{-3} & .48884 \times 10^{-3} & -.37037 \times 10^{-3} \\
.24319 \times 10^{-3} & .12718 \times 10^{-1} & .24319 \times 10^{-1} & -.18519 \times 10^{-1} \\
.48884 \times 10^{-3} & .24319 \times 10^{-1} & .50627 \times 10^{-1} & -.37037 \times 10^{-1} \\
-.37037 \times 10^{-3} & -.18519 \times 10^{-1} & -.37037 \times 10^{-1} & .11111 \times 10
\end{bmatrix}.$$

The parameters for this model have interesting interpretations. The parameter β_1^{II} represents the increase in affective value for each dollar of salary increase. Similarly, β_2^{II} represents the increase for each additional day of vacation, and β_3^{II} represents the increase per each 1% increase in company contribution to retirement benefit. Since the average salaries of these subjects is about \$10,000 per annum, the cost to the company of one day of vacation is about \$38.00; the cost of a 1% increase in retirement benefit is about \$100.00 per annum. We can therefore calculate the increase in affective value per dollar cost to the company of these options as follows:

$$\text{Vacation} \qquad .10328/38 = .00272$$

$$\text{Retirement} \qquad .32453/100 = .00325$$

Both these figures are lower than .00358, the rate of increase of affective value per dollar of salary increase. By these estimates, the affective value per dollar for salary increase is about 10% higher than that for increased contribution in retirement and about 32% higher than that for additional vacation time.

The parameter β_4^{II}, representing the effect of diversity of options, can be put on a dollar basis by comparing it with β_1^{II}. The ratio $\beta_4^{II}/\beta_1^{II}$ represents the number of dollars increase in salary which would be necessary to increase affective value by an amount equal to that contributed by diversity of options. The ratio of the corresponding estimates is

$$.32490/.00358 = 90.75$$

dollars per annum. It is therefore to the company's advantage to divide the cost of increased compensation between two options, or perhaps more. The data of the present example show that the inclusion of two options in the plans increases the affective value, at no cost to the company, by about the same amount that would result from a \$90.00 per annum increase in salary.

7.4   Group Differences in Paired-comparison Response

Suppose the subjects in a paired-comparison experiment are drawn from two or more identified (sub)groups of some population. The question may then arise as to whether subjects in different groups respond differently to the objects in the experiment. In statistical terminology this question can be phrased as a null hypothesis that the response probabilities for each pair are equal for all groups. Thus, if there are m groups and P_{jkl} is the parametric probability that object j is preferred to object k by subjects in population group l, the null hypothesis is $P_{jk1} = P_{jk2} = \cdots = P_{jkm}$. If the sample proportions estimating these probabilities are independent, this hypothesis may be tested by the standard χ^2 test for the homogeneity of proportions. The statistic for this purpose is made up of quantities

$$\chi_{jk}^2 = \sum_{l=1}^{m} \frac{N_{jkl}(p_{jkl} - p_{jk.})^2}{p_{jk.}(1 - p_{jk.})}, \qquad \text{d.f.} = m - 1 \tag{7.16}$$

corresponding to each pair in the experiment. $p_{jk.}$ is the " marginal " proportion for this pair calculated by dividing the total number of subjects who preferred object j to k by the total number of subjects who judged this pair. On the null hypothesis, (7.16) is distributed as a central chi square with $m - 1$ degrees of freedom. Moreover, the over-all statistic is the sum of the quantities (7.16) for all independent comparisons. On the null hypothesis this sum is a central chi square with degrees of freedom equal to the number of independent comparisons times $(m - 1)$.

This χ^2 test can be strengthened if the paired-comparison model can be assumed to hold within groups. The hypothesis may then be rephrased in terms of equality of the vectors of affective values of the m groups. The null hypothesis then is

$$\alpha_1 = \alpha_2 = \cdots = \alpha_m.$$

A test of this hypothesis is particularly simple if the judgments have been obtained by single-judgment sampling for a complete paired-comparison design and the angular response function is assumed. Under these conditions the homogeneity of the affective values may be tested in a simple weighted analysis of variance as follows.

Suppose that the affective values for n objects have been estimated in each of m groups by the solution of Section 6.5.2, or of Section 6.6, if an order-effect model is assumed. Let the weighted mean affective value for object X_j be

$$\hat{\alpha}_{j.} = \frac{1}{N} \sum_{l=1}^{m} N_l \hat{\alpha}_{jl},$$

where N_l is the number of subjects sampled from the lth group and $N = \Sigma_{l=1}^{m} N_l$. The sum of squares for between-group differences in affective values of the n objects is

$$SSB = \sum_{j=1} \left[\sum_{l=1} N_l \hat{\alpha}_{jl}^2 - N \hat{\alpha}_{j.}^2 \right].$$

If the paired-comparison model employed in the estimation of the affective values holds within each group, this sum of squares is, under the null hypothesis, proportional to a central χ^2 on $(m-1)(n-1)$ degrees of freedom. If the estimated affective values have been obtained by the conventional solution in Section 6.5.2, the constant of proportionality is n, and $\chi^2 = n$SSR. If they have been obtained by the order-effect solution this constant is $2n$, and $\chi^2 = 2n$SSR.

When the order-effect solution has been used, it may also be of interest to test the hypothesis of equality of order effects. Let the weighted mean of the estimated order effect be

$$\hat{\mu}. = \sum_{l=1}^{m} N_l \hat{\mu}_l / N .$$

Then the quantity

$$\chi^2 = n(n-1) \sum_{l=1}^{m} N_l \hat{\mu}_l^2 - N \hat{\mu}_.^2$$

is distributed under the null hypothesis as a central chi square with $m-1$ degrees of freedom.

Example 7.4

This example is based on an unpublished thesis by G. W. Gross (1954).[2] In a study to determine the most preferred level of salt or sugar in creamed cottage cheese, Gross obtained judgments from consumers in 337 households. Single-judgment sampling was used. Each household was sent two samples of cottage cheese in containers coded by color. Each subject tasted the creamed cottage cheese under normal conditions of eating and responded to a preference questionnaire by identifying the preferred sample or by stating no preference. The order of presentation of the samples was determined by the investigator and was recorded with the preference judgment.

In many households, more than one member returned a preference questionnaire. For purposes of this example, however, we have randomly selected one adult subject from each family, with the restriction that the number of men and women in the sample should be approximately equal (see Noel, 1964, for details). We have used the resulting data to investigate sex differences in the responses to levels of salt in the cottage cheese, the salt concentrations in question having been set in the experiment at 0.25, 0.75, 1.00, 1.25, and 1.50 grams of salt per 100 grams of cottage cheese.

The responses of 167 men and those of 170 women are shown in Table 7.21. The fraction in each cell of these tables shows, in the numerator, the

---

[2] We are indebted to Professor E. J. Finnegan, University of Georgia, for providing these data.

TABLE 7.21. Preference for Level of Salt in Cottage Cheese: Proportion of Subjects Expressing Positive Preference for Sample in Row

Sample presented first	Sample presented second				
	1	2	3	4	5
Men					
1		5/9	3/9	2/9	2/8
2	6/9		2/9	3/9	7/9
3	4/8	5/7	·	4/9 ·	5/9
4	4/7	3/8	3/8		3/8
5	7/8	3/8	3/8	3/8	
Women					
1		6/9	4/9	3/8	2/9
2	7/8		2/8	2/9	5/8
3	6/9	5/8		3/9	4/9
4	7/8	6/8	6/8		5/9
5	5/9	6/9	6/8	7/8	

number of subjects who expressed a positive preference for the sample designated on the left and, in the denominator, the number of subjects responding to each pair. Subjects expressing no preference were pooled with those expressing dislike.

The proportions in Table 7.21 were transformed to angular deviates and analyzed by means of the order-effect model of Section 6.6. The small variation in the number of subjects per cell was ignored and the harmonic mean of these numbers, shown at the bottom of Table 7.22, was used in calculating the theoretical variance of the angular deviates.

TABLE 7.22. Estimated Order Effect and Affective Value for the Cottage Cheese Data

	Men	Women	Weighted mean
Order effect	−.0459	.1695	.0629
Affective values			
1	−.2673	−.2728	−.2701
2	−.0049	−.1464	−.0764
3	.1375	−.0271	.0543
4	.0679	.2258	.1628
5	.0068	.1904	.1292
Harmonic mean sample size	8.2963	8.4706	

The analyses of variance for the fitting of the order-effect model to these data are shown in Table 7.23. There is no evidence of departure from the model in either sample. The female subjects show clearly significant order effect and effects of the different levels of salt in the samples (object effect). The male subjects, on the other hand, show no evidence of order effect, and the object effect is of borderline significance.

TABLE 7.23. Partition of χ^2 for the Order-effect Model Within the Groups

Source of χ^2	d.f.	Sum of squares	χ^2	p
		Men		
Order effect	1	.0421	.35	$p > .50$
Object effect	4	.9945	8.25	$.10 > p > .05$
Error	15	1.9849	16.47	$p > .30$
Total	20	3.0215		
		Women		
Order effect	1	.5745	4.87	$.05 > p > .025$
Object effect	4	1.9827	16.79	$.005 > p > .001$
Error	15	2.0242	17.15	$p > .30$
Total	20	4.5814		

The order effects and affective values for the objects estimated from the two samples are shown in Table 7.22, where the weighted means of the estimates are also shown. The harmonic means of the sample numbers were used as the weights. We will use the estimates in Table 7.22 to test the hypothesis of no group differences in the order and object effects. As for the order effect, the χ^2 (d.f. = 1) for between-group difference is

$$5 \times 4[8.2963(-.0459)^2 + 8.4706(.1695)^2 - 16.7669(.06291)^2] = 3.89 .$$

The probability of this value of χ^2 is between .05 and .025, indicating that the two groups differ significantly in the effect of order of presentation of stimuli. The men show essentially no order effect, whereas the women show some tendency to prefer the first presented sample.

The χ^2 for between-group differences in affective value (object effect) is calculated as follows:

$$2 \times 5\{8.2963[(-.2673)^2 + (-.0049)^2 + (.1375)^2 + (.0679)^2 + (.0668)^2]$$
$$+ 8.4706[(-.2728)^2 + (-.1464)^2 + (-.0271)^2 + (.2558)^2 + (.1904)^2]$$
$$- 16.7669[(-.2701)^2 + (-.0764)^2 + (.0543)^2 + (.1628)^2 + (.1292)^2]\}$$
$$= 4.10; \quad \text{d.f.} = 4 .$$

Since this value of χ^2 is very nearly equal to expectation, there is no evidence for differences in the responses of the subjects to the objects as such. Such differences in response proportions as are evident in Table 7.21 may be attributed to the effects of order of presentation and sampling variation. In view of the significantly different order effect, it would not be desirable to ignore sex of subject and apply the paired-comparison solution to the combined data. To do so would cause the sampling variance of the angular deviates to depart somewhat from its theoretical value. Instead, the estimates of the common affective values for the objects should be the weighted means of the within-group estimates as shown in Table 7.22. We note that these means show a regular change of affective value with salt concentration with a maximum near object 4, i.e. in the vicinity of 1.25 gram percent.

8 The Method of
Successive Categories

For the method of successive categories, data are collected by use of the so-called rating scale. To avoid confusion, let us refer to the format by which ratings are recorded as a rating *form*, retaining the use of the term scale for the results of applying a formal scaling model. A rating form is a set of categories by which a subject is required to partition a set of stimuli into mutually exclusive classes. A rating form might be defined, for example, by categories labeled *low*, *medium*, and *high*, with a subject asked to place each of a number of stimulus objects into that category which best represents his preference for the object.

The intermediate purpose of the method of successive categories is the estimation of parameters which characterize the distribution of discriminal processes associated with a given attitude (preference, for example) toward a set of stimuli. Thus, a reference scale is established by use of a response function; the normal response function typically is selected (the law of categorical judgment, to use the nomenclature of Torgerson, 1958); and a mean and variance of "scale values" associated with the stimuli are estimated from the data. The reference scale provided by the Thurstonian model brings rating-form data into a form comparable to that obtained by the constant method and the method of paired comparisons.

The method of successive categories differs in one prominent way from both the method of paired comparisons and the method of rank order. For the latter methods, judges assess stimulus objects directly in terms of other objects; successive-categories judgments, however, depend upon an intervening frame of reference provided by the labels which define categories on the rating form. To the extent that interpretation of these labels depends upon the set of stimuli being rated, results may not be comparable from one stimulus set to another (see Section 8.2.3).

Despite this reservation, results from the method of successive categories have proved remarkably comparable from one study to another when the same general universe of stimulus objects is under investigation (Jones, 1959c). When the same stimuli are judged by different samples of individuals using rating forms which differ in terms of number of categories and labels defining these categories, estimates of scale parameters, both affective values and discriminal dispersions of stimuli, are practically identical. When different stimuli selected from the same universe of objects are judged by different samples of individuals on identical rating forms, estimates of category widths are essentially identical. When the normal response function which is typically invoked in use of the method of successive categories (Eq. (8.2)) is replaced by an assumption of normally distributed differences between repeated ratings of objects by the same judges, affective values as well as discriminal dispersions are found to be linearly related to those derived by ordinary application of the method. Finally, results from the method of successive categories repeatedly have been found to predict with considerable accuracy results obtained on the same stimuli by the method of paired comparisons (Saffir, 1937; Edwards and Thurstone, 1952; Thurstone, 1952), to predict proportion of choice of one stimulus from a set of three (Section 9.1), and even to allow prediction of purchase of competing consumer objects (Jones, 1959a; Example 9.1b). These findings attest to the adequacy of the scaling model over a wide range of conditions and to its usefulness for predictive purposes.

A second, more general use for successive-category scale results should also be mentioned. Not infrequently in experimental psychology, preference, utility, or perceived attribute values of stimuli are required as dependent variables. It is desired to obtain measures of these variables using some interpretable reference scale, in order that they may be amenable to quantitative treatment within the framework of experimental design and analysis. The scaling model is well suited to provide the required interpretable reference scale.

The prominent advantage of the method of successive categories over the method of paired comparisons is a practical one. To estimate the mean discriminal processes for n stimuli requires n responses from each subject, rather than the $n(n-1)/2$ demanded by a complete paired-comparisons procedure. A subsidiary advantage is, as will be seen, the provision for estimating the σ_j rather than assuming them equal, as in the method of paired comparisons.

8.1 The Experimental Design

The method of successive categories depends upon data collected as follows.

(1) A set of stimuli, $X_1, X_2, \ldots, X_n$, is prepared. Frequently, in application of this method, stimulus objects are simply denoted by names, and not actually presented to subjects for direct sensory evaluation.

(2) Each stimulus X_j is presented to subject i, $i = 1, 2, \ldots, N$, randomly selected from a large population of subjects. Temporal positions of the X_j are independently randomized for each subject.

(3) Subject i is required to judge each stimulus in terms of an explicitly defined attribute, and to classify each into one and only one ordered attribute category k, where $k = 1, 2, \ldots, m$. The subject is instructed to respond in this way to all n stimuli. (The method of successive categories thus is defined to involve a multiple-response condition.)

(4) Data are recorded in the form p_{jk}, the proportions of judgments, over the N subjects, in which stimulus X_j is assigned below the upper bound of category k.

8.2   The Model for Categorical Judgment

As in earlier chapters, following Thurstone, we consider a discriminal process

$$v_j = \mu_j + \varepsilon_j \, ;$$

where μ_j is a fixed component, specific to X_j, but common to all subjects, and ε_j is a random component characteristic of stimulus X_j and a randomly selected subject. For successive categories, we postulate a second discriminal process which pertains to the perception of a given point on the rating form,

$$v_k = \tau_k + \pi + \varepsilon_k \, ;$$

τ_k is a fixed component associated with point k on the continuum represented by the rating form. π is an individual difference component, dependent upon the over-all interpretation of the rating form by a particular subject. (Although π does not affect derivation of the method of successive categories, it does assume importance in Chapter 9, devoted to prediction of choice.) The component ε_k is a random component, allowing for variability of interpretations, over subjects, of point k on the rating form.

We assume the joint distribution of ε_j and $\pi + \varepsilon_k$ to be bivariate normal, with means of zero, variances δ_j^2 and γ_k^2, and intercorrelation zero. We assume further that $\gamma_k^2 = \gamma^2$ for all k.

The response of subject i is assumed to be determined as follows. Stimulus j will be rated at or below point k if

$$v_{jki} = v_{ji} - v_{ki} = \mu_j - \tau_k - \pi_i + \varepsilon_{ji} - \varepsilon_{ki} \leq 0.$$

Clearly, v_{jk} is normally distributed, with mean

$$\mathscr{E}(v_{jk}) = \mu_j - \tau_k,$$

and variance

$$\mathscr{V}(v_{jk}) = \delta_j^2 + \gamma_k^2 = \sigma_j^2, \text{ say}.$$

The probability that a randomly selected subject will judge X_j at or below point k on the rating form, is then

$$P_{jk} = \frac{1}{\sqrt{2\pi}\,\sigma_j} \int_{-\infty}^{0} \exp\left(-\frac{1}{2}\frac{[y - (\mu_j - \tau_k)]^2}{\sigma_j^2}\right) dy. \qquad (8.1)$$

Let us introduce the change of variable

$$z = \frac{y - (\mu_j - \tau_k)}{\sigma_j}.$$

Then

$$dz = \frac{1}{\sigma_j}\, dy.$$

When

$$y = 0,$$

$$z = (\tau_k - \mu_j)/\sigma_j.$$

With this change of variable, (8.1) becomes

$$P_{jk} = \frac{1}{\sqrt{2\pi}} \int_{-\infty}^{(\tau_k - \mu_j)/\sigma_j} \exp\left(-\frac{1}{2}z^2\right) dz, \qquad (8.2)$$

the normal response function for the method of successive categories. Given the parameters μ_j, τ_k, and σ_j, we could determine from (8.2) the probability that stimulus X is judged at or below point k on the rating form.

In the notation of previous chapters, (8.2) may be written

$$P_{jk} = \Phi[(\tau_k - \mu_j)/\sigma_j]. \qquad (8.3)$$

The inverse of this function is

$$(\tau_k - \mu_j)/\sigma_j = \Phi^{-1}(P_{jk}). \qquad (8.4)$$

Data from the experimental design of Section 8.1 may be cast in the form of observed proportions p_{jk}, the proportions of judgments of X_j at or below t_k, the upper boundary of the kth rating category. Then, according to the model,

$$(\tau_k - \mu_j)/\sigma_j \cong \mathscr{E}[\Phi^{-1}(p_{jk})]$$

$$\cong \mathscr{E}(y_{jk}). \qquad (8.5)$$

It will be recognized that y_{jk} is the normal deviate corresponding to the proportion p_{jk} in the lower tail of the unit normal distribution.

8.3 A Graphical Solution

Ratings obtained from N subjects for each of n objects may be recorded as shown in the $n \times m$ matrix of Table 8.1 where n is the number of stimuli

TABLE 8.1. Frequencies of Ratings over Nine Successive Categories for Twelve Food Items

Food item	\multicolumn{9}{c}{Successive category}									N	No response
	1	2	3	4	5	6	7	8	9		
1. Sweetbreads	24	31	26	29	47	37	32	13	4	243	12
2. Cauliflower	15	6	10	26	27	62	72	30	6	254	1
3. Fresh pineapple	4	1	2	7	16	40	75	77	31	253	2
4. Parsnips	17	30	31	45	47	32	33	11	4	250	5
5. Baked beans	4	5	6	17	27	60	72	56	7	254	1
6. Wieners	0	2	7	9	28	76	91	38	2	253	2
7. Chocolate cake	0	1	2	7	20	33	74	85	32	254	1
8. Salmon loaf	8	9	11	23	36	74	64	25	3	253	2
9. Blueberry pie	2	0	3	14	24	41	70	70	28	252	3
10. Turnips	19	30	33	48	35	40	32	15	1	253	2
11. Liver	21	16	10	15	23	42	71	46	9	253	2
12. Spaghetti	1	1	8	9	24	61	92	46	12	254	1

and m is the number of rating categories. In Table 8.1 are presented actual data from a sample of 255 U.S. Army enlisted men instructed to rate their preference for each of 12 food items on a nine-category "hedonic" rating form.[1] The frequency of ratings are transformed into cumulative proportions of ratings, as in Table 8.2. From a table of the normal probability distribution,

TABLE 8.2. Cumulative Proportions, p_{jk}, of Ratings over Nine Successive Categories for Twelve Food Items

Food item	\multicolumn{9}{c}{Successive category}								
	1	2	3	4	5	6	7	8	9
1	099	226	333	453	646	798	930	984	1.000
2	059	083	122	224	331	575	858	976	1.000
3	016	020	028	055	119	277	573	877	1.000
4	068	188	312	492	680	808	940	984	1.000
5	015	035	059	126	232	469	752	972	1.000
6	000	008	036	071	182	482	842	992	1.000
7	000	004	012	039	118	248	539	874	1.000
8	032	067	111	202	344	636	889	988	1.000
9	008	008	020	075	171	333	611	889	1.000
10	075	194	324	514	652	810	937	996	1.000
11	083	146	186	245	336	502	783	964	1.000
12	004	008	039	075	169	409	772	953	1.000

[1] When the purpose of a study is to detect differences among the μ_j, evidence from unpublished studies suggests that this aim is better met in general when m is selected to be an even number rather than an odd number as in this example.

these proportions, p_{jk}, may be transformed into normal deviates, y_{jk}, and another matrix may be formed, or order n by $(m - 1)$ with entries y_{jk}; in Table 8.3 appear the y_{jk} corresponding to the p_{jk} of Table 8.2.

The sampling variability of normal deviates, given by Equation (2.23), is large as the parametric deviate approaches either extreme of the normal distribution function. Particularly for sample values of p_{jk} more extreme than .01 or .99, the sampling variance of y_{jk} is intolerably large. For this reason, in tables of the form of Table 8.3, it is not recommended that y values be recorded when p exceeds .99 or is less than .01. For such situations, a y value is estimated as follows. The mean difference between the recorded y_{jk} in two adjacent columns of Table 8.3 is found, based upon only those rows of a table in which a y_{jk} value is recorded in each of the two columns. This mean difference then is taken as the expected increment in y values in those cases where no entry exists.

To exemplify the procedure, look at column 2 of Table 8.3. No y_{jk} values are determined directly from the values of p_{jk} for food items 6, 7, 9, or 12, since in each of those cases the p_{jk} (Table 8.2) is less than .010. To estimate values for these entry cells, we require the mean difference between the y values in columns 3 and 2 of Table 8.3. The sum of the difference, $\Sigma(y_{j2} - y_{j3})$, for the eight values of j for which an entry appears in both columns, is found to be -2.172. The mean difference, $-2.172/8$, is $-.272$, which is then added to each of the entries in column 3 in rows 6, 7, 9, and 12 to obtain the estimates -2.071, -2.529, -2.326, and -2.034. These estimates are recorded in parentheses in the appropriate cells or column 2.

In like manner, estimates are obtained for the missing y_{jk} estimates in column 1, Table 8.3. The mean difference between entries in columns 1 and 2, for the eight rows in which this can be determined, is $-.379$. Adding this value to the estimates in parentheses, column 2, yields the estimates in parentheses, column 1.

The other missing values of y_{jk}, column 8, are also estimated by this procedure. For the ten pairs of y values which appear in both column 7 and column 8, the mean difference is .934. Adding .934 to 1.003 in row 6, column 7 yields 1.937, which is recorded in row 6, column 8; adding .934 to 1.530 in row 10, column 7 yields 2.464, which is recorded in row 10, column 8.

For a graphical solution, $\hat{\tau}_k$ is defined as the estimate of the scale value associated with the upper bound of category k, for $k = 1, 2, \ldots, (m - 1)$. To effect a solution, we begin by substituting sample values for expected values in Equation (8.5) over j, summing and dividing both sides by n, thus obtaining the $(m - 1)$ equations

$$\frac{1}{n}\sum_j y_{jk} = \frac{\hat{\tau}_k}{n}\sum_j \frac{1}{\hat{\sigma}_j} - \frac{1}{n}\sum_j \frac{\hat{\mu}_j}{\hat{\sigma}_j}, \tag{8.6}$$

TABLE 8.3. Normal Deviates, y_{jk}, Associated with the p_{jk} of Table 8.2

Food item	\multicolumn{8}{c}{Successive category}								Sum
	1	2	3	4	5	6	7	8	
1	−1.287	−.752	.432	−.118	.374	.834	1.476	2.144	2.239
2	−1.563	−1.385	−1.165	−.759	−.437	.189	1.071	1.977	−2.072
3	−2.144	−2.054	−1.911	−1.598	−1.180	−.592	.184	1.160	−8.135
4	−1.491	−.885	−.490	−.020	.468	.870	1.555	2.144	2.151
5	−2.170	−1.812	−1.563	−1.146	−.732	−.078	.681	1.911	−4.909
6	(−2.450)	(−2.071)	−1.799	−1.468	−.908	−.045	1.003	(1.937)	−5.801
7	(−2.908)	(−2.529)	−2.257	−1.762	−1.185	.681	.098	1.146	−10.078
8	−1.852	−1.498	−1.221	.834	−.402	−.348	1.221	2.257	−1.981
9	(−2.705)	(−2.326)	−2.054	−1.440	.950	−.432	.282	1.221	−8.404
10	−1.440	−.863	−.456	.035	.391	.878	1.530	(2.464)	2.539
11	−1.385	−1.054	.893	.690	−.423	−.005	.782	1.799	−1.859
12	(−2.413)	(−2.034)	−1.762	−1.440	−.958	−.230	.745	1.675	−6.417
$\sum y_{jk}$	−23.808	−19.263	−16.003	−11.240	−5.942	1.066	10.628	21.835	−42.727
$\sum y_{jk}/12$	−1.984	−1.605	−1.333	−.937	−.495	.089	.886	1.820	
d_k	.379	.272	.396	.442	.584	.797	.934		
$\hat{\tau}_k$	−1.268	−.889	−.617	−.221	.221	.805	1.602	2.536	

$$c = (.937 + .495)/2 = .716$$

where $k = 1, 2, \ldots, (m - 1)$. (Since $\hat{\tau}_k$ is the upper bound of category k, the mth value of $\hat{\tau}_k$ is indeterminantly large.) Equation (8.6) determines $\hat{\tau}_k$ except for location and scale.

An algebraic solution for $\hat{\mu}_j$ and $\hat{\sigma}_j$ is derived as follows. Subtracting the $(k - 1)$st equation (8.6) from the kth equation (8.6) yields

$$\frac{1}{n}\left(\sum_j y_{jk} - \sum_j y_{j,k-1}\right) = \frac{1}{n}(\hat{\tau}_k - \hat{\tau}_{k-1})\sum_j \frac{1}{\hat{\sigma}_j}. \qquad (8.7)$$

For each stimulus object l, $l = 1, 2, \ldots, j, \ldots, n$, we may divide both sides of (8.7) by $(y_{lk} - y_{l,k-1})$ to obtain

$$\frac{\left(\sum_j y_{jk} - \sum_j y_{j,k-1}\right)}{n(y_{lk} - y_{l,k-1})} = \frac{(\hat{\tau}_k - \hat{\tau}_{k-1})}{n(\hat{\tau}_k - \hat{\tau}_{k-1})/\hat{\sigma}_l}\sum_j \frac{1}{\hat{\sigma}_j} = \frac{\hat{\sigma}_l}{n}\sum_j \frac{1}{\hat{\sigma}_j} \qquad (8.8)$$

since, from (8.5),

$$y_{lk} - y_{l,k-1} = (\hat{\tau}_k - \hat{\tau}_{k-1})/\hat{\sigma}_l.$$

Equation (8.8) determines $\hat{\sigma}_l(=\hat{\sigma}_j)$. Note that (8.8) also serves to fix the scale unit. For, summing the reciprocal of (8.8) with respect to $l = 1, 2, \ldots, n$,

$$\frac{n\left(\sum_l y_{lk} - \sum_l y_{l,k-1}\right)}{\left(\sum_j y_{jk} - \sum_j y_{j,k-1}\right)} = n = \sum_l \frac{n}{\hat{\sigma}_l\left(\sum_j \frac{1}{\hat{\sigma}_j}\right)},$$

a condition satisfied when

$$\sum_j \frac{1}{\hat{\sigma}_j} = n. \qquad (8.9)$$

Finally, summing (8.5) over k and dividing by $m - 1$ yields

$$\frac{\hat{\sigma}_j \sum_k y_{jk}}{m - 1} = \frac{\sum_k \hat{\tau}_k}{m - 1} - \hat{\mu}_j, \qquad (8.10)$$

which determines $\hat{\mu}_j$ except for location. Let us fix location by setting

$$\sum_j \frac{\hat{\mu}_j^0}{\hat{\sigma}_j} = 0. \qquad (8.11)$$

Substituting (8.9) and (8.11) in (8.6),

$$\hat{\tau}_k^0 = \frac{1}{n}\sum_j y_{jk}. \qquad (8.6a)$$

In one form of graphical solution, the observed deviates are plotted against the values of the category boundaries given by (8.6a) and a straight line is fitted by eye. The slopes of these lines are determined to obtain $\hat{\sigma}_j$ and the values of $\hat{\mu}_j^0$ are the points on the scale of boundaries corresponding to the zero points of observed deviates as determined by the fitted lines. The use of this graphical procedure in place of (8.8) and (8.10) improves somewhat the estimates of σ_j and μ_j with fallible data.

Frequently it is useful to shift the scale origin from that given by (8.11) so that zero mean discriminal process is associated with that point on the rating form which most nearly corresponds to "neutrality" or "indifference" of judgment. This is illustrated in Table 8.3. The fifth category of the rating form is labeled " neither like nor dislike," a neutral category. The midpoint of the fifth category, equidistant from the upper bound of category 4 and the upper bound of category 5, is associated with a $\Sigma y_{jk}/n$ value of $-.716$. Consider a shift of origin to be given by

$$\hat{\tau}_k = \hat{\tau}_k^0 + c. \tag{8.12}$$

From (8.12), when $\hat{\tau}_k = 0$ and $\hat{\tau}_k^0 = -.716$, $c = .716$. The resulting scale values, for $\hat{\tau}_k$ as well as for $\hat{\mu}_j$, are expressed in terms of an origin at the point of neutrality.

The $\bar{d}_k$ values in Table 8.3 are defined as

$$\bar{d}_k = \sum_j y_{jk}/n - \sum_j y_{j,k-1}/n;$$

each $\bar{d}_k$ estimates the width of the kth category on the rating form. The $\hat{\tau}_k$ values are determined by (8.12) and appear as the final row of Table 8.3.

The graphical solution for the μ_j and σ_j may be performed directly from the p_{jk} (rather than from the y_{jk}), as illustrated in studies of Jones and Thurstone (1955); Jones, Peryam, and Thurstone (1955); and Morris and Jones (1955). We first plot, on normal probability paper, the cumulative proportions of response (Table 8.2) against the values $\hat{\tau}_k$. For the 12 food items, these plots are exhibited in Figures 8.1–8.4. To make such plots, vertical lines are drawn to correspond with scale values $\hat{\tau}_k$ of the $(m-1)$ upper category bounds. Cumulative proportion of response then is plotted and a straight line is drawn so as to minimize approximately the vertical discrepancies, in proportion units, of points from the line. The intercept of the line of best fit with the value $p = .50$ provides an estimate for $\hat{\mu}_j$; the reciprocal of the slope of the line gives an estimate for σ_j, taking as unit distance on the ordinate the distance spanned by one standard deviation, i.e. the distance between $p = .50$ and $p = .84$ (or between $p = .50$ and $p = .16$). In Figure 8.1, the scale value of food item 1, sweetbreads, corresponding with $p = .50$, is read from the abscissa to be $-.10$. The scale distance between $p = .50$ and $p = .84$ is $-.10 - (-1.23) = +1.13$, yielding 1.13 as the estimate of σ for this preference distribution. In Figure 8.1, μ_2 is estimated as .62 and σ_2 as 1.05; μ_3 is found to be 1.41 and σ_3 is 1.02. The values for $\hat{\mu}_j$ for the twelve food items, obtained

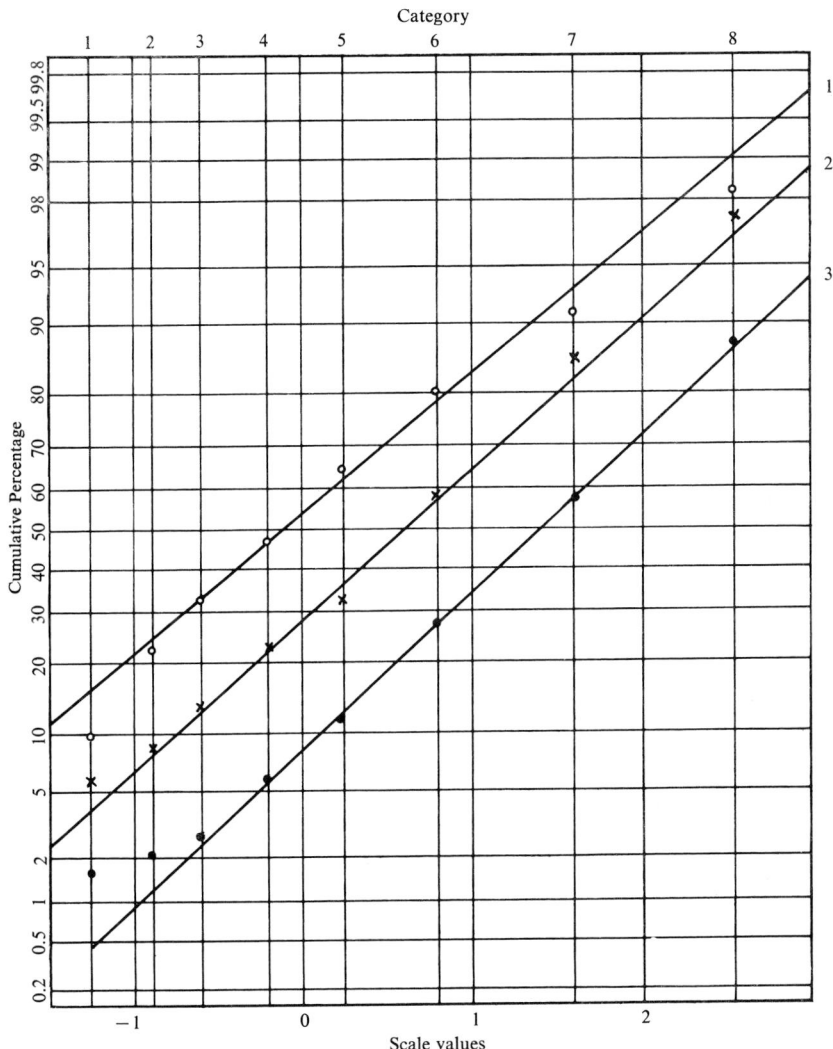

FIG. 8.1. p_{jk} plotted against τ_k, food items 1–3.

in this graphical fashion, appear in Table 8.4. Also in Table 8.4 are the estimates of σ_j.

It is appropriate to comment on the unusual aspects of the list of twelve foods included in this example, and to note that the assumption of normality of preference distribution is violated much more seriously for this sample of foods than is typically the case (see Edwards and Thurstone, 1952; Jones and

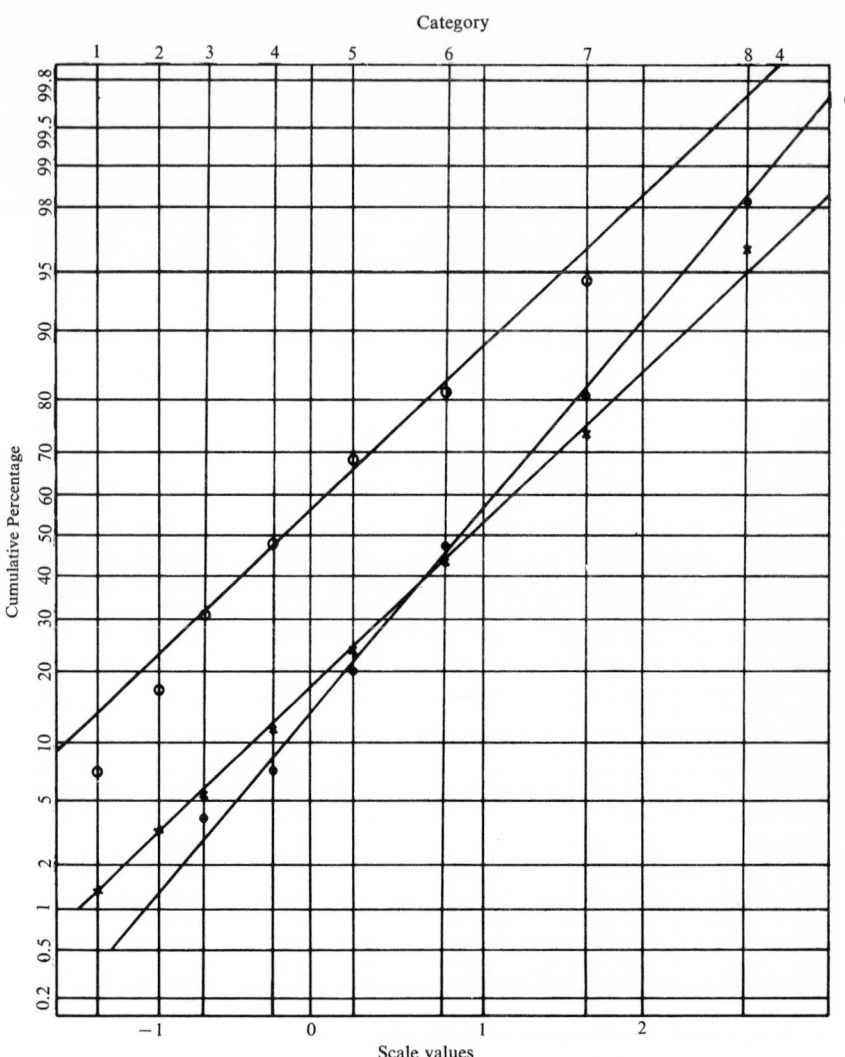

FIG. 8.2. p_{jk} plotted against τ_k, food items 4–6.

Thurstone, 1954; Jones, 1959c). Particularly, food items 1, 4, 10, and 11, exhibit distributions markedly different from the Gaussian distribution, as is attested by the systematic nonlinear components of the plots for those food items in Figures 8.1, 8.2, and 8.4. For food items 1, 4, and 10, sweetbreads, parsnips, and turnips, the distributions are leptokurtic, with a preponderance of the distribution close to the mean of the distribution, and fewer cases

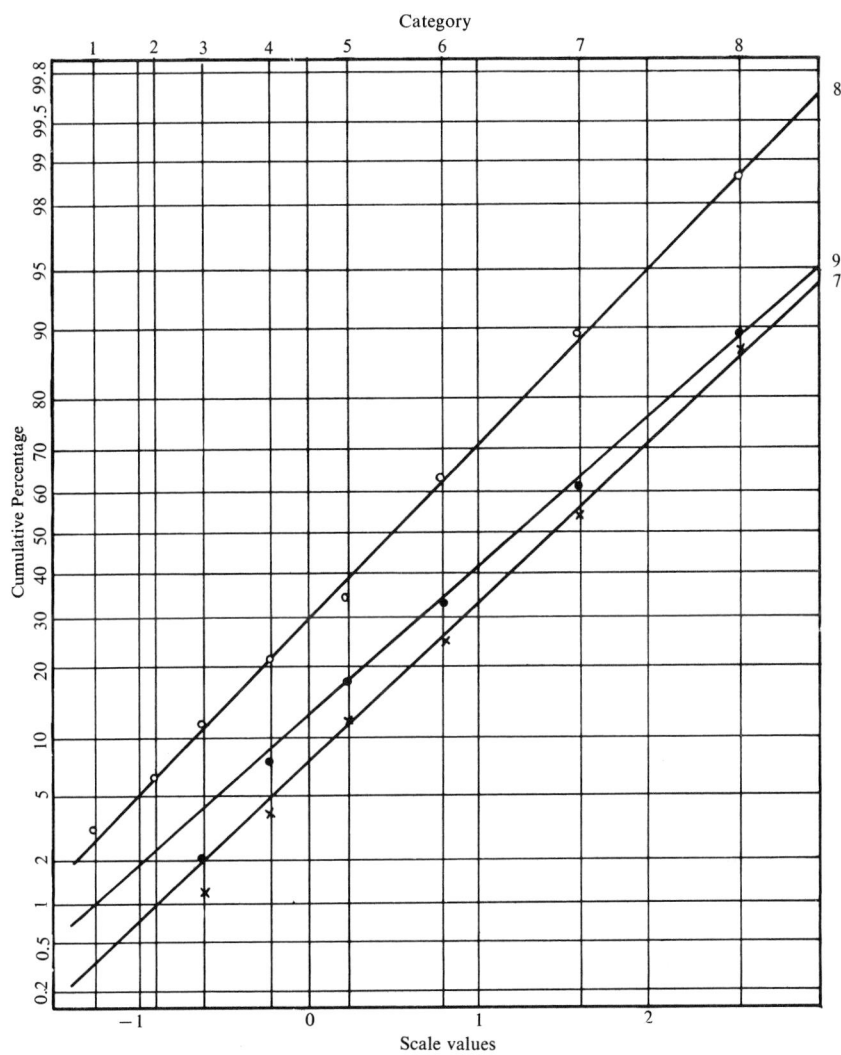

FIG. 8.3. p_{jk} plotted against τ_k, food items 7–9.

toward the tails, as compared with a normal distribution with the same mean and standard deviation. For food item 11, liver, the distribution is platykurtic, with more cases toward both extremes of preference than would be expected when sampling from a normal distribution.

The substitution of estimates from Table 8.4 in (8.2) gives estimates of the expected proportion of subjects assigning the objects to the respective

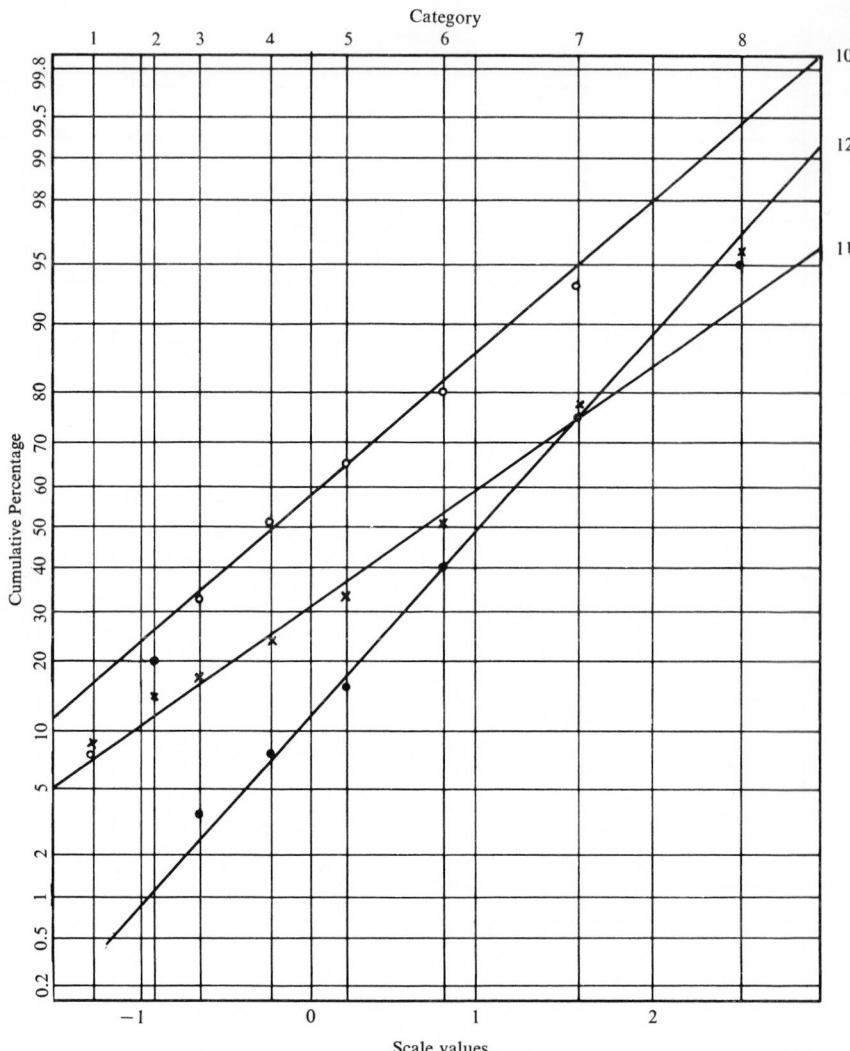

FIG. 8.4. p_{jk} plotted against τ_k, food items 10–12.

categories. The conformity of the observed proportions of response in each category, designated $p_{jk} - p_{j,k-1}$ with those derived from the model designated $\hat{P}_{jk} - \hat{P}_{j,k-1}$, may be tested by computing a total χ^2 for the discrepancies between them:

$$\chi^2 = \sum_{j=1}^{n} \sum_{k=1}^{m-1} \frac{\{[(p_{jk} - p_{j,k-1}) - (\hat{P}_{jk} - \hat{P}_{j,k-1})]N_j\}^2}{(\hat{P}_{jk} - \hat{P}_{j,k-1})N_j}. \tag{8.13}$$

TABLE 8.4. Graphical Estimates for $\hat{\mu}_j$ and $\hat{\sigma}_j$, Twelve Food Items

Food item	$\hat{\mu}_j$	$\hat{\sigma}_j$
1. Sweetbreads	− .10	1.13
2. Cauliflower	.62	1.05
3. Fresh pineapple	1.41	1.02
4. Parsnips	− .18	1.00
5. Baked beans	.88	.97
6. Wieners	.82	.72
7. Chocolate cake	1.46	1.00
8. Salmon loaf	.52	.89
9. Blueberry pie	1.25	1.07
10. Turnips	− .20	1.06
11. Liver	.67	1.30
12. Spaghetti	.99	.83

For the present example, this sum, given separately for each j, is as follows:

Foods	χ^2	Foods	χ^2
1	15.4	7	3.9
2	11.3	8	3.4
3	10.2	9	5.4
4	32.9	10	22.8
5	4.3	11	15.6
6	6.7	12	9.2

Total $\chi^2 = 141.51$,   d.f. $= 66$, $p < .01$

To determine the degrees of freedom for the total χ^2, we note that there are $n(m − 1)$ independent observed proportions (according to the assumptions stated above). From this total $2(n − 1)$ degrees of freedom are consumed by the estimates of μ_j and σ_j not determined by the estimates of τ_k, and $m − 1$ are consumed by the estimates of τ_k. Thus, the residual variation is on $(n − 1) \times (m − 3)$ degrees of freedom, and it is necessary to use not less than four categories and two objects if the model is to be tested.

The value of the total χ^2 indicates that the observations depart significantly from the model. If we neglect the degrees of freedom consumed by the estimates of τ_k, the expectation for the χ^2's for each food would be about six. Relative to this figure only the distributions for food items 4 and 10 show remarkable departure from expectation.

8.4 Minimum Normit χ^2 Solution

It is of interest to determine whether conformity to the model can be improved by a more efficient method of estimating τ_k, σ_j, and μ_j. We use a method given by Bock (1958b) for this purpose. The approach is to minimize the normit χ^2 attributable to discrepancies between the normal deviates obtained from the observed cumulative proportions and those reproduced from the model.

According to the law of categorical judgment,

$$\mathcal{E}(y_{jk}) \cong \Phi^{-1}(P_{jk}) \cong (\tau_k - \mu_j)/\sigma_j.$$

To compute the variance of y_{jk} we introduce the independent formal variate (see Section 2.7):

$s_{jk} = 1$, with probability P_{jk} when the jth object is assigned to category $1, 2, \ldots,$ or k in a random judgment;

$s_{jk} = 0$, with probability $Q_{jk} = 1 - P_{jk}$ when the jth object is assigned to category $k + 1, k + 2, \ldots, m - 1,$ or m in a random judgment.

Then

$$p_{jk} = \sum_{i=1}^{N_j} s_{jki}/N_j, \quad \text{and} \quad \mathcal{E}(p_{jk}) = N_j[\mathcal{E}(s_{jk}/N_j)] = P_{jk};$$

$$\mathcal{V}(p_{jk}) = N_j[\mathcal{E}(s_{jk}^2/N^2) - \mathcal{E}^2(s_{jk}/N)]$$

$$= P_{jk}Q_{jk}/N_j;$$

then by Rao's lemma (see p. 150), in the limit

$$\mathcal{V}(y_{jk}) = P_{jk}Q_{jk}/N_j h^2(Y_{jk}).$$

Similarly, a second cumulative proportion, say p_{jl}, $l > k$, can be expressed as the mean of two formal variates

$$p_{jl} = \sum_{i=1}^{N_j} (s_{jki} + t_{jli})/N_j,$$

where

$t_{jl} = 1$, with probability $P_{jl} - P_{jk}$ when the jth object is assigned to category $k + 1, k + 2, \ldots, l - 1,$ or l in a random judgment;

$t_{jl} = 0$, with probability $1 - P_{jl} = Q_{jl}$ when the jth object is assigned to category $l + 1, l + 2, \ldots, m - 1,$ or m in a random judgment.

Thus the covariance of p_{jk} and p_{jl} is

$$\mathcal{V}(p_{jk}, p_{jl}) = \frac{1}{N_j} [\mathcal{E}(s_{jk})(s_{jk} + t_{jl}) - \mathcal{E}(s_{jk})\mathcal{E}(s_{jk} + t_{jl})]$$

$$= (P_{jk} - P_{jk}P_{jl})/N_j$$

$$= P_{jk}Q_{jl}/N_j,$$

since $s_{jk} = 0$ when $t_{jl} = 1$ and vice versa. Then

$$\mathcal{V}(y_{jk}, y_{jl}) = P_{jk}Q_{jl}/N_j h(Y_{jk})h(Y_{jl}).$$

The limiting covariance of the observed normal deviates for the jth object is therefore of the form (suppressing j within the matrix):

$$A_j = \frac{1}{N_j} \begin{bmatrix} \dfrac{P_1 Q_1}{h^2(Y_1)} & \dfrac{P_1 Q_2}{h(Y_1)h(Y_2)} & \cdots & \dfrac{P_1 Q_{m-1}}{h(Y_1)h(Y_{m-1})} \\[2ex] \dfrac{Q_2 P_1}{h(Y_2)h(Y_1)} & \dfrac{P_2 Q_2}{h^2(Y_2)} & \cdots & \dfrac{P_2 Q_{m-1}}{h(Y_2)h(Y_{m-1})} \\[2ex] \vdots & \vdots & & \vdots \\[2ex] \dfrac{Q_{m-1} P_1}{h(Y_{m-1})h(Y_1)} & \dfrac{Q_{m-1} P_2}{h(Y_{m-1})h(Y_2)} & \cdots & \dfrac{P_{m-1} Q_{m-1}}{h^2(Y_{m-1})} \end{bmatrix}$$

The matrix A_j is a function of the population cumulative proportions, which are in general unknown. If the N_j are very large, the observed proportions might be substituted for the population proportions, but there is some probability that a value of p_{jk} (or q_{jl}) will be zero, making A_j singular. A better method is to use the expected proportions already computed from the graphical solution. Estimates of P_{jk} (or Q_{jl}) from this solution can be zero only if a category k is void for all objects, in which case the category can be dropped.

In order to express simply the normit χ^2 for successive-categories data, it is necessary to assume that the proportions for different objects are independently distributed. Actually, this cannot be strictly true since the same individuals are responding to all the objects. In the extreme case, when objects are presented to all the subjects in the same order and two similar objects follow one another, all the subjects may perseverate and give the same rating to both objects. Then the distribution for the two objects will be identical and any error due to sampling subjects which occurs in the first will also occur in the second.

Randomization of the order in which the objects are presented to different subjects should suppress some, perhaps much, of this type of dependency. If correlation of the error remains, however, and is positive, the sampling theory presented here shows that the sum of squares attributable to discrepancies between the observations and the model will be decreased. Hence, if in practice the residual sum of squares is frequently found smaller than its expectation computed on the assumption of independence, the possibility of correlated error should be considered. Such correlation would complicate the theory presented here but would not vitiate it entirely. If we find, for example, that the correlation of the error term in certain applications is roughly constant and can be assigned plausible bounds, the expressions for the expected sums of squares and sampling variances of the estimators can easily be generalized to the correlated case. Substitution of the bounds in the generalized formulas would then produce limits on standard errors and criteria for goodness of fit which should be useful in practical problems. The sampling theory presented here does not explicitly treat the correlated case, but it provides some basis for handling it if the necessity arises.

In the uncorrelated case, the normit χ^2 is

$$\chi^2 = \sum_j \sum_{k,l} a_j^{kl} [y_{jk} - (\tau_k - \mu_j)/\sigma_j][y_{jl} - (\tau_l - \mu_j)/\sigma_j], \qquad (8.14)$$

where a_j^{kl} is the kl element of the inverse of A_j. The (in general nonsingular, positive definite) matrix A_j is one of a large class of patterned matrices of interest in statistical applications which have very simple inverses (Roy and Sarhan, 1956). The inverse of A_j may be obtained as follows.

Suppressing the subscript j and writing $1 - P_{jk}$ for Q_{jk}, we may resolve the matrix A_j into the form

$$A = \frac{1}{N} D[P - \mathbf{P'P}]D,$$

where

$$P - \mathbf{P'P} = \begin{bmatrix} P_1 & P_1 & \cdots & P_1 \\ P_1 & P_2 & \cdots & P_2 \\ & & \vdots & \\ & & \vdots & \\ P_1 & P_2 & \cdots & P_{m-1} \end{bmatrix} - \begin{bmatrix} P_1 \\ P_2 \\ \vdots \\ \\ P_{m-1} \end{bmatrix} [P_1 P_2 \cdots P_{m-1}]$$

and

$$D = \begin{bmatrix} h^{-1}(Y_1) & & & \\ & h^{-1}(Y_2) & & \\ & & \ddots & \\ & & & h^{-1}(Y_{m-1}) \end{bmatrix}.$$

It is well known (Bodewig, 1959, p. 217) and may be verified directly that a matrix M of the form $M = R \pm \mathbf{qq'}$, which is the sum of a nonsingular matrix R and the matrix product, of similar order, of an arbitrary vector $\mathbf{q}$, may be inverted by use of the relation

$$M^{-1} = R^{-1} \pm \frac{R^{-1}\mathbf{qq'}R^{-1}}{1 \pm \mathbf{q'}R^{-1}\mathbf{q}}.$$

Thus, if we let $R = P$, then A^{-1} may be evaluated easily once P^{-1} is obtained. The most direct approach to computing P^{-1} is to border P above and on the right with identity matrices.

$$\begin{array}{c} I \\ \cdots \\ P \ \vdots I \end{array}$$

Subtracting neighboring rows in $P \mathrel{\vdots} I$, and then neighboring columns in the result yields, say,

$$
\begin{array}{c}
J \\
\cdots \\
H \mathrel{\vdots} K
\end{array}
\begin{bmatrix}
1 & -1 & 0 & \cdots & 0 \\
0 & 1 & -1 & \cdots & 0 \\
0 & 0 & 1 & \cdots & 0 \\
\vdots & \vdots & \vdots & & \vdots \\
0 & 0 & 0 & \cdots & 1
\end{bmatrix}
$$

$$
=
\begin{bmatrix}
P_1 & & & & \\
& P_2 - P_1 & & & \\
& & P_3 - P_2 & & \\
& & & \ddots & \\
& & & & P_{m-1} - P_{m-2}
\end{bmatrix}
\begin{bmatrix}
1 & 0 & 0 & \cdots & 0 \\
-1 & 1 & 0 & \cdots & 0 \\
0 & -1 & 1 & \cdots & 0 \\
\vdots & & \ddots & & \\
0 & 0 & 0 & \cdots & 1
\end{bmatrix}.
$$

Then since $P^{-1} = JH^{-1}K$, we find

$$
P^{-1} =
\begin{bmatrix}
\left(\dfrac{1}{P_1} + \dfrac{1}{P_2 - P_1}\right) & -\dfrac{1}{P_2 - P_1} & 0 & \cdots & 0 \\[2mm]
-\dfrac{1}{P_2 - P_1} & \left(\dfrac{1}{P_2 - P_1} + \dfrac{1}{P_3 - P_2}\right) & -\dfrac{1}{P_3 - P_2} & \cdots & 0 \\[2mm]
0 & -\dfrac{1}{P_3 - P_2} & \left(\dfrac{1}{P_3 - P_2} + \dfrac{1}{P_4 - P_3}\right) & \cdots & 0 \\[2mm]
\vdots & \vdots & \vdots & & \vdots \\[2mm]
0 & 0 & 0 & \cdots & \dfrac{1}{P_{m-1} - P_{m-2}}
\end{bmatrix}.
$$

Substitution of P^{-1} for R^{-1} and $[P_1, P_2, \ldots, P_{m-1}]$ for $\mathbf{q}'$ reveals that all the terms in $R^{-1}\mathbf{q}\mathbf{q}'R^{-1}/(1 - \mathbf{q}'R^{-1}\mathbf{q})$ go to zero except that for the element in the $m - 1, m - 1$ position, which proves to be $1/(1 - P_{m-1})$. Adding this value to $D^{-1}P^{-1}D^{-1}$ and premultiplying by D^{-1} gives the inverse in Figure 8.5.

The normal equations from (8.14) are expressed most conveniently in a combination of summatory and matrix notation. Let

$\mathbf{y}_j =$ the $(m - 1) \times 1$ row vector of observed deviates,
$W_j =$ the $(m - 1) \times (m - 1)$ matrix A_j^{-1},
$\boldsymbol{\tau} =$ the $(m - 1) \times 1$ row vector of category boundaries,
$\mu_j =$ the (scalar) mean for the jth object,
$\sigma_j =$ the (scalar) discriminal dispersion for the jth object,
$\mathbf{1} =$ the $(m - 1) \times 1$ row vector $[1, 1, \ldots, 1]$.

$$A_J^{-1} = W_J = N_J$$

$$
\begin{bmatrix}
h^2(Y_1)\left(\dfrac{1}{P_1} + \dfrac{1}{P_2 - P_1}\right) & \dfrac{-h(Y_1)h(Y_2)}{P_2 - P_1} & 0 & \cdots & 0 \\[2ex]
\dfrac{-h(Y_2)h(Y_1)}{P_2 - P_1} & h^2(Y_2)\left(\dfrac{1}{P_2 - P_1} + \dfrac{1}{P_3 - P_2}\right) & \dfrac{-h(Y_2)h(Y_3)}{P_3 - P_2} & \cdots & 0 \\[2ex]
0 & \dfrac{-h(Y_3)h(Y_2)}{P_3 - P_2} & h^2(Y_3)\left(\dfrac{1}{P_3 - P_2} + \dfrac{1}{P_4 - P_3}\right) & \cdots & 0 \\[2ex]
\vdots & & \vdots & \cdots & \vdots \\[2ex]
0 & 0 & 0 & \cdots & h^2(Y_{m-1})\left(\dfrac{1}{P_{m-1} - P_{m-2}} + \dfrac{1}{1 - P_{m-1}}\right)
\end{bmatrix}
$$

FIG. 8.5. The matrix $A_J^{-1} = W_J$.

Then (8.14) may be written

$$\chi^2 = \sum_j \left[\mathbf{y}_j - \left(\frac{\tau - \mu_j \mathbf{1}}{\sigma_j} \right) \right]' W_j \left[\mathbf{y}_j - \left(\frac{\tau - \mu_j \mathbf{1}}{\sigma_j} \right) \right]. \tag{8.15}$$

In the following we make use of the fact that quadratic forms may be freely transposed, e.g., $\mathbf{y}_j' W_j \tau = \tau' W_j \mathbf{y}_j$. Differentiating the right member of (8.15) with respect to μ_j, σ_j, and τ, in turn, and equating to zero yields the following normal equations:

for μ_j $(\hat{\tau} - \hat{\sigma}_j \mathbf{y}_j)' W_j \mathbf{1} - \hat{\mu}_j \mathbf{1}' W_j \mathbf{1} = 0$;

for σ_j $\dfrac{\mathbf{y}_j' W_j (\hat{\tau} - \hat{\mu}_j \mathbf{1})}{\hat{\sigma}_j^2} - \dfrac{(\hat{\tau} - \hat{\mu}_j \mathbf{1})' W_j (\hat{\tau} - \hat{\mu}_j \mathbf{1})}{\hat{\sigma}_j^3} = 0$. $\qquad$ (8.16)

But $\hat{\sigma}_j$ cannot be zero, so we may multiply by $\hat{\sigma}_j^3$.

$$\hat{\sigma}_j \mathbf{y}_j' W_j (\hat{\tau} - \hat{\mu}_j \mathbf{1}) = (\hat{\tau} - \hat{\mu}_j \mathbf{1})' W_j (\hat{\tau} - \hat{\mu}_j \mathbf{1}).$$

Substituting for $\hat{\mu}_j$ the solution for (8.16), $\hat{\mu}_j = (\hat{\tau} - \hat{\sigma}_j \mathbf{y}_i)' W_j \mathbf{1}/\mathbf{1}' W_j \mathbf{1}$, gives the estimate for σ_j :

$$\hat{\sigma}_j = \frac{\hat{\tau}' \left(W_j - \dfrac{W_j \mathbf{11}' W_j}{\mathbf{1}' W_j \mathbf{1}} \right) \hat{\tau}}{\mathbf{y}_j' \left(W_j - \dfrac{W_j \mathbf{11}' W_j}{\mathbf{1}' W_j \mathbf{1}} \right) \hat{\tau}}.$$

Writing B_j in place of the matrix $W_j - (W_j \mathbf{11}' W_j / \mathbf{1}' W_j \mathbf{1})$ we obtain

$$\hat{\sigma}_j = \frac{\hat{\tau}' B_j \hat{\tau}}{\mathbf{y}_j' B_j \hat{\tau}}. \tag{8.17}$$

Finally, the normal equation for τ is

$$\sum \left\{ -\frac{\hat{\tau}' W_j}{\hat{\sigma}_j^2} + \frac{\mathbf{y}_j' W_j}{\hat{\sigma}_j} - \frac{\hat{\mu}_j \mathbf{1}' W_j}{\hat{\sigma}_j^2} \right\} = 0.$$

Substituting for $\hat{\mu}_j$,

$$\sum \left\{ -\frac{\hat{\tau}'}{\hat{\sigma}_j^2} \left(W_j - \frac{W_j \mathbf{11}' W_j}{\mathbf{1}' W_j \mathbf{1}} \right) + \frac{\mathbf{y}_j'}{\hat{\sigma}_j} \left(W_j - \frac{W_j \mathbf{11}' W_j}{\mathbf{1}' W_j \mathbf{1}} \right) \right\} = 0$$

or

$$\hat{\tau}' \left(\sum \frac{1}{\hat{\sigma}_j^2} B_j \right) = \sum \frac{\mathbf{y}_j}{\hat{\sigma}_j} B_j. \tag{8.18}$$

Note, however, that

$$B_j \mathbf{1} = W_j \mathbf{1} - \frac{W_j \mathbf{11}' W_j \mathbf{1}}{\mathbf{1}' W_j \mathbf{1}} = W_j \mathbf{1} - W_j \mathbf{1} = 0.$$

That is, the rows (and columns) of B_j sum to zero and B_j is singular. Thus, an explicit solution for $\hat{\mathbf{t}}$ can be obtained only be setting one of the values of $\hat{t}_k$, say $\hat{t}_1$, equal to zero and deleting the corresponding row and column. The result is the nonsingular matrix B_j^*, and,

$$\hat{\mathbf{t}}^{*\prime} = \sum \frac{\mathbf{y}_j^{*\prime}}{\hat{\sigma}_j} B_j^* (\Sigma B_j^*/\hat{\sigma}_j^2)^{-1}, \tag{8.19}$$

where the asterisks indicate the dropping of the first variate. The same subsidiary condition used in the graphical solution to determine location can then be used to obtain $\hat{\mathbf{t}}$ from $\hat{\mathbf{t}}^*$, namely $\Sigma_j \hat{\mu}_j/\hat{\sigma}_j = 0$. For, by substituting for $\hat{\mathbf{t}}$ in (8.16), we may put the subsidiary condition in the form

$$\sum \frac{\mathbf{y}_j' W_j \mathbf{1}}{\mathbf{1}' W_j \mathbf{1}} = (\hat{\mathbf{t}}^{*\prime} + \hat{t}_1 \mathbf{1}') \sum \frac{W_j \mathbf{1}}{\hat{\sigma}_j \mathbf{1}' W_j \mathbf{1}}$$

$$\hat{t}_1 \sum \frac{1}{\hat{\sigma}_j} = \sum \frac{\mathbf{y}_j' W_j \mathbf{1}}{\mathbf{1}' W_j \mathbf{1}} - \hat{\mathbf{t}}^{*\prime} \sum \frac{W_j \mathbf{1}}{\hat{\sigma}_j \mathbf{1}' W_j \mathbf{1}}$$

or, writing $\bar{y}_j$ for $\mathbf{y}_j' W_j \mathbf{1}/\mathbf{1}' W_j \mathbf{1}$,

$$\hat{t}_1 = \left(\sum \bar{y}_j - \tau^{*\prime} \sum \frac{W_j \mathbf{1}}{\hat{\sigma}_j \mathbf{1}' W_j \mathbf{1}} \right) \Big/ \sum \frac{1}{\hat{\sigma}_j} \tag{8.20}$$

and

$$\hat{\mathbf{t}} = (\hat{\mathbf{t}}^* + \hat{t}_1 \mathbf{1}). \tag{8.21}$$

Although direct simultaneous solution of (8.16), (8.17), and (8.19) is not possible, an iterative solution is feasible and appears to converge rapidly. The best approach is to substitute in (8.19) the estimates of $\hat{\sigma}_j$ obtained from the graphical solution. The $(m-2) \times (m-2)$ matrix $\Sigma B_j^*/\hat{\sigma}_j$ is obtained and inverted. It will be found well conditioned and easy to invert. A first estimate of $\hat{\mathbf{t}}^*$ is calculated from (8.19). New estimates of $\hat{\sigma}_j$ are then obtained from (8.17) and (8.19) is entered again to improve the estimate of $\hat{\mathbf{t}}^*$. Two or three iterations should yield essentially stationary values of $\hat{\sigma}_j$ and $\hat{\mathbf{t}}^*$. Then $\hat{\mathbf{t}}$ is obtained from (8.21) and $\hat{\mu}_j$ from (8.16). For purposes of computation it is useful to note that, because $\hat{\mathbf{t}}' B_j = (\hat{\mathbf{t}}^{*\prime} + \hat{t}_1 \mathbf{1}') B_j = \hat{\mathbf{t}}^{*\prime} B_j$, by (8.18), the $\hat{\sigma}_j$ determined from (8.17) are independent of the location of $\hat{\mathbf{t}}$. As a result $\hat{\mathbf{t}}^*$ may be used without adjustment at each stage of the iterations. If it is desired to make the estimates obtained from this solution correspond in scale to those from the graphical solution, $\hat{\mathbf{t}}$, $\hat{\sigma}_j$, and $\hat{\mu}_j$ may be multiplied by the factor $k = (1/n)\Sigma(1/\hat{\sigma}_j)$.

THE MINIMUM NORMIT χ^2. The minimum normit χ^2 may be evaluated by substituting the estimates $\hat{\mu}_j$, $\hat{\sigma}_j$, and $\hat{\mathbf{t}}$ for the parameters in Equation (8.15). The result simplifies as follows:

$$\text{SSE} = \sum \left\{ \mathbf{y}_j' W_j \mathbf{y}_j - \frac{\hat{\mathbf{t}}' B_j \hat{\mathbf{t}}}{\hat{\sigma}_j^2} - \bar{y}_j^2 \mathbf{1}' W_j \mathbf{1} \right\} \tag{8.22}$$

where $\bar{y}_j$ is defined as in (8.20). Note that the term $\hat{\tau}'B_j\hat{\tau}/\hat{\sigma}_j^2$ is independent of both the location constant $\hat{\tau}_1$ and the scale constant k; hence, the residual sum of squares can be computed from the unadjusted estimates taken directly from the solution.

The total sum of squares thus may be partitioned as shown in Table 8.5.

TABLE 8.5. Analysis of Variance

Source of variation	d.f.	Sum of squares, χ^2	Expected sum of squares*
Regression	$(n-1)+(m-2)$	$SSR = \sum_j \dfrac{\hat{\tau}'B_j\hat{\tau}}{\hat{\sigma}_j^2}$	$\mathscr{E}(SSR) = \sum_j \dfrac{\tau'B_j\tau}{\sigma_j^2} + [(n-1) + (m-2)]\sigma^2$
Means	n	$SSM = \sum_j \bar{y}_j^2 1'W_j 1$	$\mathscr{E}(SSM) = \sum_j \bar{Y}_j 1'W_j 1 + n\sigma^2$
Error	$(n-1)(m-3)$	$SSE = SST - SSR - SSM$	$\mathscr{E}(SSE) = (n-1)(m-3)\sigma^2$
Total	$n(m-1)$	$SST = \sum_j y'_j W_j y_j$	

* These $\mathscr{E}(SS)$ are slightly approximated (see text); $\sigma^2 = 1$.

SAMPLING VARIANCES OF THE ESTIMATES. Because the estimators of the response parameters are not linear functions of the observations, it is extremely difficult to derive their exact sampling variances. On certain assumptions, however, some useful approximate results may be obtained.

It is not possible to derive a simple sampling variance for $\hat{\sigma}_j$. But for the discriminal precision, say $b_j = 1/\hat{\sigma}_j$, a useful result may be found if we neglect the variance of the $\hat{\tau}$ and substitute the fixed value τ. This is a reasonable assumption if the number of objects is fairly large, since $\hat{\tau}$ depends on all the data whereas the other terms in the estimator of b_j depend only upon the observations for the jth object. Thus if n is not too small, we may use (8.23), below, replacing τ by its estimate $\hat{\tau}$ to approximate the sampling variance of b_j. For

$$b_j = 1/\hat{\sigma}_j = \frac{(Y'_j + \varepsilon'_j)B_j\tau}{\tau'B_j\tau},$$

$$\mathscr{E}(b_j) = 1/\sigma_j,$$

$$\mathscr{V}(b_j) = \mathscr{E}\left\{\frac{\tau'B_j(Y_j+\varepsilon_j)(Y_j+\varepsilon_j)'B_j\tau}{(\tau B_j\tau)^2}\right\} - \frac{1}{\sigma_j}$$

$$= \frac{\tau'B_j A_j B_j\tau}{(\tau'B_j\tau)^2}$$

$$= \frac{\tau'B_j A_j\left(W_j - \dfrac{W_j 11'W_j}{1'W_j 1}\right)\tau}{(\tau'B_j\tau)^2},$$

or, since $A_j W_j = I$ and $B_j \mathbf{1} = 0$,

$$\mathscr{V}(b_j) = 1/\tau' B_j \tau. \tag{8.23}$$

The preceding expressions become quite unmanageable if the assumption of fixed τ is relaxed. It appears then that b_j is no longer an unbiased estimate of $1/\sigma_j$ and that (8.23) is slightly too large because $\hat{\tau}' B_j \hat{\tau}$, as an estimate of $\tau' B_j \tau$, is biased downward slightly. Thus (8.23) is a conservative estimate of the sampling variance of b_j.

Like $\hat{\sigma}_j$, the estimate of the mean, $\hat{\mu}_j$, does not admit a simple expression for its variance. However, the estimate of μ_j/σ_j, the standardized mean for the jth distribution, is more tractable. If the σ_j are homogeneous, μ_j/σ_j may be used as a parameter of the models for prediction of choice in Chapter 9, and the sampling variance of its estimator is of interest:

$$\widehat{\mu_j/\sigma_j} = (\hat{\tau}'/\hat{\sigma}_j - \mathbf{y}_j') W_j \mathbf{1}/\mathbf{1}' W_j \mathbf{1}.$$

Again assuming $\hat{\tau}$ fixed,

$$\widehat{\mu_j/\sigma_j} = \frac{(\mathbf{Y}_j' + \boldsymbol{\varepsilon}_j') B_j \tau \mathbf{1}' W_j \tau}{\tau' B_j \tau\, \mathbf{1}' W_j \mathbf{1}} - \frac{(\mathbf{Y}_j' + \boldsymbol{\varepsilon}_j') W_j \mathbf{1}}{\mathbf{1}' W_j \mathbf{1}}$$

$$\mathscr{E}(\widehat{\mu_j/\sigma_j}) = \mu_j/\sigma_j$$

$$\mathscr{V}(\widehat{\mu_j/\sigma_j}) = \frac{1}{\mathbf{1}' W_j \mathbf{1}} + \frac{\tau' W_j \mathbf{1} \tau' B_j \tau \mathbf{1}' W_j \tau}{(\tau' B_j \tau)^2 (\mathbf{1}' W_j \mathbf{1})^2},$$

since $\mathbf{1}' B_j = B_j \mathbf{1} = 0$, or, defining $\bar{\tau}_j = \tau' W_j \mathbf{1}/\mathbf{1}' W_j \mathbf{1}$,

$$\mathscr{V}(\widehat{\mu_j/\sigma_j}) = \frac{1}{\mathbf{1}' W_j \mathbf{1}} + \frac{\bar{\tau}_j^2}{\tau' B_j \tau}. \tag{8.24}$$

Replacing τ by $\hat{\tau}$ in (8.24), we have an expression for a sampling variance in which the error of assuming $\tau = \hat{\tau}$ affects only the quadratic term. The effect of this approximation should quickly become negligible as n increases.

Finally, for the variance of the interval boundaries, $\hat{\tau}^*$, it is convenient to define

$$\hat{\tau}^* = \tau^* + \xi^* = \left(\sum_j \frac{B_j^*}{\hat{\sigma}_j^2}\right)^{-1} \sum_j B_j^* \left(\frac{\mathbf{Y}_j^* + \boldsymbol{\varepsilon}_j^*}{\hat{\sigma}_j}\right).$$

Then

$$\tau^* = \left(\sum_j \frac{B_j^*}{\hat{\sigma}_j^2}\right)^{-1} \sum_j B_j^* \left(\frac{\mathbf{Y}_j^*}{\hat{\sigma}_j}\right)$$

and

$$\xi^* = \left(\sum_j \frac{B_j^*}{\hat{\sigma}_j^2}\right)^{-1} \sum_j B_j^* \left(\frac{\boldsymbol{\varepsilon}_j^*}{\hat{\sigma}_j}\right),$$

where the asterisk indicates that one of the $m - 1$ variates has been dropped.

Since the $\hat{\sigma}_j$ appear only as weights in sums and are typically homogeneous, we may treat the $\hat{\sigma}_j$ as fixed and substitute σ_j.

Then

$$\mathscr{E}(\xi^*) = 0\,;$$

$$\mathscr{V}(\hat{\mathfrak{t}}^*) = \mathscr{V}(\xi^*)$$

$$= (\Sigma B_j^*/\sigma_j^2)^{-1}\mathscr{E}\left(\Sigma\frac{B_j^*}{\sigma_j}\,\varepsilon_j^*\right)\left(\Sigma\frac{B_j^*}{\sigma_j}\,\varepsilon_j^*\right)'(\Sigma B_j^*/\sigma_j^2)^{-1}$$

$$= (\Sigma B_j^*/\sigma_j^2)^{-1}\mathscr{E}\left[\frac{B_1^*\varepsilon_1^*\varepsilon_1^{*\prime}B_1^*}{\sigma_1^2} + \frac{B_1\varepsilon_1^*\varepsilon_2'\,B_2^*}{\sigma_1\sigma_2} + \cdots + \frac{B_1^*\varepsilon_1^*\varepsilon_n^{*\prime}B_n^*}{\sigma_1\sigma_n}\right.$$

$$+ \frac{B_2^*\,\varepsilon_2^*\,\varepsilon_1^{*\prime}B_1^*}{\sigma_2\sigma_1} + \frac{B_2^*\,\varepsilon_2^*\,\varepsilon_2^{*\prime}B_2^*}{\sigma_2^2} + \cdots + \frac{B_2^*\,\varepsilon_2^*\,\varepsilon_n^{*\prime}B_n^*}{\sigma_2\sigma_n} + \cdots$$

$$\left.+ \frac{B_n^*\varepsilon_n^*\varepsilon_1^{*\prime}B_1^*}{\sigma_n\sigma_1} + \cdots + \frac{B_n^*\varepsilon_n^*\varepsilon_n^{*\prime}B_n^*}{\sigma_n^2}\right](\Sigma B_j^*/\sigma_j^2)^{-1}\,.$$

At this point the assumption of independence of the sampling error for separate objects is required. On this assumption we have

$$\mathscr{E}(\varepsilon_i^*\varepsilon_j^{*\prime}) = 0, \qquad \text{for } i \neq j\,,$$

and the sum in the brackets reduces to

$$\Sigma\frac{B_j^*\varepsilon_j^*\varepsilon_j^{*\prime}B_j^*}{\sigma_j^2} = \Sigma\frac{B_j^*A_j^*B_j^*}{\sigma_j^2}$$

$$= \Sigma\frac{B_j^*A_j^*}{\sigma_j^2}\left(W_j^* - \frac{W_j^*\mathbf{11}'W_j^*}{\mathbf{1}'W^*\mathbf{1}}\right)$$

$$= \Sigma\frac{B_j^*}{\sigma_j^2}\,.$$

Then,

$$\mathscr{V}(\hat{\mathfrak{t}}^*) = \left(\Sigma\frac{B_j^*}{\sigma_j^2}\right)^{-1}\,. \tag{8.25}$$

If the errors are correlated, the terms $\mathscr{E}(\varepsilon_j^*\varepsilon_j^{*\prime})$, $i \neq j$, will not vanish. If the correlation is positive, as probably would be the case in practice, the contribution of these terms could considerably increase the sampling variance and covariance of the $\hat{\mathfrak{t}}_k^*$. As can be seen by inspecting the expressions for the expected mean square below, positive correlation will also increase SSR, thus decreasing SSE and causing the fit of the model to appear better than it is in fact.

DERIVATION OF THE EXPECTED SUMS OF SQUARES IN TABLE 8.5. On certain assumptions it is possible to express in familiar form the expected sums of squares for the partition given by (8.22).

(a) $\text{SST} = \Sigma \mathbf{y}_j' W_j \mathbf{y}_j$.

If the errors for separate objects are uncorrelated,

$$\mathscr{E}(\text{SST}) = \Sigma[\mathbf{Y}_j' W_j \mathbf{Y}_j + \mathscr{E}(\boldsymbol{\varepsilon}_j' W_j \boldsymbol{\varepsilon}_j)]$$

$$= \Sigma[\mathbf{Y}_j' W_j \mathbf{Y}_j + \mathscr{E}(\boldsymbol{\varepsilon}_j' T_j T_j' \boldsymbol{\varepsilon}_j)]$$

$$= \sum_{j=1}^{n} \left(\frac{\boldsymbol{\tau}' W_j \boldsymbol{\tau}}{\sigma_j^2} + \frac{2\mu_j \mathbf{1}' W_j \boldsymbol{\tau}}{\sigma_j} + \frac{\mu_j^2 \mathbf{1}' W_j \mathbf{1}}{\sigma_j^2} \right) + \sum_{j=1}^{n} \mathscr{E}(\mathbf{f}_j' \mathbf{f}_k),$$

where $T_j T_j' = W_j$ (see Computing Note A), and

$$\sum_{j=1}^{n} \mathscr{E}(\mathbf{f}_j' \mathbf{f}_j) = n(m - 1).$$

(b) $\text{SSM} = \Sigma \bar{y}_j^2 \mathbf{1}' W_j \mathbf{1}$.

$$\mathscr{E}(\text{SSM}) = \Sigma \left(\frac{\mathbf{1}' W_j \mathbf{Y}_j \mathbf{Y}_j' W_j \mathbf{1}}{\mathbf{1}' W_j \mathbf{1}} + \frac{\mathbf{1}' W_j \mathscr{E}(\boldsymbol{\varepsilon}_j \boldsymbol{\varepsilon}_j') W_j \mathbf{1}}{\mathbf{1}' W_j \mathbf{1}} \right)$$

$$= \Sigma \left(\frac{\boldsymbol{\tau}' W_j \mathbf{1}\mathbf{1}' W_j \boldsymbol{\tau}}{\sigma_j^2 \mathbf{1}' W_j \mathbf{1}} + \frac{2\mu_j \mathbf{1}' W_j \boldsymbol{\tau}}{\sigma_j} + \frac{\mu_j^2 \mathbf{1}' W_j \mathbf{1}}{\sigma_j^2} \right) + \Sigma \frac{\mathbf{1}' W_j A_j W_j \mathbf{1}}{\mathbf{1}' W_j \mathbf{1}}$$

where, of course,

$$\sum_{j=1}^{n} \frac{\mathbf{1}' W_j A_j W_j \mathbf{1}}{\mathbf{1}' W_j \mathbf{1}} = n.$$

$\hat{\boldsymbol{\tau}}$ is assumed fixed.

The derivation for SSR is less straightforward.

(c) $\text{SSR} = \Sigma b_j^2 \hat{\boldsymbol{\tau}}^{*\prime} B_j \hat{\boldsymbol{\tau}}^*$.

Initially assume both b_j and $\hat{\boldsymbol{\tau}}^*$ subject to error and write

$$\text{SSR} = \sum_j \{ b_j^2 (\boldsymbol{\tau}^* + \boldsymbol{\xi}^*)' B_j (\boldsymbol{\tau}^* + \boldsymbol{\xi}^*) \}$$

$$\mathscr{E}(\text{SSR}) = \sum_j \left[\boldsymbol{\tau}^{*\prime} B_j \boldsymbol{\tau}^* \mathscr{E}(b_j^2) + 2\mathscr{E}\left\{ \boldsymbol{\xi}^{*\prime} \left(\sum_j \frac{B_j}{\hat{\sigma}_j^2} \right) \boldsymbol{\tau}^* \right\} + \mathscr{E}\left\{ \boldsymbol{\xi}^{*\prime} \left(\sum_j \frac{B_j}{\hat{\sigma}_j^2} \right) \boldsymbol{\xi}^* \right\} \right],$$

replacing b_j^2 with $1/\hat{\sigma}^2$ in the two terms on the right. In the first term of this expansion we may enter the result already contained in (8.23)

$$\mathscr{E}(b_j^2) = \frac{1}{\boldsymbol{\tau}^{*\prime} B_j \boldsymbol{\tau}^*} + \frac{1}{\sigma^2}.$$

The second term is an odd function of the errors and vanishes. The third term may be evaluated if $\hat{\sigma}_j^2$ is assumed fixed. Writing σ_j in place of $\hat{\sigma}_j$, we have by an argument similar to that used in calculating $\mathscr{E}(\text{SST})$,

$$\mathscr{E}\left\{\xi^{*\prime}\left(\sum_j \frac{B_j}{\sigma_j^2}\right)\xi^*\right\} = m - 2, \text{ since } \mathscr{E}(\xi^*\xi^{*\prime}) = \left(\sum_j \frac{B_j}{\sigma_j^2}\right)^{-1}.$$

Again the independence of errors for different objects is assumed. Since one of the b_j is determined once $\hat{t}^*$ is fixed, it would appear that only $n - 1$ of the b_j contribute error to SSR; hence,

$$\mathscr{E}(\text{SSR}) = \sum_{j=1}^{n-1} \frac{\tau^{*\prime} B_j \tau^*}{\tau^{*\prime} B_j \tau^*} + \sum_{j=1}^{n} \frac{\tau^{*\prime} B_j \tau^*}{\sigma_j^2} + m - 2$$

$$= n - 1 + \sum_{j=1}^{n} \left(\frac{\tau' W_j \tau}{\sigma_j^2} - \frac{\tau' W_j \mathbf{1} \mathbf{1}' W_j \tau}{\sigma_j^2 \mathbf{1}' W_j \mathbf{1}} \right) + m - 2.$$

(d)   SSE = SST − SSM − SSR.

Subtracting the expectations of SSM and SSR from SST yields

$$\mathscr{E}(\text{SSE}) = n(m - 1) - n - (n - 1) - (m - 2) = (n - 1)(m - 3).$$

This expression is free of the parameters of the model. By appeal to Cochran's theorem (Cramér, 1951, p. 117) and on the stated assumptions, the error sum of squares in the analysis of variance is distributed as a central χ^2 on $(n - 1)$ $(m - 3)$ degrees of freedom when departure from the model is due only to sampling of individuals. This result is approximate, of course, but improves with increasing numbers of objects and should be useful in many applications for testing the conformity of the observed proportions to the response function.

Example 8.4

The data illustrating the graphical solution of Section 8.3 were reanalyzed by the foregoing method. Expected proportions for computing the matrices W_j were taken from the graphical solution as given in Section 8.3. The iterations for $\hat{\sigma}_j$, shown in Table 8.6, were essentially complete in two stages. The final values for $\hat{t}$, $\hat{\sigma}_j$, and $\hat{\mu}_k$, adjusted for scale by the constant $k = 1.017591$, are shown in Table 8.7.

The analysis of regression given in Table 8.5 was computed using unadjusted values of $\hat{t}^*$ and $\hat{\sigma}_j$. The resulting sums of squares with the contributions of each object kept separate are shown in Table 8.8.

The value of the residual χ^2 in Table 8.8 is reduced from that of the graphical solution but remains significant with $p < .01$. There is no evidence that positive correlation of error between ratings of different foods is reducing the

TABLE 8.6. Values of $\hat{\sigma}_j$ at Successive Stages of Iteration

Objects	Graphical	First iteration	Second iteration
1	1.13	1.101	1.090
2	1.05	1.065	1.060
3	1.02	1.051	1.055
4	1.00	.975	.974
5	.97	.963	.962
6	.72	.741	.742
7	1.00	.988	.993
8	.89	.929	.926
9	1.07	1.059	1.062
10	1.06	.987	.978
11	1.30	1.272	1.265
12	.83	.869	.871

TABLE 8.7. Adjusted Estimates of τ, σ_j, and μ_j

Categories	$\hat{\tau}$	Objects	$\hat{\sigma}_j$	$\hat{\mu}_j$
1	-2.159	1	1.109	$-$ .818
2	-1.688	2	1.079	$-$ .160
3	-1.338	3	1.074	.703
4	$-$ .939	4	.992	$-$ .824
5	$-$ .508	5	.979	.170
6	.073	6	.755	.131
7	.893	7	1.010	.778
8	1.935	8	.942	$-$ .212
		9	1.081	.587
		10	.995	$-$ .831
		11	1.287	$-$ .116
		12	.887	.293

TABLE 8.8. Analysis of Regression

Objects	Total (SST)	Means (SSM)	Regression (SSR)	Residual error (SSE $= \chi^2$)
1	431.64	.65	421.99	9.00
2	458.04	.15	444.71	13.17
3	391.69	1.86	385.76	4.07
4	457.32	.41	437.20	19.71
5	480.88	.31	476.05	4.52
6	422.20	2.45	414.01	5.73
7	424.97	3.37	417.74	3.86
8	522.35	3.09	513.35	5.91
9	446.49	3.69	430.16	12.64
10	592.58	.24	480.02	12.32
11	454.54	.18	437.42	16.94
12	422.81	1.32	414.07	7.42
Total	5405.51	16.73	5272.48	115.30

residual sum of squares as conjectured in the first section. However, it is pointed out in Section 8.3 that the fit of these data to the regression lines in the graphical solution appears worse than has typically been the case for food preferences. Deviation from the model may be so great in this example as to completely mask the correlation effect. Further investigation with more typical objects will be necessary to determine whether some tendency toward significantly small residuals actually exists. Direct estimation of the correlation of the errors could also be attempted.

Note that much of the improvement of the least squares solution over the graphical solution is an improved fit for objects 4 and 10. The graphical solution could have been improved somewhat by adjusting the regression lines for these objects in order to reduce their contribution to the residual χ^2. The least squares solution would remain somewhat better, however, because values of $\hat{\tau}_k$ in this solution are chosen to allow the best fit for all the objects.

The approximate sampling variances for the quantities b_j, $\widehat{\mu_j/\sigma_j}$, and $\hat{\tau}_k^*$ computed from (8.23), (8.24), and (8.25) are shown in Table 8.9.

8.5 Analysis of a Factorial Experiment in which the Response is Obtained by Means of a Rating Form

A class of experiments widely used in consumer product development studies consists of ratings by judges of product prototypes fabricated in various ways. Data from these experiments are often analyzed by means of the standard linear models for factorial experimental designs. Since these models assume a continuous response, the rating categories are usually arbitrarily assigned numerical values, such as $1, 2, 3, \ldots, m$, so that the conventional analysis may be applied. This arbitrary assignment of values to categories can be avoided, however, by incorporating the linear model of the factorial design into the measurement model for the method of successive intervals. For the case in which the discriminal dispersions are equal, a solution for the parameters of the combined model may be obtained as follows.

Assume a factorial experiment in which the response to the various treatment combinations consists of independent judgments made with the aid of a rating form. In this section, let us specify $m + 1$ successive categories which might be defined by a succession of adjectives, e.g., poor, fair, good, excellent, etc.

Assume that the distribution of judgments into these categories follows Thurstone's law of categorical judgment. That is, the probability that a response to the hth treatment combination, say, will fall in or below the kth successive category is

$$P_{hk} = \int_{-\infty}^{Y_{hk} = (\tau_k - \mu_h)/\sigma_h} g(z)\, dz, \qquad (8.26)$$

where τ_k is a parameter specifying the upper boundary of an interval associated with the kth category of the rating scale. μ_h is a parameter specifying the effect of the h treatment combination, σ_h is a scale parameter for the h treatment combination, and $g(z)$ is a probability density function.

TABLE 8.9. Sampling Variances of b_j, $\widehat{\mu_j/\sigma_j}$, and $\hat{\tau}^*$

$$\mathcal{V}(\hat{\tau}^*) = c^2\left(\sum B_j^*/\hat{\sigma}_j^2\right)^{-1}$$

Objects	$\mathcal{V}(b_j)$	$\mathcal{V}(\widehat{\mu_j/\sigma_j})$	Categories	Categories						
				1	2	3	4	5	6	7
1	.00193	.00433	1	.00387						
2	.00193	.00410	2	.00298	.00315					
3	.00225	.00431	3	.00259	.00270	.00279				
4	.00232	.00437	4	.00223	.00229	.00234	.00245			
5	.00219	.00410	5	.00198	.00201	.00203	.00209	.00220		
6	.00424	.00427	6	.00175	.00176	.00176	.00179	.00184	.00196	
7	.00234	.00433	7	.00137	.00137	.00137	.00138	.00140	.00144	.00159
8	.00219	.00393				(Symmetric)				
9	.00199	.00424								
10	.00210	.00431								
11	.00138	.00412								
12	.00307	.00421								

To illustrate the fact that $g(z)$ need not be the normal density function, let us assume the logistic density

$$g(z) = \frac{1}{4} \operatorname{sech}^2 \frac{z}{2}.$$

Then

$$P_{hk} = 1/(1 + e^{-Y_{hk}})$$

and

$$Y_{hk} = \ln \left[P_{hk}/(1 - P_{hk}) \right].$$

If σ_h is sufficiently homogeneous, we may assume $\sigma_h = \sigma = 1$, by choice of scaling unit. In this case, a linear model of the effects for, say, n treatment combinations, may be expressed as

$$\underset{n \times 1}{\boldsymbol{\mu}} = \underset{n \times m}{A} \ \underset{m \times 1}{\boldsymbol{\zeta}}$$

If A is singular of rank $l < m$, $l \le n$, a reparameterization of the model in terms of l linear parametric functions of the parameters, $\boldsymbol{\theta} = \underset{l \times m}{L} \boldsymbol{\zeta}$, will be necessary (see Section 6.7.2). Then

$$\underset{n \times l}{\boldsymbol{\mu}} = \underset{l \times 1}{K} \ \underset{l \times 1}{\boldsymbol{\theta}} \ ;$$

$$\mu_h = \mathbf{k}_h' \boldsymbol{\theta}, \qquad h = 1, 2, \ldots, n.$$

where $\mathbf{k}_h'$ is the row of K corresponding to treatment combination h.

Making use of the foregoing assumptions, we may write the response model (8.26) as

$$P_{hk} = \frac{1}{2} \int_{-\infty}^{Y_{hk} = \tau_k - \mathbf{k}_h' \boldsymbol{\theta}} \operatorname{sech}^2 \frac{z}{2} \, dz. \tag{8.27}$$

We wish to estimate $\boldsymbol{\tau}$ and $\boldsymbol{\theta}$ with data from independent judgments randomly sampled from populations defined by (8.27). These data may be represented as shown in Table 8.10.

TABLE 8.10. Form of Successive Categories Data

Treatment combinations	Categories				
	1	2	$\ldots$	$m+1$	Total
1	n_{11}	n_{12}		$n_{1,m+1}$	$n_{1.}$
2	n_{21}	n_{22}		$n_{2,m+1}$	$n_{2.}$
$\cdot$					
$\cdot$					
$\cdot$					
n	$n_{n,1}$	$n_{n,2}$		$n_{n,m+1}$	$n_{n.}$

Corresponding to treatment combination h and category k we may define the sample cumulative proportion

$$p_{hk} = (n_{h1} + n_{h2} + \cdots + n_{hk})/n_{h.}.$$

Its expectation is P_{hk} and the covariance matrix for the first m cumulative proportions is

$$\underset{r \times 1}{\mathcal{V}(\mathbf{p}_h)} = \frac{1}{n_{h.}} \begin{bmatrix} P_{h1}Q_{h1} & P_{h2}Q_{h1} & \cdots & P_{hm}Q_{h1} \\ Q_{h1}P_{h2} & P_{h2}Q_{h2} & \cdots & P_{hm}Q_{h2} \\ & & \vdots & \\ Q_{h1}P_{hm} & Q_{h2}P_{hm} & & P_{hm}Q_{hm} \end{bmatrix}.$$

In the limit as $n_{h.} \to \infty$, the logistic transformations of these proportions,

$$[y_{hk}] = \ln[p_{hk}/(1 - p_{hk})], \qquad k = 1, 2, \ldots, m,$$

are multivariate normally distributed with mean

$$\underset{m \times 1}{\tau_k} - \underset{1 \times l}{(\mathbf{k}_h'} \ \underset{l \times 1}{\boldsymbol{\theta})} \ \underset{m \times 1}{\mathbf{1}_m},$$

where $\mathbf{1}_m$ is an $m \times 1$ vector of unities. Their covariance matrix is

$$\mathcal{V}(\mathbf{y}_h) = \frac{1}{n_{h.}} \begin{bmatrix} 1/P_{h1}Q_{h1} & 1/P_{h2}Q_{h1} & 1/P_{h3}Q_{h1} & \cdots & 1/P_{hm}Q_{h1} \\ 1/Q_{h1}P_{h2} & 1/P_{h2}Q_{h2} & 1/P_{h3}Q_{h2} & \cdots & 1/P_{hm}Q_{h2} \\ 1/Q_{h1}P_{h3} & 1/Q_{h2}P_{h3} & 1/P_{h3}Q_{h3} & \cdots & 1/P_{hm}Q_{h3} \\ & & \vdots & & \\ 1/Q_{h1}P_{hm} & 1/Q_{h2}P_{hm} & 1/P_{h3}Q_{hm} & \cdots & 1/P_{hm}Q_{hm} \end{bmatrix}, \quad (8.28)$$

where $Q_{hk} = 1 - P_{hk}$.

The inverse of (8.28) is tri-diagonal of the form

$$\mathcal{V}^{-1}(\mathbf{y}_h) = n_{h.} \begin{bmatrix} P_{h1}Q_{h1} & -P_{h1}Q_{h1}Q_{h2} & \cdots & 0 \\ -P_{h1}Q_{h1}Q_{h2} & P_{h2}Q_{h2} & \cdots & 0 \\ 0 & -P_{h2}Q_{h2}Q_{h3} & \cdots & 0 \\ & & \vdots & \\ 0 & 0 & \cdots & P_{hm}Q_{hm} \end{bmatrix}$$

$$= W_h, \text{ say}.$$

Assuming independence of responses under different treatment combinations we may define the logit χ^2 for the sample as follows:

$$Q = (\mathbf{y} - \mathbf{1}_n \times \tau + K\boldsymbol{\theta} \times \mathbf{1}_m)' W^* (\mathbf{y} - \mathbf{1}_n \times \tau + K\boldsymbol{\theta} \times \mathbf{1}_m) \qquad (8.29)$$

where $\mathbf{y}$ is a vector of all observed logits written in the natural order of the experimental design and category subscripts,

$$\underset{nm \times 1}{\mathbf{y}} = \begin{bmatrix} \mathbf{y}_1 \\ \mathbf{y}_2 \\ \vdots \\ \mathbf{y}_n \end{bmatrix};$$

$\mathbf{1}_n$ is a vector of n unities; W^* is the diagonal super matrix,

$$\underset{nm \times nm}{W^*} = \begin{bmatrix} W_1 & \cdot & \cdots & \cdot \\ \cdot & W_2 & \cdots & \cdot \\ \cdot & \cdot & \cdots & W_m \end{bmatrix};$$

and the operation $\times$ symbolizes the Kronecker (direct) product defined by

$$\underset{\substack{p \times q \quad r \times s \\ pq \times rs}}{A \ \times \ B} = \begin{bmatrix} a_{11}B & a_{12}B & \cdots & a_{1q}B \\ a_{21}B & a_{22}B & \cdots & a_{2q}B \\ & & \vdots & \\ a_{p1}B & a_{p2}B & \cdots & a_{pq}B \end{bmatrix}.$$

In minimizing (8.29) with respect to variation in τ and θ, we employ symbolic vector differentiation, differentiating first with respect to θ:

$$\frac{1}{2}\frac{\partial Q}{\partial \theta} = (K' \times \mathbf{1}'_m)W^*(\mathbf{y} - \mathbf{1}_n \times \tau + K\theta \times \mathbf{1}_m). \tag{8.30}$$

To simplify (8.30), let

$$\left. \begin{array}{r} [\mathbf{1}'_m W_h \mathbf{y}_h] = \underset{n \times 1}{\mathbf{y}_n} \\ [\mathbf{1}'_m W_h] = \underset{n \times m}{C} \\ \mathrm{diag}[\mathbf{1}'_m W_h \mathbf{1}_m] = \underset{n \times n}{D} \end{array} \right\} \quad h = 1, 2, \ldots, n.$$

Then the normal equation for θ is

$$K'\mathbf{y}_n - K'C\hat{\tau} + K'DK\hat{\theta} = 0. \tag{8.31}$$

Differentiating (8.29) with respect to τ,

$$-\frac{1}{2}\frac{2\theta}{\partial \tau} = (\mathbf{1}_n \times I_m)W^*(\mathbf{y} - \mathbf{1}_n \times \tau + K\theta \times \mathbf{1}_m).$$

Let

$$\underset{m \times m}{W.} = W_1 + W_2 + \cdots + W_m$$

and

$$\underset{m \times 1}{\mathbf{y}.} = W_1\mathbf{y}_1 + W_2\mathbf{y}_2 + \cdots + W_m\mathbf{y}_m.$$

Then the normal equations for τ may be written

$$-\mathbf{y}. + W.\hat{\tau} - C'K\hat{\theta} = 0 \tag{8.32}$$

or

$$\hat{\tau} = W.^{-1}(\mathbf{y}. + C'K\hat{\theta}).$$

Eliminating $\hat{\tau}$ from (8.31) gives

$$K'(\mathbf{y}_n - CW_*^{-1}\mathbf{y}.) + K'(D - CW_*^{-1}C')K\boldsymbol{\theta}.$$

Let $(D - CW_*^{-1}C) = B$ and solve for $\hat{\boldsymbol{\theta}}$:

$$\hat{\boldsymbol{\theta}} = (K'BK)^{-1}K'(\mathbf{y}_n - CW_*^{-1}\mathbf{y}.).$$

Similarly, eliminating $\hat{\boldsymbol{\theta}}$ from (8.32),

$$\hat{\tau} = W_*^{-1}[\mathbf{y}. + C'K(K'BK)^{-1}K'(\mathbf{y}_n - CW_*^{-1}\mathbf{y}.)].$$

The calculation of these estimates is illustrated in the following example. The study reported in the example is not a factorial experiment, but is rather a sampling study with cross-classification of the population. Since the linear model for the effects of the cross-classification of the subjects is the same as that for a factorial design on the objects, the example serves to illustrate a successive intervals solution in both of these types of investigation.

Example 8.5

The data, which refer to preference for black olives, were obtained in a survey of U.S. Armed Forces personnel conducted by the Acceptance Branch of the Food and Container Institute for the Armed Forces. Preferences were obtained by a nine-category rating scale. Subjects have been classified in a 2×3 crossed design, i.e. (rural, urban) vs (Northeast (NE), Midwest (MW), Southwest (SW)). After some response categories were combined, the frequency and the cumulative proportions of preference were tabulated as in Tables 8.11 and 8.12.

TABLE 8.11. Observed Frequencies of Preferences

	Rural			Urban		
	NE	MW	SW	NE	MW	SW
Categories	(11)	(12)	(13)	(21)	(22)	(23)
1	23	30	11	18	20	12
2,3	18	22	9	17	15	9
4,5	20	21	26	18	12	23
6	18	17	19	18	17	21
7	10	8	17	6	16	19
8,9	15	12	24	25	28	30
$n_{\cdot h}$	104	110	106	102	108	114

TABLE 8.12. Cumulative Proportions

Categories	11	12	13	21	22	23
1	.22115	.27273	.10377	.17647	.18519	.10526
2,3	.39423	.47273	.18868	.34314	.32407	.18421
4,5	.58654	.66364	.43396	.51961	.43519	.38596
6	.75962	.81818	.61321	.69608	.59259	.57018
7	.85577	.89091	.77358	.75490	.74074	.73684
8,9	1.00000	1.00000	1.00000	1.00000	1.00000	1.00000

The analyses were performed with two models, the one involving only the main effects (model I), and the other including also the interaction effects (model II). The procedures of calculation are exactly the same for both models except that in the model I the last two columns of the basis matrix were deleted.

The basis for the model, K, was constructed from simple contrasts as follows:

Let $K_i = [\mathbf{1}_i, C_i]$, where $C_i = L_i(L_i L_i')^{-1}$. Then, $\underset{ab \times ab}{K} = [K_a \times K_b]$ with $L_a = [1, -1]$ and

$$L_b = \begin{bmatrix} 1 & -1 & 0 \\ 1 & 0 & -1 \end{bmatrix}.$$

Therefore,

$$K = \begin{bmatrix} 1 & -1/3 & -1/3 & 1/2 & -1/6 & -1/6 \\ 1 & 2/3 & -1/3 & 1/2 & 1/3 & -1/6 \\ 1 & -1/3 & 2/3 & 1/2 & -1/6 & 1/3 \\ 1 & -1/3 & -1/3 & -1/2 & 1/6 & 1/6 \\ 1 & 2/3 & -1/3 & -1/2 & -1/3 & 1/6 \\ 1 & -1/3 & 2/3 & -1/2 & 1/6 & -1/3 \end{bmatrix}.$$

(See Section 6.7.2.)

Since the general effect is absorbed in τ_k, $\mathbf{1}_m'(D - CW^{-1}C') = 0$, and the first column must be deleted, thus reducing K to a (6×3) matrix (model I), and a (6×5) matrix (model II).

Some of the results are summarized in Tables 8.13–8.18. The covariance matrix and its inverse for rural–NE are shown as examples (Tables 8.13 and 8.14).

TABLE 8.13. Covariance Matrix $\mathscr{V}(\mathbf{y}_{11})$

$$\frac{1}{104} \cdot \begin{bmatrix} 5.80576 & \text{(Symmetric)} & & & \\ 3.25684 & 4.18738 & & & \\ 2.18901 & 2.81446 & 4.12353 & & \\ 1.69025 & 2.17318 & 3.18398 & 5.47653 & \\ 1.50034 & 1.92901 & 2.82624 & 4.86121 & 8.10191 \end{bmatrix}$$

TABLE 8.14. Inverse of $\mathscr{V}(\mathbf{y}_{11})$

$$104 \cdot \begin{bmatrix} .31778 & -.24716 & \cdot & \cdot & \cdot \\ -.24716 & .65111 & -.31320 & \cdot & \cdot \\ \cdot & -.31320 & .67143 & -.26608 & \cdot \\ \cdot & \cdot & -.26608 & .56098 & -.24378 \\ \cdot & \cdot & \cdot & -.24378 & .27463 \end{bmatrix}$$

TABLE 8.15. Expected Effects

Contrast	$\hat{\theta}_I$	$\hat{\theta}_{II}$
NE–MW	.04380	.04196
NE–SW	−.57051	−.58004
Rural–urban	−.43343	−.43476
(Interactions)		.51975
		−.18323

TABLE 8.16. Category Boundaries (τ_k)

Categories	$\hat{\tau}_I$	$\hat{\tau}_{II}$
	$-\infty$	$-\infty$
1: Dislike extremely	−1.42039	−1.40806
2,3: Dislike very much, dislike moderately	− .68809	− .68017
4,5: Dislike slightly, neither like nor dislike	− .00513	− .00332
6: Like slightly	.67496	.67061
7: Like moderately	1.21089	1.20356
8,9: Like very much, like extremely	$+\infty$	$+\infty$

TABLE 8.17. Expected Cumulative Proportions

		Treatment combinations			
11	12	13	21	22	23
.26342	.27200	.16815	.18821	.19499	.11586
.42654	.43729	.29599	.32533	.33501	.21418
.59556	.60606	.45425	.48839	.49934	.35047
.74404	.75229	.62165	.65331	.66317	.51578
.83244	.83846	.73740	.76307	.77089	.64544

TABLE 8.18. Logits (y_0, Original Logits; $\hat{Y}_I$, Logits Reproduced from Model I)

11		12		13	
y_0	$\hat{Y}_I$	y_0	$\hat{Y}_I$	y_0	$\hat{Y}_I$
−1.25898	−1.02829	− .98082	− .98449	−2.15602	−1.59879
− .42957	− .29598	− .10919	− .25218	−1.45861	− .86649
.34968	.38698	.67956	.43078	− .26571	− .18353
1.15060	1.06707	1.50407	1.11087	.46085	.49656
1.78059	1.60299	2.10007	1.64679	1.22864	1.03249
21		22		23	
y_0	$\hat{Y}_I$	y_0	$\hat{Y}_I$	y_0	$\hat{Y}_I$
−1.54045	−1.46171	−1.48157	−1.41791	−2.14010	−2.03222
− .64933	− .72941	− .73513	− .68561	−1.48808	−1.29992
.07848	− .04645	− .26071	− .00265	− .46433	− .61696
.82870	.63364	.37468	.67744	.28422	.06313
1.12492	1.16957	1.04982	1.21337	1.02961	.59906

If we refer to Table 8.15, noting at the same time the contrasts in L_a and L_b, $\hat{\theta}_I$ shows that SW has relatively high preference for black olives and that the urban group also has the same tendency. On the other hand, $\hat{\theta}_{II}$ suggests there is some amount of interaction. To test for possible interaction, we may assume that the difference between two χ^2's for model I and model II is distributed as χ^2 with two degrees of freedom. χ^2's were computed by the following formula:

$$\chi^2 = \sum \frac{n_{\cdot h}[(p_{hk} - p_{h,k-1}) - (\hat{P}_{hk} - \hat{P}_{h,k-1})]^2}{\hat{P}_{hk} - \hat{P}_{h,k-1}}$$

with d.f. $= mh - (k + 1)$. χ_I^2 was 32.39953 and χ_{II}^2 was 29.89618. χ^2 for interaction is not significant so that the interaction terms should not be included in the model. Both of the individual χ^2's proved to be nonsignificant, with $.05 < p < .10$ for both χ_I^2 and χ_{II}^2, which means that the logistic response function fits the preference data for black olives fairly well. However, the χ^2 for model II distributes over the groups as follows:

rural–NE	1.98472
rural–MW	2.61370
rural–SW	11.88603
urban–NE	3.31461
urban–MW	2.78705
urban–SW	7.31007

Since each is on about four degrees of freedom, rural–SW shows considerable departure from expectation. Presumably, this is because individual differences in preference for this group are heterogeneous and not distributed logistically.

9 Prediction of Choice

When a paired-comparison or rating experiment is performed in order to estimate the parameters of the judgmental model, the purpose is not merely to reproduce the distribution of judgments in the particular experiment, but ultimately to predict behavior in other and more realistic situations. If such prediction is to be possible, however, another and wider class of models must be formulated, models which specify how the parameters of the judgmental model control behavior of the subjects in these situations. Our purpose in the present chapter is to present a number of models in this wider class. Models applicable to the following predictive problems will be considered:

(1) Prediction of the frequency with which each object in a specified set of more than two objects will be chosen as "most preferred."

(2) Prediction of the frequency of choice for compound objects which are comprised of combinations of distinct objects.

These types of problems are of obvious practical importance since, on the one hand, choices in most realistic situations (purchasing, voting, etc.) require a first choice among more than two objects, and on the other hand, many situations require choice among composite objects (a "package" of commodities, a slate of candidates, etc.). Moreover they have theoretical implications in extending the generality of the judgmental models.

Attention to predictive problems of these types is comparatively new in the study of behavior. In the field of psychology, Thurstone's paper "The Prediction of Choice" (1945) marks its beginning. In the field of economics, Arrow's book *Social Choice and Individual Values* (1951) appears to have been the first to consider economic phenomena from this point of view. More recently Luce (1959) and Restle (1961), in psychology, and Marschak (1960) in economics, have continued the work in these areas.

Much of the study of choice behavior has up to this time been theoretical and speculative. The models proposed have seldom been subjected to empirical tests. This is not the case in the present work, however. Each of the models discussed in this chapter is applied to data and, in most cases, the goodness of fit is assessed.

9.1 Prediction of First Choices

The Thurstonian judgmental models can be generalized in order to predict the proportion of times each object will be chosen when the subjects are given a choice of one out of n objects. For simplicity we consider initially the problem of predicting the proportion of first choice when one object is chosen from among three. That is, for objects X_h, X_j, and X_k we require the probability of the event

$$(v_h > v_j) \cap (v_h > v_k),$$

where v_h, v_j, and v_k are the discriminal processes of a randomly sampled individual, and their distributions are assumed $N(\mu_h, \sigma_h)$, $N(\mu_j, \sigma_j)$, and $N(\mu_k, \sigma_k)$, with $\mathscr{V}(v_h, v_j) = \rho_{hj}\sigma_h\sigma_j$, etc. Designating the differences between these affective values as v_{hj} and v_{hk}, we may write the required probability as $P[(v_{hj} \cap v_{hk}) > 0]$.

The joint distribution of v_{hj} and v_{hk} is bivariate normal, and its parameters may be denoted as follows:

$$N(\mu_{hj}, \mu_{hk}, \sigma_{hj}, \sigma_{hk}, \rho_{hj,hk}).$$

Expressing these parameters in terms of those of the distributions of the original processes, we have

$$\mu_{hj} = \mathscr{E}(v_h - v_j) = \mu_h - \mu_j.$$

Similarly,

$$\mu_{hk} = \mu_h - \mu_k. \tag{9.1}$$

Also

$$\sigma_{hj}^2 = \mathscr{E}(v_h - v_j)^2 - \mathscr{E}^2(v_h - v_j)$$
$$= \sigma_h^2 + \sigma_j^2 - 2\sigma_h\sigma_j\rho_{hj}, \tag{9.2}$$

and

$$\sigma_{hk}^2 = \sigma_h^2 + \sigma_k^2 - 2\sigma_h\sigma_k\rho_{hk}. \tag{9.3}$$

Finally,

$$\sigma_{hj}\sigma_{hk}\rho_{hj,hk} = \mathscr{E}(v_h - v_j)(v_h - v_k) - \mathscr{E}(v_h - v_j)\mathscr{E}(v_h - v_k)$$
$$= \sigma_h^2 - \sigma_h\sigma_j\rho_{hj} - \sigma_h\sigma_k\rho_{hk} + \sigma_j\sigma_k\rho_{jk}. \tag{9.4}$$

It will be convenient to refer to $\rho_{hj,hk}$ as a "comparatal correlation."

The proportion of times that v_h can be expected to exceed both v_j and v_k, so that object X_h receives a first choice, is given by the volume of the positive quadrant of the bivariate normal distribution, say,

$$P[(v_{hj} \cap v_{hk}) > 0] = \int_0^\infty \int_0^\infty \phi(\mu_{hj}, \mu_{hk}, \sigma_{hj}, \sigma_{hk}, \rho_{hj,hk}) \, dw \, dx. \quad (9.5)$$

Introducing the new variables

$$y = (w - \mu_{hj})/\sigma_{hj} \quad \text{and} \quad z = (x - \mu_{hk})/\sigma_{hk},$$

we may write (9.5) in unit bivariate normal form,

$$P[(v_{hj} \cap v_{hk}) > 0] = \int_{-\frac{\mu_{hk}}{\sigma_{hk}}}^\infty \int_{-\frac{\mu_{hj}}{\sigma_{hj}}}^\infty \phi(0, 0, 1, 1, \rho_{hj,hk}) \, dy \, dz. \quad (9.6)$$

Note that when σ_h^2 is larger than σ_j^2 and σ_k^2, the covariance of this distribution will be always positive and will increase as σ_h^2 increases relative to σ_j^2 and σ_k^2. This means that an increasing fraction of the bivariate normal volume will lie in the positive quadrant and the proportion of first choices received by object X_h will increase at the expense of those received by the others. Thus, we could occasionally expect to encounter the paradoxical situation in which the mean affective value of object X_h is somewhat less than that of object X_j and X_k, yet X_h receives a plurality of first choices. A similar observation has been made by Thurstone (1945).

An experimental test of the multivariate normal model specified by (9.6) is presented in the following numerical example.

Example 9.1a

This example is based on data reported in Thurstone (1952). The experiment consisted of (1) determining the preferences of 254 men for 40 foods by means of a nine-interval successive-categories rating form, and (2) obtaining their first choices among foods grouped in sets of two, three, four, and five foods. The problem was to predict the proportion of first choices for the foods in each set on the basis of the preference data. For the purposes of this example only the four sets of three foods from Thurstone's study will be considered.

We wish to compare the observed proportion of first choices for each food with those predicted from the successive-categories data by use of (9.6). For this purpose we need estimates of the mean affective values, discriminal dispersions, and correlations for the foods in the various sets of three.

Estimates of the mean values and discriminal dispersions are available from the minimum normit χ^2 solution in Chapter 8, which was illustrated with data from this experiment. The solution in Chapter 8 can also be used to determine class marks for the categories. A class mark is that value to be associated with each category in order to estimate correlations between preference values of pairs of foods by the customary formula for grouped data. The method is as follows.

(1) In terms of the category boundaries, $\hat{t}_k$, from Table 8.7 (which are assumed to bound intervals under the normal curve), the centroid of the kth interval for the jth object, say x_{jk}, may be obtained by Pearson's formula

$$x_{jk} = \frac{h(\hat{Y}_{jk}) - h(\hat{Y}_{j,k+1})}{\Phi(\hat{Y}_{j,k+1}) - \Phi(\hat{Y}_{jk})}, \qquad k = 0, 1, 2, \ldots, n-1.$$

$\hat{Y}_{jk}$ is the deviate corresponding to the upper boundary of the kth category for the jth food as determined in the successive intervals solution

$$\hat{Y}_{jk} = (\hat{t}_k - \hat{\mu}_j)/\hat{\sigma}_j.$$

For example, the deviate for the upper boundary of category 1 for food 12 is $(-2.159 - .293)/.887 = -2.764$. (The deviate of the lower boundary of the first category is, of course, $-\infty$.) As in previous chapters $h(\hat{Y}_{jk})$ is the ordinate and $\Phi(\hat{Y}_{jk})$ the area of the normal curve at the deviate $\hat{Y}_{jk}$. Thus the class mark for the first category of food 12 is

$$\frac{0 - .00874}{.00284 - 0} = -3.077.$$

(2) To express the formula for computing the correlation of judgments for two foods in terms of the respective class marks of their distributions, let the foods be h and j, say. The cross-tabulation of judgments of N subjects for these foods may be represented

	Food j	
Food h	$n_{hj,kl}$	$n_{h,k}$
	$n_{j,l}$	N

$j = 1, 2, \ldots, n$
$h = 1, 2, \ldots, n$
$j \neq h$
$k = 1, 2, \ldots, m$
$l = 1, 2, \ldots, m$

$n_{hj,kl}$ is the number of judgments in the k,l-cell of the cross-classified ratings; $n_{h,k}$ is the total number of judgments in the kth category for the hth food; $n_{j,l}$ is a similar total for the lth category for the jth food; and N is the total number of subjects. Then the correlation of judgments, which we take as an estimate of the correlation of the underlying discriminal processes, may be computed from

$$\rho_{hj} = \frac{N \sum_k \sum_l x_{hk} x_{jl} n_{hj,kl} - \sum_k x_{hk} n_{h,k} \sum_l x_{jl} n_{j,l}}{\{[N \sum_k x_{hk}^2 n_{h,k} - (\Sigma x_{nk} n_{h,k})^2][N \sum_l x_{jl}^2 n_{j,l} - (\Sigma x_{jl} n_{j,l})^2]\}^{1/2}}.$$

For the four sets of three foods in the prediction of choice experiment the estimated mean affective values, discriminal dispersions, and correlations

TABLE 9.1. Preference Data for Twelve Foods

Set	Food item	Mean affective value, $\hat{\mu}_j$	Discriminal Dispersions, $\hat{\sigma}_j$	Correlations $\hat{\rho}_{hj}$		
	12 Spaghetti	.293	.887	1.000		
1	5 Baked beans	.170	.979	.165	1.000	
	8 Salmon loaf	−.212	.942	−.018	.135	1.000
	9 Blueberry pie	.587	1.081	1.000		
2	7 Chocolate cake	.778	1.010	.196	1.000	
	3 Pineapple	.703	1.074	.116	.033	1.000
	11 Liver	−.116	1.287	1.000		
3	6 Wieners	.131	.755	.001	1.000	
	1 Sweetbreads	−.818	1.109	.256	.003	1.000
	4 Parsnips	−.824	.992	1.000		
4	10 Turnips	−.831	.995	.638	1.000	
	2 Cauliflower	−.160	1.079	.353	.318	1.000

so computed are shown in Table 9.1. From these data are estimated the mean affective differences, say,

$$\hat{\mu}_{hj} = \hat{\mu}_h - \hat{\mu}_j,$$

the comparatal dispersions

$$\hat{\sigma}_{hj} = (\hat{\sigma}_h^2 + \hat{\sigma}_j^2 - 2\hat{\rho}_{hj}\hat{\sigma}_h\hat{\sigma}_j)^{1/2},$$

and the comparatal correlations

$$\hat{\rho}_{hj,hk} = (\hat{\sigma}_h^2 - \hat{\rho}_{hj}\hat{\sigma}_h\hat{\sigma}_j - \hat{\rho}_{hk}\hat{\sigma}_h\hat{\sigma}_k + \hat{\rho}_{jk}\hat{\sigma}_j\hat{\sigma}_k)/\hat{\sigma}_{hj}\hat{\sigma}_{hk}.$$

(k now refers to a food rather than to a category.) The affective differences are converted to unit deviates by dividing by the corresponding comparatal dispersions. They are shown in this form in Table 9.2 along with the comparatal correlations.

TABLE 9.2. Prediction of First Choices by the Normal Response Model

Set	Food item	Deviates		Comparatal correlation	$P(v_{hj} \cap v_{hk}) > 0$		
		j	k	ρ	Predicted	Observed ($N = 254$)	Deviations
	12 Spaghetti	.1018	.3868	.497	.429	.427	−.002
1	5 Baked beans	−.1018	.3023	.443	.351	.349	−.003
	8 Salmon loaf	−.3023	−.3868	.558	.220	.224	.004
	9 Blueberry pie	−.1439	−.0810	.450	.280	.337	.057
2	7 Chocolate cake	.1439	.0517	.470	.375	.400	.025
	3 Pineapple	−.0517	.0810	.576	.345	.263	−.082
	11 Liver	−.1656	.4782	.590	.381	.416	.035
3	6 Wieners	.1656	.7078	.466	.490	.482	−.008
	1 Sweetbreads	−.7078	−.4782	.437	.129	.102	−.027
	4 Parsnips	.0083	−.5627	.319	.191	.130	−.061
4	10 Turnips	−.0083	−.5532	.397	.194	.178	−.016
	2 Cauliflower	.5532	.5627	.751	.615	.692	.077

Call the deviates and correlations in any row of Table 9.2, j, k, and ρ, respectively. Then, the integral in (9.6) may be expressed in terms of observable quantities as

$$P[(v_{hj} \cap v_{hk}) > 0] = \int_{-j}^{\infty} \int_{-k}^{\infty} \phi(0, 0, 1, 1, \rho) \, dy \, dz. \qquad (9.7)$$

For example, (9.7) may represent the shaded quadrant of the normal distribution shown in Figure 9.1. The area of this quadrant can be evaluated from tables of the univariate and bivariate normal distribution[1] as follows.

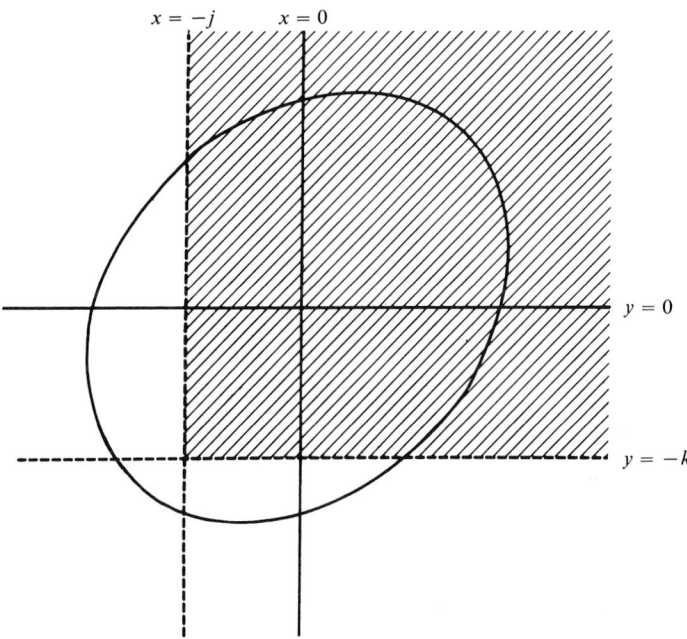

Fig. 9.1. A representation of Equation (9.7).

From the univariate tables the area to the left of $-j$ and below $-k$ may be obtained, giving $P(z < -j)$ and $P(y < -k)$. From the bivariate table, the area below and to the left of $-j$ and $-k$ may be obtained, giving $P[(z < -j) \cap (y < -k)]$. Then

$$P[(z > -j) \cap (y > -k)]$$
$$= 1 - \{P(z < -j) + P(y < -k) - P[(z < -j) \cap (y < -k)]\}. \quad (9.8)$$

---

[1] National Bureau of Standards, *Tables of Bivariate Normal Distribution Functions and Related Functions*, Applied Math. Series No. 50, U.S. Government Printing Office, Washington, D.C., 1956.

For the data of Table 9.1 the predicted proportions of first choices obtained from the bivariate normal model for the difference processes are compared with the observed proportions of first choices in Table 9.2.

Two factors appear to influence the goodness of fit of the multivariate normal model. One is the extent of separation between the mean affective values of the foods, and the other is the closeness of the approximation to normal marginal distributions as revealed in the successive-categories solution. Where these factors are favorable, as in set 1, prediction under the model is excellent. This is to be expected since, from Table 8.9, where the residual χ^2 in the minimum normit χ^2 successive-intervals solution is shown for each food separately, we find that foods 12, 5, and 8 in set 1 have χ^2's very near expectation (which is approximately 6). Similarly, Table 9.1 shows their means to be well separated.

In set 2, the fit of the marginal distributions is good, except possibly for food 9 ($\chi^2 = 12.64$), but the foods have very similar mean values, especially foods 3 and 7. This puts the mean affective difference toward the center of the bivariate normal distribution where small discrepancies in the deviates result in relatively large changes in proportions. Prediction for this set is much poorer than for the first set; indeed, the predicted order of proportion of first choices is not correct.

In set 3, the mean affective values are well separated and prediction is better, but appears to be limited by lack of normality of the marginal distribution for liver ($\chi^2 = 16.94$). Inspection of Figure 8.4 suggests that there is a bimodal distribution of preference for liver—the subjects tend to either like or dislike it, and are infrequently neutral toward it.

Finally, in set 4 two foods (4 and 10) have very similar mean values and all show somewhat poor fit in the successive-intervals solution ($\chi^2 = 19.71$, 12.32, and 13.17 for foods 4, 10, and 2, respectively). Prediction is poor as a result. This set is also interesting in that the discriminal correlations are appreciable and the comparatal correlation is far removed from the value of $1/2$ expected under Case V assumptions.

If the discriminal correlations are assumed zero, prediction of first choices is much poorer. Proportions of approximately .23, .22, and .55 are then predicted for foods 4, 10, and 2. The substantial correlation of foods 4 and 10, parsnips and turnips, undoubtedly reflects the close physical similarity of these vegetables. The effect of the correlations on rating-scale methods is particularly marked when objects are similar in affective value. If correlation is not present, first choices for such objects tend to split evenly; if correlation is present, the object which is slightly higher in affective value tends to receive disproportionately many first choices. This occurs although the discriminal processes have wide distribution over subjects because the discriminal processes for the two objects tend to be of the same order within subjects. To some extent this is the case for turnips and parsnips in the example. Their mean affective values are extremely close, but turnips receive more first choices.

Example 9.1b

Jones (1959a) reports a study in which actual purchases are predicted by a generalized model for comparative judgment. The objects are competing entrees on luncheon menus at the faculty club of the University of Chicago. A seven-category successive-category rating form was mailed to each of the 430 faculty members who were also active members of the faculty club at the University of Chicago. The addressee was instructed to complete the form by placing a check mark to indicate the degree to which he liked or disliked each menu item. Included on the schedule were the names of the 15 entrees served at the club during a criterion period. A total of 297 completed forms were returned, comprising 69% of those mailed.

Five criterion days were selected. On no criterion day was there a shortage of a luncheon item at the club, and on each day more than 100 members patronized the regular dining room facilities. The frequency of purchase of the three competing luncheon entrees on each of the five days serve as criteria.

From the preference ratings, approximate least squares successive-intervals estimates for scale values and discriminal dispersions were obtained by the graphical method (see Section 8.1). Based upon these preference parameters, and upon the assumption of the normality of distributions of preference along the underlying scale continuum, one may utilize Equation (9.6) to predict the proportion of consumers who would select each of three competing consumer objects. The resulting predicted proportions appear in Table 9.3, column A, and in Figure 9.2. A comparison of these predicted proportions with actual observed proportions of choice indicates that discrepancies are considerable. The average error in predicting proportions is .194.

It is evident from Figure 9.2 that the price of the entrees must be taken into account in order to predict purchase. A straightforward approach is to assume that the discriminal process for each entree includes a component with negative value which may be called the utility of its price. Then let the discriminal process of a random subject for the jth food when offered at price q be

$$v_{jq} = \mu_j + v_q + \varepsilon_{jq},$$

where μ_j is the mean affective value of the item, v_q is the utility of its price, and ε_{jq} a random component normally distributed in the population of subjects. The difference process for items h at price p and j at price q is

$$v_{hp,jq} = v_{hp} - v_{jq}$$
$$= (\mu_h - \mu_j) + (v_p - v_q) + (\varepsilon_{hp} - \varepsilon_{jq})$$
$$= \mu_{hj} + v_{pq} + \varepsilon_{hj}.$$

TABLE 9.3. Observed and Predicted Proportions of Purchase

N	Entree	Price, $	Observed proportions	Predicted proportions Model A	Model B
116	Roast round of beef	1.20	.405	.707	.402
	Smoked tongue	1.00	.319	.120	.279
	Creamed mushrooms on toast	.85	.276	.173	.319
107	Fried chicken leg with country gravy	1.20	.215	.510	.236
	Meat loaf with brown gravy	1.05	.505	.273	.473
	Welsh rarebit on toast	.80	.280	.217	.291
123	Roast leg of lamb	1.20	.268	.623	.326
	Smoked Thüringer sausage	.95	.342	.200	.396
	French-fried smelts with tartar sauce	.90	.390	.177	.278
102	Roast leg of lamb	1.20	.441	.651	.351
	Braised ox joints	1.00	.304	.152	.314
	Baked beans	.80	.255	.197	.335
139	Roast round of beef	1.20	.295	.586	.286
	Creamed chicken with hot biscuit	1.00	.439	.244	.448
	Apple fritters, bacon, and syrup	.85	.266	.170	.266
Mean deviation |pred-obs|				.194	.03

We here assume that utility of price does not systematically contribute to discriminal dispersions or correlations, so that the joint distribution of $v_{hp,jq}$ and $v_{hp,kr}$ is bivariate normal with parameters

$$N[\mu_{hj} + v_{pq}, \mu_{hk} + v_{pr}, \sigma_{hj}, \sigma_{hk}, \rho_{hj,hk}].$$

With these specifications, we may write the model in unit bivariate form analogously to (9.6), as

$$P[(v_{hp} > v_{jq}) \cap (v_{hp} > v_{kr})] = \int_{\frac{-\mu_{hk} - v_{pr}}{\sigma_{hk}}}^{\infty} \int_{\frac{-\mu_{hj} - v_{pq}}{\sigma_{hj}}}^{\infty} (0, 0, 1, 1, \rho_{hj,hk}) \, dy \, dz.$$

$$(9.9)$$

Data in this example were analyzed by the method of successive categories to provide estimates of the μ's, σ's, and ρ's. However, no knowledge of the utilities of price, the v's, is available from the successive categories data.

With three competing consumer objects and empirically known proportions of purchase of each, there are three equations of the form of (9.9), one yielding $P_{(hp>jq,kr)}$, another $P_{(jq>hp,kr)}$, and the third (not independent), $P_{(kr>jq,hp)}$. Using these values, tables of the bivariate normal distribution function allow iterative solutions for the three estimates of utility, $\hat{v}_p$, $\hat{v}_q$, and $\hat{v}_r$, simultaneously adjusting them until (9.9), with successive-categories

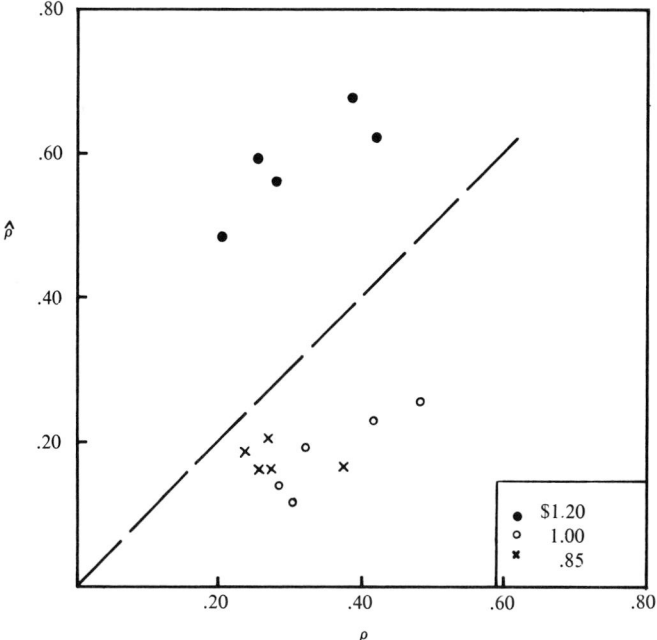

Fig. 9.2. Predicted vs observed proportions of purchase; price not considered in the model.

estimates $\hat{\mu}$, $\hat{\sigma}$, and $\hat{\rho}$ replacing corresponding parameters, serves to reproduce the observed proportions of purchase. Finally, if data are available for several sets of three competing consumer objects, each set containing one object at price p, one at price q, and one at price r, then several estimates may be found and checked for consistency, for each utility of price.

To obtain unique estimates for each utility, we may set the utility of $0.85 equal to zero. The resulting estimates obtained by fitting (9.9) for each criterion day separately are shown in Table 9.4. It will be noted that the most

TABLE 9.4. Estimates of Utility Values*

Criterion day	$\hat{v}_{1.20}$	$\hat{v}_{1.00}$	$\hat{v}_{.85}$
1	−.810	.420	.000
2	−.967	.265	.000
3	−1.395	−.257	.000
4	−.547	.353	.000
5	−.916	.154	.000
Mean	−.927	.187	.000

* $\hat{v}_{.85}$ is arbitrarily assigned zero utility.

divergent values are those for criterion day 3. The lowest-cost entree on that day is french-fried smelts. That the day was a Friday appears to have added a determinant of purchase which is not included in the model.

It is also of interest to note from Table 9.4 the relative strength of negative utility for the three prices. The values for $\hat{u}_{.85}$ and $\hat{u}_{1.20}$ are consistently more negative than $\hat{u}_{1.00}$. Although \$1.20 is the least preferred price, \$1.00 is a price preferred to \$0.85. In other words, in this study, utility of price is not monotonically related to price.

Utilizing the mean values for the three utilities, final predictions are made, the results of which appear in column B, Table 9.3 and in Figure 9.3.

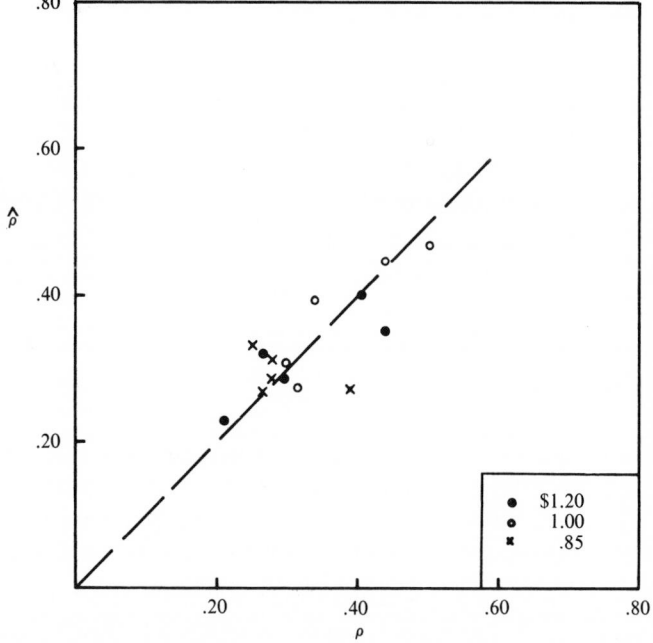

FIG. 9.3. Predicted vs observed prediction of purchase; price included in the model.

The improvement of fit is demonstrated by the relatively small average discrepancy of predicted from observed proportions, .038, and lends credence to the model.

The finding that faculty members when lunching at the faculty club prefer paying \$1.00 to paying \$0.85 may come as a surprise. However, we might conjecture that the social psychology of publicly ordering lunch at a table with colleagues provides a disposition away from the cheapest meal.

The present study, of course, provides no evidence as to the source of the finding. Nor may we legitimately generalize the findings to any other situations. Nevertheless, it might not be surprising to find such non-monotonic relations between price and utility for numerous consumer commodities: cosmetics, articles of clothing, household drug supplies, indeed, any items where the consumer evaluation of quality is difficult or impossible to make independent of the factor of price.

9.1.1 Other Models for Prediction of First Choices

Application of the general multivariate normal model for the prediction of first choices is severely limited by the extreme difficulty of integrating the multivariate normal density function when the number of variates exceeds two. Thus it is not feasible at present to apply the results of the previous section to even as many as four objects, since this would involve a trivariate distribution of the difference processes. Reduction methods have been proposed for performing the required integration (Plackett, 1954), but cannot easily be carried beyond the four-variate case even with machine computation.

Useful approximate solutions for the case of four or more objects are available, however, if the comparatal correlation is taken as 1/2. This is in fact its population value under Case V assumptions, since from (9.2);

$$\rho_{hj,hk} = \sigma^2(1 - \rho - \rho + \rho)/\sigma^2\sqrt{2(1 - \rho)}\sqrt{2(1 - \rho)} = 1/2.$$

A convenient multivariate distribution with correlation 1/2 is obtained by generalizing the bivariate logistic distribution introduced by Gumbel (1961). The marginal distributions are logistic,

$$P(y) = 1/(1 - e^{-y}),$$

with mean and median at $y = 0$ and variance of $\pi^2/3$. This is the same distribution proposed in Section 6.5.1 as an alternative to the normal response function. The logistic response function generalized for n variates, y_1, y_2, $\ldots, y_n$, is

$$P(\alpha_1, \alpha_2, \ldots, \alpha_{n-1})$$

$$= \int_{-\alpha_{n-1}}^{\infty} \cdots \int_{-\alpha_2}^{\infty} \int_{-\alpha_1}^{\infty} \lambda(y_1, y_2, \ldots, y_{n-1}) \, dy_1 \, dy_2 \cdots dy_{n-1}$$

$$= 1/(1 + e^{-\alpha_1} + e^{-\alpha_2} + \cdots + e^{-\alpha_{n-1}}). \tag{9.10}$$

Each of the $n(n - 1)/2$ pairwise correlations of the variates is equal to 1/2. To use this function it is necessary to adjust the scale of the variates to fit the normal distribution. This may be done by equating variances in the marginal distributions, i.e. by using $\pi/\sqrt{3}$ times the unit normal deviates as logistic deviates. Then the probability that object X_j will be chosen first from among n objects is approximated by (9.10) with

$$\alpha_1 = 1.813799 \hat{\mu}_{j1}/\hat{\sigma}_{j1},$$

$$\alpha_2 = 1.813799 \hat{\mu}_{j1}/\hat{\sigma}_{j2},$$

$$\vdots$$

$$\alpha_{n-1} = 1.813799 \hat{\mu}_{j,n-1}/\hat{\sigma}_{j,n-1}.$$

It is instructive to relate prediction of first choices with the multivariate logistic model to the Bradley-Terry-Luce model of Section 6.5.1. Recall that, according to the latter model, the affective differences estimated assuming Case V of the law of comparative judgment and the logistic response function have composition

$$\mu_{jk} = \ln(\pi_j/\pi_k).$$

In Case V the comparatal dispersions are equal and may be set to unity, so that (9.10) becomes

$$P(X_j > X_1, \ldots, X_{j-1}, X_{j+1}, \ldots, X_n)$$

$$= \frac{1}{1 + e^{-\mu_{j1}} + \cdots + e^{-\mu_{j,j-1}} + e^{-\mu_{j,j+1}} + \cdots + e^{-\mu_{j,n}}}$$

$$= \frac{1}{(\pi_1 + \pi_2 + \cdots + \pi_n)/\pi_j}$$

$$= \frac{\pi_j}{\pi_1 + \pi_2 + \cdots + \pi_n}. \tag{9.11}$$

This result will be recognized as the general form of the model for paired comparisons given by Equation (6.6).

Example 9.1.1

Predicted proportions of first choices computed by the bivariate logistic and the Bradley-Terry-Luce model were computed for the data of Example 9.1.1 by formulas (9.10) and (9.11), respectively. The resulting proportions, together with the results for the bivariate normal model are shown in Table 9.5. It is apparent that whenever the comparatal correlations are near the value of 1/2 assumed by the bivariate logistic model, for example, with foods 12, 8, 9, 7, and 6 (see Table 9.2) the logistic model provides approximations

TABLE 9.5. Prediction of First Choices by Normal and Logistic Models

Set	Food	Observed (N = 254)	Normal model		Logistic model		B-T-L model*	
			Predicted	Deviation	Predicted	Deviation	Predicted	Deviation
	12 Spaghetti	.427	.429	−.002	.430	−.003	.402	.025
1	5 Baked beans	.349	.351	−.002	.360	−.011	.355	−.006
	8 Salmon loaf	.224	.220	.004	.211	.013	.243	−.019
	9 Blueberry pie	.337	.280	.057	.289	.048	.300	.037
2	7 Chocolate cake	.400	.375	.025	.373	.027	.363	.037
	3 Pineapple	.263	.345	−.082	.338	−.075	.337	−.074
	11 Liver	.416	.381	.035	.361	.055	.360	.056
3	6 Wieners	.482	.490	−.008	.496	−.014	.461	.021
	1 Sweetbreads	.102	.129	−.027	.143	−.041	.179	−.077
	4 Parsnips	.130	.191	−.061	.210	−.080	.254	−.124
4	10 Turnips	.178	.194	−.016	.210	−.032	.252	−.074
	2 Cauliflower	.692	.615	.077	.579	.113	.494	.198

* Predictions from application of the Bradley-Terry–Luce model.

to the predictions of the multivariate normal model which are remarkably good. Where the correlations depart from 1/2, as in set 4, results from the normal and logistic models diverge. When the correlations of the judgments are small and the discriminal dispersions uniform, as in set 2, the Bradley-Terry-Luce model also approximates well the predictions of the normal model.

Neither of the alternative models fit the observed choices as well as the multivariate normal model. Doubtless this is partly the result of the use of the normal distribution as the response function for the successive categories solution in Chapter 8. If the original preference ratings were scaled, assuming a logistic rather than a normal response function for the marginal distributions, the fit to the data certainly would be improved. In any case, the results in Table 9.5 suggest that the multivariate logistic model may be a sufficiently accurate approximation to the normal model for some practical purposes.

9.1.2 Distribution-free Methods

When the successive-intervals solution fails to normalize the marginal distributions for each stimulus object, as indicated by significant residual variation in the minimum normit χ^2 solution, the joint distribution of affective differences cannot be multivariate normal. Prediction of choice by the normal model or its logistic alternative may not then be satisfactorily accurate. However, by use of distribution-free methods accurate prediction may still be possible. If preference data can be obtained by the method of rank order, for example, a solution for prediction of first choices is straightforward. It is only necessary to examine the ranking made by each subject in order to determine the number of subjects who rank a given object above all others in a specified subset. This number divided by the number of subjects in the sample is an estimate of the proportion of the population which assigns first choice to the given object.

Thurstone (1945) has suggested a modification of this procedure which is suitable for data obtained by the method of successive categories. The number of subjects who rate the given object a category above those of all other objects in a specified subset is counted. If a subject rates *two* objects in the same category but above those of all other objects, each of the two objects is assigned a count of one half; if a subject rates *three* objects in the same category above those of the other objects, each of the three objects get one third of a count, etc. The tallies for each object obtained in this way are divided by the total for all objects in the specified subset to obtain an estimated proportion of first choices for each object. Some evidence for the accuracy of this procedure may be obtained by applying it to the data of Example 9.1.1. The results obtained are shown in Table 9.6. (The result for the normal model is again shown for purposes of comparison.)

TABLE 9.6. Comparison of the Distribution-free Method and the Multivariate Normal Model for Prediction of First Choices

Set	Foods	Observed ($N = 254$)	Normal model		Distribution-free method	
			Predicted	Deviation	Predicted	Deviation
1	12 Spaghetti	.427	.429	−.002	.444	−.017
	5 Baked beans	.349	.351	−.002	.333	.016
	8 Salmon loaf	.224	.220	.004	.223	.001
2	9 Blueberry pie	.337	.280	.057	.320	.017
	7 Chocolate cake	.400	.375	.025	.390	.010
	3 Pineapple	.263	.345	−.082	.290	−.027
3	11 Liver	.416	.381	.035	.381	.035
	6 Wieners	.482	.490	−.008	.503	−.021
	1 Sweetbreads	.102	.129	−.027	.116	−.014
4	4 Parsnips	.130	.191	−.061	.169	−.039
	10 Turnips	.178	.194	−.016	.144	.034
	2 Cauliflower	.692	.615	.077	.687	.005

As we might expect, Table 9.6 shows that the distribution-free method tends for the most part to give as good or better predictions than the normal model. The exception is for foods in set 1, where distribution assumptions seem to be well satisfied and the normal model is slightly superior. In set 3 the two methods appear equally accurate. In sets 2 and 4, however the distribution-free method appears to give slightly better prediction. These results suggest that for data obtained by the method of rank order or successive categories, this distribution-free method for prediction of first choices can be recommended for practical work. Methods based on the normal or logistic models continue to be of interest, however, since they are characterized by greater generality and their parameters may be estimated by any of the methods based on comparative or categorical judgment.

In his 1945 paper, Thurstone presented another distribution-free method which does not require examination of responses of individual subjects. This method assumes independent judgments, however, and does not give accurate results when correlation is present. For example, the predicted proportions for foods in sets 1 and 4 obtained by this method are as follows:

Set	Foods	Observed	Predicted	Deviation
	12	.426	.410	.016
1	5	.349	.373	−.024
	8	.224	.216	.008
	4	.130	.235	.105
4	10	.178	.341	.163
	2	.692	.424	.268

This second distribution-free method is evidently much inferior to the method based on tallies of first choices and cannot be generally recommended.

9.2 Prediction of Choice for Compound Objects

Given the results of scaling preferences for each of a set of objects, to what extent is it possible to predict relative preference for combinations or "packages" of the objects? In this section, we shall note alternative models which have been suggested for this problem, then we shall present results from several empirical studies.

Gulliksen (1956) discusses several alternative models by which one might predict scale values of composite stimuli from the scale values of their components. The models are distinguished by the different relations assumed between scale values (y) and physical stimulus magnitudes (x). (A fifth law has been utilized by Cliff, 1959.) In the typical application of scaling to compound objects, the interest is in stimulus objects for which physical magnitude is only vaguely defined. When judges are asked to assess their preference for objects or to respond in accordance with their attitudes toward objects, the physical stimulus magnitude often remains completely undefined. In such cases, selection of a scaling model can be made only by analogy with the sensory psychophysical problem where judges respond with an estimate closely contingent upon their direct perception of physical stimulus magnitude.

As has been previously noted, when a study is designed for paired-comparisons judgments, the range of stimuli prepared for the study must be relatively narrow in order to avoid observed proportions p_{jk} of zero or one.

Within the restricted range of stimuli presented in a given paired-comparisons study, it may be tenable to assume a linear psychophysical model, as presented in Section 2.4, Equation (2.9). Under less restricted conditions, a logarithmic psychophysical model may be assumed.

9.2.1   Prediction of Choice for Compounds Using Paired Comparisons

The experimental procedure for assessing preference values for compound stimuli as well as for component stimuli differs from that of Section 6.2 only in the definition of compound stimuli. Included in the same experiment are not only a set of n distinct stimulus objects X_1, X_2, ..., X_n, but a set of $n(n-1)/2$ "double" stimuli, say, X_{12}, X_{13}, ..., X_{1n}, X_{23}, ..., X_{2n}, X_{34}, ..., $X_{n-1,n}$, where X_{jk} represents the composite objects X_j and X_k. In such an experiment, incomplete designs are favored over complete designs, for if all objects are desirable, the task of judging the pair (X_i, X_{ij}) becomes trivial; X_{ij} includes not only X_i but X_j as well, and as a consequence all subjects are likely to prefer X_{ij}.

Based upon the law of comparative judgment, the response of a random subject to each pair of stimuli is assumed determined by the discriminal processes, for single stimuli

$$v_j = \alpha_j + \varepsilon_j,$$

for double stimuli,

$$v_{(kl)} = \alpha_{(kl)} + \varepsilon_{(kl)}.$$

For single stimuli, as in Chapter 6, it is assumed that the discriminal process v_j is normally distributed with mean α_j and variance σ_j^2, for all $j = 1, 2, \ldots, n$.

A LINEAR "CASE V" SCALING MODEL.[2] We assume, as in Thurstone's Case V, that discriminal dispersions for single stimuli, σ_j, are constant. It is convenient to set the unit of measurement by

$$\sigma_j = \sigma = 1, \qquad \text{for } j = 1, 2, \ldots, n.$$

Assume further that, for single stimuli, correlations between the v_j and v_k for all j and k are zero.

Under a linear model of combination for preference values for a compound stimulus

$$v_{(jk)} = v_j + v_k = \alpha_j + \alpha_k + \varepsilon_j + \varepsilon_k.$$

Thus, $v_{(jk)}$, the sum of independent normally distributed variates, is normally distributed with mean $\alpha_{(jk)} = \alpha_j + \alpha_k$ and variance $\sigma_{(jk)}^2 = \sigma_j^2 + \sigma_k^2 = 2$.

---

[2] This Section and Example 9.2.1a are adapted from Thurstone and Jones (1957).

Then, comparatal dispersions are, for single-single comparisons, $v_j - v_k$,

$$\sigma_{(jk)} = \sqrt{2};$$

for single-double comparisons, $v_{(jk)} - v_l$ (where l is distinct from j and k),

$$\sigma_{(jk)l} = \sqrt{3};$$

and for double-double comparisons, $v_{(jk)} - v_{(lm)}$ (where all component stimuli are distinct),

$$\sigma_{(jk)(lm)} = \sqrt{4} = 2.$$

To bring all comparisons to the same scale, these comparatal dispersions are multiplicative "stretching factors" to be applied to the appropriate sets of normal deviates generated from observed proportions. From the adjusted deviates, a solution for the $\hat{\alpha}^*$ or $\hat{\alpha}^0$ values (depending upon choice of arbitrary origin) may be effected by the method of Section 6.4.

Let us consider the problem of finding a "rational" scale origin, in the sense that such an origin will be consistent with the linear additivity condition

$$\alpha_{(jk)} = \alpha_j + \alpha_k.$$

Such an origin, if it exists, will be C units removed from the arbitrarily selected origin, where C is an unknown constant. That is,

$$\alpha^*_{(jk)} + C = \alpha^*_j + C + \alpha^*_k + C,$$

or

$$\alpha^*_{(jk)} = \alpha^*_j + \alpha^*_k + C. \tag{9.12}$$

Thus an unbiased estimate of C is

$$c = \hat{\alpha}^*_{(jk)} - \hat{\alpha}^*_j - \hat{\alpha}^*_k. \tag{9.13}$$

Each of the $n(n-1)/2$ equations of form (9.13) provides an estimate c of the required translation from arbitrary to rational origin. The homogeneity of these c values is a measure of adequacy of the linear model for predicting preference values for compound from composite stimuli. Another relative measure of adequacy is the "additivity index" suggested by Hicks and Campbell (1965), the ratio of the standard deviation of the α_{jk} to the standard deviation of the obtained estimates of C.

Example 9.2.1a

Thurstone and Jones (1957) used the above linear model to predict preference values for compound stimuli, after solving for preference values of the component stimuli. Their study was motivated by a desire to solve for a rational zero point on the preference scale. Presented to 194 college-student subjects were all ten distinct pairs of five stimuli. New stimuli were defined, each consisting of a pair of the original stimuli. With birthday gifts serving as stimulus objects, subjects were required to provide paired-comparisons judgments of three types: to express preference for one gift or another (single-single comparisons), for one gift or a pair of others (single-double comparisons), or for one pair of gifts or another pair of gifts (double-double comparisons). The incomplete paired-comparisons design utilized in this study is that displayed in Table 7.1.

In order to describe adequately the stimulus objects, each was illustrated with a picture and a catalog description. This detailed information was presented on the first page of a schedule to which the subject could refer at will while recording his preferences. To ensure differentiation in the scale values of these five items it seemed desirable that they differ somewhat (but not extremely) in monetary value. It was expected that the actual choices would be determined mainly by individual interests and habits. Nevertheless, extreme differences in price would probably result in extreme proportions of preferences near unity or zero. The scale values would then be unstable and hence less useful in testing the additivity hypothesis of this study.

Objects selected as stimuli were (A) briefcase, (B) portable three-speed record player, (C) Parker "51" pen and pencil set, (D) fluorescent desk lamp, and (E) Webster's International Unabridged Dictionary. Subjects were instructed to select, for each comparison, the article (or pair of articles in the case of a double stimulus) which would be preferred as birthday gifts. They were asked to judge the articles as if they did not already possess the objects, and were instructed to consider the articles for their own personal use—not to be sold.

The 194 subjects were male undergraduate students in the School of Business Administration, University of North Carolina. Proportions of paired-comparison responses were obtained for 55 pairs of stimuli, from which were derived the normal deviates of Table 7.1. An incomplete design was utilized in order to avoid repetition of the same object on either side of a comparison.

Using the estimated preference value contrasts given in Table 7.2, values of c may be found by invoking Equation (9.13). These values are given in Table 9.7. The mean of the ten estimates, $\bar{c} = 3.029$, represents a single best estimate for C, and is added to each of the $\hat{\alpha}^*$ values of Table 7.2 to produce the $\hat{\alpha}$'s of Table 9.7.

It is instructive to compare these values of $\hat{\alpha}$ with corresponding values determined by Thurstone and Jones (1957) from an unweighted solution. The relation between the two sets of estimates is shown in Figure 9.4; only slight differences appear between the two sets of preference values.

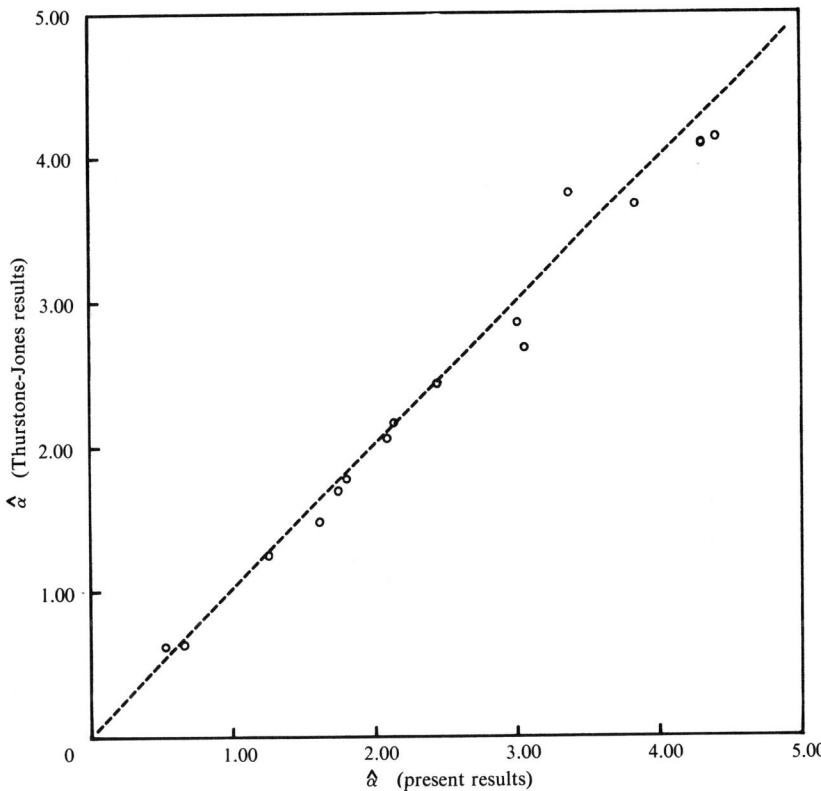

FIG. 9.4. Preference values from Thurstone and Jones (1957) compared with those from Table 9.7.

TABLE 9.7. Estimates c and $\hat{\alpha}$

Stimulus	c	$\hat{\alpha}$
A		.648
B		.550
C		3.000
D		1.270
E		1.741
AB	3.441	1.610
AC	2.701	3.316
AD	3.188	2.078
AE	3.086	2.436
BC	3.276	3.793
BD	2.997	1.789
BE	2.855	2.106
CD	3.000	4.238
CE	2.686	4.384
DE	3.056	3.029

$$\bar{c} = 3.029$$
$$\sigma_c = .227$$

The additivity assumption of (9.13) may be checked by determining, for each pair of single stimuli, the value $\hat{\alpha}_j + \hat{\alpha}_k$, and comparing this with the preference value for corresponding composite stimuli $\hat{\alpha}_{jk}$. The plot of Figure 9.5 demonstrates that preference values for the composite stimuli approximate closely the sums of preference values for corresponding single stimuli. A line of unit slope and zero intercept, sketched in Figure 9.5, fits the data reasonably well.

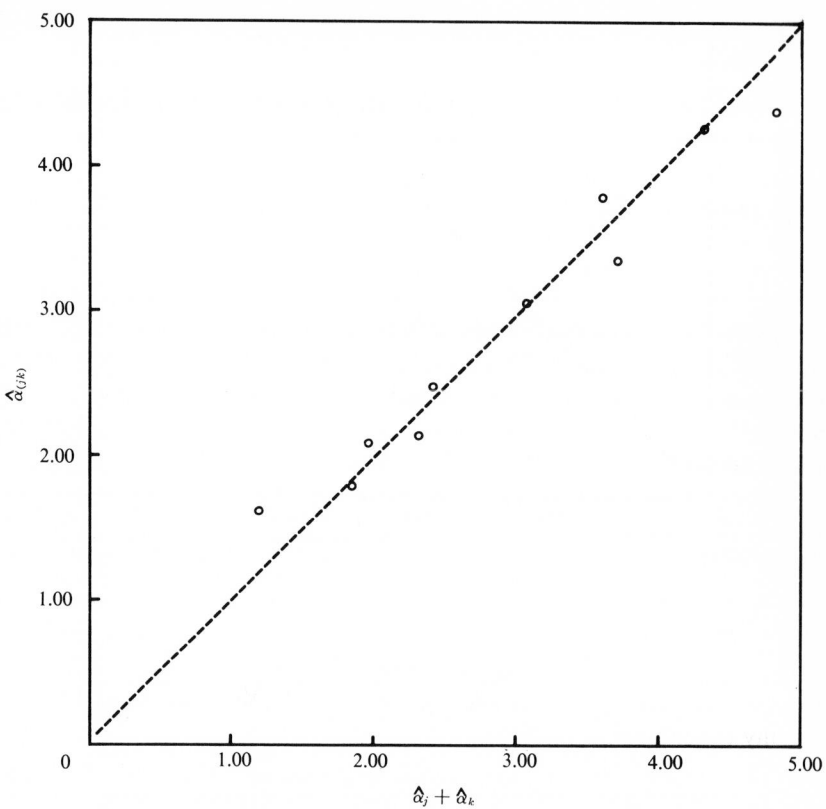

FIG. 9.5. Plot of $\hat{\alpha}_{jk}$ vs $(\hat{\alpha}_j + \hat{\alpha}_k)$ from results in Table 9.7.

A related check upon the additivity assumption involves the "additivity index," given as a ratio of standard deviation for composite scale values to standard deviation for estimates of C. From Table 9.7, the index is found to be 4.27. For purposes of a statistical test of regression, each value of c may be considered a departure from the regression line (of Figure 9.5). Then variability of the $\hat{\alpha}_{jk}$ may be decomposed into a source attributable to regression and a source attributable to the c's. The ratio of the variance estimates from these two sources, when the additive model fails to fit the data except for random effects, is approximately distributed as F with $l - 1$ and $l - 1$ degrees of freedom where l is the number of composite stimuli (10 in this example). For these data, $F = 17.38$ with 9 and 9 degrees of freedom, a highly significant regression effect.

Results from this study thus demonstrate the prediction of preference values of composite stimuli from preference values of their components when all are measured on the same preference scale and from the same rational point of origin.

A LOGARITHMIC " CASE VI " MODEL. The linear Case V model, assuming distinct comparatal dispersions for different classes of comparisons, appeared to provide an adequate fit for compound stimuli in the Thurstone-Jones study. However, Hicks and Campbell (1965) have published data from a series of studies which suggest limitations of this Case V solution. In three successive studies, involving paired-comparisons judgments of sets of birthday gifts selected to represent high, neutral, or low ranges of value, Hicks and Campbell report large systematic differences in the mean values of C for different stimulus ranges. Their results suggest that the additive relation of (9.13) fails to provide a uniform solution over changes in range of value of stimulus objects.[3] Similar results were obtained for judgments of severity of traffic accidents and bizarreness of behavior disorders.

The results reported by Hicks and Campbell would be expected if, over a wide range of stimuli, discriminal dispersions were not constant but rather were linearly related to mean discriminal values of the stimulus objects, i.e.

$$\sigma_j = a + b\alpha_j \quad \text{for all } j,$$

where a is a positive constant and b has the same sign as α_j. Then, with appropriate choice of unit on the logarithmic scale, the discriminal difference for any two stimuli is given by

$$y_{jk} = \log \hat{\alpha}_j - \log \hat{\alpha}_k \qquad (9.14)$$

(see Section 6.4.1).

Under this model, the Thurstone Case V solution yields, for each stimulus

$$\frac{1}{n} \sum_{k=1}^{n} y_{jk} = \log \hat{\alpha}_j - \frac{1}{n} \sum_{k=1}^{n} \log \hat{\alpha}_k,$$

---

[3] The major analysis reported by Hicks and Campbell is a Case V solution assuming equal comparatal dispersions for all comparisons, single-single, single-double, and double-double. However, the dependence of the estimates of C upon stimulus values also is evident when differing comparatal dispersions are assumed, as in the Thurstone-Jones development.

where n is the number of stimuli in the set being scaled. (We assume the availability of a complete $n \times n$ matrix of the y_{jk}.) A provisional origin on the logarithmic scale is appropriately established by setting

$$\sum_{k=1}^{n} \log \hat{\alpha}_k = 0. \tag{9.15}$$

Then the desired estimates of scale values are found to be

$$\hat{\alpha}_j = \text{antilog}\left(\sum_{k=1}^{n} \frac{y_{jk}}{n} \right). \tag{9.16}$$

Equation (9.16) provides estimates of mean affective values for composite as well as single stimuli. For these estimates, Equation (9.13) may be invoked to provide an estimate of the additive constant:

$$c = \hat{\alpha}_{jk} - \hat{\alpha}_j - \hat{\alpha}_k.$$

Accepting $\bar{c}$, the mean value of c, as the best estimate for C, we may shift the origin of affective value for all single and composite stimuli:

$$\hat{\alpha}' = \hat{\alpha} + \bar{c}.$$

Then,

$$\hat{\alpha}'_{jk} = \hat{\alpha}'_j + \hat{\alpha}'_k \quad \text{for all } j \neq k.$$

Example 9.2.1b

Jones (1967) has reanalyzed the data presented by Hicks and Campbell, using this log normal model. We exemplify the solution here for the case of birthday gifts.

Hicks and Campbell selected nine "gifts," and ordered them a priori according to estimated value, from a television set (gift A) to a dictionary (gift I). Further selection of subsets of these gifts provided stimuli for three distinct studies: a "high-context" condition, using gifts A, B, C, D, and E, a "neutral-context" condition, with gifts A, C, E, G, and I, and a "low-context" condition, with gifts E, F, G, H, and I. Subjects in each condition submitted paired-comparisons judgments involving the five single gifts and the ten possible composite pairs.

The results from Hicks and Campbell (1965), based upon a Case V solution assuming equal comparatal dispersions for all comparisons are graphically presented in Figure 9.6. Allowing differing comparatal dispersions for single-single, single-double, and double-double comparisons, following the model of Thurstone and Jones, produced the results of Figure 9.7. Neither solution is invariant over stimulus context.

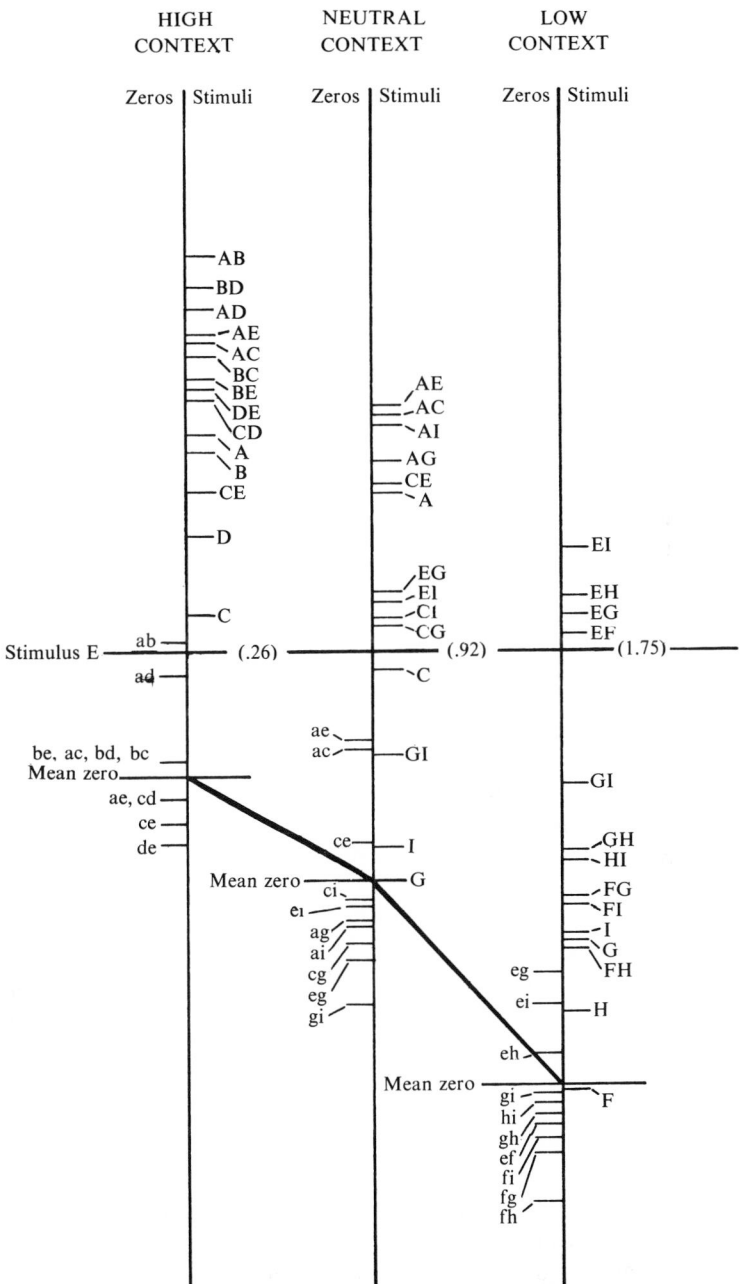

Fig. 9.6. Preference values and zero-point determinations assuming Case V.

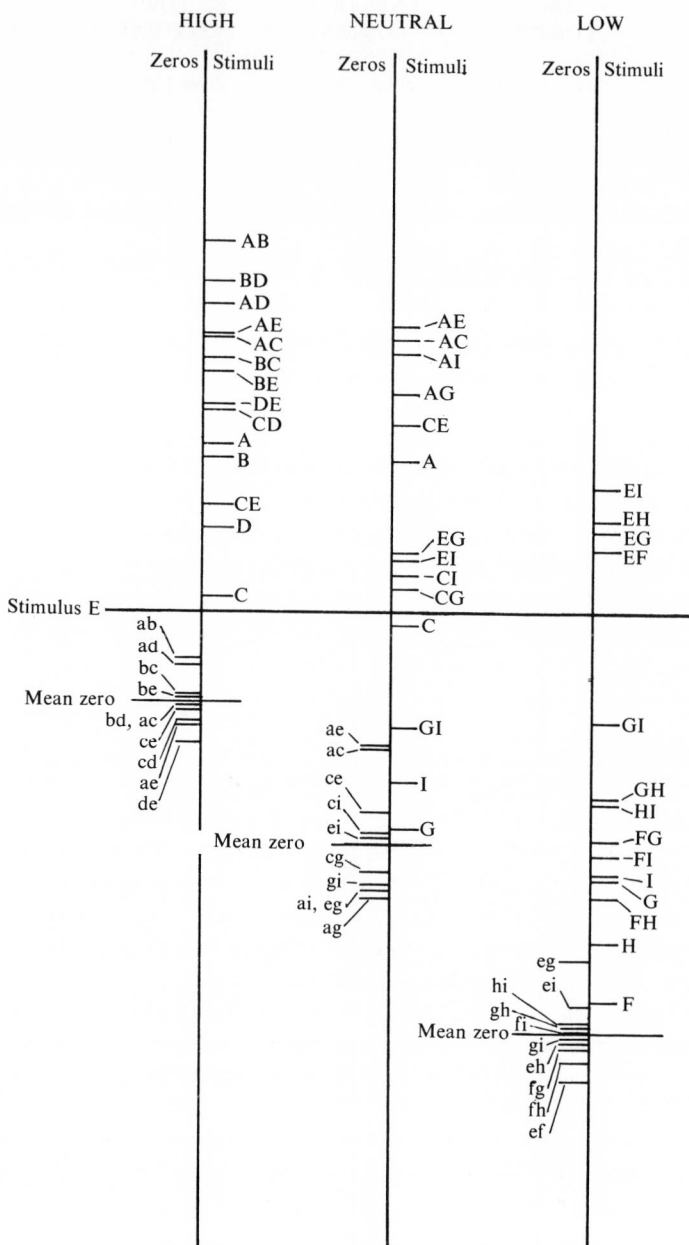

Fig. 9.7. Preference values and zero-point determinations assuming the model of Thurstone and Jones (1957).

Using a Case VI model separately for each stimulus context, it is clear that we are left with a distinct arbitrary scale unit for each solution, namely, from (9.16),

$$\prod_{k=1}^{n} \hat{\alpha}_k = 1,$$

for that set of $n = 15$ stimuli comprising the high-, neutral-, or low-context condition.

To equate scale unit across context conditions, the scale unit has been adjusted. The unit for the high-context condition is matched with that for the neutral condition by equating distance between stimulus E and stimulus A, common to the two conditions. The unit for the low-context condition is matched with that for the neutral condition by equating distances between stimulus E and stimulus G.[4]

Using this model for the data of Hicks and Campbell provides the results of Figure 9.8. Following their convention, the scale value α' for stimulus E is taken as a common reference point for the three context conditions, and zero determinations are plotted as distances below E.

Contrasting Figure 9.6 with Figures 9.7 and 9.8, it is seen that for all three context conditions the variability of zero-point determinations is greatest in Figure 9.6, suggesting that both the Thurstone-Jones Case V model and the Case VI model are much more adequate than the "unweighted" Case V for treatment of these data. Determination of additivity indices, suggested by Hicks and Campbell, confirm this impression. A striking finding, for the Case VI results of Figure 9.8, is the absence of systematic differences in mean zero points as a function of stimulus context.

Eisler (1965, p. 278) has stated ". . . it can be concluded that data obtained from an experiment of paired comparisons do not permit a distinction between Case V and Case VI." This is clearly true when only single stimuli are presented, since there is provided no internal evidence to distinguish the Case V solution, $y_{jk} = \hat{\alpha}_j - \hat{\alpha}_k$, from the Case VI solution of Equation (9.14). However, the imposition of an additive scale model and collection of data for both single and composite stimuli, does permit a distinction between goodness of fit for Case V and Case VI. Results of the present analysis argue strongly for Case VI for the data of Hicks and Campbell. Also, results from the Case VI solution lead to a completely distinct conclusion regarding the rational zero point. Under the Case VI analysis, the zero point is found to be remarkably invariant under changes in stimulus context. This finding, alone, would

---

[4] This scale adjustment was not made by Hicks and Campbell. However, their results would be relatively unaffected by the adjustment, as is clear from Figure 9.6. The adjustment serves only as a "scale factor," and in no significant way influences the estimators of the rational zero point.

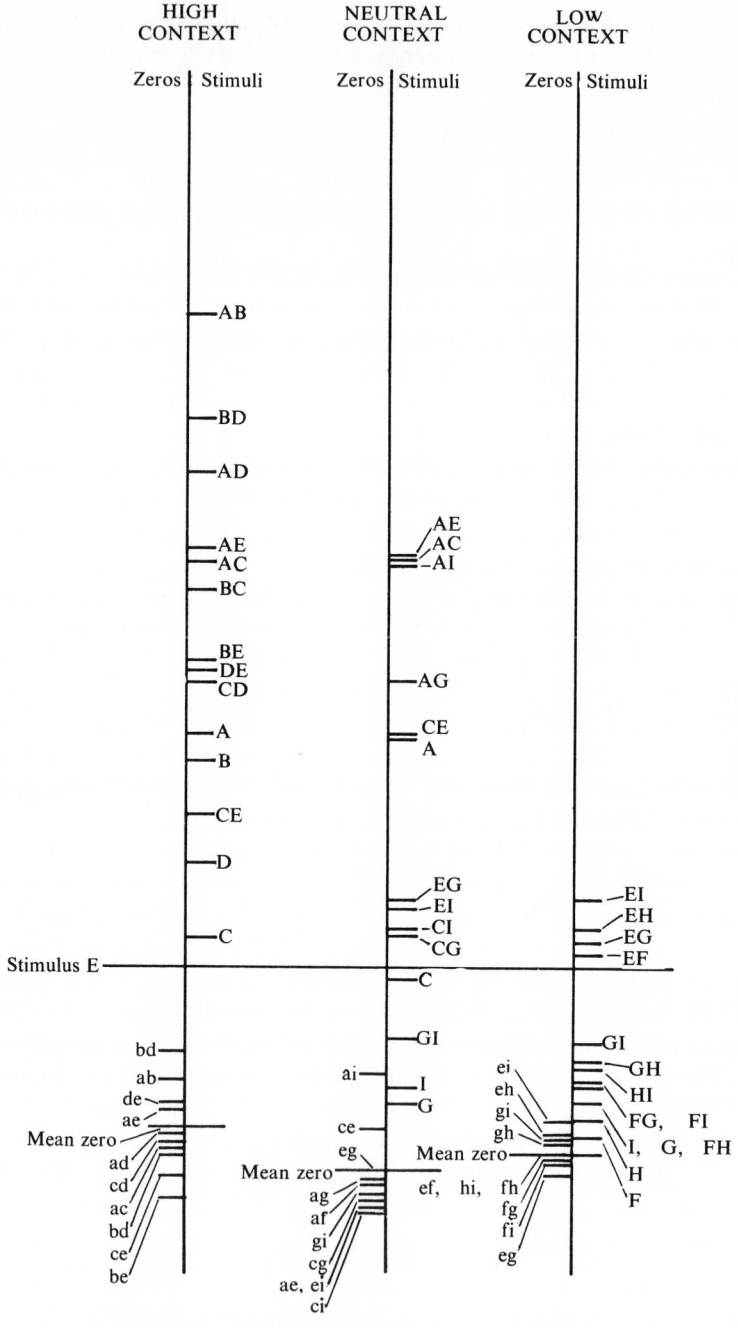

FIG. 9.8. Preference values and zero-point determinations assuming Case VI.

seem sufficient justification for preferring the log normal response function of Case VI to the normal response function of Case V.

9.2.2 Prediction of Choice for Compounds Using Contingent Paired Comparisons[5]

A modification of the method of paired comparisons, suggested by Shuford, Jones, and Bock (1960), provides another method of estimating the rational origin on the preference continuum. In this method of "contingent paired comparisons" subjects are required to make paired-comparison choices in which each alternative of a pair of stimuli represents a risky rather than a certain outcome. Thus the expressed preferences depend not only upon the objects, but also upon the probability that, if one side of the pair of stimuli is "selected" by the subject, the object would be "acquired." The method of contingent paired comparisons may be employed for determining preference values on a scale with a rational origin. For this purpose, a subject's judgment of a stimulus pair is defined by his answer to the following question: "Would you prefer to receive object A with probability p or object B with probability $1 - p$?" Selection of the former alternative provides an opportunity for "receiving" object A with probability p or of receiving nothing with probability $1 - p$; selection of the latter provides for receipt of object B with probability $1 - p$ or nothing with probability p. Explicit solution for the preference value of "nothing" provides a rational zero point for the preference scale.

As in Chapter 6, let v_j and v_k represent the discriminal processes of objects j and k, respectively, for a random subject. Let the joint distribution of v_j and v_k be bivariate normal: $N(\alpha_j, \alpha_k \sigma_j, \sigma_k, \rho_{jk})$. Then $v_{jk} = v_j - v_k$ is normally distributed with mean $\alpha_j - \alpha_k$ and variance $\sigma_j^2 + \sigma_k^2 - 2\sigma_j \sigma_k \rho_{jk}$.

In the contingent paired-comparisons situation, the alternative options are (i) receipt of object j with probability p_l or "nothing" with probability $(1 - p_l)$; (ii) receipt of object k with probability $(1 - p_l)$ or "nothing" with probability p_l. If the preference for the status quo is equal to a constant value, θ, for all subjects, then the difference between the expected preference values for the alternative options in a contingent paired-comparison item is normally distributed with mean

$$\alpha_{(jk)l} = p_l \alpha_j + (1 - p_l)\theta - p_l\theta - (1 - p_l)\alpha_k$$
$$= p_l \alpha_j - (1 - p_l)\alpha_k + (1 - 2p_l)\theta$$

and variance

$$\sigma_{(j,k)l}^2 = p_l^2 \sigma_j^2 + (1 - p_l)^2 \sigma_k^2 - 2p_l(1 - p_l)\sigma_j \sigma_k \rho_{jk}. \tag{9.17}$$

---

[5] This section is an abridgment of Shuford, Jones, and Bock (1960).

The unit normal deviates associated, in the population, with mean utility differences for the two alternative options have the composition

$$\mu_{(j,k)l} = \frac{p_l \alpha_j - (1 - p_l)\alpha_k + (1 - 2p_l)\theta}{\sigma_{(j,k)l}}.$$
(9.18)

Assuming as in Case V of Thurstone's law of comparative judgment $\sigma_j^2 = \sigma_k^2 = 1$, and assuming $\sigma_{jk} = 0$, for all j, k, (9.17) becomes

$$\sigma_{(j,k)l}^2 = p_l^2 + (1 - p_l)^2 = \omega_l^2.$$
(9.19)

Substituting ω_l for $\sigma_{(j,k)l}$ in the denominator of (9.18), multiplying both sides of (9.18) by ω_l, and summing over all probability levels l, yields

$$\sum_{l=1}^{r} \omega_l \mu_{(j,k)l} = \alpha_j \sum_{l=1}^{r} p_l - \alpha_k \sum_{l=1}^{r} (1 - p_l) + \theta \sum_{l=1}^{r} (1 - 2p_l).$$
(9.20)

We now introduce an important restriction upon the design of the experimental study, namely that, for the r values selected for p_l,

$$\frac{1}{r} \sum_{l=1}^{r} p_l = \frac{1}{2}.$$
(9.21)

Under this restriction,

$$\sum_{l=1}^{r} p_l = \sum_{l=1}^{r} (1 - p_l) = \frac{r}{2}$$
(9.22)

and

$$\sum_{l=1}^{r} (1 - 2p_l) = 0.$$
(9.23)

Substituting (9.22) and (9.23) in (9.20),

$$\sum_{l=1}^{r} \omega_l \mu_{(j,k)l} = \frac{r}{2} (\alpha_j - \alpha_k),$$

or

$$\alpha_j - \alpha_k = \frac{2}{r} \sum_{l=1}^{r} \omega_l \mu_{(j,k)l}.$$
(9.24)

Note that (9.24) implies a skew–symmetric matrix of summed (weighted) normal deviates $\Sigma_l \omega_l \mu_{(j,k)l}$, since (9.24) demands that

$$\sum_{l} \omega_l \mu_{(j,k)l} = -\sum_{l} \omega_l \mu_{(k,j)l} \quad \text{and} \quad \sum_{l} \omega_l \mu_{(j,k)l} = 0.$$

TABLE 9.8. Matrix Elements to be Summed in Equation (9.25)

$\alpha_2 p_l - \alpha_1(1 - p_l)$ $+ \theta(1 - 2p_l)$		$\cdots$
$\alpha_3 p_l - \alpha_1(1 - p_l)$ $+ \theta(1 - 2p_l)$	$\alpha_3 p_l - \alpha_2(1 - p_l)$ $+ \theta(1 - 2p_l)$	$\cdots$
$\vdots$	$\vdots$	$\vdots$
$\alpha_n p_l - \alpha_1(1 - p_l)$ $+ \theta(1 - 2p_l)$	$\alpha_n p_l - \alpha_2(1 - p_l)$ $+ \theta(1 - 2p_l)$	$\cdots$
		$a_n p_l - \alpha_{n-1}(1 - p_l)$ $+ \theta(1 - 2p_l)$

Except for the known constant $2/r$, the parametric form of the contingent paired comparisons under restriction (9.11) is the same as that assumed in ordinary paired comparisons. This fact will be used later (Eq. (9.24a)) to express the relative affective value for the jth object.

Now for each level of p_l write only those elements of the matrix $\omega_l \mu_{(j,k)l}$ below the diagonal, where $j > k$ as in Table 9.8. The sum of these elements for $j > k$ is

$$\omega_l \sum_{j=2}^{n} \sum_{k=1}^{j-1} \mu_{(j,k)l} = (n-1)p_l \sum_{j=1}^{n} \alpha_j - \sum_{k=1}^{n-1}(n-k)\alpha_k + \frac{n(n-1)}{2}(1 - 2p_l)\theta.$$

(9.25)

Each value, α_j, in (9.25) may be considered a sum of two components, one the scale distance, a_j^0, of the jth stimulus from an arbitrary *provisional* scale origin, the other a constant, γ, representing the distance of that arbitrary origin from the rational origin. That is,

$$\alpha_j = \alpha_j^0 + \gamma.$$

(9.26)

Let the provisional origin be given by the restriction

$$\sum_{j=1}^{n} \alpha_j^0 = 0.$$

(9.27)

Substituting (9.26) and (9.27) in (9.25) and simplifying,

$$\omega_l \sum_{j=2}^{n} \sum_{k=1}^{j-1} \mu_{(j,k)l} = -\sum_{k=1}^{n-1}(n-k)\alpha_k^0 + \frac{n(n-1)}{2}(1 - 2p_l)(\theta - \gamma).$$

(9.28)

Replacing parameters by estimates, (9.28) becomes

$$\omega_l \sum_{j=2}^{n} \sum_{k=1}^{j-1} y_{(j,k)l} = -\sum_{k=1}^{n-1}(n-k)\hat{a}_k^0 + \frac{n(n-1)}{2}(1 - 2p_l)(\theta - \gamma),$$

(9.29)

where $\hat{\alpha}_k^0$ estimates α_k^0, and $y_{(j,k)l}$ is the normal deviate associated with $p_{(j,k)l}$, the sample proportion of choice of the option which includes outcome j with probability p_l over the option which includes outcome k with probability $(1 - p_l)$.

Equation (9.29) is a linear expression denoting the random variate $\omega_l \Sigma\Sigma y_{(j,k)l}$ and the fixed variate $(1 - 2p_l)$ for $l = 1, 2, \ldots, r$. The quantity $-\sum_{k-1}^{n-1}(n - k)\hat{\alpha}_k^0$, which does not involve l, is a location constant of no particular interest. On the other hand $(\theta - \gamma)$, the slope of the line represented by (9.29), is of interest. It is the amount which must be added to transform relative utilities into absolute utilities, taken from the point which represents the utility of the status quo. With fallible data the constant $(\theta - \gamma)$ may be estimated by plotting $\omega_l \Sigma\Sigma y_{(j,k)l}$ against $(1 - 2p_l)$ for all l and determining graphically the slope of the line of best fit. Alternatively, if we wish to minimize the squared discrepancy between the observed $\omega_l \Sigma\Sigma y_{(j,k)l}$ and those predicted from (9.29) the usual least squares solution yields

$$(\hat{\theta} - \hat{\gamma}) = \frac{2\sum_{l=1}^{r}(1 - 2p_l)\omega_l \sum_{j=2}^{n}\sum_{k=1}^{j-1} y_{(j,k)l}}{n(n - 1)\sum_{l=1}^{r}(1 - 2p_l)^2}. \qquad (9.30)$$

Note that, because of (9.21), the mean of $(1 - 2p_l)$ is zero. Allowing $\hat{\theta}$ to be zero, then $\hat{\gamma}$ may be found from (9.30), after multiplying both sides of the equation by -1. Adding $\hat{\gamma}$ to each $\hat{\alpha}_j^0$ yields an estimate of absolute utility, $\hat{\alpha}_j$ (see Equation (9.27)). The $\hat{\alpha}_j^0$ values are determined from the sample analogs to (9.24),

$$\hat{\alpha}_j^0 - \hat{\alpha}_k^0 = \frac{2}{r}\sum_{l=1}^{r}\omega_l y_{(j,k)l}. \qquad (9.24a)$$

But

$$\sum_{k=1}^{n}\hat{\alpha}_k^0 = 0; \qquad (9.27a)$$

thus

$$\hat{\alpha}_j^0 = \frac{2}{nr}\sum_{k=1}^{n}\sum_{l=1}^{n}\omega_l y_{(j,k)l} \qquad (9.31)$$

and the estimated absolute value for object j is given by (9.26).

It should be noted that only the parametric solution for contingent paired-comparisons model has been discussed here. It is not difficult, however, to derive the normal equations for least squares estimation of the utilities of the objects. One finds that even for a single level of p_l the matrix of coefficients of these equations is nonsingular (unlike conventional paired comparisons). Thus in principle one may estimate the absolute utilities directly without the restriction $\Sigma p_l = r/2$. The much greater simplicity of the parametric solution recommends it for practical use, particularly since the restriction on p_l is easy to meet. However, use of the restriction may be wasteful in some applications, particularly if average utilities of the objects differ extremely.

Example 9.2.2

A questionnaire was administered to 146 male students in General Psychology classes at the University of North Carolina. Data for the 141 subjects who responded to all items in the questionnaire form the basis for analysis.

An outcome of each lottery in the questionnaire was the (pretended) receipt of a gift. Each student was presented with a form containing line drawings and catalog descriptions of the four gifts: (A) record player, (B) pen and pencil set, (C) briefcase, and (D) desk lamp. (Subjects had had previous experience with the gifts since they had rated their preference for these and other gifts on successive-intervals forms immediately prior to the administration of the questionnaire described.) Subjects were instructed to "assume that you do not already own any of the articles, and that they are gifts for your own personal use, which you may not sell."

Each of the 34 items consisted of two alternative lottery options, represented by two rectangles, each containing five squares. In some squares appeared identical line drawings of a gift; the other squares were blank. Subjects were instructed to imagine that the five squares within each rectangle were tickets which would be placed in a box and thoroughly mixed. One ticket would be randomly selected and the subject would receive as a gift the article pictured on the ticket. If a blank ticket were drawn he would receive nothing. A sample item appears as Figure 9.9.

The contingent paired-comparisons items consisted of a lottery offering gift j with probability p and nothing with probability $(1 - p)$ and a lottery offering gift k with probability $(1 - p)$ and nothing with probability p, where p takes on the values 1/5, 2/5, 3/5, and 4/5. The four probability levels and six possible pairs of gifts yielded 24 options of this type (Table 9.10). These contingent paired-comparisons items are used to measure the average utilities of the gifts with respect to a rational origin, the utility of the status quo.

The remaining 10 items provided internal checks on the scaling model. Six of these were paired-comparisons items; i.e. one lottery offered gift j with probability 1, the other lottery gift k with probability 1. Each of the other four items contained all four gifts as outcomes; i.e. one lottery offered

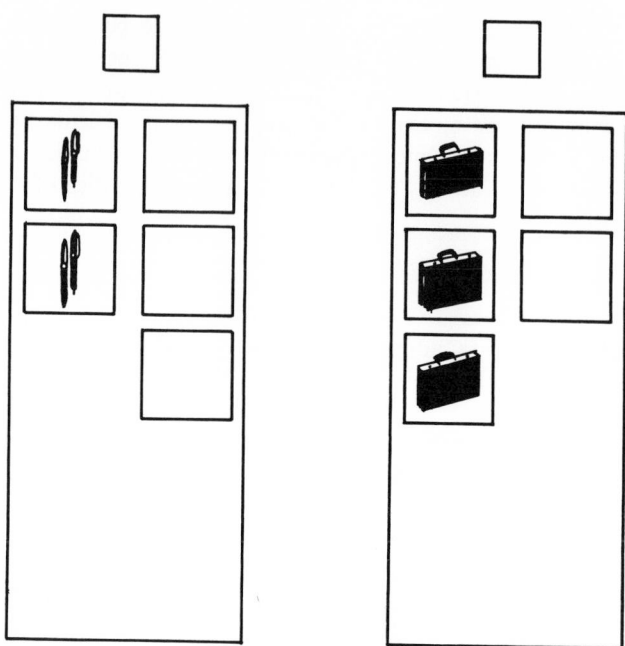

FIG. 9.9. Sample item—contingent paired comparisons.

gift h with probability p and gift j with probability $(1 - p)$, the other lottery, gift k with probability $(1 - p)$ and gift m with probability p, with p taking on the values of 1/5, 2/5, 3/5, and 4/5.

   The subjects indicated their choices by placing a check mark in a small box above the desired option (see Figure 9.9). The proportion of subjects who chose the first lottery over the second lottery was determined for each item and transformed to a normal deviate. The average utility of each of the four gifts was estimated from the contingent paired-comparisons data by using the parametric solution, Equations (9.27a) and (9.31). The estimates $\hat{\alpha}_j$ are 2.84, 1.35, .70, and 1.87 for gifts A, B, C, and D.

   To evaluate the consistency of the data, the estimated utilities were used to reconstruct the normal deviates and thus the proportions for the contingent paired-comparisons items. Table 9.10 gives the observed proportion (column A), the reconstructed proportion (column B), and the absolute difference between the two (column C) for each of the 34 items in the questionnaire. The average absolute difference for the 24 contingent paired-comparisons is .056.

   A smaller average absolute difference, .051, is found for the six paired-comparisons items even though they were not used to estimate the utilities.

TABLE 9.10. Comparison Between Observed Proportions and
Reconstructed and Predicted Proportions

Option					*A* Observed proportion	*B* Reconstructed proportion	*C* Error $|A-B|$
I vs II							
A	B				.894	.854	.040
A	C				.950	.935	.105
A	D				.872	.754	.118
B	C				.752	.677	.075
B	D				.390	.357	.033
C	D				.227	.204	.023
						Average	.051
.2A	.8B				.348	.266	.082
.4A	.6B				.830	.672	.158
.6A	.4B				.936	.946	.010
.8A	.2B				.964	.997	.033
.2A	.8C				.447	.504	.057
.4A	.6C				.894	.839	.055
.6A	.4C				.972	.976	.004
.8A	.2C				.986	.995	.009
.2A	.8D				.220	.131	.089
.4A	.6D				.688	.492	.196
.6A	.4D				.908	.907	.001
.8A	.2D				.972	.989	.017
.2B	.8C				.234	.364	.130
.4B	.6C				.518	.568	.050
.6B	.4C				.823	.770	.053
.8B	.2C				.908	.874	.034
.2B	.8D				.057	.069	.012
.4B	.6D				.220	.211	.009
.6B	.4D				.553	.534	.019
.8B	.2D				.844	.805	.039
.2C	.8D				.007	.050	.043
.4C	.6D				.078	.122	.044
.6C	.4D				.390	.324	.066
.8C	.2D				.730	.589	.141
						Average	.056
.2A,	.8C	.2B,	.8D		.447	.292	.155
.4A,	.6C	.4B,	.6D		.624	.459	.165
.6A,	.4C	.6B,	.4D		.830	.660	.170
.8A,	.2C	.8B,	.2D		.897	.794	.085
						Average	.144

Probably this occurs because fewer assumptions are required for the paired-comparisons model or, alternatively, because a paired-comparisons judgment is easier to make than a contingent paired-comparisons judgment. This latter explanation is supported by the finding of a much larger average absolute difference of .144 for the more complex items involving all four gifts.

It is instructive to predict, from results from contingent paired-comparisons, the preference values of compound stimuli obtained in Section 9.2.1. With four stimuli common to the two studies, we may plot the values $\hat{\alpha}_{jk}$ from Example 9.2.1a against values for corresponding $\hat{\alpha}_j + \hat{\alpha}_k$ from the present results, as shown in Figure 9.10. The congruence is consistent with the

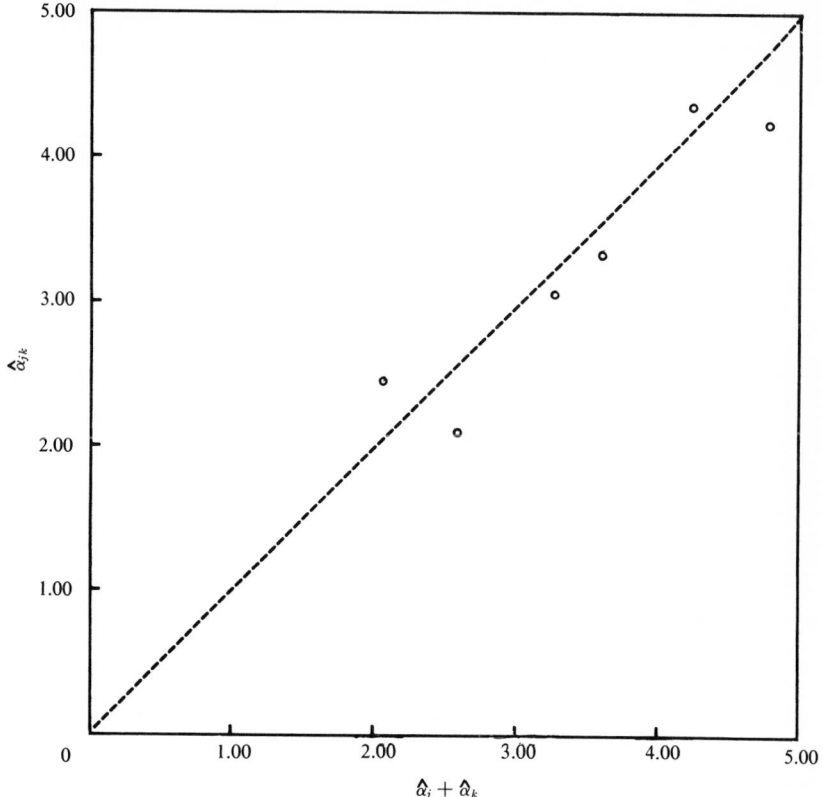

FIG. 9.10. Plot of $\hat{\alpha}_{jk}$ values from Table 9.7 vs $(\hat{\alpha}_j + \hat{\alpha}_k)$ as determined from contingent paired comparisons.

conclusion that the preference scales found in the two studies have the same unit of measurement and rational origin, and that the linear model for predicting compound from composite stimuli once again has been supported.

9.2.3   Prediction of Choice for Compounds Using Successive Categories

It might be expected that the method of successive categories, as described in Chapter 8, would provide a solution to the problem of predicting preference values of compound from composite stimuli. As in Section 9.2.1, we would consider a set of single stimuli, $X_1, X_2, \ldots, X_n$, and the possible $n(n-1)/2$ double stimuli, $X_{12}, X_{13}, \ldots, X_{1n}, X_{23}, \ldots, X_{2n}, \ldots$, each presented for assignment by subjects to one of m preference categories.

However, the problem of fixing the unit of measurement on the scale of the double stimuli seriously complicates the successive categories model. The unit of measurement for single stimuli is given by Equation (8.9) to be

$$\sum_{j=1}^{n} \frac{1}{\hat{\sigma}_j} = n.$$

If the scale solution for single stimuli were completely independent of that for double stimuli, and if the conventional method of successive categories were adopted for double stimuli, then the unit of measurement for double stimuli would arbitrarily be set by

$$\sum_{j<k} \frac{1}{\hat{\sigma}_{(jk)}} = \frac{n(n-1)}{2}. \tag{9.32}$$

Then the average discriminal dispersion for single stimuli would be precisely equal to the average for double stimuli. However, as described in Section 9.2.1, the scaling model leads us to anticipate discriminal dispersions for double stimuli unequal to and generally larger than those for single stimuli. From the law of categorical judgment, it might be specified that

$$\sigma'_{(jk)} \simeq (\sigma_j^2 + \sigma_k^2 + 2\rho_{jk}\sigma_j\sigma_k)^{1/2}, \tag{9.33}$$

where $\sigma'_{(jk)}$ is a prediction of the discriminal dispersion for double stimuli, σ_j and σ_k are discriminal dispersions for the component single stimuli, and ρ_{jk} is the product-moment correlation coefficient between distributions of preference (v_j and v_k) for the two single stimuli.

There have been several attempts to establish the validity of an additive linear model of successive categories, that of Kelton (1956), an analysis by Jones (1957) of data earlier presented by Rimoldi (1956), and an empirical study by Jones (1959b) replicating Kelton's study with slightly different experimental conditions. In each case, there was evidence for a clear linear relation between preference values $\hat{\alpha}_{jk}$ of double stimuli and $\hat{\alpha}_j + \hat{\alpha}_k$, the sum of values for component single stimuli. In the reanalysis of the Rimoldi data (Jones, 1957) evidence was compelling that the intercept of the line of best linear fit corresponded to the center of the successive category at the "neutral" point of the rating form. In every case, however, the slope of the linear relation differed from unity. (Results consistent with these also have been reported more recently by Hicks, 1962, and by Hicks and Campbell, 1965.)

On the basis of these studies using successive categories, it would appear that subjects' responses follow neither the expectation provided by Equation (9.32) nor that of (9.33). The unit of measurement (and thus the scale values associated with the various rating categories) clearly is not equivalent for single and double stimuli, but neither is it that predicted from the rational model of stimulus combination, Equation (9.33). The context of judgment, single or double stimuli, thus appears to influence the judges' interpretation of the "meaning" connoted by the rating categories. As a consequence, no general additive model for the method of successive categories may be found adequate to predict combination of preference values. Unlike the methods of paired comparisons and rank order, the method of successive categories depends not upon direct comparison of stimuli but upon comparison via an intervening frame of reference—that provided by the labels of the categories on the rating form. And to the extent that the interpretation of those categories shifts from one judgmental context to another, results will not be strictly comparable.

9.2.4 Prediction of Choice for Compounds Using Rank Order

Motivated by the failure of verification of an additive linear model for preference values of compound stimuli by the method of successive categories, McKeon (1961) investigated the method of rank order (see Section 6.8) for prediction of choice for compounds. With 10 single and 45 composite items, the same stimuli as those selected earlier by Kelton (1956), a total of 55 stimuli were to be assessed on a single scale. McKeon utilized a partially balanced incomplete block design (PBIB) selected from Bose et al. (1954). Each subject ranked 10 stimuli in order of preference (1, 2, ..., 10) for each of 11 blocks of stimuli. The first block contained the 10 single stimuli and each of the 10 following blocks contained one single and nine double stimuli. Each single or double stimulus appeared in two different blocks.

In place of the usual rating form an experimental procedure especially suited to ranking judgments was used. The names of the single or double items were printed on IBM cards. The subjects were asked to rank the cards in each block in order of preference. When the experiment was completed the cards were run through an IBM 407, programmed to punch a set of 11 summary cards for each subject, giving the subject's rankings for each block.

The use of punched cards for presenting stimuli to judges has the following advantages: (1) The ranking process is made easier; (2) the arrangement of cards within blocks may be randomized; (3) punched card systems conveniently may be used for processing data; (4) the original cards are not altered by the analysis and may be used over again a number of times.

One hundred seventy eight undergraduates at the University of North Carolina served as subjects. The experiment was conducted on a group basis. Following a ten-minute introductory explanation of the experiment, each subject was given a pack of 110 cards, 11 blocks of 10 cards each, and a booklet describing each of the 10 gift items. They were instructed to arrange the items, whether single or double, in the order of their suitability as gifts for friends. To avoid purely economic evaluation, they were told the gifts could not be resold. The ten gift items were as follows:

(1) camera	(6) pen and pencil set
(2) typewriter	(7) cigarette case and lighter
(3) portable radio	(8) briefcase
(4) record player	(9) bookcase
(5) dictionary	(10) desk lamp

The rankings of the 11 blocks took about 35 minutes, or averaged about 3 minutes per block.

The analysis of the data was performed by a computer program. In this application, rather than directly generating for each block a paired-comparison matrix of proportions by the method of Section 6.8, this matrix was approximated by an analytic procedure (McKeon, 1961, p. 40). From data of each block, a complete weighted least squares solution was obtained under Case V assumptions for preference values of all stimuli which appeared in that block (Section 6.4.2). Then, using estimated affective values derived from each of the 11 blocks as "observations," the PBIB design was solved for the scale values of all stimuli by the intra-block solution of Bose et al. (1954).

In McKeon's solution, not only were the usual Müller-Urban weights employed, but also observed normal deviates were multiplied by the theoretically expected standard deviations. Assuming unit variance for the distribution of discriminal processes associated with each single stimulus, variances for the difference processes (the comparatal variances) are expected to be as in Section 9.2.1:

for single-single comparisons, $\mathscr{V}(v_j - v_k) = 2,$
for single-double comparisons, $\mathscr{V}(v_j + v_k - v_l) = 3,$
for double-double comparisons, $\mathscr{V}(v_j + v_k - v_l - v_m) = 4.$

The estimation of preference values for single and double stimuli on the same scale allows for the solution of a rational zero point for the scale and a test of the linear model for combination of preference values, namely

$$\hat{\alpha}_{jk} = \hat{\alpha}_j + \hat{\alpha}_k,$$

where $\hat{\alpha}_{jk}$ is the estimated preference value for a double stimulus, $\hat{\alpha}_j$ and $\hat{\alpha}_k$

estimates for the corresponding single stimuli. The solution is obtained from the estimated preference values on a scale with arbitrary origin by setting

$$(\hat{\alpha}_{jk}^0 + c) = (\hat{\alpha}_j^0 + c) + (\hat{\alpha}_k^0 + c).$$

Then

$$c = \hat{\alpha}_{jk}^0 - (\hat{\alpha}_j + \hat{\alpha}_k),$$

and from $n(n-1)/2$ double stimuli,

$$c = \frac{2}{n(n-1)} \sum_{j<k}^{\cdot} [\hat{\alpha}_{jk}^0 - (\hat{\alpha}_j^0 + \hat{\alpha}_k^0)]$$

$$= \frac{2}{n(n-1)} \left[\sum_{j<k} \hat{\alpha}_{jk}^0 - (n-1) \sum_j \hat{\alpha}_j^0 \right].$$

Since the $\hat{\alpha}^0$'s are defined so that

$$\sum_j \hat{\alpha}_j^0 + \sum_{j<k} \hat{\alpha}_{jk}^0 = 0,$$

then

$$c = \frac{-2}{n-1} \sum_{j=1}^n \hat{\alpha}_j^0.$$

In McKeon's study, with $n = 10$, $\sum_{j=1}^{10} \hat{\alpha}_j = -6.954$, and $c = 1.545$. Adjusting all preference values so that $\hat{\alpha} = \hat{\alpha}^0 + 1.545$ yields the estimates given in Table 9.11. The values are plotted in Figure 9.11.

TABLE 9.11. Preference Values for Single and Double Items

Singles		Doubles			Doubles			Doubles		
1	1.744	1,	2	3.374	2,	9	2.790	5,	6	.824
2	2.093	1,	3	3.305	2,	10	2.453	5,	7	.144
3	1.893	1,	4	3.288	3,	4	3.244	5,	8	.390
4	1.528	1,	5	2.123	3,	5	2.193	5,	9	1.082
5	.554	1,	6	2.210	3,	6	2.048	5,	10	.742
6	.085	1,	7	1.421	3,	7	1.558	6,	7	.118
7	−.485	1,	8	1.745	3,	8	1.908	6,	8	.137
8	−.189	1,	9	2.362	3,	9	2.523	6,	9	.869
9	.988	1,	10	2.230	3,	10	2.258	6,	10	.471
10	.286	2,	3	3.589	4,	5	1.977	7,	8	.243
		2,	4	3.307	4,	6	1.817	7,	9	.293
		2,	5	2.306	4,	7	1.415	7,	10	−.046
		2,	6	2.329	4,	8	1.756	8,	9	.643
		2,	7	1.186	4,	9	2.347	8,	10	.334
		2,	8	1.956	4,	10	1.884	9,	10	1.443

The results lend support to the additive linear model, with possible exceptions at the lower end of the scale. The two lowest preference values for single stimuli, for item 7 (cigarette case and lighter) and item 8 (briefcase)

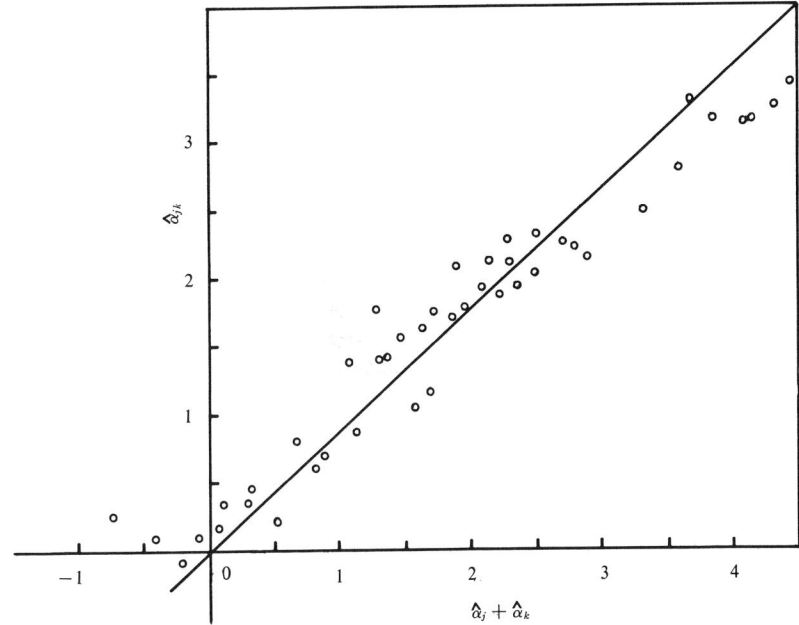

Fig. 9.11. Plot of $\hat{\alpha}_{jk}$ vs $(\hat{\alpha}_j + \hat{\alpha}_k)$ as determined from the method of rank order.

are negative, and the preference value for item 6 (pen and pencil set) is near zero. The pairs containing combinations of items 6, 7, and 8 tend to have greater preference values than those predicted from the sums of values for their composites.

The results of McKeon using the method of rank order are consistent with findings from the methods of paired comparisons and contingent paired comparisons with respect to the adequacy of a linear model of combination of preference values. It might be noted, however, that while the results of McKeon are internally consistent with the scaling model, preference values for particular stimuli exhibit little systematic relation with preference values for the identical stimuli as found in paired comparisons, Section 9.2.1, or contingent paired comparisons, Section 9.2.2. A probable explanation for this discrepancy, and for the finding of several negative preference values, is that it is a result of the form of instructions to subjects. In the studies reported in Sections 9.2.1 and 9.2.2, subjects were asked to judge stimulus objects (doubles as well as singles) as to how much they would like to receive the objects as gifts. In McKeon's study, subjects "were instructed to arrange the items, whether single or double, in the order of their suitability as gifts for friends." If double gifts were considered by college-student subjects as not particularly suitable gifts for friends, then the apparent zero point would be elevated, and McKeon's findings would be expected to differ in the way they were found to differ from results of the earlier studies.

9.2.5 Prediction of Paired-comparison Preference Values for Compounds from Successive Categories Preference Values of Components

In an unpublished study, Jones and Bock (1959) investigated an extension of Thurstonian scaling methods for the prediction of choice for food combinations, given the "rating-form" preference responses of subjects for the constituent food items.

Suppose one is interested in providing meals comprised of three preselected components, a meat dish, a vegetable, and a starch. If the selection may be among r meats, s vegetables, and t starches, the number of possible meals which may be formed, $r \times s \times t$, quickly becomes large with increases in r, s, and t. It is hardly practical to attempt a direct evaluation of acceptability of all possible meals. Great economy would be effected by a model which allows accurate estimation of the preference of a complete meal from knowledge of the preference of its parts.

Let us postulate a model of preference combination such that the mean affective value for a meat-vegetable-starch kind of meal could be predicted knowing affective values for the single foods—the meat, the vegetable, and the starch—and the affective values of pairs of these foods in interaction —the meat-vegetable pair, the meat-starch pair, and the vegetable-starch pair. To make predictions of preference for the three-component meals, using such a model, we require $r + s + t$ ratings of single foods and $rs + rt + st$ ratings of pairs of foods. With r, s, and t each equal to four, this model already results in economy of measurement compared with the alternative of direct assessment of preference for all three-component menus. As r, s, and t increase, the relative economy rapidly increases.

The dependent variable in this study is a scaled measure of preference for each of a specified set of meals. Meals are scaled by the method of paired comparisons. The independent variables are scaled affective values for the single foods and for the pairs of foods, determined from responses to a category rating form by the method of successive categories.

A general linear regression model is used to determine a prediction equation, predicting preference for meals from the independent variables. The model is displayed in Table 9.12. The meat dishes are designated as Class X, the vegetables as Y, the starches as Z. Then the expected mean affective values for given foods may be represented by the expressions in Section A of Table 9.12. Here, χ_i, ϕ_j, and ω_k are absolute scale values for a given meat, a vegetable, and a starch, respectively. ν, ξ, and π are unknown location adjustments, since the scale for each class of foods is allowed a

TABLE 9.12. Generation of a Linear Regression Model for Predicting (D), the
Affective Values for Meals

(A)	$X_i = \alpha(\chi_i - \nu)$, $Y_j = \beta(\phi_j - \xi)$, $Z_k = \gamma(\omega_k - \pi)$.
(B)	$(XY)_{ij} = \delta[\chi_i + \phi_j + (\chi\phi)_{ij} - \rho]$. $(XZ)_{ik} = \varepsilon[\chi_i + \omega_k + (\chi\omega)_{ik} - \sigma]$. $(YZ)_{jk} = \zeta[\phi_j + \omega_k + (\phi\omega)_{jk} - \tau]$.
(C)	$(XYZ)_{ijk} = \eta[\chi_i + \phi_j + (\chi\phi)_{ij} + (\chi\omega)_{ik} + (\phi\omega)_{jk} - \theta]$.
(D)	$V_{ijk} = a(XY)_{ij} + b(XZ)_{ik} + c(YZ)_{jk} - dX_i - eY_j - fZ_k - g$.

distinct arbitrary origin. α, β, and γ are unknown scale adjustments, to allow for distinct units of measurement for the three classes of food. (The model thus recognizes the probable differences in location and scale parameters for differing classes of stimuli, as discussed in Section 9.2.3.)

The expected mean affective values for pairs of foods are specified in Section B of Table 9.12, and the expected mean affective value for a three-item meal is given in Section C. This final composition includes interactions of pairs of foods, but excludes all three-way interactions which are assumed to play no appreciable part in determining preference for a meal. Finally, solving from the expressions in Sections A and B for the parameters of the expression in Section C, we have the result of Section D, Table 9.12. Under the model, then, the scale values of the meals, V_{ijk}, may be estimated by a linear combination of the observed scale values for single and paired constituents; the lowercase letters represent unknown positive constants. Although this final expression does not specify the magnitudes of the coefficients, it indicates that the signs of the coefficients for double items should be positive, while those for the singles should be negative. To evaluate the sign pattern and the empirical fit of the model, a least squares solution is utilized to estimate the coefficients, and a test of significance is performed upon the residual variation in the analysis of regression.

Subjects for the study were 307 troops from the specialty training program at Fort Lee, Virginia. About half of the subjects completed paired-comparisons ratings of the menus prior to successive-categories ratings of the foods, while the order of tasks was reversed for the other half. Eleven distinct menus were considered, each containing one of eleven meat items, one of seven vegetables, and one of nine starches.

An incomplete paired-comparisons design allowed estimation of mean affective values for the 11 menus from only 25 of the 55 possible pairwise judgments. Subjects indicated their preferences for menus by recording a check mark beside the preferred menu in each of 25 pairs of menus. Other sections of the questionnaire required ratings of single foods and pairs of foods on a nine-category rating schedule. A successive-intervals solution for mean affective values of the 27 single foods and 33 pairs of foods was determined from these ratings.

The regression solution for this problem is somewhat complicated by the lack of independence of observations of the dependent variable. The same subjects evaluate each of the 11 menus. However, estimates may be obtained for the variances and covariances of the scaled affective values of the menus by the methods of Section 6.7.4. With this information, a regression analysis for correlated observation may be performed by the method of Section 6.7.2. For the regression solution, the predictor variables, mean affective values for constituent food items, are assumed to be fixed variates, a reasonable assumption when category ratings have been obtained from large samples of consumers.

The full solution is shown in Figure 9.12, together with a plot of predicted against observed affective values for the 11 menus. The sign pattern in the equation for the complete model is roughly that expected. Although the signs for starches (Z) and vegetable-starch (YZ) are reversed from the expected signs, the values of these coefficients are close to zero. If these coefficients are considered zero the expected sign pattern holds.

SINGLES and DOUBLES

$$\hat{V} = 2.308(XY)_{ij} + .886(XZ)_{ik} - .107(YZ)_{jk} - 1.495X_i - .502Y_j + .108Z_k + .451$$

$R^2 = .9597$

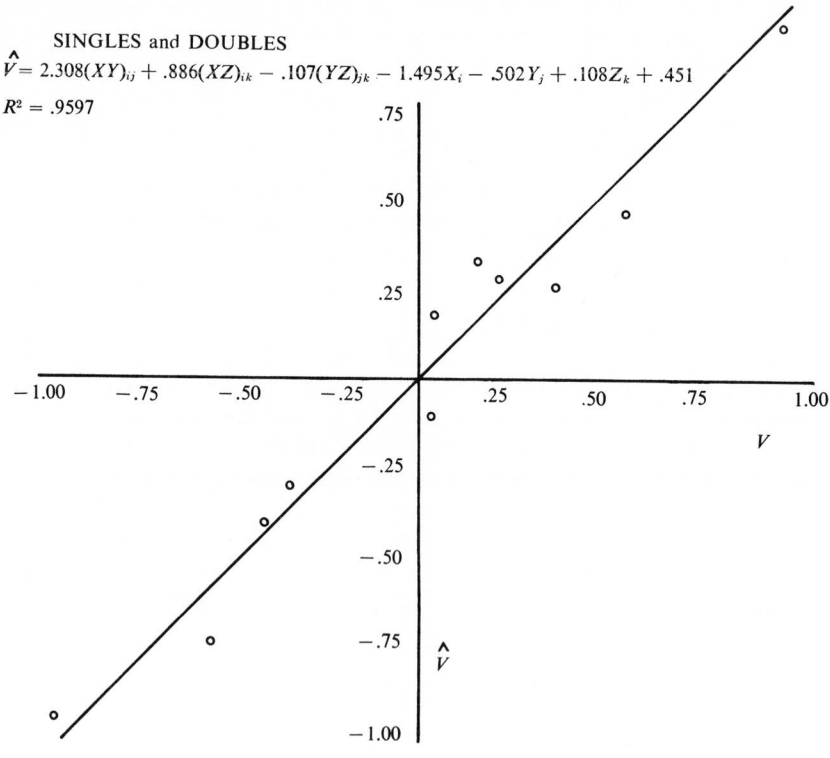

FIG. 9.12. The complete regression solution.

It is seen that the model accounts for about 96% of the variance in the menu scale values, the R^2 being .9597. The remaining variance, although small, is significant. This may result from departure from the paired-comparisons model, departure from the successive-categories model, contribution of a nonzero triple interaction component, or nonlinearity of the relation between paired-comparison and successive-intervals solutions. Nonlinearity is unlikely, as is seen from the graph, which displays no systematic nonlinear trend.

Using a sample size as large as 307, severe shrinkage of the multiple R would not be anticipated if the regression equation were applied to a new sample of subjects. It appears, then, that from preference ratings of these individual foods and pairs of foods, we may predict rather accurately the proportion of subjects who will choose each of two competing menus.

It is of considerable interest to determine how much of the predictive power of the full equation is due to the interaction terms of the model. With this question in mind, consider Figure 9.13, which presents results from a

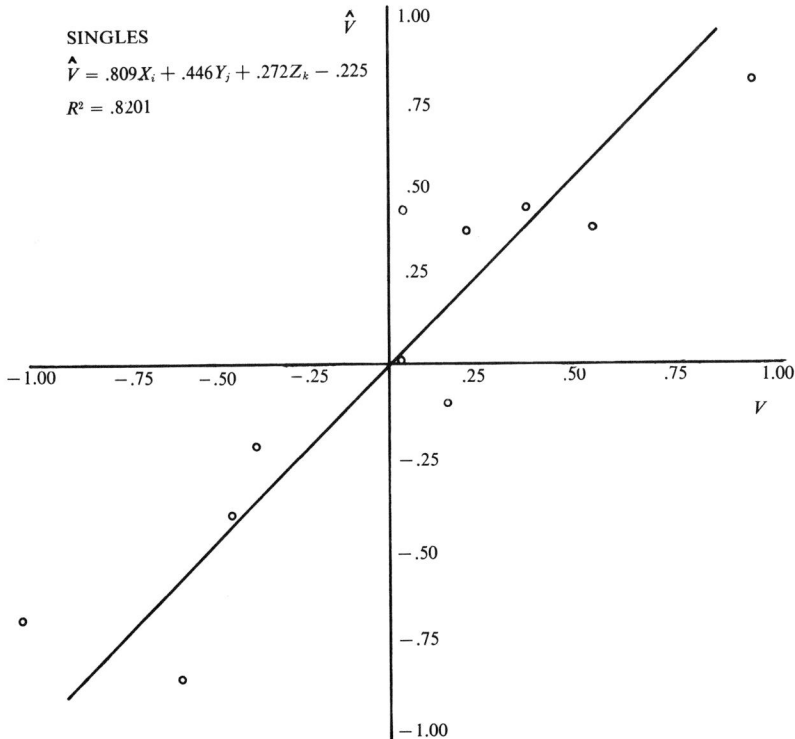

FIG. 9.13. A regression solution based upon single constituents.

regression analysis including only terms due to the single constituents of the menus. The multiple R^2 is found to be .82, as contrasted with .96 for the full solution. Fourteen percent of the variance in menu preference is attributable to interaction effects, a portion which is statistically significant. Prediction of menu preference from successive-categories scale values for single items is appreciably worse than that from the full model, for the particular menu items selected for study. However, these menu items were chosen with the aim of including appreciable interaction effects. It is conceivable that a large class of menus exists for which interaction effects are negligible. And it is remarkable that, from knowledge of ratings only of single components, preference for meals may be predicted even as well as displayed in the graphs.

It might be anticipated that prediction would be even better using ratings of acceptance of pairs of foods, since such preferences would include both effects of the single foods and an interaction effect. The results in Figure 9.14 show this to be the case. From preference ratings for doubles, prediction is

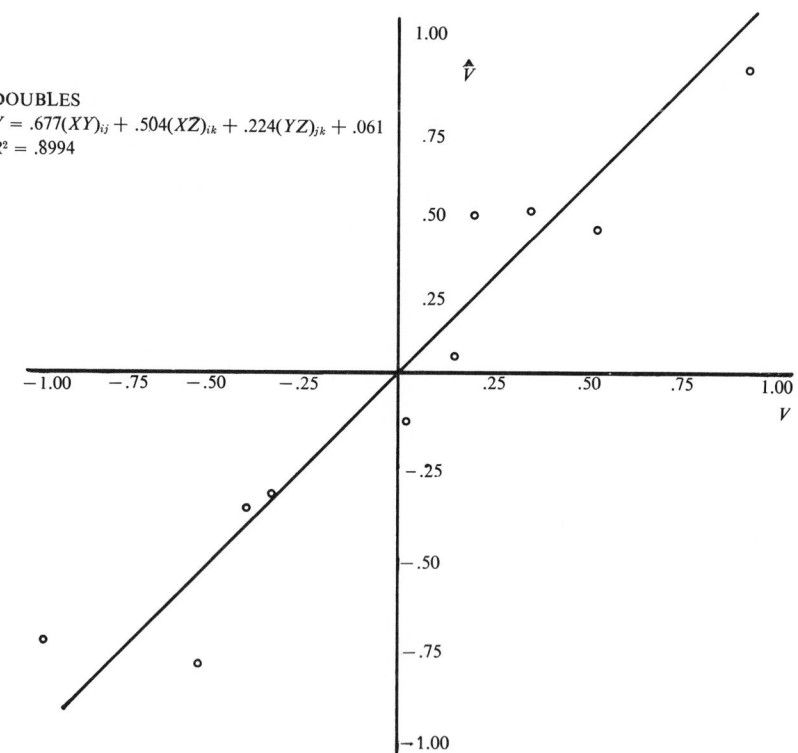

FIG. 9.14. A regression solution based upon double constituents.

considerably better than that from only singles; R^2 is .90 as compared with .82. The result clearly is intermediate between the success of the complete model and that of prediction of menus only from data concerning the individual food constituents.

The existence of interaction effects in preference for menus suggests an interesting application of the model to planning of institutional menus. Suppose an institution, such as a school or industrial cafeteria, a hospital, or a military unit has available a selection of foods in definite amounts for some period. Assume that interactions of foods on a particular menu were *not* a consideration. Then it would not matter, in terms of acceptability of the meals, which combination from the various classes of foods comprised the meal. When interaction is present, on the other hand, the average preference of meals will depend on how frequently constituent foods interact favorably, or unfavorably. Then there should be a unique or very limited set of menus for which the average affective value is a maximum. Given the necessary data on preference for the foods and their pairwise combinations, it would be possible to compute (by machine methods) the affective values of all possible meals from the given set of foods, and find that subset which maximizes preference under the restrictions that all the foods must be used in a certain number of meals, that certain classes of foods will appear in every meal, and that the same meal will be repeated only a permissible number of times. In this way the best set of menus possible for foods of some fixed total cost could be found. Whether such optimizing would be practical, however, would depend upon the cost of obtaining and processing the necessary information.

Appendix I *Tables*

Function: $P = \dfrac{1}{\sqrt{2\pi}} \displaystyle\int_{-\infty}^{Y} \exp(-z^2/2)\, dz; \quad -2.99 \leq Y \leq 0$

Decimal places: 4

Note: For positive deviates ($Y > 0$) subtract the tabled entries from unity.

Examples:

Y	P
-1.97	.0244
.85	.8023

$-Y$	0	1	2	3	4	5	6	7	8	9	$-Y$
0.0	5000	4960	4920	4880	4840	4801	4761	4721	4681	4641	0.0
0.1	4602	4562	4522	4483	4443	4404	4364	4325	4286	4247	0.1
0.2	4207	4168	4129	4090	4052	4013	3974	3936	3897	3859	0.2
0.3	3821	3783	3745	3707	3669	3632	3594	3557	3520	3483	0.3
0.4	3446	3409	3372	3336	3300	3264	3228	3192	3156	3121	0.4
0.5	3085	3050	3015	2981	2946	2912	2877	2843	2810	2776	0.5
0.6	2743	2709	2676	2643	2611	2578	2546	2514	2483	2451	0.6
0.7	2420	2389	2358	2327	2297	2266	2236	2206	2177	2148	0.7
0.8	2119	2090	2061	2033	2005	1977	1949	1922	1894	1867	0.8
0.9	1841	1814	1788	1762	1736	1711	1685	1660	1635	1611	0.9
1.0	1587	1562	1539	1515	1492	1469	1446	1423	1401	1379	1.0
1.1	1357	1335	1314	1292	1271	1251	1230	1210	1190	1170	1.1
1.2	1151	1131	1112	1093	1075	1056	1038	1020	1003	0985	1.2
1.3	0968	0951	0934	0918	0901	0885	0869	0853	0838	0823	1.3
1.4	0808	0793	0778	0764	0749	0735	0721	0708	0694	0681	1.4
1.5	0668	0655	0643	0630	0618	0606	0594	0582	0571	0559	1.5
1.6	0548	0537	0526	0516	0505	0495	0485	0475	0465	0455	1.6
1.7	0446	0436	0427	0418	0409	0401	0392	0384	0375	0367	1.7
1.8	0359	0351	0344	0336	0329	0322	0314	0307	0301	0294	1 8
1.9	0287	0281	0274	0268	0262	0256	0250	0244	0239	0233	1.9
2.0	0228	0222	0217	0212	0207	0202	0197	0192	0188	0183	2.0
2.1	0179	0174	0170	0166	0162	0158	0154	0150	0146	0143	2.1
2.2	0139	0136	0132	0129	0125	0122	0119	0116	0113	0110	2.2
2.3	0107	0104	0102	0099	0096	0094	0091	0089	0087	0084	2.3
2.4	0082	0080	0078	0075	0073	0071	0069	0068	0066	0064	2.4
2.5	0062	0060	0059	0057	0055	0054	0052	0051	0049	0048	2.5
2.6	0047	0045	0044	0043	0041	0040	0039	0038	0037	0036	2.6
2.7	0035	0034	0033	0032	0031	0030	0029	0028	0027	0026	2.7
2.8	0026	0025	0024	0023	0023	0022	0021	0021	0020	0019	2.8
2.9	0019	0018	0018	0017	0016	0016	0015	0015	0014	0014	2.9

TABLE A2. The Normal Ordinate (Decimal Points Omitted)

Function: $h(Y) = (1/\sqrt{2\pi})\exp(-Y^2/2)/$

Decimal places: 4

Examples:

	Y	h(Y)
	1.03	.2347
	−.55	.3429

|Y|	0	1	2	3	4	5	6	7	8	9	|Y|
0.0	3989	3989	3989	3988	3986	3984	3982	3980	3977	3973	0.0
0.1	3970	3965	3961	3956	3951	3945	3939	3932	3925	3918	0.1
0.2	3910	3902	3894	3885	3876	3867	3857	3847	3836	3825	0.2
0.3	3814	3802	3790	3778	3765	3752	3739	3725	3712	3697	0.3
0.4	3683	3668	3653	3637	3621	3605	3589	3572	3555	3538	0.4
0.5	3521	3503	3485	3467	3448	3429	3410	3391	3372	3352	0.5
0.6	3332	3312	3292	3271	3251	3230	3209	3187	3166	3144	0.6
0.7	3123	3101	3079	3056	3034	3011	2989	2966	2943	2920	0.7
0.8	2897	2874	2850	2827	2803	2780	2756	2732	2709	2685	0.8
0.9	2661	2637	2613	2589	2565	2541	2516	2492	2468	2444	0.9
1.0	2420	2396	2371	2347	2323	2299	2275	2251	2227	2203	1.0
1.1	2179	2155	2131	2107	2083	2059	2036	2012	1989	1965	1.1
1.2	1942	1919	1895	1872	1849	1826	1804	1781	1758	1736	1.2
1.3	1714	1691	1669	1647	1626	1604	1582	1561	1539	1518	1.3
1.4	1497	1476	1456	1435	1415	1394	1374	1354	1334	1315	1.4
1.5	1295	1276	1257	1238	1219	1200	1182	1163	1145	1127	1.5
1.6	1109	1092	1074	1057	1040	1023	1006	0989	0973	0957	1.6
1.7	0940	0925	0909	0893	0878	0863	0848	0833	0818	0804	1.7
1.8	0790	0775	0761	0748	0734	0721	0707	0694	0681	0669	1.8
1.9	0656	0644	0632	0620	0608	0596	0584	0573	0562	0551	1.9
2.0	0540	0529	0519	0508	0498	0488	0478	0468	0459	0449	2.0
2.1	0440	0431	0422	0413	0404	0395	0387	0379	0371	0363	2.1
2.2	0355	0347	0339	0332	0325	0317	0310	0303	0297	0290	2.2
2.3	0283	0277	0270	0264	0258	0252	0246	0241	0235	0229	2.3
2.4	0224	0219	0213	0208	0203	0198	0194	0189	0184	0180	2.4
2.5	0175	0171	0167	0163	0158	0154	0151	0147	0143	0139	2.5
2.6	0136	0132	0129	0126	0122	0119	0116	0113	0110	0107	2.6
2.7	0104	0101	0099	0096	0093	0091	0088	0086	0084	0081	2.7
2.8	0079	0077	0075	0073	0071	0069	0067	0065	0063	0061	2.8
2.9	0060	0058	0056	0055	0053	0051	0050	0048	0047	0046	2.9

TABLE A3. Normal Deviates in Terms of *P* (Decimal Points Omitted)

Function: Inverse normal transformation: $Y = \Phi^{-1}(P)$

Decimal places: 4

Note: Proportions *less than* .500 are read from the left and top margins. Proportions *greater than* .500 are read from the right and bottom margins. For proportions less than .500 a minus sign should precede the tabled entry.

Examples:

	P	Y
	.191	−.8742
	.900	1.2816

(*continued*)

TABLE A3 (*continued*). Normal Deviates in Terms of *P* (Decimal Points Omitted)

P	0	1	2	3	4	5	6	7	8	9	10	
00		30902	28782	27478	26521	25758	25121	24573	24089	23656	23263	99
01	23263	22904	22571	22262	21973	21701	21444	21201	20969	20749	20537	98
02	20537	20335	20141	19954	19774	19600	19431	19268	19110	18957	18808	97
03	18808	18663	18522	18384	18250	18119	17991	17866	17744	17624	17507	96
04	17507	17392	17279	17169	17060	16954	16849	16747	16646	16546	16449	95
05	16449	16352	16258	16164	16072	15982	15893	15805	15718	15632	15548	94
06	15548	15464	15382	15301	15220	15141	15063	14985	14909	14833	14758	93
07	14758	14684	14611	14538	14466	14395	14325	14255	14187	14118	14051	92
08	14051	13984	13917	13852	13787	13722	13658	13595	13532	13469	13408	91
09	13408	13346	13285	13225	13165	13106	13047	12988	12930	12873	12816	90
10	12816	12759	12702	12646	12591	12536	12481	12426	12372	12319	12265	89
11	12265	12212	12160	12107	12055	12004	11952	11901	11850	11800	11750	88
12	11750	11700	11650	11601	11552	11503	11455	11407	11359	11311	11264	87
13	11264	11217	11170	11123	11077	11031	10985	10939	10893	10848	10803	86
14	10803	10758	10714	10669	10625	10581	10537	10494	10451	10407	10364	85
15	10364	10322	10279	10237	10194	10152	10110	10069	10027	9986	9945	84
16	9945	9904	9863	9822	9782	9741	9701	9661	9621	9581	9542	83
17	9542	9502	9463	9424	9385	9346	9307	9269	9230	9192	9154	82
18	9154	9116	9078	9040	9002	8965	8927	8890	8853	8816	8779	81
19	8779	8742	8706	8669	8633	8596	8560	8524	8488	8452	8416	80
20	8416	8381	8345	8310	8274	8239	8204	8169	8134	8099	8064	79
21	8064	8030	7995	7961	7926	7892	7858	7824	7790	7756	7722	78
22	7722	7688	7655	7621	7588	7554	7521	7488	7455	7421	7388	77
23	7388	7356	7323	7290	7257	7225	7192	7160	7128	7095	7063	76
24	7063	7031	6999	6967	6935	6903	6871	6840	6808	6776	6745	75
25	6745	6713	6682	6651	6620	6588	6557	6526	6495	6464	6433	74
26	6433	6403	6372	6341	6311	6280	6250	6219	6189	6158	6128	73
27	6128	6098	6068	6038	6008	5978	5948	5918	5888	5858	5828	72
28	5828	5799	5769	5740	5710	5681	5651	5622	5592	5563	5534	71
29	5534	5505	5476	5446	5417	5388	5359	5330	5302	5273	5244	70
30	5244	5215	5187	5158	5129	5101	5072	5044	5015	4987	4959	69
31	4959	4930	4902	4874	4845	4817	4789	4761	4733	4705	4677	68
32	4677	4649	4621	4593	4565	4538	4510	4482	4454	4427	4399	67
33	4399	4372	4344	4316	4289	4261	4234	4207	4179	4152	4125	66
34	4125	4097	4070	4043	4016	3989	3961	3934	3907	3880	3853	65
35	3853	3826	3799	3772	3745	3719	3692	3665	3638	3611	3585	64
36	3585	3558	3531	3505	3478	3451	3425	3398	3372	3345	3319	63
37	3319	3292	3266	3239	3213	3186	3160	3134	3107	3081	3055	62
38	3055	3029	3002	2976	2950	2924	2898	2871	2845	2819	2793	61
39	2793	2767	2741	2715	2689	2663	2637	2611	2585	2559	2533	60
40	2533	2508	2482	2456	2430	2404	2378	2353	2327	2301	2275	59
41	2275	2250	2224	2198	2173	2147	2121	2096	2070	2045	2019	58
42	2019	1993	1968	1942	1917	1891	1866	1840	1815	1789	1764	57
43	1764	1738	1713	1687	1662	1637	1611	1586	1560	1535	1510	56
44	1510	1484	1459	1434	1408	1383	1358	1332	1307	1282	1257	55
45	1257	1231	1206	1181	1156	1130	1105	1080	1055	1030	1004	54
46	1004	0979	0954	0929	0904	0878	0853	0828	0803	0778	0753	53
47	0753	0728	0702	0677	0652	0627	0602	0577	0552	0527	0502	52
48	0502	0476	0451	0426	0401	0376	0351	0326	0301	0276	0251	51
49	0251	0226	0201	0175	0150	0125	0100	0075	0050	0025	0000	50
	10	9	8	7	6	5	4	3	2	1	0	P

TABLE A4. Phi Coefficients Corresponding to Various Two-fold Partitions of the Bivariate Normal Surface with Correlation 1/2
(Decimal Points Omitted)

Function: $\rho_{k,l} = \dfrac{P_{k,l} - P_k P_l}{\sqrt{P_k Q_k P_l Q_l}} = F(Y_k, Y_l)$

where Prob $(z > Y_k) = P_k$
where Prob $(z > Y_l) = P_l$

Decimal places: 4

Note: The tabled values may be used in a minimum normit χ^2 solution for the multiple-judgment case of paired comparisons, as described in Section 6.7.4. From $Y_{jk,\text{prov}}$ and $Y_{jl,\text{prov}}$ (Y_k and Y_l, above), the terms $\rho_{jk,jl}$, $\sqrt{P_{jk} Q_{jk}}$, and $\sqrt{P_{jl} Q_{jl}}$, necessary for determining $\mathcal{V}(y_{jk}, y_{jl})$, may be read from the table.

Symmetric properties of $\rho_{k,l}$ are as follows.

$$F(Y_k, Y_l) = F(-Y_k, -Y_l) = F(Y_l, Y_k) = F(-Y_l, -Y_k)$$
$$F(Y_k, -Y_l) = F(-Y_k, Y_l) = F(-Y_l, Y_k) = F(Y_l, -Y_k)$$

Consequently, for any value of Y_l, $P_l = P_k$ and $\sqrt{P_l Q_l} = \sqrt{P_k Q_k}$ with l set equal to k, and the marginal entries P_k and $\sqrt{P_k Q_k}$ also suffice to find P_l and $\sqrt{P_l Q_l}$.

Examples:

Y_k	Y_l	$\rho_{k,l}$	P_k	P_l	$\sqrt{P_k Q_k}$	$\sqrt{P_l Q_l}$
2.5	0.1	.0742	.0062	.4602	.0788	.4984
-2.5	-0.1	.0742	.9938	.5398	.0788	.4984
0.1	2.5	.0742	.4602	.0062	.4984	.0788
-0.1	-2.5	.0742	.5398	.9938	.4984	.0788
0.1	-2.5	.0665	.4602	.9938	.4984	.0788
-0.1	2.5	.0665	.5398	.0062	.4984	.0788
-2.5	0.1	.0665	.9938	.4602	.0788	.4984
2.5	-0.1	.0665	.0062	.5398	.0788	.4984

(continued)

TABLE A4 (continued). Phi Coefficients (Decimal Points Omitted)

Y_k							Y_t							
	0	0.1	0.2	0.3	0.4	0.5	0.6	0.7	0.8	0.9	1.0	1.1	1.2	1.3
2.5	0698	0742	0786	0831	0876	0921	0964	1007	1048	1086	1122	1154	1182	1206
2.4	0800	0848	0897	0946	0994	1041	1088	1132	1175	1214	1250	1281	1308	1330
2.3	0903	0955	1008	1061	1113	1163	1212	1258	1302	1341	1377	1407	1432	1451
2.2	1013	1070	1127	1183	1238	1291	1342	1389	1433	1473	1507	1535	1558	1572
2.1	1130	1192	1252	1312	1369	1425	1477	1525	1569	1607	1640	1665	1683	1694
2.0	1254	1319	1384	1446	1506	1563	1616	1664	1707	1743	1773	1795	1808	1813
1.9	1384	1453	1520	1585	1647	1704	1757	1804	1845	1879	1905	1922	1930	1929
1.8	1518	1591	1661	1727	1790	1848	1900	1945	1983	2013	2034	2046	2048	2039
1.7	1657	1732	1804	1872	1934	1991	2042	2084	2119	2144	2160	2165	2160	2143
1.6	1799	1876	1949	2017	2079	2134	2182	2221	2251	2270	2279	2277	2264	2239
1.5	1942	2020	2093	2161	2221	2274	2318	2352	2377	2390	2392	2382	2360	2326
1.4	2085	2164	2237	2302	2360	2409	2449	2478	2495	2501	2495	2477	2446	2402
1.3	2227	2306	2377	2440	2494	2539	2573	2595	2605	2603	2589	2561	2520	2467
1.2	2367	2443	2512	2572	2622	2661	2688	2703	2705	2695	2671	2633	2583	2520
1.1	2502	2576	2641	2697	2741	2773	2793	2800	2794	2774	2741	2694	2633	2561
1.0	2631	2702	2763	2813	2850	2876	2888	2886	2870	2841	2798	2741	2671	2589
0.9	2754	2820	2875	2918	2949	2966	2969	2959	2934	2894	2841	2774	2695	2603
0.8	2867	2928	2977	3013	3035	3044	3038	3018	2983	2934	2870	2794	2705	2605
0.7	2971	3026	3067	3095	3109	3108	3093	3062	3018	2959	2886	2800	2703	2595
0.6	3063	3111	3144	3164	3168	3158	3133	3093	3038	2969	2888	2793	2688	2573
0.5	3144	3183	3208	3218	3213	3193	3158	3108	3044	2966	2876	2773	2661	2539
0.4	3211	3242	3257	3258	3243	3213	3168	3109	3035	2949	2850	2741	2622	2494
0.3	3264	3285	3292	3282	3258	3218	3164	3095	3013	2918	2813	2697	2572	2440
0.2	3302	3314	3311	3292	3257	3208	3144	3067	2977	2875	2763	2641	2512	2377
0.1	3326	3328	3314	3285	3242	3183	3111	3026	2928	2820	2702	2576	2443	2306
0.0	3333	3326	3302	3264	3211	3144	3064	2971	2867	2754	2631	2502	2367	2227

(continued)

TABLE A4 (continued). Phi Coefficients (Decimal Points Omitted)

Y_k	Y_t 1.4	1.5	1.6	1.7	1.8	1.9	2.0	2.1	2.2	2.3	2.4	2.5	P_k	$\sqrt{P_k Q_k}$
2.5	1224	1237	1244	1245	1238	1226	1207	1181	1148	1110	1066	1014	0062	0788
2.4	1346	1355	1357	1353	1340	1321	1295	1262	1223	1177	1126	1066	0082	0902
2.3	1463	1467	1465	1454	1436	1410	1376	1336	1288	1236	1177	1110	0107	1030
2.2	1580	1579	1570	1553	1528	1495	1453	1405	1349	1288	1223	1148	0139	1171
2.1	1696	1689	1674	1649	1616	1575	1525	1468	1405	1336	1262	1181	0179	1325
2.0	1809	1795	1772	1740	1699	1648	1590	1525	1453	1376	1295	1207	0228	1491
1.9	1917	1896	1865	1824	1774	1715	1648	1575	1495	1410	1321	1226	0287	1670
1.8	2020	1991	1951	1901	1842	1774	1699	1616	1528	1436	1340	1238	0359	1861
1.7	2116	2077	2029	1969	1901	1824	1740	1649	1553	1454	1353	1245	0446	2063
1.6	2203	2155	2097	2029	1951	1865	1772	1674	1570	1465	1357	1244	0548	2276
1.5	2280	2223	2155	2077	1991	1896	1795	1689	1579	1467	1355	1237	0668	2497
1.4	2347	2280	2203	2116	2020	1917	1809	1696	1580	1463	1346	1224	0808	2725
1.3	2402	2326	2239	2143	2039	1929	1813	1694	1572	1451	1330	1206	0968	2957
1.2	2446	2360	2264	2160	2048	1930	1808	1683	1558	1432	1308	1182	1151	3191
1.1	2477	2382	2277	2165	2046	1922	1795	1665	1535	1407	1281	1154	1357	3424
1.0	2495	2392	2279	2160	2034	1905	1773	1640	1507	1377	1250	1122	1587	3654
0.9	2501	2390	2270	2144	2013	1879	1743	1607	1473	1341	1214	1086	1841	3875
0.8	2495	2377	2251	2119	1983	1845	1707	1569	1433	1302	1175	1048	2119	4086
0.7	2478	2352	2221	2084	1945	1804	1664	1525	1389	1258	1132	1007	2420	4283
0.6	2449	2318	2182	2042	1900	1757	1616	1477	1342	1212	1088	0964	2743	4461
0.5	2409	2274	2134	1991	1848	1704	1563	1425	1291	1163	1041	0921	3085	4619
0.4	2360	2221	2079	1934	1790	1647	1506	1369	1238	1113	0994	0876	3446	4752
0.3	2302	2161	2017	1872	1727	1585	1446	1312	1183	1061	0946	0831	3821	4859
0.2	2237	2093	1949	1804	1661	1520	1384	1252	1127	1008	0897	0786	4207	4937
0.1	2164	2020	1876	1732	1591	1453	1319	1192	1070	0955	0848	0742	4602	4984
0.0	2085	1942	1799	1657	1518	1384	1254	1130	1013	0903	0800	0698	5000	5000

(continued)

TABLE A4 (continued). Phi Coefficients (Decimal Points Omitted)

Y_k	0	0.1	0.2	0.3	0.4	0.5	0.6	0.7	0.8	0.9	1.0	1.1	1.2	1.3
−0.1	3326	3308	3275	3228	3166	3091	3004	2905	2796	2677	2552	2420	2283	2143
−0.2	3302	3275	3233	3177	3108	3026	2932	2827	2714	2592	2464	2330	2193	2054
−0.3	3264	3228	3177	3113	3036	2948	2849	2740	2623	2499	2369	2235	2099	1961
−0.4	3211	3166	3108	3036	2953	2859	2755	2643	2524	2398	2268	2135	2000	1865
−0.5	3144	3091	3026	2948	2854	2761	2653	2539	2418	2292	2163	2032	1899	1767
−0.6	3064	3004	2932	2849	2755	2653	2544	2428	2307	2182	2054	1925	1796	1667
−0.7	2971	2905	2827	2740	2643	2539	2428	2312	2191	2068	1943	1817	1691	1567
−0.8	2867	2796	2714	2623	2524	2418	2307	2191	2072	1952	1830	1708	1587	1468
−0.9	2754	2677	2592	2499	2398	2292	2182	2068	1952	1834	1716	1598	1483	1369
−1.0	2631	2552	2464	2369	2268	2163	2054	1943	1830	1716	1602	1490	1380	1272
−1.1	2502	2420	2330	2235	2135	2032	1925	1817	1708	1598	1490	1383	1279	1177
−1.2	2367	2283	2193	2099	2000	1899	1796	1691	1587	1483	1380	1279	1181	1085
−1.3	2227	2143	2054	1961	1865	1767	1667	1567	1468	1369	1272	1177	1085	0997
−1.4	2085	2001	1914	1823	1730	1636	1540	1445	1351	1259	1168	1079	0994	0911
−1.5	1942	1859	1774	1686	1597	1507	1417	1327	1239	1152	1067	0985	0906	0830
−1.6	1799	1718	1636	1552	1467	1381	1296	1212	1130	1049	0971	0895	0822	0752
−1.7	1657	1580	1501	1420	1340	1260	1181	1102	1026	0951	0879	0810	0743	0680
−1.8	1518	1444	1369	1294	1218	1143	1070	0998	0927	0859	0793	0729	0669	0611
−1.9	1384	1313	1243	1172	1102	1033	0965	0898	0834	0772	0712	0654	0599	0547
−2.0	1254	1188	1122	1056	0991	0928	0865	0805	0746	0690	0636	0584	0534	0487
−2.1	1130	1069	1007	0947	0887	0829	0773	0718	0665	0614	0565	0519	0474	0433
−2.2	1013	0956	0900	0844	0790	0738	0686	0637	0589	0544	0500	0459	0419	0382
−2.3	0903	0851	0799	0749	0700	0652	0607	0562	0520	0479	0440	0404	0369	0336
−2.4	0800	0753	0706	0661	0617	0574	0533	0494	0456	0420	0386	0354	0323	0294
−2.5	0698	0665	0623	0582	0543	0505	·0468	0433	0400	0368	0338	0309	0282	0257

(continued)

TABLE A4 (continued). Phi Coefficients (Decimal Points Omitted)

Y_k	Y_i												P_k	$\sqrt{P_k Q_k}$
	1.4	1.5	1.6	1.7	1.8	1.9	2.0	2.1	2.2	2.3	2.4	2.5		
−0.1	2001	1859	1718	1580	1444	1313	1188	1069	0956	0851	0753	0665	5398	4984
−0.2	1914	1774	1636	1501	1369	1243	1122	1007	0900	0799	0706	0623	5793	4937
−0.3	1823	1686	1552	1420	1294	1172	1056	0947	0844	0749	0661	0582	6179	4859
−0.4	1730	1597	1467	1340	1218	1102	0991	0887	0790	0700	0617	0543	6554	4752
−0.5	1636	1507	1381	1260	1143	1033	0928	0829	0738	0652	0574	0505	6915	4619
−0.6	1540	1417	1296	1181	1070	0965	0865	0773	0686	0607	0533	0468	7257	4461
−0.7	1445	1327	1212	1102	0998	0898	0805	0718	0637	0562	0494	0433	7580	4283
−0.8	1351	1239	1130	1026	0927	0834	0746	0665	0589	0520	0456	0400	7881	4086
−0.9	1259	1152	1049	0951	0859	0772	0690	0614	0544	0479	0420	0368	8159	3875
−1.0	1168	1067	0971	0879	0793	0712	0636	0565	0500	0440	0386	0338	8413	3654
−1.1	1079	0985	0895	0810	0729	0654	0584	0519	0459	0404	0354	0309	8643	3424
−1.2	0994	0906	0822	0743	0669	0599	0534	0474	0419	0369	0323	0282	8849	3191
−1.3	0911	0830	0752	0680	0611	0547	0487	0433	0382	0336	0294	0257	9032	2957
−1.4	0832	0757	0686	0619	0556	0498	0443	0393	0347	0305	0267	0233	9192	2725
−1.5	0757	0688	0623	0562	0504	0451	0402	0356	0314	0276	0241	0211	9332	2497
−1.6	0686	0623	0564	0508	0456	0407	0362	0321	0283	0249	0217	0190	9452	2276
−1.7	0619	0562	0508	0457	0410	0366	0326	0288	0254	0223	0195	0171	9554	2063
−1.8	0556	0504	0456	0410	0367	0328	0292	0258	0228	0200	0175	0152	9641	1861
−1.9	0498	0451	0407	0366	0328	0293	0260	0230	0203	0178	0156	0136	9713	1670
−2.0	0443	0402	0362	0326	0292	0260	0231	0205	0181	0158	0138	0121	9772	1491
−2.1	0393	0356	0321	0288	0258	0231	0205	0181	0160	0140	0123	0107	9821	1325
−2.2	0347	0314	0283	0254	0228	0203	0181	0160	0140	0124	0108	0094	9861	1171
−2.3	0305	0276	0249	0223	0200	0178	0158	0140	0124	0108	0095	0083	9893	1030
−2.4	0267	0241	0217	0195	0175	0156	0138	0123	0108	0095	0083	0072	9918	0902
−2.5	0233	0211	0190	0171	0152	0136	0121	0107	0094	0083	0072	0063	9938	0788

TABLE A5. The Angular Transformation for Binomial Proportions (Decimal Points Omitted)

Function: $Y = 2 \sin^{-1} \sqrt{P} - \pi/2$

Decimal places: 4

Notes: Proportions *less than* .500 are read from the left and top margins. Proportions *greater than* .500 are read from the right and bottom margins.
For proportions *less than* .500, *change the sign of the tabled entry.*

Examples:

P	Y
.125	−.8481
.690	.3898

Adapted with permission from A. Hald, *Statistical Tables and Formulas*, Wiley, New York, 1952.

P	0	1	2	3	4	5	6	7	8	9	10	
00	15708	15075	14813	14612	14442	14293	14157	14033	13917	13808	13705	99
01	13705	13607	13513	13423	13336	13252	13171	13093	13017	12942	12870	98
02	12870	12799	12731	12663	12597	12532	12469	12407	12346	12285	12226	97
03	12226	12168	12111	12055	11999	11944	11890	11837	11784	11732	11681	96
04	11681	11630	11580	11530	11481	11433	11385	11337	11290	11244	11198	95
05	11198	11152	11107	11062	11018	10974	10930	10886	10844	10801	10759	94
06	10759	10717	10675	10634	10593	10552	10512	10472	10432	10392	10353	93
07	10353	10314	10275	10236	10198	10160	10122	10084	10047	10010	9973	92
08	9973	9936	9900	9863	9827	9791	9755	9720	9684	9649	9614	91
09	9614	9579	9545	9510	9476	9442	9408	9374	9340	9306	9273	90
10	9273	9240	9207	9174	9141	9108	9076	9043	9011	8979	8947	89
11	8947	8915	8883	8851	8820	8788	8757	8726	8695	8664	8633	88
12	8633	8602	8572	8541	8511	8481	8450	8420	8390	8361	8331	87
13	8331	8301	8271	8242	8213	8183	8154	8125	8096	8067	8038	86
14	8038	8009	7981	7952	7923	7895	7867	7838	7810	7782	7754	85
15	7754	7726	7698	7670	7643	7615	7587	7560	7532	7505	7478	84
16	7478	7450	7423	7396	7369	7342	7315	7288	7262	7235	7208	83
17	7208	7182	7155	7129	7102	7076	7050	7023	6997	6971	6945	82
18	6945	6919	6893	6867	6841	6816	6790	6764	6739	6713	6687	81
19	6687	6662	6637	6611	6586	6561	6535	6510	6485	6460	6435	80
	10	9	8	7	6	5	4	3	2	1	0	P

(continued)

TABLE A5 (continued). Angular Transformation (Decimal Points Omitted)

P	0	1	2	3	4	5	6	7	8	9	10	
20	6435	6410	6385	6360	6335	6311	6286	6261	6237	6212	6187	79
21	6187	6163	6138	6114	6089	6065	6041	6016	5992	5968	5944	78
22	5944	5920	5896	5872	5848	5824	5800	5776	5752	5728	5704	77
23	5704	5681	5657	5633	5610	5586	5562	5539	5515	5492	5469	76
24	5469	5445	5422	5398	5375	5352	5329	5305	5282	5259	5236	75
25	5236	5213	5190	5167	5144	5121	5098	5075	5052	5029	5007	74
26	5007	4984	4961	4938	4916	4893	4870	4848	4825	4803	4780	73
27	4780	4757	4735	4713	4690	4668	4645	4623	4601	4578	4556	72
28	4556	4534	4512	4489	4467	4445	4423	4401	4379	4357	4335	71
29	4335	4312	4290	4268	4247	4225	4203	4181	4159	4137	4115	70
30	4115	4093	4072	4050	4028	4006	3985	3963	3941	3920	3898	69
31	3898	3876	3855	3833	3812	3790	3769	3747	3726	3704	3683	68
32	3683	3661	3640	3618	3597	3576	3554	3533	3512	3491	3469	67
33	3469	3448	3427	3405	3384	3363	3342	3321	3300	3278	3257	66
34	3257	3236	3215	3194	3173	3152	3131	3110	3089	3068	3047	65
35	3047	3026	3005	2984	2963	2942	2921	2901	2880	2859	2838	64
36	2838	2817	2796	2776	2755	2734	2713	2692	2672	2651	2630	63
37	2630	2610	2589	2568	2547	2527	2506	2486	2465	2444	2424	62
38	2424	2403	2383	2362	2341	2321	2300	2280	2259	2239	2218	61
39	2218	2198	2177	2157	2136	2116	2095	2075	2054	2034	2014	60
40	2014	1993	1973	1952	1932	1912	1891	1871	1851	1830	1810	59
41	1810	1790	1769	1749	1729	1708	1688	1668	1647	1627	1607	58
42	1607	1587	1566	1546	1526	1506	1486	1465	1445	1425	1405	57
43	1405	1384	1364	1344	1324	1304	1284	1263	1243	1223	1203	56
44	1203	1183	1163	1143	1122	1102	1082	1062	1042	1022	1002	55
45	1002	982	962	941	921	901	881	861	841	821	801	54
46	801	781	761	741	721	701	681	660	640	620	600	53
47	600	580	560	540	520	500	480	460	440	420	400	52
48	400	380	360	340	320	300	280	260	240	220	200	51
49	200	180	160	140	120	100	80	60	40	20	00	50
	10	9	8	7	6	5	4	3	2	1	0	P

TABLE A6. Weighting Coefficients for the Constant Method
(Decimal Points Omitted)

Function: $W = h^2(Y)/PQ$

Decimal places: 4

Note: In the solutions for the constant method enter Table A6 with Y_{prov}.

Examples:

	Y_{prov}	W
	.43	.5950
	−2.79	.0253

$\|Y\|$	0	1	2	3	4	5	6	7	8	9	$\|Y\|$
0.0	6365	6365	6366	6365	6362	6359	6357	6356	6352	6347	0.0
0.1	6345	6337	6334	6328	6323	6315	6308	6299	6291	6283	0.1
0.2	6273	6264	6255	6244	6233	6224	6212	6201	6187	6174	0.2
0.3	6161	6146	6132	6118	6103	6087	6072	6055	6041	6021	0.3
0.4	6006	5988	5971	5950	5930	5911	5892	5871	5851	5830	0.4
0.5	5811	5789	5767	5745	5721	5697	5674	5651	5628	5603	0.5
0.6	5577	5554	5529	5503	5478	5453	5426	5397	5370	5342	0.6
0.7	5317	5289	5261	5231	5202	5173	5146	5117	5086	5055	0.7
0.8	5026	4996	4964	4934	4901	4872	4841	4807	4780	4748	0.8
0.9	4714	4683	4650	4618	4586	4553	4518	4486	4454	4420	0.9
1.0	4386	4356	4317	4285	4251	4218	4184	4152	4117	4082	1.0
1.1	4048	4015	3979	3946	3911	3873	3843	3806	3774	3737	1.1
1.2	3703	3671	3633	3600	3563	3530	3498	3463	3425	3394	1.2
1.3	3360	3323	3290	3254	3225	3189	3154	3123	3085	3051	1.3
1.4	3017	2984	2955	2918	2890	2854	2822	2787	2755	2725	1.4
1.5	2690	2660	2626	2596	2563	2530	2501	2468	2435	2407	1.5
1.6	2374	2347	2315	2283	2256	2224	2193	2162	2135	2109	1.6
1.7	2074	2052	2021	1991	1965	1935	1909	1879	1854	1828	1.7
1.8	1803	1773	1743	1723	1693	1668	1643	1619	1589	1568	1.8
1.9	1544	1519	1499	1474	1449	1424	1399	1379	1354	1334	1.9
2.0	1309	1289	1269	1244	1223	1203	1183	1163	1142	1122	2.0
2.1	1101	1086	1066	1045	1024	1003	0988	0972	0957	0935	2.1
2.2	0919	0898	0882	0866	0856	0834	0817	0801	0790	0773	2.2
2.3	0757	0746	0722	0711	0700	0682	0671	0658	0640	0630	2.3
2.4	0617	0604	0586	0581	0569	0556	0549	0529	0516	0510	2.4
2.5	0497	0490	0476	0469	0456	0442	0441	0426	0419	0404	2.5
2.6	0395	0389	0380	0371	0365	0355	0346	0337	0328	0319	2.6
2.7	0310	0301	0298	0289	0280	0277	0268	0265	0262	0253	2.7
2.8	0241	0238	0235	0232	0220	0217	0214	0202	0199	0196	2.8
2.9	0190	0187	0175	0178	0176	0163	0167	0154	0158	0151	2.9

TABLE A7. Weighting Coefficients for the Determination of Absolute
Thresholds by the Constant Method (Decimal Points Omitted)

Function: $W' = h^2(Y')/4PQ$

Decimal places: 4

Note: For threshold solutions enter Table A7 with Y'_{prov}.

Examples:
Y'_{prov}	W'
1.50	.1299
−1.50	.0168

Y'	0	1	2	3	4	5	6	7	8	9	Y'
−0.0	2122	2110	2099	2088	2075	2063	2051	2039	2026	2012	−0.0
−0.1	2000	1985	1972	1959	1945	1931	1917	1902	1887	1873	−0.1
−0.2	1858	1843	1828	1813	1797	1783	1767	1751	1735	1719	−0.2
−0.3	1704	1687	1671	1655	1638	1622	1605	1589	1573	1556	−0.3
−0.4	1539	1522	1506	1488	1471	1455	1438	1421	1404	1387	−0.4
−0.5	1370	1353	1336	1319	1302	1285	1268	1251	1235	1217	−0.5
−0.6	1201	1184	1167	1150	1134	1118	1101	1084	1068	1052	−0.6
−0.7	1036	1020	1004	0987	0972	0956	0940	0925	0909	0894	−0.7
−0.8	0879	0864	0848	0834	0819	0804	0790	0775	0761	0747	−0.8
−0.9	0733	0719	0705	0692	0678	0665	0652	0639	0626	0613	−0.9
−1.0	0601	0588	0576	0564	0552	0540	0529	0517	0506	0495	−1.0
−1.1	0484	0473	0462	0451	0441	0431	0421	0411	0401	0391	−1.1
−1.2	0382	0373	0364	0355	0346	0337	0329	0321	0312	0304	−1.2
−1.3	0297	0289	0281	0274	0267	0259	0252	0245	0239	0232	−1.3
−1.4	0226	0219	0213	0207	0201	0195	0190	0184	0179	0174	−1.4
−1.5	0168	0164	0159	0154	0149	0145	0140	0136	0132	0127	−1.5
−1.6	0123	0120	0116	0112	0108	0105	0101	0098	0095	0092	−1.6
−1.7	0089	0086	0083	0080	0077	0075	0072	0069	0067	0065	−1.7
−1.8	0062	0060	0058	0056	0054	0052	0050	0048	0046	0045	−1.8
−1.9	0043	0042	0040	0038	0037	0036	0034	0033	0032	0030	−1.9
−2.0	0029	0028	0027	0026	0025	0024	0023	0022	0021	0020	−2.0
−2.1	0019	0019	0018	0017	0016	0016	0015	0014	0014	0013	−2.1
−2.2	0013	0012	0011	0011	0011	0010	0010	0009	0009	0008	−2.2
−2.3	0008	0008	0007	0007	0007	0006	0006	0006	0006	0005	−2.3
−2.4	0005	0005	0005	0004	0004	0004	0004	0004	0003	0003	−2.4
−2.5	0003	0003	0003	0003	0002	0002	0002	0002	0002	0002	−2.5
−2.6	0002	0002	0002	0002	0001	0001	0001	0001	0001	0001	−2.6
−2.7	0001	0001	0001	0001	0001	0001	0001	0001	0001	0001	−2.7
−2.8	0001	0001	0001	0001	0001	0000	0000	0000	0000	0000	−2.8
0.0	2122	2133	2145	2155	2165	2175	2186	2196	2206	2215	0.0
0.1	2224	2232	2242	2250	2259	2266	2274	2281	2287	2295	0.1
0.2	2301	2307	2314	2319	2325	2331	2336	2341	2345	2349	0.2
0.3	2354	2357	2360	2364	2366	2368	2371	2373	2375	2376	0.3
0.4	2378	2379	2380	2379	2379	2379	2379	2378	2377	2377	0.4
0.5	2376	2374	2372	2370	2366	2363	2361	2358	2354	2350	0.5
0.6	2346	2343	2338	2333	2329	2323	2317	2311	2305	2299	0.6
0.7	2293	2286	2279	2272	2265	2256	2249	2241	2233	2224	0.7
0.8	2216	2207	2198	2189	2179	2170	2160	2148	2140	2131	0.8
0.9	2119	2108	2097	2086	2075	2064	2052	2040	2030	2017	0.9

(*continued*)

TABLE A7 (*continued*). Weights for the Determination of Thresholds
(Decimal Points Omitted)

Y′	0	1	2	3	4	5	6	7	8	9	Y′
1.0	2005	1993	1980	1968	1954	1943	1929	1918	1905	1891	1.0
1.1	1878	1865	1850	1837	1824	1809	1796	1781	1767	1753	1.1
1.2	1740	1727	1710	1697	1682	1667	1653	1638	1624	1611	1.2
1.3	1595	1580	1564	1549	1533	1523	1507	1494	1475	1462	1.3
1.4	1445	1432	1418	1401	1390	1374	1360	1342	1328	1316	1.4
1.5	1299	1287	1271	1256	1241	1225	1212	1197	1184	1171	1.5
1.6	1154	1143	1126	1111	1101	1086	1071	1057	1044	1032	1.6
1.7	1013	1003	0991	0974	0964	0950	0936	0921	0912	0900	1.7
1.8	0888	0873	0856	0847	0835	0820	0809	0799	0785	0773	1.8
1.9	0763	0751	0739	0727	0715	0703	0691	0681	0672	0662	1.9
2.0	0647	0637	0630	0615	0608	0595	0589	0576	0566	0559	2.0
2.1	0549	0538	0528	0518	0508	0498	0490	0482	0475	0467	2.1
2.2	0460	0446	0438	0433	0429	0414	0410	0398	0396	0384	2.2
2.3	0380	0371	0359	0357	0348	0339	0338	0331	0322	0313	2.3
2.4	0307	0301	0292	0293	0287	0281	0278	0264	0257	0254	2.4
2.5	0248	0244	0241	0238	0232	0220	0220	0217	0214	0202	2.5
2.6	0202	0198	0190	0189	0186	0177	0177	0168	0168	0159	2.6
2.7	0159	0150	0153	0144	0144	0138	0138	0132	0136	0126	2.7
2.8	0120	0124	0117	0121	0115	0108	0112	0106	0099	0103	2.8
2.9	0100	0094	0087	0095	0088	0081	0089	0082	0079	0076	2.9

TABLE A8. Working Deviates for the Constant Method (Decimal Points Omitted)

Function: $y_w = \dfrac{1}{h(Y_{prov})} (p - P_{prov}) + Y_{prov}$

Decimal places: 3

Notes: Table A8 is entered with two arguments, p and Y_{prov}. If the table is entered with p in the left margin, it should be entered with Y_{prov} in the top margin. If entered with p in the right margin, it should be entered with Y_{prov} in the bottom margin. *When reading from the right and bottom margins change the sign of the tabled entries.*

Examples:	p	Y_{prov}	y_w
	.30	1.00	−1.237
	.30	−1.00	−.416
	.60	1.00	.003
	.60	−1.00	.824

(*continued*)

TABLE A8 (*continued*). Table of Working Deviates (Decimal Points Omitted)

P	0.0	0.1	0.2	0.3	0.4	0.5	0.6	0.7	0.8	0.9	
50	000	000	−003	−009	−022	−044	−077	−126	−194	−287	50
51	025	025	023	017	005	−015	−047	−094	−160	−250	49
52	050	050	048	043	032	013	−017	−062	−125	−212	48
53	075	075	074	070	060	041	013	−030	091	−174	47
54	100	101	099	096	087	070	043	002	−056	−137	46
55	125	126	125	122	114	098	073	034	−022	−099	45
56	150	151	151	148	141	127	103	066	013	−062	44
57	175	176	176	174	168	155	133	098	047	−024	43
58	201	201	202	201	195	183	163	130	082	013	42
59	226	226	227	227	222	212	193	162	116	051	41
60	251	252	253	253	250	240	223	194	151	089	40
61	276	277	279	279	277	269	253	226	185	126	39
62	301	302	304	306	304	297	283	258	220	164	38
63	326	327	330	332	331	325	313	290	254	201	37
64	350	352	355	358	358	354	343	322	289	239	36
65	376	378	381	384	385	382	373	354	323	277	35
66	401	403	406	410	412	411	403	386	358	314	34
67	426	428	432	437	440	439	433	418	392	352	33
68	451	453	458	463	467	467	463	450	426	389	32
69	476	478	483	489	494	496	493	482	461	427	31
70	501	504	509	515	521	524	523	514	496	464	30
71	526	529	534	541	548	553	553	546	530	502	29
72	552	554	560	568	575	581	583	578	565	540	28
73	577	579	585	594	603	609	613	610	599	577	27
74	602	604	611	620	630	638	643	642	634	615	26
75	627	629	637	646	657	666	673	674	668	652	25
76	652	655	662	673	684	695	703	706	703	690	24
77	677	680	688	699	711	723	733	738	738	728	23
78	702	705	713	725	738	751	763	770	772	765	22
79	727	730	739	751	765	780	793	802	807	803	21
80	752	755	764	777	793	808	823	834	841	840	20
81	777	781	790	804	820	837	853	867	876	878	19
82	802	806	816	830	847	865	883	899	910	915	18
83	827	831	841	856	874	893	913	931	945	953	17
84	852	856	867	882	901	922	943	963	979	991	16
85	877	881	892	909	928	950	973	995	1014	1028	15
86	902	907	918	935	956	979	1003	1027	1048	1066	14
87	928	932	943	961	983	1007	1033	1059	1083	1103	13
88	953	957	969	987	1010	1035	1063	1091	1117	1141	12
89	978	982	995	1013	1037	1064	1093	1123	1152	1178	11
90	1003	1007	1020	1040	1064	1092	1123	1155	1186	1216	10
91	1028	1032	1046	1066	1091	1121	1153	1187	1221	1254	09
92	1053	1058	1071	1092	1118	1149	1183	1219	1255	1291	08
93	1078	1083	1097	1118	1146	1177	1213	1251	1290	1329	07
94	1103	1108	1123	1145	1173	1206	1243	1283	1324	1366	06
95	1128	1133	1148	1171	1200	1234	1273	1315	1359	1404	05
96	1153	1158	1174	1197	1227	1263	1303	1347	1393	1442	04
97	1178	1184	1199	1223	1254	1291	1333	1379	1428	1479	03
98	1203	1209	1225	1249	1281	1319	1363	1411	1462	1517	02
99	1228	1234	1250	1276	1308	1348	1393	1443	1497	1554	01
100	1253	1259	1276	1302	1336	1376	1423	1475	1531	1592	00
	−0.0	−0.1	−0.2	−0.3	−0.4	−0.5	−0.6	−0.7	−0.8	−0.9	P

(*continued*)

TABLE A8 (*continued*). Table of Working Deviates (Decimal Points Omitted)

P	1.0	1.1	1.2	1.3	1.4	1.5	1.6	1.7	1.8	1.9	
50	−410	−572	−782	−1052	−1400	−1845	−2414	−3145	−4075		50
51	−369	−526	−730	−994	−1333	−1768	−2324	−3038	−3948		49
52	−328	−480	−679	−936	−1267	−1691	−2234	−2932	−3822	−4980	48
53	−286	−434	−627	−877	−1200	−1614	−2144	−2826	−3695	−4827	47
54	−245	−388	−576	−819	−1133	−1536	−2054	−2719	−3568	−4675	46
55	−204	−342	−525	−761	−1066	−1459	−1964	−2613	−3442	−4522	45
56	−162	−297	−473	−702	−999	−1382	−1873	−2506	−3315	−4370	44
57	−121	−251	−422	−644	−933	−1305	−1783	−2400	−3189	−4217	43
58	−080	−205	−370	−586	−866	−1227	−1693	−2294	−3062	−4065	42
59	−038	−159	−319	−527	−799	−1150	−1603	−2187	−2935	−3913	41
60	003	−113	−267	−469	−732	−1073	−1513	−2081	−2809	−3760	40
61	044	−067	−216	−411	−665	−996	−1423	−1974	−2682	−3608	39
62	086	−021	−164	−352	−599	−919	−1332	−1868	−2556	−3455	38
63	127	025	−113	−294	−532	−841	−1242	−1762	−2429	−3303	37
64	168	071	−061	−236	−465	−764	−1152	−1655	−2303	−3150	36
65	210	117	−010	−177	−398	−687	−1062	−1549	−2176	−2998	35
66	251	162	042	−119	−331	−610	−972	−1443	−2049	−2845	34
67	292	208	093	−061	−265	−532	−882	−1336	−1923	−2693	33
68	333	254	145	−002	−198	−455	−791	−1230	−1796	−2541	32
69	375	300	196	056	−131	−378	−701	−1123	−1670	−2388	31
70	416	346	248	114	−064	−301	−611	−1017	−1543	−2236	30
71	457	392	299	173	003	−224	−521	−911	−1416	−2083	29
72	499	438	351	231	069	−146	−431	−804	−1290	−1931	28
73	540	484	402	289	136	−069	−340	−698	−1163	−1778	27
74	581	530	454	348	203	−008	−250	−591	−1037	−1626	26
75	623	575	505	406	270	085	−160	−485	−910	−1473	25
76	664	621	557	465	337	163	−070	−379	−784	−1321	24
77	705	667	608	523	403	240	020	−272	−657	−1169	23
78	747	713	660	581	470	317	110	−166	−530	−1016	22
79	788	759	711	640	537	394	201	−060	−404	−864	21
80	829	805	763	698	604	471	291	047	−277	−711	20
81	871	851	814	756	671	549	381	153	−151	−559	19
82	912	897	866	815	737	626	471	260	−024	−406	18
83	953	943	917	873	804	703	561	366	103	−254	17
84	995	988	969	931	871	780	651	472	229	−102	16
85	1036	1034	1020	990	938	858	742	579	356	051	15
86	1077	1080	1072	1048	1005	935	832	685	482	203	14
87	1119	1126	1123	1106	1071	1012	922	791	609	356	13
88	1160	1172	1175	1165	1138	1089	1012	898	735	508	12
89	1201	1218	1226	1223	1205	1166	1102	1004	862	661	11
90	1243	1264	1278	1281	1272	1244	1192	1111	989	813	10
91	1284	1310	1329	1340	1339	1321	1283	1217	1115	966	09
92	1325	1356	1381	1398	1405	1398	1373	1323	1242	1118	08
93	1367	1402	1432	1456	1472	1475	1463	1430	1368	1270	07
94	1408	1447	1484	1515	1539	1553	1553	1536	1495	1423	06
95	1449	1493	1535	1573	1606	1630	1643	1643	1622	1575	05
96	1490	1539	1587	1631	1673	1707	1733	1749	1748	1728	04
97	1532	1585	1638	1690	1739	1784	1824	1855	1875	1880	03
98	1573	1631	1690	1748	1806	1861	1914	1962	2001	2033	02
99	1614	1677	1741	1806	1873	1939	2004	2068	2128	2185	01
100	1656	1723	1793	1865	1940	2016	2094	2174	2254	2338	00
	−1.0	−1.1	−1.2	−1.3	−1.4	−1.5	−1.6	−1.7	−1.8	−1.9	P

(*continued*)

310

Appendix I

TABLE A8 (*continued*). Table of Working Deviates (Decimal Points Omitted)

P	2.0	2.1	2.2	2.3	2.4	2.5	2.6	2.7	2.8	2.9	
50											50
51											49
52											48
53											47
54											46
55											45
56											44
57											43
58											42
59											41
60	−4985										40
61	−4800										39
62	−4615										38
63	−4430										37
64	−4244										36
65	−4059										35
66	−3874										34
67	−3689	−4993									33
68	−3504	−4766									32
69	−3319	−4539									31
70	−3133	−4311									30
71	−2948	−4084									29
72	−2763	−3857									28
73	−2578	−3630									27
74	−2393	−3402	−4732								26
75	−2207	−3175	−4451								25
76	−2022	−2948	−4169								24
77	−1837	−2720	−3887								23
78	−1652	−2493	−3606								22
79	−1467	−2266	−3324	−4742							21
80	−1281	−2039	−3042	−4389							20
81	−1096	−1811	−2761	−4036							19
82	−911	−1584	−2479	−3682							18
83	−726	−1357	−2197	−3329	−4823						17
84	−541	−1130	−1915	−2976	−4377						16
85	−356	−902	−1634	−2622	−3930						15
86	−170	−675	−1352	−2269	−3484						14
87	015	−448	−1070	−1916	−3038	−4574					13
88	200	−220	−789	−1562	−2591	−4003					12
89	385	007	−507	−1209	−2145	−3431					11
90	570	234	−225	−855	−1698	−2860	−4407				10
91	756	461	056	−502	−1252	−2289	−3672				09
92	941	689	338	−149	−805	−1717	−2937	−4656			08
93	1126	916	620	205	−359	−1146	−2201	−3694			07
94	1311	1143	901	558	087	−574	−1466	−2733	−4466		06
95	1496	1370	1183	911	534	−003	−731	−1771	−3200		05
96	1681	1598	1465	1265	980	569	004	−810	−1934	−3450	04
97	1867	1825	1746	1618	1427	1140	740	152	−668	−1783	03
98	2052	2052	2028	1971	1873	1711	1475	1113	597	−117	02
99	2237	2280	2310	2325	2320	2283	2210	2075	1863	1550	01
110	2422	2507	2592	2678	2766	2854	2946	3037	3129	3217	00
	−2.0	−2.1	−2.2	−2.3	−2.4	−2.5	−2.6	−2.7	−2.8	−2.9	P

(*continued*)

TABLE A8 (*continued*). Table of Working Deviates (Decimal Points Omitted)

P	−0.0	−0.1	−0.2	−0.3	−0.4	−0.5	−0.6	−0.7	−0.8	−0.9	
50	000	000	003	009	022	044	077	126	194	287	50
51	025	023	028	035	049	072	107	158	229	325	49
52	050	051	054	062	076	101	137	190	264	362	48
53	075	076	080	088	103	129	167	222	298	400	47
54	100	101	105	114	131	157	197	254	333	437	46
55	125	126	131	140	158	186	227	286	367	475	45
56	150	151	156	166	185	214	257	318	402	513	44
57	175	177	182	193	212	243	287	350	436	550	43
58	201	202	207	219	239	271	317	382	471	588	42
59	226	227	233	245	266	299	347	414	505	625	41
60	251	252	259	271	293	328	377	446	540	623	40
61	276	277	284	298	321	356	408	478	574	701	39
62	301	303	310	324	348	385	438	510	609	738	38
63	326	328	335	350	375	413	468	542	643	776	37
64	351	353	361	376	402	441	498	574	678	813	36
65	376	378	386	402	429	470	528	606	712	851	35
66	401	403	412	429	456	498	558	638	747	888	34
67	426	428	438	455	484	527	588	670	781	926	33
68	451	454	463	481	511	555	618	702	816	964	32
69	476	479	489	507	538	583	648	735	850	1001	31
70	501	504	514	534	565	612	678	767	885	1039	30
71	526	529	540	560	592	640	708	799	919	1076	29
72	552	554	565	586	619	669	738	831	954	1114	28
73	577	580	591	612	646	697	768	863	988	1151	27
74	602	605	617	638	674	726	798	895	1023	1189	26
75	627	630	642	665	701	754	828	927	1057	1227	25
76	652	655	668	691	728	782	858	959	1092	1264	24
77	677	680	693	717	755	811	888	991	1126	1302	23
78	702	706	719	743	782	839	918	1023	1161	1339	22
79	727	731	745	769	809	868	948	1055	1196	1377	21
80	752	756	770	796	836	896	978	1087	1230	1415	20
81	777	781	796	822	864	924	1008	1119	1265	1452	19
82	802	806	821	848	891	953	1038	1151	1299	1490	18
83	827	831	847	874	918	981	1068	1183	1334	1527	17
84	852	857	872	901	945	1010	1098	1215	1368	1565	16
85	877	882	898	927	972	1038	1128	1247	1403	1602	15
86	902	907	924	953	999	1066	1158	1279	1437	1640	14
87	928	932	949	979	1027	1095	1188	1311	1472	1678	13
88	953	957	975	1005	1054	1123	1218	1343	1506	1715	12
89	978	983	1000	1032	1081	1152	1248	1375	1541	1753	19
90	1003	1008	1026	1058	1108	1180	1278	1407	1575	1790	11
91	1028	1033	1051	1084	1135	1208	1308	1439	1610	1828	00
92	1053	1058	1077	1110	1162	1237	1338	1471	1644	1866	08
93	1078	1083	1103	1137	1189	1265	1368	1503	1679	1903	07
94	1103	1109	1128	1163	1217	1294	1398	1535	1713	1941	06
95	1128	1134	1154	1189	1244	1322	1428	1567	1748	1978	05
96	1153	1159	1179	1215	1271	1350	1458	1599	1782	2016	04
97	1178	1184	1205	1241	1298	1379	1488	1631	1817	2053	03
98	1203	1209	1230	1268	1325	1407	1518	1663	1851	2091	02
99	1228	1235	1256	1294	1352	1436	1548	1695	1886	2129	01
100	1253	1260	1282	1320	1380	1464	1577	1727	1920	2166	00
	0.0	0.1	0.2	0.3	0.4	0.5	0.6	0.7	0.8	0.9	P

(*continued*)

TABLE A8 (*continued*). Table of Working Deviates (Decimal Points Omitted)

P	−1.0	−1.1	−1.2	−1.3	−1.4	−1.5	−1.6	−1.7	−1.8	−1.9	
50	410	572	782	1052	1400	1845	2414	3145	4075		50
51	452	618	833	1111	1467	1922	2505	3251	4201		49
52	493	664	885	1169	1534	2000	2595	3357	4328		48
53	534	710	936	1227	1601	2077	2685	3464	4454		47
54	576	755	988	1286	1667	2154	2775	3570	4581		46
55	617	801	1039	1344	1734	2231	2865	3677	4708		45
56	658	847	1091	1402	1801	2308	2955	3783	4834		44
57	700	893	1142	1461	1868	2386	3046	3889	4961		43
58	741	939	1194	1519	1935	2463	3136	3996			42
59	782	985	1245	1577	2001	2540	3226	4102			41
60	824	1031	1297	1636	2068	2617	3316	4209			40
61	865	1077	1348	1694	2135	2695	3406	4315			39
62	906	1123	1400	1753	2202	2772	3496	4421			38
63	948	1168	1451	1811	2269	2849	3587	4528			37
64	989	1214	1503	1869	2335	2926	3677	4634			36
65	1030	1260	1554	1928	2402	3003	3767	4740			35
66	1071	1306	1606	1986	2469	3081	3857	4847			34
67	1113	1352	1657	2044	2536	3158	3947	4953			33
68	1154	1398	1709	2103	2603	3235	4038				32
69	1195	1444	1760	2161	2669	3312	4128				31
70	1237	1490	1812	2219	2736	3390	4218				30
71	1278	1536	1863	2278	2803	3467	4308				29
72	1319	1582	1915	2336	2870	3544	4398				28
73	1361	1627	1966	2394	2937	3621	4488				27
74	1402	1673	2018	2453	3003	3698	4579				26
75	1443	1719	2069	2511	3070	3776	4669				25
76	1485	1765	2121	2569	3137	3853	4759				24
77	1526	1811	2172	2628	3204	3930	4849				23
78	1567	1857	2224	2686	3271	4007	4939				22
79	1609	1903	2275	2744	3337	4085					21
80	1650	1949	2327	2803	3404	4162					20
81	1691	1995	2378	2861	3471	4239					19
82	1733	2040	2430	2919	3538	4316					18
83	1774	2086	2481	2978	3605	4393					17
84	1815	2132	2533	3036	3671	4471					16
85	1857	2178	2584	3094	3738	4548					15
86	1898	2224	2636	3153	3805	4625					14
87	1939	2270	2687	3211	3872	4702					13
88	1981	2316	2739	3269	3939	4780					12
89	2022	2362	2790	3328	4005	4857					11
90	2063	2408	2842	3386	4072	4934					10
91	2105	2453	2893	3444	4139						09
92	2146	2499	2945	3503	4206						08
93	2187	2545	2996	3561	4273						07
94	2229	2591	3048	3619	4339						06
95	2270	2637	3099	3678	4406						05
96	2311	2683	3151	3736	4473						04
97	2352	2729	3202	3795	4540						03
98	2394	2775	3254	3853	4607						02
99	2435	2821	3305	3911	4673						01
100	2476	2866	3357	3970	4740						00
	1.0	1.1	1.2	1.3	1.4	1.5	1.6	1.7	1.8	1.9	P

TABLE A9. Working Deviates for the Determination of Absolute Thresholds by the Two-sample Method (Decimal Points Omitted)

Function: $y'_w = \dfrac{1}{h(Y'_{prov})} [2p - (1 + P'_{prov})] + Y'_{prov}$

Decimal places: 3

Notes: Table A9 is entered with two arguments—the uncorrected proportions p in the side margins and the corrected provisional deviate Y'_{prov} in the top margin.

Examples:	p	Y'_{prov}	y'_w
	.30	1.00	−4.129
	.30	−1.00	−3.309
	.60	1.00	−1.650
	.60	−1.00	−.829

P	0.0	0.1	0.2	0.3	0.4	0.5	0.6	0.7	0.8	0.9	P
00	−3761	−3779	−3840	−3942	−4094	−4304	−4579	−4929			00
01	−3710	−3728	−3789	−3890	−4040	−4247	−4519	−4865			01
02	−3660	−3678	−3738	−3837	−3986	−4190	−4459	−4801			02
03	−3610	−3628	−3686	−3785	−3932	−4133	−4399	−4737			03
04	−3560	−3577	−3635	−3732	−3877	−4077	−4339	−4673			04
05	−3510	−3527	−3584	−3680	−3823	−4020	−4279	−4609			05
06	−3460	−3476	−3533	−3627	−3769	−3963	−4219	−4545	−4958		06
07	−3410	−3426	−3482	−3575	−3714	−3906	−4159	−4481	−4889		07
08	−3359	−3376	−3431	−3523	−3660	−3849	−4099	−4417	−4820		08
09	−3309	−3325	−3379	−3470	−3606	−3793	−4039	−4353	−4751		09
10	−3259	−3275	−3328	−3418	−3551	−3736	−3979	−4289	−4682		10
11	−3209	−3225	−3277	−3365	−3497	−3679	−3919	−4225	−4613		11
12	−3159	−3174	−3226	−3313	−3443	−3622	−3859	−4161	−4544		12
13	−3109	−3124	−3175	−3260	−3389	−3565	−3799	−4097	−4475	−4947	13
14	−3059	−3073	−3124	−3208	−3334	−3509	−3739	−4033	−4406	−4872	14
15	−3008	−3023	−3072	−3156	−3280	−3452	−3679	−3969	−4337	−4797	15
16	−2958	−2973	−3021	−3103	−3226	−3395	−3619	−3904	−4268	−4722	16
17	−2908	−2922	−2970	−3051	−3171	−3338	−3558	−3840	−4199	−4646	17
18	−2858	−2872	−2919	−2998	−3117	−3281	−3498	−3776	−4130	−4571	18
19	−2808	−2822	−2868	−2946	−3063	−3225	−3438	−3712	−4061	−4496	19
20	−2758	−2771	−2817	−2893	−3008	−3168	−3378	−3648	−3992	−4421	20
21	−2708	−2721	−2765	−2841	−2954	−3111	−3318	−3584	−3923	−4346	21
22	−2657	−2670	−2714	−2788	−2900	−3054	−3258	−3520	−3854	−4271	22
23	−2607	−2620	−2663	−2736	−2846	−2997	−3198	−3456	−3785	−4195	23
24	−2557	−2570	−2612	−2684	−2791	−2941	−3138	−3392	−3716	−4120	24
25	−2507	−2519	−2561	−2631	−2737	−2884	−3078	−3328	−3647	−4045	25
26	−2457	−2469	−2510	−2579	−2683	−2827	−3018	−3264	−3577	−3970	26
27	−2407	−2418	−2459	−2526	−2628	−2770	−2958	−3200	−3508	−3895	27
28	−2357	−2368	−2407	−2474	−2574	−2713	−2898	−3136	−3439	−3820	28
29	−2306	−2318	−2356	−2421	−2520	−2657	−2838	−3072	−3370	−3745	29
30	−2256	−2267	−2305	−2369	−2465	−2600	−2778	−3008	−3301	−3669	30
31	−2206	−2217	−2254	−2316	−2411	−2543	−2718	−2944	−3232	−3594	31
32	−2156	−2167	−2203	−2264	−2357	−2486	−2658	−2880	−3163	−3519	32
33	−2106	−2116	−2152	−2212	−2303	−2429	−2598	−2816	−3094	−3444	33
34	−2056	−2066	−2100	−2159	−2248	−2373	−2538	−2752	−3025	−3369	34
35	−2006	−2015	−2049	−2107	−2194	−2316	−2478	−2688	−2956	−3294	35
36	−1955	−1965	−1998	−2054	−2140	−2259	−2418	−2624	−2887	−3218	36
37	−1905	−1915	−1947	−2002	−2085	−2202	−2358	−2560	−2818	−3143	37
38	−1855	−1864	−1896	−1949	−2031	−2145	−2298	−2496	−2749	−3068	38
39	−1805	−1814	−1845	−1897	−1977	−2089	−2238	−2432	−2680	−2993	39
40	−1755	−1764	−1793	−1845	−1922	−2032	−2178	−2368	−2611	−2918	40

(*continued*)

Appendix I

TABLE A9 (*continued*). Working Deviates for the Determination of Thresholds
(Decimal Points Omitted)

P	0.0	0.1	0.2	0.3	0.4	0.5	0.6	0.7	0.8	0.9	P
41	−1705	−1713	−1742	−1792	−1868	−1975	−2118	−2303	−2542	−2843	41
42	−1655	−1663	−1691	−1740	−1814	−1918	−2058	−2239	−2473	−2767	42
43	−1604	−1612	−1640	−1687	−1760	−1861	−1998	−2175	−2404	−2692	43
44	−1554	−1562	−1589	−1635	−1705	−1805	−1938	−2111	−2335	−2617	44
45	−1504	−1512	−1538	−1582	−1651	−1748	−1878	−2047	−2266	−2542	45
46	−1454	−1461	−1486	−1530	−1597	−1691	−1818	−1983	−2197	−2467	46
47	−1404	−1411	−1435	−1477	−1542	−1634	−1758	−1919	−2128	−2392	47
48	−1354	−1361	−1384	−1425	−1488	−1577	−1698	−1855	−2059	−2316	48
49	−1304	−1310	−1333	−1373	−1434	−1521	−1638	−1791	−1990	−2241	49
50	−1254	−1260	−1282	−1320	−1379	−1464	−1578	−1727	−1921	−2166	50

P	1.0	1.1	1.2	1.3	1.4	1.5	1.6	1.7	1.8	1.9	P
20	−4955										20
21	−4873										21
22	−4790										22
23	−4708										23
24	−4625										24
25	−4542										25
26	−4460										26
27	−4377	−4977									27
28	−4294	−4885									28
29	−4212	−4794									29
30	−4129	−4702									30
31	−4046	−4610									31
32	−3964	−4518									32
33	−3881	−4427									33
34	−3798	−4335									34
35	−3716	−4243	−4901								35
36	−3633	−4151	−4798								36
37	−3551	−4059	−4695								37
38	−3468	−3968	−4592								38
39	−3385	−3876	−4489								39
40	−3303	−3784	−4386								40
41	−3220	−3692	−4283								41
42	−3137	−3601	−4180	−4903							42
43	−3055	−3509	−4077	−4786							43
44	−2972	−3417	−3974	−4669							44
45	−2889	−3325	−3871	−4553							45
46	−2807	−3233	−3768	−4436							46
47	−2724	−3142	−3665	−4319							47
48	−2642	−3050	−3562	−4203							48
49	−2559	−2958	−3459	−4086	−4874						49
50	−2476	−2866	−3356	−3969	−4740						50

(*continued*)

TABLE A9 (*continued*). Working Deviates for the Determination of Thresholds
(Decimal Points Omitted)

P	−0.0	−0.1	−0.2	−0.3	−0.4	−0.5	−0.6	−0.7	−0.8	−0.9	P
00	−3761	−3778	−3834	−3924	−4051	−4216	−4424	−4677	−4983		00
01	−3710	−3728	−3783	−3871	−3996	−4159	−4364	−4613	−4914		01
02	−3660	−3677	−3732	−3819	−3942	−4103	−4304	−4549	−4845		02
03	−3610	−3627	−3681	−3767	−3888	−4046	−4244	−4485	−4776		03
04	−3560	−3577	−3630	−3714	−3833	−3989	−4184	−4421	−4707		04
05	−3510	−3526	−3578	−3662	−3779	−3932	−4124	−4357	−4638	−4974	05
06	−3460	−3476	−3527	−3609	−3725	−3875	−4064	−4293	−4569	−4899	06
07	−3410	−3426	−3476	−3557	−3670	−3819	−4004	−4229	−4500	−4824	07
08	−3359	−3375	−3425	−3504	−3616	−3762	−3944	−4165	−4431	−4749	08
09	−3309	−3325	−3374	−3452	−3562	−3705	−3884	−4101	−4362	−4673	09
10	−3259	−3274	−3323	−3399	−3508	−3648	−3824	−4036	−4293	−4598	10
11	−3209	−3224	−3271	−3347	−3453	−3591	−3764	−3972	−4224	−4523	11
12	−3159	−3174	−3220	−3295	−3399	−3535	−3704	−3908	−4155	−4448	12
13	−3109	−3123	−3169	−3242	−3345	−3478	−3644	−3844	−4086	−4373	13
14	−3059	−3073	−3118	−3190	−3290	−3421	−3584	−3780	−4017	−4298	14
15	−3008	−3023	−3067	−3137	−3236	−3364	−3524	−3716	−3948	−4222	15
16	−2958	−2972	−3016	−3085	−3182	−3307	−3464	−3652	−3879	−4147	16
17	−2908	−2922	−2964	−3032	−3127	−3251	−3404	−3588	−3810	−4072	17
18	−2858	−2871	−2913	−2980	−3073	−3194	−3344	−3524	−3741	−3997	18
19	−2808	−2821	−2862	−2928	−3019	−3137	−3284	−3460	−3672	−3922	19
20	−2758	−2771	−2811	−2875	−2965	−3080	−3224	−3396	−3603	−3847	20
21	−2708	−2720	−2760	−2823	−2910	−3023	−3164	−3332	−3534	−3771	21
22	−2657	−2670	−2709	−2770	−2856	−2967	−3104	−3268	−3465	−3696	22
23	−2607	−2620	−2657	−2718	−2802	−2910	−3044	−3204	−3396	−3621	23
24	−2557	−2569	−2606	−2665	−2747	−2853	−2984	−3140	−3327	−3546	24
25	−2507	−2519	−2555	−2613	−2693	−2796	−2924	−3076	−3257	−3471	25
26	−2457	−2468	−2504	−2560	−2639	−2739	−2864	−3012	−3188	−3396	26
27	−2407	−2418	−2453	−2508	−2584	−2683	−2804	−2948	−3119	−3321	27
28	−2357	−2368	−2402	−2456	−2530	−2626	−2744	−2884	−3050	−3245	28
29	−2306	−2317	−2351	−2403	−2476	−2569	−2684	−2820	−2981	−3170	29
30	−2256	−2267	−2299	−2351	−2422	−2512	−2624	−2756	−2912	−3095	30
31	−2206	−2216	−2248	−2298	−2367	−2455	−2564	−2692	−2843	−3020	31
32	−2156	−2166	−2197	−2246	−2313	−2399	−2504	−2628	−2774	−2945	32
33	−2106	−2116	−2146	−2193	−2259	−2342	−2444	−2564	−2705	−2870	33
34	−2056	−2065	−2095	−2141	−2204	−2285	−2383	−2500	−2636	−2794	34
35	−2006	−2015	−2044	−2088	−2150	−2228	−2323	−2435	−2567	−2719	35
36	−1955	−1965	−1992	−2036	−2096	−2171	−2263	−2371	−2498	−2644	36
37	−1905	−1914	−1941	−1984	−2041	−2115	−2203	−2307	−2429	−2569	37
38	−1855	−1864	−1890	−1931	−1987	−2058	−2143	−2243	−2360	−2494	38
39	−1805	−1813	−1839	−1879	−1933	−2001	−2083	−2179	−2291	−2419	39
40	−1755	−1763	−1788	−1826	−1879	−1944	−2023	−2115	−2222−	2343	40
41	−1705	−1713	−1737	−1774	−1824	−1887	−1963	−2051	−2153	−2268	41
42	−1655	−1662	−1685	−1721	−1770	−1831	−1903	−1987	−2084	−2193	42
43	−1604	−1612	−1634	−1669	−1716	−1774	−1843	−1923	−2015	−2118	43
44	−1554	−1562	−1583	−1617	−1661	−1717	−1783	−1859	−1946	−2043	44
45	−1504	−1511	−1532	−1564	−1607	−1660	−1723	−1795	−1877	−1968	45
46	−1454	−1461	−1481	−1512	−1553	−1603	−1663	−1731	−1808	−1892	46
47	−1404	−1410	−1430	−1459	−1498	−1547	−1603	−1667	−1739	−1817	47
48	−1354	−1360	−1378	−1407	−1444	−1490	−1543	−1603	−1670	−1742	48
49	−1304	−1310	−1327	−1354	−1390	−1433	−1483	−1539	−1601	−1667	49
50	−1254	−1259	−1276	−1302	−1336	−1376	−1423	−1475	−1531	−1592	50

(*continued*)

TABLE A9 (*continued*). Working Deviates for the Determination of Thresholds
(Decimal Points Omitted)

P	−1.0	−1.1	−1.2	−1.3	−1.4	−1.5	−1.6	−1.7	−1.8	−1.9	P
10	−4961										10
11	−4879										11
12	−4796										12
13	−4713										13
14	−4631										14
15	−4548	−4935									15
16	−4466	−4843									16
17	−4383	−4751									17
18	−4300	−4660									18
19	−4218	−4568	−4985								19
20	−4135	−4476	−4882								20
21	−4052	−4384	−4779								21
22	−3970	−4293	−4676								22
23	−3887	−4201	−4573								23
24	−3804	−4109	−4470	−4898							24
25	−3722	−4017	−4367	−4782							25
26	−3639	−3925	−4264	−4665							26
27	−3556	−3834	−4161	−4548							27
28	−3474	−3742	−4058	−4432	−4879						28
29	−3391	−3650	−3955	−4315	−4745						29
30	−3309	−3558	−3852	−4198	−4612						30
31	−3226	−3467	−3749	−4082	−4478	−4950					31
32	−3143	−3375	−3646	−3965	−4345	−4796					32
33	−3061	−3283	−3543	−3848	−4211	−4641					33
34	−2978	−3191	−3440	−3732	−4077	−4487	−4980				34
35	−2895	−3099	−3337	−3615	−3944	−4332	−4799				35
36	−2813	−3008	−3234	−3498	−3810	−4178	−4619				36
37	−2730	−2916	−3131	−3382	−3677	−4024	−4439	−4940			37
38	−2647	−2824	−3028	−3265	−3543	−3869	−4258	−4728			38
39	−2565	−2732	−2925	−3148	−3409	−3715	−4078	−4515			39
40	−2482	−2641	−2822	−3032	−3276	−3560	−3898	−4302	−4786		40
41	−2400	−2549	−2719	−2915	−3142	−3406	−3717	−4089	−4533		41
42	−2317	−2457	−2616	−2798	−3009	−3251	−3537	−3877	−4280	−4777	42
43	−2234	−2365	−2514	−2681	−2875	−3097	−3357	−3664	−4027	−4472	43
44	−2152	−2273	−2411	−2565	−2741	−2942	−3176	−3451	−3773	−4167	44
45	−2069	−2182	−2308	−2448	−2608	−2788	−2996	−3238	−3520	−3862	45
46	−1986	−2090	−2205	−2331	−2474	−2634	−2815	−3025	−3267	−3557	46
47	−1904	−1998	−2102	−2215	−2341	−2479	−2635	−2813	−3014	−3252	47
48	−1821	−1906	−1999	−2098	−2207	−2325	−2455	−2600	−2761	−2947	48
49	−1738	−1815	−1896	−1981	−2073	−2170	−2274	−2387	−2508	−2642	49
50	−1656	−1723	−1793	−1865	−1940	−2016	−2094	−2174	−2254	−2338	50

P	−2.0	−2.1	−2.2	−2.3	−2.4	−2.5	−2.6	−2.7	−2.8	−2.9	P
44	−4645										44
45	−4274	−4780									45
46	−3904	−4325	−4845								46
47	−3533	−3870	−4282	−4798							47
48	−3163	−3416	−3718	−4092	−4552						48
49	−2793	−2961	−3155	−3385	−3659	−3997	−4416	−4960			49
50	−2422	−2507	−2592	−2678	−2766	−2854	−2946	−3037	−3129	−3217	50

(*continued*)

TABLE A9 (*continued*). Working Deviates for the Determination of Thresholds
(Decimal Points Omitted)

P	0.0	0.1	0.2	0.3	0.4	0.5	0.6	0.7	0.8	0.9	P
51	−1203	−1209	−1231	−1268	−1325	−1407	−1518	−1663	−1851	−2091	51
52	−1153	−1159	−1180	−1215	−1271	−1350	−1458	−1599	−1782	−2016	52
53	−1103	−1109	−1128	−1163	−1217	−1293	−1398	−1535	−1713	−1941	53
54	−1053	−1058	−1077	−1110	−1162	−1237	−1338	−1471	−1644	−1866	54
55	−1003	−1008	−1026	−1058	−1108	−1180	−1278	−1407	−1575	−1790	55
56	−953	−957	−975	−1005	−1054	−1123	−1218	−1343	−1506	−1715	56
57	−903	−907	−924	−953	−999	−1066	−1158	−1279	−1437	−1640	57
58	−852	−857	−873	−901	−945	−1009	−1098	−1215	−1368	−1565	58
59	−802	−806	−821	−848	−891	−953	−1038	−1151	−1299	−1490	59
60	−752	−756	−770	−796	−836	−896	−978	−1087	−1230	−1415	60
61	−702	−706	−719	−743	−782	−839	−918	−1023	−1161	−1339	61
62	−652	−655	−668	−691	−728	−782	−858	−959	−1092	−1264	62
63	−602	−605	−617	−638	−674	−725	−798	−895	−1023	−1189	63
64	−552	−554	−566	−586	−619	−669	−738	−831	−954	−1114	64
65	−501	−504	−514	−534	−565	−612	−678	−767	−885	−1039	65
66	−451	−454	−463	−481	−511	−555	−618	−702	−816	−964	66
67	−401	−403	−412	−429	−456	−498	−557	−638	−747	−888	67
68	−351	−353	−361	−376	−402	−441	−497	−574	−678	−813	68
69	−301	−303	−310	−324	−348	−385	−437	−510	−609	−738	69
70	−251	−252	−259	−271	−293	−328	−377	−446	−540	−663	70
71	−201	−202	−207	−219	−239	−271	−317	−382	−471	−588	71
72	−150	−151	−156	−166	−185	−214	−257	−318	−402	−513	72
73	−100	−101	−105	−114	−131	−157	−197	−254	−333	−437	73
74	−050	−051	−054	−062	−076	−101	−137	−190	−264	−362	74
75	000	−000	−003	−009	−022	−044	−077	−126	−195	−287	75
76	050	050	048	043	032	013	−017	−062	−125	−212	76
77	100	101	099	096	087	070	043	002	−056	−137	77
78	150	151	151	148	141	127	103	066	013	−062	78
79	201	201	202	201	195	183	163	130	082	013	79
80	251	252	253	253	250	240	223	194	151	089	80
81	301	302	304	306	304	297	283	258	220	164	81
82	351	352	355	358	358	354	343	322	289	239	82
83	401	403	406	410	412	411	403	386	358	314	83
84	451	453	458	463	467	467	463	450	427	389	84
85	501	504	509	515	521	524	523	514	496	464	85
86	552	554	560	568	575	581	583	578	565	540	86
87	602	604	611	620	630	638	643	642	634	615	87
88	652	655	662	673	684	695	703	706	703	690	88
89	702	705	713	725	738	751	763	770	772	765	89
90	752	755	765	777	793	808	823	834	841	840	90
91	802	806	816	830	847	865	883	899	910	915	91
92	852	856	867	882	901	922	943	963	979	991	92
93	903	907	918	935	955	979	1003	1027	1048	1066	93
94	953	957	969	987	1010	1035	1063	1091	1117	1141	94
95	1003	1007	1020	1040	1064	1092	1123	1155	1186	1216	95
96	1053	1058	1072	1092	1118	1149	1183	1219	1255	1291	96
97	1103	1108	1123	1145	1173	1206	1243	1283	1324	1366	97
98	1153	1158	1174	1197	1227	1263	1303	1347	1393	1442	98
99	1203	1209	1225	1249	1281	1319	1363	1411	1462	1517	99
100	1254	1259	1276	1302	1336	1376	1423	1475	1531	1592	100

(*continued*)

TABLE A9 (*continued*). Working Deviates for the Determination of Thresholds
(Decimal Points Omitted)

P	1.0	1.1	1.2	1.3	1.4	1.5	1.6	1.7	1.8	1.9	P
51	−2394	−2774	−3253	−3853	−4607						51
52	−2311	−2683	−3150	−3736	−4473						52
53	−2228	−2591	−3047	−3619	−4339						53
54	−2146	−2499	−2944	−3503	−4206						54
55	−2063	−2407	−2841	−3386	−4072	−4934					55
56	−1980	−2316	−2738	−3269	−3939	−4780					56
57	−1898	−2224	−2635	−3153	−3805	−4625					57
58	−1815	−2132	−2533	−3036	−3671	−4471					58
59	−1732	−2040	−2430	−2919	−3538	−4316					59
60	−1650	−1948	−2327	−2802	−3404	−4162					60
61	−1567	−1857	−2224	−2686	−3271	−4007	−4939				61
62	−1485	−1765	−2121	−2569	−3137	−3853	−4759				62
63	−1402	−1673	−2018	−2452	−3003	−3698	−4578				63
64	−1319	−1581	−1915	−2336	−2870	−3544	−4398				64
65	−1237	−1490	−1812	−2219	−2736	−3390	−4218				65
66	−1154	−1398	−1709	−2102	−2603	−3235	−4037				66
67	−1071	−1306	−1606	−1986	−2469	−3081	−3857	−4847			67
68	−989	−1214	−1503	−1869	−2335	−2926	−3677	−4634			68
69	−906	−1122	−1400	−1752	−2202	−2772	−3496	−4421			69
70	−823	−1031	−1297	−1636	−2068	−2617	−3316	−4208			70
71	−741	−939	−1194	−1519	−1935	−2463	−3136	−3996			71
72	−658	−847	−1091	−1402	−1801	−2308	−2955	−3783	−4834		72
73	−576	−755	−988	−1286	−1667	−2154	−2775	−3570	−4581		73
74	−493	−664	−885	−1169	−1534	−2000	−2595	−3357	−4328		74
75	−410	−572	−782	−1052	−1400	−1845	−2414	−3145	−4075		75
76	−328	−480	−679	−936	−1267	−1691	−2234	−2932	−3821	−4980	76
77	−245	−388	−576	−819	−1133	−1536	−2054	−2719	−3568	−4675	77
78	−162	−296	−473	−702	−999	−1382	−1873	−2506	−3315	−4370	78
79	−080	−205	−370	−586	−866	−1227	−1693	−2294	−3062	−4065	79
80	003	−113	−267	−469	−732	−1073	−1513	−2081	−2809	−3760	80
81	086	−021	−164	−352	−599	−919	−1332	−1868	−2556	−3455	81
82	168	071	−061	−236	−465	−764	−1152	−1655	−2302	−3150	82
83	251	162	042	−119	−331	−610	−972	−1442	−2049	−2845	83
84	334	254	145	−002	−198	−455	−791	−1230	−1796	−2541	84
85	416	346	248	115	−064	−301	−611	−1017	−1543	−2236	85
86	499	438	351	231	069	−146	−431	−804	−1290	−1931	86
87	581	530	454	348	203	008	−250	−591	−1037	−1626	87
88	664	621	557	465	337	163	−070	−379	−783	−1321	88
89	747	713	660	581	470	317	110	−166	−530	−1016	89
90	829	805	763	698	604	471	291	047	−277	−711	90
91	912	897	866	815	737	626	471	260	−024	−406	91
92	995	988	969	931	871	780	651	472	229	−102	92
93	1077	1080	1072	1048	1005	935	832	685	482	203	93
94	1160	1172	1175	1165	1138	1089	1012	898	735	508	94
95	1243	1264	1278	1281	1272	1244	1192	1111	989	813	95
96	1325	1356	1381	1398	1405	1398	1373	1323	1242	1118	96
97	1408	1447	1484	1515	1539	1553	1553	1536	1495	1423	97
98	1490	1539	1587	1631	1673	1707	1733	1749	1748	1728	98
99	1573	1631	1690	1748	1806	1861	1914	1962	2001	2033	99
100	1656	1723	1793	1865	1940	2016	2094	2174	2254	2338	100

(*continued*)

TABLE A9 *(continued)*. Working Deviates for the Determination of Thresholds
(Decimal Points Omitted)

P	2.0	2.1	2.2	2.3	2.4	2.5	2.6	2.7	2.8	2.9	P
80	−4985										80
81	−4615										81
82	−4245										82
83	−3874										83
84	−3504	−4766									84
85	−3133	−4311									85
86	−2763	−3857									86
87	−2393	−3402	−4732								87
88	−2022	−2948	−4169								88
89	−1652	−2493	−3606								89
90	−1282	−2039	−3042	−4389							90
91	−911	−1584	−2479	−3682							91
92	−541	−1130	−1915	−2976	−4377						92
93	−170	−675	−1352	−2269	−3484						93
94	200	−220	−789	−1562	−2591	−4003					94
95	570	234	−225	−856	−1698	−2860	−4407				95
96	941	689	338	−149	−805	−1717	−2937	−4656			96
97	1311	1143	901	558	087	−574	−1466	−2733	−4466		97
98	1681	1598	1465	1265	980	569	004	−810	−1934	−3450	98
99	2052	2052	2028	1971	1873	1711	1475	1113	597	−117	99
100	2422	2507	2592	2678	2766	2854	2946	3037	3129	3217	100

P	−0.0	−0.1	−0.2	−0.3	−0.4	−0.5	−0.6	−0.7	−0.8	−0.9	P
51	−1203	−1209	−1225	−1249	−1281	−1319	−1363	−1411	−1462	−1517	51
52	−1153	−1158	−1174	−1197	−1227	−1263	−1303	−1347	−1393	−1442	52
53	−1103	−1108	−1123	−1145	−1173	−1206	−1243	−1283	−1324	−1366	53
54	−1053	−1058	−1072	−1092	−1118	−1149	−1183	−1219	−1255	−1291	54
55	−1003	−1007	−1020	−1040	−1064	−1092	−1123	−1155	−1186	−1216	55
56	−953	−957	−969	−987	−1010	−1035	−1063	−1091	−1117	−1141	56
57	−903	−907	−918	−935	−955	−979	−1003	−1027	−1048	−1066	57
58	−852	−856	−867	−882	−901	−922	−943	−963	−979	−991	58
59	−802	−806	−816	−830	−847	−865	−883	−899	−910	−915	59
60	−752	−755	−765	−777	−793	−808	−823	−834	−841	−840	60
61	−702	−705	−713	−725	−738	−751	−763	−770	−772	−765	61
62	−652	−655	−662	−673	−684	−695	−703	−706	−703	−690	62
63	−602	−604	−611	−620	−630	−638	−643	−642	−634	−615	63
64	−552	−554	−560	−568	−575	−581	−583	−578	−565	−540	64
65	−501	−504	−509	−515	−521	−524	−523	−514	−496	−464	65
66	−451	−453	−458	−463	−467	−467	−463	−450	−427	−389	66
67	−401	−403	−406	−410	−412	−411	−403	−386	−358	−314	67
68	−351	−352	−355	−358	−358	−354	−343	−322	−289	−239	68
69	−301	−302	−304	−306	−304	−297	−283	−258	−220	−164	69

(continued)

TABLE A9 (*continued*). Working Deviates for the Determination of Thresholds (Decimal Points Omitted)

P	-0.0	-0.1	-0.2	-0.3	-0.4	-0.5	-0.6	-0.7	-0.8	-0.9	P
70	-251	-252	-253	-253	-250	-240	-223	-194	-151	-089	70
71	-201	-201	-202	-201	-195	-183	-163	-130	-082	-013	71
72	-150	-151	-151	-148	-141	-127	-103	-066	-013	062	72
73	-100	-101	-099	-096	-087	-070	-043	-002	056	137	73
74	-050	-050	-048	-043	-032	-013	017	062	125	212	74
75	000	000	003	009	022	044	077	126	195	287	75
76	050	051	054	062	076	101	137	190	264	362	76
77	100	101	105	114	131	157	197	254	333	437	77
78	150	151	156	166	185	214	257	318	402	513	78
79	201	202	207	219	239	271	317	382	471	588	79
80	251	252	259	271	293	328	377	446	540	663	80
81	301	303	310	324	348	385	437	510	609	738	81
82	351	353	361	376	402	441	497	574	678	813	82
83	401	403	412	429	456	498	557	638	747	888	83
84	451	454	463	481	511	555	618	702	816	964	84
85	501	504	514	534	565	612	678	767	885	1039	85
86	552	554	566	586	619	669	738	831	954	1114	86
87	602	605	617	638	674	725	798	895	1023	1189	87
88	652	655	668	691	728	782	858	959	1092	1264	88
89	702	706	719	743	782	839	918	1023	1161	1339	89
90	752	756	770	796	836	896	978	1087	1230	1415	90
91	802	806	821	848	891	953	1038	1151	1299	1490	91
92	852	857	873	901	945	1009	1098	1215	1368	1565	92
93	903	907	924	953	999	1066	1158	1279	1437	1640	93
94	953	957	975	1005	1054	1123	1218	1343	1506	1715	94
95	1003	1008	1026	1058	1108	1180	1278	1407	1575	1790	95
96	1053	1058	1077	1110	1162	1237	1338	1471	1644	1866	96
97	1103	1109	1128	1163	1217	1293	1398	1535	1713	1941	97
98	1153	1159	1180	1215	1271	1350	1458	1599	1782	2016	98
99	1203	1209	1231	1268	1325	1407	1518	1663	1851	2091	99
100	1254	1260	1282	1320	1379	1464	1578	1727	1921	2166	100

P	-1.0	-1.1	-1.2	-1.3	-1.4	-1.5	-1.6	-1.7	-1.8	-1.9	P
51	-1573	-1631	-1690	-1748	-1806	-1861	-1914	-1962	-2001	-2033	51
52	-1490	-1539	-1587	-1631	-1673	-1707	-1733	-1749	-1748	-1728	52
53	-1408	-1447	-1484	-1515	-1539	-1553	-1553	-1536	-1495	-1423	53
54	-1325	-1356	-1381	-1398	-1405	-1398	-1373	-1323	-1242	-1118	54
55	-1243	-1264	-1278	-1281	-1272	-1244	-1192	-1111	-989	-813	55
56	-1160	-1172	-1175	-1165	-1138	-1089	-1012	-898	-735	-508	56
57	-1077	-1080	-1072	-1048	-1005	-935	-832	-685	-482	-203	57
58	-995	-988	-969	-931	-871	-780	-651	-472	-229	102	58
59	-912	-897	-866	-815	-737	-626	-471	-260	024	406	59
60	-829	-805	-763	-698	-604	-471	-291	-047	277	711	60
61	-747	-713	-660	-581	-470	-317	-110	166	530	1016	61
62	-664	-621	-557	-465	-337	-163	070	379	783	1321	62
63	-581	-530	-454	-348	-203	-008	250	591	1037	1626	63
64	-499	-438	-351	-231	-069	146	431	804	1290	1931	64
65	-416	-346	-248	-115	064	301	611	1017	1543	2236	65
66	-334	-254	-145	002	198	455	791	1230	1796	2541	66
67	-251	-162	-042	119	331	610	972	1442	2049	2845	67
68	-168	-071	061	236	465	764	1152	1655	2302	3150	68
69	-086	021	164	352	599	919	1332	1868	2556	3455	69

(*continued*)

TABLE A9 (*continued*). Working Deviates for the Determination of Thresholds (Decimal Points Omitted)

P	−1.0	−1.1	−1.2	−1.3	−1.4	−1.5	−1.6	−1.7	−1.8	−1.9	P
70	−003	113	267	469	732	1073	1513	2081	2809	3760	70
71	080	205	370	586	866	1227	1693	2294	3062	4065	71
72	162	296	473	702	999	1382	1873	2506	3315	4370	72
73	245	388	576	819	1133	1536	2054	2719	3568	4675	73
74	328	480	679	936	1267	1691	2234	2932	3821	4980	74
75	410	572	782	1052	1400	1845	2414	3145	4075		75
76	493	664	885	1169	1534	2000	2595	3357	4328		76
77	576	755	988	1286	1667	2154	2775	3570	4581		77
78	658	847	1091	1402	1801	2308	2955	3783	4834		78
79	741	939	1194	1519	1935	2463	3136	3996			79
80	823	1031	1297	1636	2068	2617	3316	4208			80
81	906	1122	1400	1752	2202	2772	3496	4421			81
82	989	1214	1503	1869	2335	2926	3677	4634			82
83	1071	1306	1606	1986	2469	3081	3857	4847			83
84	1154	1398	1709	2102	2603	3235	4037				84
85	1237	1490	1812	2219	2736	3390	4218				85
86	1319	1581	1915	2336	2870	3544	4398				86
87	1402	1673	2018	2452	3003	3698	4578				87
88	1485	1765	2121	2569	3137	3853	4759				88
89	1567	1857	2224	2686	3271	4007	4939				89
90	1650	1948	2327	2802	3404	4162					90
91	1732	2040	2430	2919	3538	4316					91
92	1815	2132	2533	3036	3671	4471					92
93	1898	2224	2635	3153	3805	4625					93
94	1980	2316	2738	3269	3939	4780					94
95	2063	2407	2841	3386	4072	4934					95
96	2146	2499	2944	3503	4206						96
97	2228	2591	3047	3619	4339						97
98	2311	2683	3150	3736	4473						98
99	2394	2774	3253	3853	4607						99
100	2476	2866	3356	3969	4740						100

P	−2.0	−2.1	−2.2	−2.3	−2.4	−2.5	−2.6	−2.7	−2.8	−2.9	P
51	−2052	−2052	−2028	−1971	−1873	−1711	−1475	−1113	−597	117	51
52	−1681	−1598	−1465	−1265	−980	−569	−004	810	1934	3450	52
53	−1311	−1143	−901	−558	−087	574	1466	2733	4466		53
54	−941	−689	−338	149	805	1717	2937	4656			54
55	−570	−234	225	856	1698	2860	4407				55
56	−200	220	789	1562	2591	4003					56
57	170	675	1352	2269	3484						57
58	541	1130	1915	2976	4377						58
59	911	1584	2479	3682							59
60	1282	2039	3042	4389							60
61	1652	2493	3606								61
62	2022	2948	4169								62
63	2393	3402	4732								63
64	2763	3857									64
65	3133	4311									65
66	3504	4766									66
67	3874										67
68	4245										68
69	4615										69
70	4985										70

TABLE A10. Confidence Limits for a Proportion (Two-sided) N = (1, 1, 30). Reproduced from E. L. Crow, F. A. Davis, and M. W. Maxfield, Statistics Manual, *Navord Report 3369, NOTS 948*, U.S. Naval Ordnance Test Station, China Lake, Calif., 1955

N = 1

r	90% lower	90% upper	95% lower	95% upper	99% lower	99% upper
0	0	.900	0	.950	0	.990
1	.100	1	.050	1	.010	1

N = 2

r	90% lower	90% upper	95% lower	95% upper	99% lower	99% upper
0	0	.684	0	.776	0	.900
1	.051	.949	.025+	.975−	.005+	.995−
2	.316	1	.224	1	.100	1

N = 3

r	90% lower	90% upper	95% lower	95% upper	99% lower	99% upper
0	0	.536	0	.632	0	.785−
1	.035−	.804	.017	.865−	.003	.941
2	.196	.965+	.135+	.983	.059	.997
3	.464	1	.368	1	.215+	1

N = 4

r	90% lower	90% upper	95% lower	95% upper	99% lower	99% upper
0	0	.500	0	.527	0	.684
1	.026	.680	.013	.751	.003	.859
2	.143	.857	.098	.902	.042	.958
3	.320	.974	.249	.987	.141	.997
4	.500	1	.473	1	.316	1

N = 5

r	90% lower	90% upper	95% lower	95% upper	99% lower	99% upper
0	0	.379	0	.500	0	.602
1	.021	.621	.010	.657	.002	.778
2	.112	.753	.076	.811	.033	.894
3	.247	.888	.189	.924	.106	.967
4	.379	.979	.343	.990	.222	.998
5	.621	1	.500	1	.398	1

N = 6

r	90% lower	90% upper	95% lower	95% upper	99% lower	99% upper
0	0	.345−	0	.402	0	.536
1	.017	.542	.009	.598	.002	.706
2	.093	.667	.063	.729	.027	.827
3	.201	.799	.153	.847	.085−	.915+
4	.333	.907	.271	.937	.173	.973
5	.458	.983	.402	.991	.294	.998
6	.655+	1	.598	1	.464	1

N = 7

r	90% lower	90% upper	95% lower	95% upper	99% lower	99% upper
0	0	.316	0	.377	0	.500
1	.015−	.500	.007	.554	.001	.643
2	.079	.684	.053	.659	.023	.764
3	.170	.721	.129	.775−	.071	.858
4	.279	.830	.225+	.871	.142	.929
5	.316	.921	.341	.947	.236	.977
6	.500	.985+	.446	.993	.357	.999
7	.684	1	.623	1	.500	1

N = 8

r	90% lower	90% upper	95% lower	95% upper	99% lower	99% upper
0	0	.255−	0	.315+	0	.451
1	.013	.418	.006	.500	.001	.590
2	.069	.582	.046	.685−	.020	.707
3	.147	.655+	.111	.711	.061	.802
4	.240	.760	.193	.807	.121	.879
5	.345−	.853	.289	.889	.198	.939
6	.418	.931	.315+	.954	.293	.980
7	.582	.987	.500	.994	.410	.999
8	.745+	1	.685−	1	.549	1

N = 9

r	90%		95%		99%	
0	0	.232	0	.289	0	.402
1	.012	.391	.006	.443	.001	.598
2	.061	.515+	.041	.558	.017	.656
3	.129	.610	.098	.711	.053	.750
4	.210	.768	.169	.749	.105+	.829
5	.232	.790	.251	.831	.171	.895−
6	.390	.871	.289	.902	.250	.947
7	.485−	.939	.442	.959	.344	.983
8	.609	.988	.557	.994	.402	.999
9	.768	1	.711	1	.598	1

N = 11

r	90%		95%		99%	
0	0	.197	0	.250	0	.359
1	.010	.315+	.005−	.369	.001	.500
2	.049	.423	.033	.500	.014	.593
3	.105−	.577	.079	.631	.043	.660
4	.169	.685−	.135+	.667	.084	.738
5	.197	.698	.200	.750	.134	.806
6	.302	.803	.250	.800	.194	.866
7	.315+	.831	.333	.865−	.262	.916
8	.423	.895+	.369	.921	.340	.957
9	.577	.951	.500	.967	.407	.986
10	.685−	.990	.631	.995+	.500	.999
11	.803	1	.750	1	.641	1

N = 10

r	90%		95%		99%	
0	0	.222	0	.267	0	.376
1	.010	.352	.005+	.397	.001	.512
2	.055−	.500	.037	.603	.016	.624
3	.116	.648	.087	.619	.048	.703
4	.188	.659	.150	.733	.093	.782
5	.222	.778	.222	.778	.150	.850
6	.341	.812	.267	.850	.218	.907
7	.352	.884	.381	.913	.297	.952
8	.500	.945+	.397	.963	.376	.984
9	.648	.990	.603	.995−	.488	.999
10	.778	1	.733	1	.624	1

N = 12

r	90%		95%		99%	
0	0	.184	0	.236	0	.321
1	.009	.294	.004	.346	.001	.445+
2	.045+	.398	.030	.450	.013	.555−
3	.096	.500	.072	.550	.039	.679
4	.154	.602	.123	.654	.076	.698
5	.184	.706	.181	.706	.121	.765+
6	.271	.729	.236	.764	.175−	.825+
7	.294	.816	.294	.819	.235−	.879
8	.398	.846	.346	.877	.302	.924
9	.500	.904	.450	.928	.321	.961
10	.602	.955−	.550	.970	.445+	.987
11	.706	.991	.654	.996	.555−	.999
12	.816	1	.764	1	.679	1

(continued)

TABLE A10 (continued). Confidence Limits for a Proportion

N = 13

r	90%		95%		99%	
0	0	.173	0	.225+	0	.302
1	.008	.276	.004	.327	.001	.429
2	.042	.379	.028	.434	.012	.523
3	.088	.470	.066	.520	.036	.594
4	.142	.545−	.113	.587	.069	.698
5	.173	.621	.166	.673	.111	.727
6	.246	.724	.224	.740	.159	.787
7	.276	.754	.260	.776	.213	.841
8	.379	.827	.327	.834	.273	.889
9	.455+	.858	.413	.887	.302	.931
10	.530	.912	.480	.934	.406	.964
11	.621	.958	.566	.972	.477	.988
12	.724	.992	.673	.996	.571	.999
13	.827	1	.775−	1	.698	1

N = 15

r	90%		95%		99%	
0	0	.154	0	.191	0	.273
1	.007	.247	.003	.302	.001	.373
2	.036	.326	.024	.369	.010	.461
3	.076	.400	.057	.448	.031	.539
4	.122	.500	.097	.552	.059	.627
5	.154	.600	.142	.631	.094	.672
6	.205+	.674	.191	.668	.135−	.727
7	.247	.675−	.192	.706	.179	.771
8	.325+	.753	.294	.808	.229	.821
9	.326	.795−	.332	.809	.273	.865+
10	.400	.846	.369	.858	.328	.906

N = 14

r	90%		95%		99%	
0	0	.163	0	.207	0	.286
1	.007	.261	.004	.312	.001	.392
2	.039	.365+	.026	.389	.011	.500
3	.081	.422	.061	.500	.033	.608
4	.131	.578	.104	.611	.064	.636
5	.163	.594	.153	.629	.102	.714
6	.224	.645+	.206	.688	.146	.751
7	.261	.739	.207	.793	.195−	.805+
8	.355−	.776	.312	.794	.249	.854
9	.406	.837	.371	.847	.286	.898
10	.422	.869	.389	.896	.364	.936
11	.578	.919	.500	.939	.392	.967
12	.635−	.961	.611	.974	.500	.989
13	.739	.993	.688	.996	.608	.999
14	.837	1	.793	1	.714	1

N = 16

r	90%		95%		99%	
0	0	.147	0	.179	0	.264
1	.007	.235+	.003	.273	.001	.357
2	.034	.305+	.023	.352	.010	.451
3	.071	.381	.053	.429	.029	.525−
4	.114	.450	.090	.500	.055+	.579
5	.147	.550	.132	.571	.088	.643
6	.189	.619	.178	.648	.125+	.705−
7	.235+	.695−	.179	.727	.166	.739
8	.299	.701	.272	.728	.212	.788
9	.305+	.765−	.273	.821	.261	.834
10	.381	.811	.352	.822	.295+	.875−

N = 15

r	90%		95%		99%	
11	.500	.878	.448	.903	.373	.941
12	.600	.924	.552	.943	.461	.969
13	.674	.964	.631	.976	.539	.990
14	.753	.993	.698	.997	.627	.999
15	.846	1	.809	1	.727	1

N = 17

r	90%		95%		99%	
0	0	.140	0	.167	0	.243
1	.006	.225+	.003	.254	.001	.346
2	.032	.290	.021	.337	.009	.413
3	.067	.364	.050	.417	.027	.500
4	.107	.432	.085−	.489	.052	.587
5	.140	.500	.124	.544	.082	.620
6	.175+	.568	.166	.594	.117	.662
7	.225+	.636	.167	.663	.155+	.757
8	.277	.710	.253	.746	.197	.758
9	.290	.723	.254	.747	.242	.803
10	.364	.775−	.337	.833	.243	.845
11	.432	.825−	.406	.834	.338	.883
12	.500	.860	.456	.876	.380	.918
13	.568	.893	.511	.915+	.413	.948
14	.636	.933	.583	.950	.500	.973
15	.710	.968	.663	.979	.587	.991
16	.775−	.994	.746	.997	.654	.999
17	.860	1	.833	1	.757	1

N = 16

r	90%		95%		99%	
11	.450	.853	.429	.868	.357	.912
12	.550	.886	.500	.910	.421	.945−
13	.619	.929	.571	.947	.475+	.971
14	.695−	.966	.648	.977	.549	.990
15	.765−	.993	.727	.997	.643	.999
16	.853	1	.821	1	.736	1

N = 18

r	90%		95%		99%	
0	0	.135−	0	.157	0	.228
1	.006	.216	.003	.242	.001	.318
2	.030	.277	.020	.325−	.008	.397
3	.063	.349	.047	.381	.025+	.466
4	.101	.419	.080	.444	.049	.534
5	.135−	.482	.116	.556	.077	.603
6	.163	.536	.156	.619	.110	.682
7	.216	.584	.157	.625+	.145+	.686
8	.257	.651	.236	.675+	.184	.772
9	.277	.723	.242	.758	.226	.774
10	.349	.743	.325−	.764	.228	.816
11	.416	.784	.375−	.843	.314	.855−
12	.464	.837	.381	.844	.318	.890
13	.518	.865+	.444	.884	.397	.923
14	.581	.899	.556	.920	.466	.951
15	.651	.937	.619	.953	.534	.975−
16	.723	.970	.675+	.980	.603	.992
17	.784	.994	.758	.997	.682	.999
18	.865+	1	.843	1	.772	1

(continued)

TABLE A10 (continued). Confidence Limits for a Proportion

N = 19

r	90%		95%		99%	
0	0	.130	0	.150	0	.218
1	.006	.209	.003	.232	.001	.305+
2	.028	.265+	.019	.316	.008	.383
3	.059	.337	.044	.365-	.024	.455+
4	.095+	.387	.075+	.426	.046	.515+
5	.130	.440	.110	.500	.073	.564
6	.151	.560	.147	.574	.103	.617
7	.209	.613	.150	.635+	.137	.695-
8	.238	.614	.222	.655+	.173	.707
9	.265+	.663	.232	.688	.212	.782
10	.337	.735-	.312	.768	.218	.788
11	.386	.762	.345-	.778	.293	.827
12	.387	.791	.365-	.850	.305+	.863
13	.440	.849	.426	.853	.383	.897
14	.560	.870	.500	.890	.436	.927
15	.613	.905-	.574	.925-	.485-	.954
16	.663	.941	.635+	.956	.545-	.976
17	.735-	.972	.684	.981	.617	.992
18	.791	.994	.768	.997	.695-	.999
19	.870	1	.850	1	.782	1

N = 20

r	90%		95%		99%	
0	0	.126	0	.143	0	.209
1	.005+	.203	.003	.222	.001	.293
2	.027	.255-	.018	.294	.008	.375-
3	.056	.328	.042	.351	.023	.424
4	.090	.367	.071	.411	.044	.500
5	.126	.422	.104	.467	.069	.576
6	.141	.500	.140	.533	.098	.601
7	.201	.578	.143	.589	.129	.637
8	.221	.633	.209	.649	.163	.707
9	.255-	.642	.222	.706	.200	.726
10	.325	.675+	.293	.707	.209	.791
11	.358	.745+	.294	.778	.274	.800
12	.367	.779	.351	.791	.293	.837
13	.422	.799	.411	.857	.363	.871
14	.500	.859	.467	.860	.399	.902
15	.578	.874	.533	.896	.424	.931
16	.633	.910	.589	.929	.500	.956
17	.672	.944	.649	.958	.576	.977
18	.745+	.973	.706	.982	.625+	.992
19	.797	.995-	.778	.997	.707	.999
20	.874	1	.857	1	.791	1

r	N = 21 90%		N = 21 95%		N = 21 99%	
0	0	.123	0	.137	0	.201
1	.005+	.192	.002	.213	.000	.283
2	.026	.245−	.017	.277	.007	.347
3	.054	.307	.040	.338	.022	.409
4	.086	.353	.068	.398	.041	.466
5	.121	.407	.099	.455+	.065+	.534
6	.130	.458	.132	.506	.092	.591
7	.191	.542	.137	.551	.122	.653
8	.192	.593	.197	.602	.155−	.661
9	.245−	.647	.213	.662	.189	.717
10	.306	.693	.276	.723	.201	.743
11	.307	.694	.277	.724	.257	.799
12	.353	.755+	.338	.787	.283	.811
13	.407	.808	.398	.803	.339	.845+
14	.458	.809	.449	.863	.347	.878
15	.542	.870	.494	.868	.409	.908
16	.593	.879	.545−	.901	.466	.935−
17	.647	.914	.602	.932	.534	.959
18	.693	.946	.662	.960	.591	.978
19	.755+	.974	.723	.983	.653	.993
20	.808	.995−	.787	.998	.717	1.000
21	.877	1	.863	1	.799	1

r	N = 22 90%		N = 22 95%		N = 22 99%	
0	0	.116	0	.132	0	.194
1	.005−	.182	.002	.205+	.000	.273
2	.024	.236	.016	.264	.007	.334
3	.051	.289	.038	.326	.021	.396
4	.082	.340	.065−	.389	.039	.454
5	.115−	.393	.094	.424	.062	.505−
6	.116	.444	.126	.500	.088	.550
7	.181	.500	.132	.576	.116	.604
8	.182	.556	.187	.582	.147	.666
9	.236	.607	.205+	.617	.179	.682
10	.289	.660	.260	.674	.194	.727
11	.290	.710	.264	.736	.242	.758
12	.340	.711	.326	.740	.273	.806
13	.393	.764	.383	.795−	.318	.821
14	.444	.818	.418	.813	.334	.853
15	.500	.819	.424	.868	.396	.884
16	.556	.884	.500	.874	.450	.912
17	.607	.885+	.576	.906	.495+	.938
18	.660	.918	.611	.935+	.546	.961
19	.711	.949	.674	.962	.604	.979
20	.764	.976	.736	.984	.666	.993
21	.818	.995+	.795−	.998	.727	1.000
22	.884	1	.868	1	.806	1

(continued)

TABLE A10 (continued). Confidence Limits for a Proportion

N = 23

r	90%		95%		99%	
	lower	upper	lower	upper	lower	upper
0	0	.111	0	.127	0	.187
1	.005−	.174	.002	.198	.000	.265+
2	.023	.228	.016	.255−	.007	.323
3	.049	.274	.037	.317	.020	.386
4	.078	.328	.062	.361	.038	.429
5	.110	.381	.090	.409	.059	.500
6	.111	.431	.120	.457	.084	.571
7	.173	.479	.127	.543	.111	.580
8	.174	.522	.178	.591	.140	.616
9	.228	.569	.198	.639	.171	.677
10	.273	.619	.247	.640	.187	.702
11	.274	.672	.255−	.683	.229	.735−
12	.328	.726	.317	.745+	.265+	.771
13	.381	.727	.360	.753	.298	.813
14	.431	.772	.361	.802	.323	.829
15	.478	.826	.409	.822	.384	.860
16	.521	.827	.457	.873	.420	.889
17	.569	.889	.543	.880	.429	.916
18	.619	.890	.591	.910	.500	.941
19	.672	.922	.639	.938	.571	.962
20	.726	.951	.683	.963	.614	.980
21	.772	.977	.745+	.984	.677	.993
22	.826	.995+	.802	.998	.735−	1.000
23	.889	1	.873	1	.813	1

N = 24

r	90%		95%		99%	
	lower	upper	lower	upper	lower	upper
0	0	.105+	0	.122	0	.181
1	.004	.165+	.002	.191	.000	.259
2	.022	.221	.015+	.246	.006	.313
3	.047	.264	.035−	.308	.019	.364
4	.075−	.317	.059	.347	.036	.416
5	.105−	.370	.086	.396	.057	.464
6	.105+	.423	.115−	.443	.080	.536
7	.165−	.448	.122	.500	.106	.584
8	.165+	.552	.169	.557	.133	.636
9	.221	.553	.191	.604	.163	.638
10	.259	.587	.234	.653	.181	.687
11	.264	.630	.246	.661	.216	.720
12	.317	.683	.308	.692	.257	.743
13	.370	.736	.339	.754	.280	.784
14	.413	.741	.347	.766	.313	.819
15	.447	.779	.396	.809	.362	.837
16	.448	.835−	.443	.831	.364	.867
17	.552	.835+	.500	.878	.416	.894
18	.577	.895−	.557	.885+	.464	.920
19	.630	.895+	.604	.914	.536	.943
20	.683	.925+	.653	.941	.584	.964
21	.736	.953	.692	.965+	.636	.981
22	.779	.978	.754	.985−	.687	.994
23	.835−	.996	.809	.998	.741	1.000
24	.895−	1	.878	1	.819	1

N = 25

r	90%		95%		99%	
0	0	.102	0	.118	0	.175+
1	.004	.159	.002	.185+	.000	.246
2	.021	.214	.014	.238	.006	.305−
3	.045−	.255−	.034	.303	.018	.352
4	.072	.307	.057	.336	.034	.403
5	.101	.362	.082	.384	.054	.451
6	.102	.390	.110	.431	.077	.500
7	.158	.432	.118	.475−	.101	.549
8	.159	.500	.161	.525+	.127	.597
9	.214	.568	.185+	.569	.155+	.648
10	.246	.610	.222	.616	.175+	.658
11	.255−	.611	.238	.664	.205+	.695+
12	.307	.640	.296	.683	.245+	.754
13	.360	.693	.317	.704	.246	.755−
14	.389	.745+	.336	.762	.305−	.795−
15	.390	.754	.384	.778	.342	.825−
16	.432	.786	.431	.815−	.352	.845−
17	.500	.841	.475−	.839	.403	.873
18	.568	.842	.525+	.882	.451	.899
19	.610	.898	.569	.890	.500	.923
20	.638	.899	.616	.918	.549	.946
21	.693	.928	.664	.943	.597	.966
22	.745+	.955+	.697	.966	.648	.982
23	.786	.979	.762	.986	.695+	.994
24	.841	.996	.815−	.998	.754	1.000
25	.898	1	.882	1	.825−	1

N = 26

r	90%		95%		99%	
0	0	.098	0	.114	0	.170
1	.004	.152	.002	.180	.000	.235−
2	.021	.209	.014	.230	.006	.298
3	.043	.247	.032	.283	.017	.342
4	.069	.299	.054	.325+	.033	.393
5	.097	.343	.079	.374	.052	.442
6	.098	.377	.106	.421	.073	.487
7	.151	.419	.114	.465−	.097	.526
8	.152	.460	.154	.506	.122	.562
9	.209	.540	.180	.542	.149	.607
10	.233	.581	.212	.579	.170	.658
11	.247	.623	.230	.626	.195−	.678
12	.299	.657	.282	.675−	.234	.702
13	.342	.658	.283	.717	.235−	.765+
14	.343	.701	.325+	.718	.298	.766
15	.377	.753	.374	.770	.322	.805+
16	.419	.767	.421	.788	.342	.830
17	.460	.791	.458	.820	.393	.851
18	.540	.848	.494	.846	.438	.878
19	.581	.849	.535−	.886	.474	.903
20	.623	.902	.579	.894	.513	.927
21	.657	.903	.626	.921	.558	.948
22	.701	.931	.675−	.946	.607	.967
23	.753	.957	.717	.968	.658	.983
24	.791	.979	.770	.986	.702	.994
25	.848	.996	.820	.998	.765+	1.000
26	.902	1	.886	1	.830	1

(continued)

TABLE A10 (*continued*). Confidence Limits for a Proportion

r	90%		95%		99%	
			N = 27			
0	0	.093	0	.110	0	.166
1	.004	.146	.002	.175−	.000	.225−
2	.020	.204	.013	.223	.006	.297
3	.042	.239	.031	.270	.017	.332
4	.066	.291	.052	.316	.032	.384
5	.093	.327	.076	.364	.050	.419
6	.094	.365+	.101	.415−	.070	.461
7	.145+	.407	.110	.437	.093	.539
8	.146	.447	.148	.500	.117	.581
9	.204	.500	.175−	.563	.143	.587
10	.221	.553	.202	.570	.166	.617
11	.239	.593	.223	.598	.185−	.668
12	.291	.635−	.269	.636	.224	.702
13	.326	.673	.270	.684	.225−	.716
14	.327	.674	.316	.730	.284	.775+
15	.365+	.709	.364	.731	.298	.776
16	.407	.761	.402	.777	.332	.815+
17	.447	.779	.430	.798	.383	.834
18	.500	.796	.437	.825+	.413	.857
19	.553	.854	.500	.852	.419	.883
20	.593	.855−	.563	.890	.461	.907
21	.635−	.906	.585+	.899	.539	.930
22	.673	.907	.636	.924	.581	.950
23	.709	.934	.684	.948	.616	.968
24	.761	.958	.730	.969	.668	.983
25	.796	.980	.777	.987	.703	.994
26	.854	.996	.825+	.998	.775+	1.000
27	.907	1	.890	1	.834	1

r	90%		95%		99%	
			N = 28			
0	0	.090	0	.106	0	.162
1	.004	.140	.002	.170	.000	.218
2	.019	.201	.013	.217	.005+	.273
3	.040	.232	.030	.259	.016	.323
4	.064	.284	.050	.307	.031	.365−
5	.089	.312	.073	.357	.048	.408
6	.090	.355−	.098	.384	.068	.449
7	.139	.396	.106	.424	.089	.500
8	.140	.435+	.142	.463	.112	.551
9	.197	.473	.170	.537	.137	.592
10	.208	.527	.192	.576	.162	.635+
11	.232	.565−	.217	.616	.175+	.636
12	.284	.604	.258	.619	.214	.677
13	.310	.645+	.259	.645+	.218	.727
14	.312	.688	.307	.693	.272	.728
15	.355−	.690	.355−	.741	.273	.782
16	.396	.716	.381	.742	.323	.786
17	.435+	.768	.384	.783	.364	.825−
18	.473	.792	.424	.808	.365−	.838
19	.527	.803	.463	.830	.408	.863
20	.565−	.860	.537	.858	.449	.888
21	.604	.861	.576	.894	.500	.911
22	.645+	.910	.616	.902	.551	.932
23	.688	.911	.643	.927	.592	.952
24	.716	.936	.693	.950	.635+	.969
25	.768	.960	.741	.970	.677	.984
26	.799	.981	.783	.987	.727	.995−
27	.860	.996	.830	.998	.782	1.000
28	.910	1	.894	1	.838	1

N = 29

r	90%		95%		99%	
0	0	.087	0	.103	0	.160
1	.004	.135−	.002	.166	.000	.211
2	.018	.190	.012	.211	.005+	.263
3	.039	.225−	.029	.251	.015+	.316
4	.062	.279	.049	.299	.030	.354
5	.086	.303	.070	.340	.046	.397
6	.087	.345−	.094	.374	.065+	.438
7	.134	.385+	.103	.413	.086	.477
8	.135−	.425−	.136	.451	.108	.523
9	.189	.463	.166	.500	.132	.562
10	.190	.500	.184	.549	.157	.603
11	.225−	.537	.211	.587	.165+	.646
12	.276	.575+	.247	.626	.206	.654
13	.294	.615−	.251	.660	.211	.684
14	.303	.655+	.299	.661	.260	.737
15	.345−	.697	.339	.701	.263	.740
16	.385+	.706	.340	.749	.316	.789
17	.425−	.724	.374	.753	.346	.794
18	.463	.775+	.413	.789	.354	.835−
19	.500	.810	.451	.816	.397	.843
20	.537	.811	.500	.834	.438	.868
21	.575+	.865+	.549	.864	.477	.892
22	.615−	.866	.587	.897	.523	.914
23	.655+	.913	.626	.906	.562	.935−
24	.697	.914	.660	.930	.603	.954
25	.721	.938	.701	.951	.646	.970
26	.775+	.961	.749	.971	.684	.985−
27	.810	.982	.789	.988	.737	.995−
28	.865+	.996	.834	.998	.789	1.000
29	.913	1	.897	1	.840	1

N = 30

r	90%		95%		99%	
0	0	.084	0	.100	0	.152
1	.004	.130	.002	.163	.000	.206
2	.018	.183	.012	.205+	.005+	.256
3	.037	.219	.028	.244	.015−	.310
4	.059	.266	.047	.292	.028	.345−
5	.083	.295−	.068	.325−	.045−	.388
6	.084	.336	.091	.364	.063	.430
7	.129	.376	.100	.403	.083	.469
8	.130	.416	.131	.440	.104	.505+
9	.182	.455+	.163	.476	.127	.538
10	.183	.492	.175+	.524	.151	.570
11	.219	.524	.205+	.560	.152	.612
12	.265−	.554	.236	.597	.198	.655+
13	.266	.584	.244	.636	.206	.671
14	.295−	.624	.292	.675+	.249	.692
15	.336	.664	.324	.676	.256	.744
16	.376	.705+	.325−	.708	.308	.751
17	.416	.734	.364	.756	.329	.794
18	.446	.735−	.403	.764	.345−	.802
19	.476	.781	.440	.795−	.388	.848
20	.508	.817	.476	.825	.430	.849
21	.545−	.818	.524	.837	.462	.873
22	.584	.870	.560	.869	.495−	.896
23	.624	.871	.597	.900	.531	.917
24	.664	.916	.636	.909	.570	.937
25	.705+	.917	.675+	.932	.612	.955+
26	.734	.941	.708	.953	.655+	.972
27	.781	.963	.756	.972	.690	.985+
28	.817	.982	.795−	.988	.744	.995−
29	.870	.996	.837	.998	.794	1.000
30	.916	1	.900	1	.848	1

TABLE A11. Some Balanced and Partially Balanced Incomplete Paired-comparison Designs (see Section 7.1.2)

1. BIB 7, 1

j	k			
1	2	4	6	$n = 7$
2	1	4	5	$r_1 = 3$
3	(3)	4	7	$\lambda_{11} = \lambda_{12} = 1$
4	1	2	3	$r_2 = 4$
5	2	(5)	7	$\lambda_{21} = \lambda_{22} = 2$
3	1	(6)	7	
7	3	5	6	

2. BIB 11, 1

j	k					
1	3	7	8	9	11	$n = 11$
2	(2)	6	7	8	10	$r_1 = 5$
3	1	5	6	7	9	$\lambda_{11} = \lambda_{12} = 2$
4	11	(4)	5	6	8	$r_2 = 6$
5	10	3	4	(5)	7	$\lambda_{21} = \lambda_{22} = 4$
6	9	2	3	4	(6)	
7	8	1	2	3	5	
8	7	11	1	2	4	
9	6	10	11	1	3	
10	5	9	(10)	11	2	
11	4	8	9	10	1	

3. BIB 13, 1

j	k				
1	2	5	8	11	$n = 13$
2	1	5	6	7	$r_1 = 4$
3	4	5	10	12	$\lambda_{11} = \lambda_{12} = 1$
4	3	5	9	13	$r_2 = 9$
5	1	2	3	4	$\lambda_{21} = \lambda_{22} = 6$
6	2	7	10	13	
7	2	6	9	12	
8	1	11	12	13	
9	4	7	(9)	11	
10	3	6	(10)	11	
11	1	8	9	10	
12	3	7	8	(12)	
13	4	6	8	(13)	

4. BIB 15, 1

j	k						
1	2	4	6	8	10	12	14	$n = 15$
2	1	4	5	8	9	12	13	$r_1 = 7$
3	(3)	4	7	8	11	12	15	$\lambda_{11} = \lambda_{12} = 3$
4	1	2	3	8	9	10	11	$r_2 = 8$
5	2	(5)	7	8	10	13	15	$\lambda_{21} = \lambda_{22} = 4$
6	1	(6)	7	8	9	14	15	
7	3	5	6	8	11	13	14	
8	1	2	3	4	5	6	7	
9	2	4	6	(9)	11	13	15	
10	1	4	5	(10)	11	14	15	
11	3	4	7	9	10	13	14	
12	1	2	3	(12)	13	14	15	
13	2	5	7	9	11	12	14	
14	1	6	7	10	11	12	13	
15	3	5	6	9	10	12	(15)	

5. BIB 16, 1

j	k					
1	4	5	12	14	15	16	$n = 16$
2	3	8	11	13	14	15	$r_1 = 6$
3	2	7	10	13	14	16	$\lambda_{11} = \lambda_{12} = 2$
4	1	6	9	13	15	16	$r_2 = 10$
5	1	8	10	11	12	16	$\lambda_{21} = \lambda_{22} = 6$
6	4	7	9	10	11	15	
7	3	6	9	1	12	14	
8	2	5	9	11	12	13	
9	4	6	7	8	12	13	
10	3	5	6	7	11	16	
11	2	5	6	8	10	15	
12	1	5	7	8	9	14	
13	2	3	4	8	9	16	
14	1	2	3	7	12	15	
15	1	2	4	6	11	14	
16	1	3	4	5	10	13	

6. C 17, 1

j	k							
1	4	6	7	8	11	12	13	15	$n = 17$
2	5	7	8	9	12	13	14	16	$r_1 = 8$
3	6	8	9	10	13	14	15	17	$\lambda_{11} = 3$
4	1	7	9	10	11	14	15	16	$\lambda_{12} = 4$
5	2	8	10	11	12	15	16	17	$r_2 = 8$
6	1	3	9	11	12	13	16	17	$\lambda_{21} = 4$
7	1	2	4	10	12	13	14	17	$\lambda_{22} = 3$
8	1	2	3	5	11	13	14	15	
9	2	3	4	6	12	14	15	16	
10	3	4	5	7	13	15	16	17	
11	1	4	5	6	8	14	16	17	
12	1	2	5	6	7	9	15	17	
13	1	2	3	6	7	8	10	16	
14	2	3	4	7	8	9	11	17	
15	1	3	4	5	8	9	10	12	
16	2	4	5	6	9	10	11	13	
17	3	5	6	7	10	11	12	14	

(continued)

TABLE A11 *(continued)*. Some Balanced and Partially Balanced Incomplete
Paired-comparison Designs

7.	S 19, 1							8.	BIB 21, 1					
j	k							j	k					
1	2	3	4	5	6	7	$n = 19$	1	2	6	10	14	18	$n = 21$
2	1	3	8	11	14	17	$r_1 = 6$	2	1	6	7	8	9	$r_1 = 5$
3	1	2	9	12	15	18	$\lambda_{11} = 1$	3	(3)	6	11	16	21	$\lambda_{11} = \lambda_{12} = 1$
4	1	5	8	15	16	19	$\lambda_{12} = 2$	4	5	6	13	15	20	$r_2 = 16$
5	1	4	10	11	16	18	$r_2 = 12$	5	4	6	12	17	19	$\lambda_{21} = \lambda_{22} = 12$
6	1	7	10	12	14	19	$\lambda_{21} = 8$	6	1	2	3	4	5	
7	1	6	9	13	16	17	$\lambda_{22} = 7$	7	2	(7)	11	15	19	
8	2	4	9	10	11	15		8	2	9	13	17	21	
9	3	7	8	10	12	17		9	2	8	12	16	20	
10	6	8	9	15	16	19		10	1	(10)	11	12	13	
11	2	5	8	12	13	18		11	3	7	10	17	20	
12	3	6	9	11	13	14		12	5	9	10	16	19	
13	4	7	11	12	16	19		13	4	8	10	15	21	
14	2	6	12	15	16	17		14	1	18	19	20	21	
15	3	4	8	14	16	18		15	4	7	13	16	18	
16	5	7	10	13	14	15		16	3	9	12	15	18	
17	2	7	9	14	18	19		17	5	8	11	(17)	18	
18	3	5	11	15	17	19		18	1	14	15	16	17	
19	4	4	10	13	17	18		19	5	7	12	14	21	
								20	4	9	11	14	(20)	
								21	3	8	13	14	19	

TABLE A12. Designs for Incomplete Multiple-judgment Paired
Comparisons (Pairs Assigned to the Same Subject Appear
Between Semicolons)*

Design
1	(1,2) (3,4); (1,4) (2,3)
2	(1,3) (2,5); (1,4) (3,5); (2,4)
3	(1,2) (3,4) (5,6); (1,6) (2,3) (4,5)
4	(1,2) (3,4) (5,6); (1,4) (2,5) (3,6); (1,6) (2,3) (4,5)
5	(1,2) (3,5) (4,6); (1,3) (2,6) (4,5); (1,4) (2,3) (5,6); (1,5) (2,4) (3,6)
6	(1,4) (2,6) (3,7); (1,5) (3,6); (2,5) (4,7)
7	(1,3) (2,6) (5,7); (1,4) (2,7) (3,6); (1,5) (2,4) (3,7); (1,6) (2,5) (4,7); (3,5) (4,6)
8	(1,2) (3,4) (5,6) (7,8); (1,8) (2,3) (4,5) (6,7)
9	(1,4) (2,6) (3,7) (5,8); (1,5) (2,7) (3,6) (4,8); (1,6) (2,5) (3,8) (4,7)
10	(1,2) (3,4) (5,6) (7,8); (1,8) (2,3) (4,5) (6,7); (1,4) (2,7) (3,6) (5,8); (1,6) (2,5) (3,8) (4,7)
11	(1,3) (2,4) (5,7) (6,8); (1,7) (2,8) (3,5) (4,6); (1,6) (2,5) (3,8) (4,7); (1,5) (2,6) (3,7) (4,8); (1,4) (2,7) (3,6) (5,8)
12	(1,2) (3,4) (5,6) (7,8); (1,8) (2,3) (4,5) (6,7); (1,3) (2,5) (4,7) (6,8); (1.6) (2,4) (3,8) (5,7); (1,7) (2,8) (3,5) (4,6); (1,4) (2,7) (3,6) (5,8)
13	(1,5) (2,6) (3,7); (1,6) (4,8) (5,9); (2,7) (3,8) (4,9)
14	(1,6) (2,7) (3,8) (4,9); (1,4) (2,5) (3,7) (6,9); (1,5) (3,6) (4,7) (5,8); (2,6) (4,8) (5,9); (1,7) (2,8) (3,9)
15	(1,2) (4,6) (5,7) (8,9); (1,5) (2,3) (4,9) (6,8); (1,8) (2,9) (3,4) (6,7); (1,3) (5,6) (4,8) (7,9); (1,6) (2,4) (3,5) (7,8); (1,9) (2,7) (3,8) (4,5); (3,7) (2,6) (5,9)
16	(1,2) (3,4) (5,6) (7,8) (9,10); (1,10) (2,3) (4,5) (6,7) (8,9)
17	(1,5) (2,7) (3,9) (4,8) (6,10); (1,6) (2,8) (3,7) (4,9) (5,10); (1,7) (2,6) (3,8) (4,10) (5,9)
18	(1,3) (2,4) (5,7) (6,9) (8,10); (1,4) (2,5) (3,10) (6,8) (7,9); (1,8) (2,9) (3,5) (4,6) (7,10); (1,9) (2,10) (3,6) (4,7) (5,8)
19	(1,2) (3,4) (5,6) (7,8) (9,10); (1,10) (2,3) (4,5) (6,7) (8,9); (1,4) (2,9) (3,6) (5,8) (7,10); (1,8) (2,5) (3,10) (4,7) (6,9); (1,6) (2,7) (3,8) (4,9) (5,10)
20	(1,3) (2,4) (5,8) (6,10) (7,9); (1,4) (2,5) (3,7) (6,9) (8,10); (1,5) (2,6) (3,9) (4,8) (7,10); (1,7) (2,8) (3,6) (4,10) (5,9); (1,8) (2,9) (3,10) (4,6) (5,7); (1,9) (2,10) (3,5) (4,7) (6,8)
21	(1,3) (2,9) (4,7) (5,8) (6,10); (1,4) (2,10) (3,8) (5,7) (6,9); (1,5) (2,4) (3,9) (6,8) (7,10); (1,6) (2,5) (3,10) (4,8) (7,9); (1,7) (2,6) (3,5) (4,9) (8,10); (1,8) (2,7) (3,6) (4,10) (5,9); (1.9) (2,8) (3,7) (4,6) (5,10)
22	(1,2) (3,9) (4,7) (5,6) (8,10); (1,3) (2,9) (4,8) (5,7) (6,10); (1,4) (2,3) (5,8) (6,9) (7,10); (1,5) (2,4) (3,10) (6,7) (8,9); (1,7) (2,5) (3,4) (6,8) (9,10); (1,8) (2,6) (3,5) (4,10) (7,9); (1,9) (2,10) (3,6) (4,5) (7,8); (1,10) (2,8) (3,7) (4,6) (5,9)

*Adapted from Linhart (1966).

TABLE A13. Parameters and Inverses for Designs in Table A12*

Design	n^{**}	r^{**}	g^{**}	v^{**}	Inverse
1	4	4	2	2	$(1/8)$ $(3, 0, -1,$
2	5	5	3	2,1	$(1/25)$ $(11, -4, 1,$
3	6	6	2	3	$(1/72)$ $(37, 7, -11, -17,$
4	6	9	3	3	$(1/18)$ $(5, 0, -1, 0,$
5	6	12	4	3	$(1/24)$ $(5, 0, 0, -1,$
6	7	7	3	3,2	$(1/49)$ $(29, -6, -13, 8,$
7	7	14	5	3,2	$(1/637)$ $(139, -29, 6, -1,$
8	8	8	2	4	$(1/64)$ $(43, 15, -5, -17, -21,$
9	8	12	3	4	$(1/448)$ $(141, -23, -35, 9, 13,$
10	8	16	4	4	$(1/32)$ $(7, 0, -1, 0, -1,$
11	8	20	5	4	$(1/3264)$ $(577, -99, 17, -3, 1,$
12	8	24	6	4	$(1/48)$ $(7, 0, 0, 0, -1,$
13	9	9	3	3	$(1/81)$ $(61, -2, -29, -20, 25,$
14	9	18	5	4,3	$(1/2997)$ $(691, -101, -123, 43, 7,$
15	9	27	7	4,3	$(1/54)$ $(8, 0, 0, -1, 0,$
16	10	10	2	5	$(1/200)$ $(167, 77, 7, -43, -73, -83,$
17	10	15	3	5	$(1/950)$ $(337, -28, -73, -93, 47, 62,$
18	10	20	4	5	$(1/200)$ $(47, -8, 2, 2, -8, -3,$
19	10	25	5	5	$(1/50)$ $(9, 0, -1, 0, -1, 0,$
20	10	30	6	5	$(1/90200)$ $(13797, -2113, 357, -193, 637, -2153,$
21	10	35	7	5	$(1/117150)$ $(15124, -1921, 244, -31, 4, -1,$
22	10	40	8	5	$(1/80)$ $(9, 0, 0, 0, 0, -1,$

*Adapted from Linhart (1966).

**n = number of objects; r = number of other objects with which each object is paired; g = number of groups of N subjects required; v = number of comparisons made by each subject.

Appendix II *Computing Notes*

A The "Square Root" Method for Computing the Inverse of a Symmetric Positive-Definite Matrix

(1) Designate the $n \times n$ matrix to be inverted by A and its elements by a_{ij}. Sum the rows of A, change the signs of the sums and record them as an additional column to the right of A. To provide a check of the arithmetic, carry this column in all subsequent computations as if it were the $n + 1$ column of the original matrix.

(2) Transform the matrix A to an upper-right triangular matrix, S', with the property

$$SS' = A \quad \text{(with the form } \triangle \cdot \triangledown = \square \text{)}.$$

The elements of S' are computed from

$$\text{first row:} \quad s_{11} = \sqrt{a_{11}}, \quad s_{1j} = a_{1j}/s_{11};$$

$$\text{ith row:} \quad s_{ii} = \left(a_{ii} - \sum_{r=1}^{i-1} s_{ri}^2\right)^{1/2},$$

$$s_{ij} = \frac{1}{s_{ii}}\left(a_{ij} - \sum_{r=1}^{i-1} s_{ri} s_{rj}\right).$$

Rows of S' must sum to zero within rounding error.

(3) Compute S^{-1}, the inverse of S, with elements s^{ij} as follows:

$$s^{ii} = 1/s_{ii}; \quad s^{ij} = -\frac{1}{s_{ii}}\left(\sum_{r=j}^{i-1} s_{ri} s^{rj}\right), \quad i > j.$$

For $i < j$, $s^{ij} = 0$. S^{-1} has the following properties:

Properties	Forms
$S^{-1}S = S'(S^{-1})' = I$	$\triangle \cdot \triangle = \triangledown \triangledown = I$
$S^{-1}A = S'$	$\triangle \cdot \square = \triangledown$

337

Properties	Forms
$A(S^{-1})' = S$	$\square \cdot \triangledown = \triangle$
$S^{-1}A(S^{-1})' = I$	$\triangle \cdot \square \cdot \triangledown = I$
$(S^{-1})'S^{-1} = A^{-1}$	$\triangledown \cdot \triangle = \square$

The elements $s^{(n+1)j}$ in the check row of S^{-1}, computed from

$$s^{(n+1)j} = -\sum_{r=j}^{i-1} s_{r(n+1)} s^{rj},$$

must equal unity within rounding error.

(4) Compute A^{-1}, the inverse of A, from $(S^{-1})'S^{-1} = A^{-1}$. The elements a^{ij} of A^{-1} (where $a^{ji} = a^{ij}$) are given by

$$a^{ii} = \sum_{r=i}^{n} (s^{ri})^2, \qquad a^{ij} = \sum_{r=i}^{n} s^{ri} s^{rj}, \ i > j.$$

To check A^{-1}, sum the products of elements in the columns of A^{-1} and the corresponding elements in the sum column of A. These values should satisfy

$$-\sum_{i=1}^{n} a^{ij} a_{i(n+1)} = 1$$

within rounding error.

Example for Computing Note A

i/j	1	2	3	4	5	6	7	Check
				The matrix A				
1	1947	−360	−354	−326	−359	−263	−285	0000
2		2051	−335	−364	−391	−304	−297	0000
3			2054	−357	−339	−349	−320	0000
4				2252	−433	−421	−351	0000
5					2191	−357	−312	0000
6	(Symmetric)					2071	−377	0000
				The matrix S′				
1	44.125	−8.159	−8.023	−7.388	−8.136	−5.960	−6.459	00.000
2		44.547	−8.990	−9.524	−10.267	−7.916	−7.850	00.000
3			43.690	−11.488	−11.366	−10.711	−10.126	−00.001
4				44.438	−16.235	−14.930	−13.273	00.000
5					40.331	−21.098	−19.234	−00.001
6	(Zero elements omitted)					34.498	−34.498	−00.001
				The matrix S^{-1}				
1	.022663					(Zero elements omitted)		1.000043
2	.004151	.022448						1.000030
3	.005016	.004619	.022889					1.000035
4	.005954	.006005	.005917	.022503				.999999
5	.009439	.009434	.008832	.009058	.024795			1.000034
6	.014775	.014954	.015069	.015279	.015164	.028988		1.000028
				The matrix $A^{-1} \times 10^3$				
1	.898848					(Symmetric)		1.000018
2	.462097	.873930						1.000007
3	.456051	.449918	.863996					1.000009
4	.445229	.449066	.443390	.821880				.999964
5	.458088	.460678	.447496	.456284	.844739			1.000009
6	.428298	.433487	.436820	.442908	.439574	.840304		.999995

B An Approximation for Computing $\hat{P} = \Phi(y)$

Given the value of a unit normal deviate, y (for $0 \le y < \infty$), it is desired to find the corresponding area $\hat{P}$, to the right of $-y$ under the normal distribution function (see Example 4.7.4):

$$\hat{P} = \Phi(y) = \frac{1}{\sqrt{2\pi}} \int_{-y}^{\infty} \exp(-z^2/2) \, dz.$$

A recommended method for machine computation is that provided by Hastings.[1] If Hastings' approximation is adapted to the function $\hat{P} = \Phi(y)$ as defined above, the approximation $\hat{P}$ for P is

$$\hat{P} = 1 - \tfrac{1}{2}(1 + a_1 y + a_2 y^2 + a_3 y^3 + a_4 y^4)^{-4},$$

where

$$a_1 = .196854, \qquad a_2 = .115195,$$

$$a_3 = .000344, \qquad a_4 = .019527.$$

For a given unit normal deviate, $y < 0$, the absolute value $|y|$ should replace y in the expression for $\hat{P}$, and the approximate area (the area to the right of $+y$) is then $1 - \hat{P}$.

The maximum error of approximation, $(\hat{P} - P)$, is on the order of 5×10^{-4}.

---

[1] C. Hastings, *Approximations for Digital Computers*, Princeton University Press, Princeton, N.J., 1955, p. 185.

C An Approximation for Computing $\hat{Y} = \Phi^{-1}(p)$

Given the value of an area in the right tail under the normal distribution function, it is desired to find the corresponding unit normal deviate $\hat{Y}$ such that

$$p = \Phi(\hat{Y}) = \frac{1}{\sqrt{2\pi}} \int_{-\hat{Y}}^{\infty} \exp(-z^2/2)\, dz \, .$$

A recommended method for machine computation involves the use of one approximate function for $.02 < p < .98$ and a distinct function for p outside that range.

For $.02 < p < .98$, a suitable function is that developed by Tucker.[1] Let $U = p - \frac{1}{2}$. Then the approximation $\hat{Y}$ for Y is given by

$$\hat{Y} = \frac{U(a_1 - a_2 U^2 + a_3 U^4)}{(1 - a_4 U^2 + a_5 U^4)} \, ,$$

where

$$a_1 = 2.5101, \quad a_2 = 12.2043, \quad a_3 = 11.2502,$$

$$a_4 = 5.8742, \quad a_5 = 7.9587 \, .$$

The maximum discrepancy $(\hat{Y} - Y)$ is less than 3×10^{-4}.

When p (or $1 - p$) $\geq .97725$, a suitable method is a modification of that given by Muller,[2] as presented by Hildebrand,[3] involving interpolation by inverted differences. It differs from that of Muller only in that a wider range of the function is approximated (Muller's method allows for $p < 1/128$ or $p > 127/128$) and in the selection of points on the curve used in the interpolation.

[1] H. Gulliksen and L. R Tucker, "An IBM 650 program for paired comparisons from balanced incomplete blocks—a 6–31 design (Parcobib 6–31)," *Res. Memo. 59–5*, Educational Testing Service, Princeton, N.J., 1959.
[2] M. E. Muller, "An inverse method for the generation of random normal deviates on large-scale computers," *Math Tables and other Aids to Computation* **12**, 167–174 (1958).
[3] F. B. Hildebrand, *Introduction to Numerical Analysis*, McGraw-Hill, New York, 1956, pp. 395–406.

The method involves use of two lists of numbers, one consisting of values of the normal integral P_k at selected points along the tail of the curve, the second list consisting of corresponding inverted divided differences a_k. Each list was arbitrarily chosen to be of length 15. These lists appear in the accompanying table. Estimates of normal deviates for a particular observed p are obtained from

$$\hat{Y} = a_0 + \frac{p - P_0}{N_1 N_2} - \frac{(p - P_0)(p - P_1)}{N_2 N_3} + \frac{(p - P_0)(p - P_1)(p - P_2)}{N_3 N_4} -$$

$$\cdots - \frac{(p - P_0)(p - P_1) \cdots (p - P_{14})}{N_{15} N_{16}}.$$

Let a_0 be the zeroth term and $(p - P_0)/N_1 N_2$ be the first term of this series. Then an expression for the kth term, for $k > 1$, is

$$r_k = \frac{(-1)^{k+1}(p - P_0)(p - P_1) \cdots (p - P_{k-1})}{N_k N_{k+1}}.$$

Values of N_k are determined recursively from

$$N_0 = 0, \quad N_1 = 1, \quad N_{k+1} = a_k N_k + (p - P_{k-1})N_{k-1}.$$

One typically uses no more than the first half of the total possible number of terms (16) of the series approximation for $\hat{Y}$. Since the series represents a divergent expansion, it is necessary to stop at an appropriate value of k. Based upon Muller's recommendation, k should be selected as the final term (a) if $|r_k| < 4 \times 10^{-4}$, (b) if $|r_k| < |r_{k+1}|$, or (c) if $k = 14$. Error of approximation, as given by Muller, is less than 4×10^{-4}.

Constants for Rational Approximation of Y from p for Extreme p

k	Y_k	P_k	a_k
0	2.00	.9772498680	2.0000000000
1	2.02	.9783083062	.05292191000
2	2.05	.9798177846	−.9654001271
3	2.10	.9821355794	.09724638020
4	2.15	.9842223926	−.6509450579
5	2.25	.9877755273	.09606653673
6	2.40	.9918024641	−.4911217717
7	2.55	.9946138540	.06260695834
8	2.75	.9970202367	−.3774911680
9	3.00	.9986501019	.02516606273
10	3.25	.9994229749	−.2865062904
11	3.50	.9997673709	+.006297099408
12	4.00	.9999683287	−.1557575105
13	4.40	.9999945874	.0008531194973
14	5.00	.9999997133	−.02425026703

D   Matrix Methods in Least Squares Analysis

Although the mathematical method of Section 2.7 is satisfactory for the solution of simple least squares problems, it does not lend itself readily to a general solution, that is, to a solution which can be applied routinely to any linear model, however complex or irregular. To express the general solution in a form which is concise and directly connected with a large body of mathematical results, the notation and methods of matrix algebra are much to be preferred. This is the practice in most of the modern treatments of least squares (e.g., Kempthorne, 1952, pp. 74ff; Graybill, 1961; Rao, 1965). A further advantage of the matrix formulation is that computer routines to perform the necessary arithmetic can be programmed directly in the matrix operations. Interpretive systems for matrix computation have been prepared for this purpose (Bock and Zyzanski, 1963; Bock and Peterson, 1967; Bargmann, 1965).

In a number of the applications of least squares which appear in this book, the solution is obtained by matrix methods, but for the reader's convenience the results are expressed both in matrix notation and in conventional algebra. An instance of this practice appears in Section 3.4, where the order-effect model for the constant method is introduced. Others appear in Chapters 5 and 9, in various solutions for the methods of paired comparisons and successive categories. The purpose of this note is to review the matrix methods for solving least squares problems. It presents these methods in the particularly simple context of Urban's solution for the constant method (Chapter 2). Other problems connected with the general solution were discussed, as they arose, in Sections 6.4 and 6.7.

The general matrix expression for a linear statistical model may be written

$$\mathbf{y} = A\pi + \xi \, ;$$

where **y** is the $n \times 1$ column of observations, A is the $n \times m$ matrix of coefficients of the model, π is the $m \times 1$ column vector of unknown parameters, and ξ is an $n \times 1$ column vector of random errors. In least square estimation the errors are assumed to have some multivariate distribution with finite mean and covariance matrix.

The psychophysical model for the constant method given by Equation (2.14) is evidently of the form $A\pi$. Ignoring δ, the bias term (which is asymptotically zero) the matrix expression of the statistical model for the observed deviates is

$$
\begin{bmatrix} y_1 \\ y_2 \\ . \\ y_n \end{bmatrix} = \begin{bmatrix} 1 & x_1 \\ 1 & x_2 \\ . & . \\ 1 & x_n \end{bmatrix} \cdot \begin{bmatrix} \alpha \\ \beta \end{bmatrix} + \begin{bmatrix} \xi_1 \\ \xi_2 \\ . \\ \xi_n \end{bmatrix}. \tag{D.1}
$$

For present purposes it is convenient to write (D.1) in terms of column vectors:

$$
\mathbf{y} = [\mathbf{1}, \mathbf{x}] \begin{bmatrix} \alpha \\ \beta \end{bmatrix} + \xi.
$$

In the context of the constant method, the error vector, ξ, has asymptotic n-variate normal distribution with zero mean and a known diagonal covariance, say,

$$
D = \text{diag}\left[\frac{P_1 Q_1}{N_1 h^2(Y_1)}, \frac{P_2 Q_2}{N_2 h^2(Y_2)}, \cdots, \frac{P_n Q_n}{N_n h^2(Y_n)} \right].
$$

The normit χ^2, Equation (2.24), may therefore be expressed as a quadratic form in the residuals $\mathbf{y} - A\pi$ and the matrix D^{-1}:

$$
Q = (\mathbf{y} - A\pi)' D^{-1} (\mathbf{y} - A\pi)
$$
$$
= (\mathbf{y} - \alpha\mathbf{1} - \beta\mathbf{x})' D^{-1} (\mathbf{y} - \alpha\mathbf{1} - \beta\mathbf{x}).
$$

To minimize this form with respect to variation in π, we employ symbolic differentiation (Dwyer and MacPhail, 1948), observing the rules

$$
\frac{\partial \mathbf{x}' B \mathbf{x}}{\partial \mathbf{x}} = 2B\mathbf{x} \qquad (B \text{ symmetric})
$$

and

$$
\frac{\partial C\mathbf{x}}{\partial \mathbf{x}} = C', \quad \text{and} \quad \frac{\partial \mathbf{x}' C'}{\partial \mathbf{x}} = C.
$$

Thus,

$$
-\frac{1}{2} \frac{\partial Q}{\partial \pi} = A' D^{-1} (\mathbf{y} - A\pi).
$$

Setting the derivatives equal to zero gives the normal equations, the simultaneous solution of which provides the best unbiased linear estimate of π.

$$A'D^{-1}\mathbf{y} - A'D^{-1}A\hat{\pi} = 0,$$

or

$$A'D^{-1}A\hat{\pi} = A'D^{-1}\mathbf{y}. \tag{D.2}$$

In the solution of (D.2), two cases must be considered according to whether the determinant of the matrix of coefficients (1) does not vanish, i.e. $A'D^{-1}A$ is nonsingular; (2) vanishes, i.e. $A'D^{-1}A$ is singular because A does not have m linearly independent columns, in which case the model is said to be of *deficient* rank; otherwise, it is said to be of *full* rank. In case 1, the normal equations have a unique solution which may be obtained by routine methods for solving m independent linear equations in m unknowns. Note that the normal equations for the constant method exemplify this case. In case 2, the equations will have a solution (which is, however, nonunique), if they are "consistent," i.e. if the constant terms are under the same linear restriction as the coefficients. Only case 1 is discussed in this computing note. The condition for consistency in case 2 is discussed in Section 6.4.2. A method for handling case 2 problems by reparameterizing the model to full rank is given in Section 6.7.2.

In case 1, the solution of the normal equations may be obtained in general by premultiplying (D.2) by the inverse of the matrix $(A'D^{-1}A)$. This solution gives the linear estimate of π:

$$\hat{\pi} = (A'D^{-1}A)^{-1}A'D^{-1}\mathbf{y}.$$

An efficient method of numerically calculating the inverse of a matrix of this type is given in Computing Note A. In many problems however, this calculation can be avoided by obtaining an explicit algebraic solution of the normal equations. A device sometimes used to simplify the algebra is a so-called "reparameterization" of the model. For example, if we write out the individual elements in the matrix form of the normal equations for the constant method, we have

$$\begin{bmatrix} \mathbf{1}'D^{-1}\mathbf{1} & \mathbf{1}'D^{-1}\mathbf{x} \\ \mathbf{x}'D^{-1}\mathbf{1} & \mathbf{x}'D^{-1}\mathbf{x} \end{bmatrix} \cdot \begin{bmatrix} \hat{\alpha} \\ \hat{\beta} \end{bmatrix} = \begin{bmatrix} \mathbf{1}'D^{-1}\mathbf{y} \\ \mathbf{x}'D^{-1}\mathbf{y} \end{bmatrix}. \tag{D.3}$$

Now let

$$\hat{\alpha} = \hat{\alpha}_0 - \hat{\beta}\mathbf{1}'D^{-1}/\mathbf{1}'D^{-1}\mathbf{1} = \hat{\alpha}_0 - \hat{\beta}\bar{x}.$$

Then the two equations represented by (D.3) become

$$\hat{\alpha}_0\mathbf{1}'D^{-1}\mathbf{1} = \mathbf{1}'D^{-1}\mathbf{y} \tag{D.4}$$

$$\hat{\alpha}_0\mathbf{x}'D^{-1}\mathbf{1} + \hat{\beta}\mathbf{x}'\left(D^{-1} - \frac{D^{-1}\mathbf{1}\mathbf{1}'D^{-1}}{\mathbf{1}'D^{-1}\mathbf{1}}\right)\mathbf{x} = \mathbf{x}'D^{-1}\mathbf{y}. \tag{D.5}$$

The solution of (D.4) provides the estimate of α_0 :

$$\hat{\alpha}_0 = \mathbf{1}'D^{-1}\mathbf{y}/\mathbf{1}'D^{-1}\mathbf{1} = \bar{y}.$$

Then multiplying (D.4) by $\mathbf{x}'D^{-1}\mathbf{1}/\mathbf{1}'D^{-1}\mathbf{1}$ and subtracting from (D.5), we have

$$\hat{\beta}\mathbf{x}'\left(D^{-1} - \frac{D^{-1}\mathbf{1}\mathbf{1}'D^{-1}}{\mathbf{1}'D^{-1}\mathbf{1}}\right)\mathbf{x} = \mathbf{x}'\left(D^{-1} - \frac{D^{-1}\mathbf{1}\mathbf{1}'D^{-1}}{\mathbf{1}'D^{-1}\mathbf{1}}\right)\mathbf{y}. \qquad \text{(D.6)}$$

Let

$$\left(D^{-1} - \frac{D^{-1}\mathbf{1}\mathbf{1}'D^{-1}}{\mathbf{1}'D^{-1}\mathbf{1}}\right) = M.$$

Then the estimate of β provided by (D.6) may be expressed as

$$\hat{\beta} = \mathbf{x}'M\mathbf{y}/\mathbf{x}'M\mathbf{x}. \qquad \text{(D.7)}$$

A solution providing an estimate of α may be then obtained as

$$\hat{\alpha} = \hat{\alpha}_0 - \hat{\beta}\bar{x} = \bar{y} - \hat{\beta}\bar{x}. \qquad \text{(D.8)}$$

These results are the matrix versions of Equations (2.25) and (2.26).

In computing expectations and variances of the estimators, we observe the following properties for the matrix analogs of the expectation and variance operators for scalar variables:

$$\mathscr{E}(A\mathbf{y} + B) = A\mathscr{E}(\mathbf{y}) + B ;$$

$$\mathscr{V}(A\mathbf{y} + B) = A\mathscr{V}(\mathbf{y})A' .$$

The symbol $\mathscr{V}(\mathbf{y})$ represents the variance–covariance matrix of the vector variable $\mathbf{y}$. Then, in general,

$$\mathscr{E}(\hat{\boldsymbol{\pi}}) = (A'D^{-1}A)^{-1}A'D^{-1}\mathscr{E}(\mathbf{y});$$

or, in particular for the constant method:

$$\mathscr{E}(\hat{\beta}) = \mathbf{x}'M\mathscr{E}(\mathbf{y})/\mathbf{x}'M\mathbf{x}$$

$$= \mathbf{x}'M(\alpha\mathbf{1} + \beta\mathbf{x})/\mathbf{x}'M\mathbf{x}$$

$$= \alpha\mathbf{x}'M\mathbf{1}/\mathbf{x}'M\mathbf{x} + \beta.$$

But $M\mathbf{1} = 0$, hence,

$$\mathscr{E}(\hat{\beta}) = \beta.$$

Then

$$\mathscr{E}(\hat{\alpha}) = \mathscr{E}(\hat{\alpha}_0) - \mathscr{E}(\hat{\beta})\bar{x}$$

$$= \frac{\mathbf{1}'D^{-1}}{\mathbf{1}'D^{-1}\mathbf{1}}(\alpha\mathbf{1} + \beta\mathbf{x}) - \beta\bar{x}$$

$$= \alpha + \beta\bar{x} - \beta\bar{x}$$

$$= \alpha.$$

As for the variances, we have in general

$$\mathscr{V}(\hat{\boldsymbol{\pi}}) = (AD^{-1}A)^{-1}A'D^{-1}\,\mathscr{V}(\mathbf{y})D^{-1}A(A'D^{-1}A)^{-1} = (A'D^{-1}A)^{-1}$$

and, in particular, for the constant method:

$$\mathscr{V}(\hat{\beta}) = \mathbf{x}'M\mathscr{V}(\mathbf{y})M\mathbf{x}/(\mathbf{x}'M\mathbf{x})^2 = \mathbf{x}'MDM\mathbf{x}/(\mathbf{x}'M\mathbf{x})^2 .$$

But $MDM = M$ (that is, M is idempotent in the metric D). Hence,

$$\mathscr{V}(\hat{\beta}) = 1/\mathbf{x}'M\mathbf{x}.$$

Similarly,

$$\mathscr{V}(\hat{\alpha}) = \mathscr{V}(\hat{\alpha}_0) + \bar{x}^2\mathscr{V}(\hat{\beta}) + 2\bar{x}\mathscr{V}(\hat{\alpha}_0 , \hat{\beta}).$$

However, $\hat{\alpha}_0$ and $\hat{\beta}$ are uncorrelated, since

$$\mathscr{V}(\hat{\alpha}_0 , \hat{\beta}) = \frac{\mathbf{1}'D^{-1}}{\mathbf{1}'D^{-1}\mathbf{1}}\,\mathscr{V}(\mathbf{y})\frac{M\mathbf{x}}{\mathbf{x}'M\mathbf{x}}$$

$$= \frac{\mathbf{1}'D^{-1}DM\mathbf{x}}{(\mathbf{1}'D^{-1}\mathbf{1})(\mathbf{x}'M\mathbf{x})}$$

$$= \mathbf{1}'M\mathbf{x}/(\mathbf{1}'D^{-1}\mathbf{1})(\mathbf{x}'M\mathbf{x}) = 0 .$$

Thus,

$$\mathscr{V}(\hat{\alpha}) = \mathscr{V}(\hat{\alpha}_0) + \bar{x}^2\mathscr{V}(\beta)$$

$$= \frac{\mathbf{1}'D^{-1}\mathscr{V}(\mathbf{y})D^{-1}\mathbf{1}}{(\mathbf{1}'D^{-1}\mathbf{1})^2} + \bar{x}^2\mathscr{V}(\beta)$$

$$= \frac{1}{\mathbf{1}'D^{-1}\mathbf{1}} + \frac{\bar{x}^2}{\mathbf{x}'M\mathbf{x}}.$$

Again, these results are the matric form of those in Section 2.7.

The analysis of variance associated with this solution may also be expressed in matrix notation as seen in Table D.1.

TABLE D.1. The Analysis of Variance Table for Urban's Solution Expressed in Matrix Notation

Source of variation	Degrees of freedom	Sum of squares	Expected sum of squares
Intercept	1	$\text{SSM} = \mathbf{y}'\left(\dfrac{D^{-1}\mathbf{1}\mathbf{1}'D^{-1}}{\mathbf{1}'D^{-1}\mathbf{1}}\right)\mathbf{y}$	$1 + (\alpha + \beta\bar{x})^2\mathbf{1}'D^{-1}\mathbf{1}$
Slope, eliminating intercept	1	$\text{SSR} = \mathbf{y}'M\mathbf{x}\,\mathbf{x}'M\mathbf{y}/\mathbf{x}'M\mathbf{x}$	$1 + \beta^2\mathbf{x}'M\mathbf{x}$
Error	$n-2$	$\text{SSE} = \mathbf{y}'\left(M - \dfrac{M\mathbf{x}\,\mathbf{x}'M}{\mathbf{x}'M\mathbf{x}}\right)\mathbf{y}$	$(n-2)$
Total	n	$\text{SST} = \mathbf{y}'D^{-1}\mathbf{y}$	

Unlike the corresponding Table 2.2, Table D.1 shows the sum of squares of the " correction term " explicitly in the first line (intercept). This form of the table reflects better the general formulation of analysis of variance than does the conventional arrangement in Table 2.2.

The general formulation of analysis of variance may be expressed in terms of a so-called " orthogonal reparameterization " of the model (see Graybill, 1961, p. 235). This reparameterization has the following characteristics: (1) The new parameters are obtained from the old by a linear transformation. (2) The unbiased estimates of the new parameters are uncorrelated and have unit variance. (3) The new parameters are " interesting " in the sense that they lead to tests of hypothesis in which some of the parameters can be tested without bias from other parameters in the model. We obtain the orthogonal reparameterization from the transposed normal equations:

$$A'D^{-1}A\pi = A'D^{-1}\mathbf{y}.$$

It can be shown (Householder, 1953, p. 66) that, in case 1, the symmetric matrix of coefficients of least square normal equations can be uniquely expressed as the product of a lower triangular matrix and its transpose (the Cholesky factorization):

$$TT'\pi = A'D^{-1}\mathbf{y}. \tag{D.9}$$

The premultiplication of π by the $m \times m$ upper triangular matrix T' defines new parameters which satisfy the above requirements. (1) The new parameters, say,

$$v = T'\pi,$$

are obtained from π by the linear transformation T'. (2) In case 1, T is nonsingular and has an inverse. Thus, the solution of (D.9) for v is obtained by premultiplying on both sides by T^{-1}:

$$\hat{v} = T^{-1}A'D^{-1}\mathbf{y} = \mathbf{u}, \quad \text{say.} \tag{D.10}$$

Then,

$$\mathscr{E}(\mathbf{u}) = T^{-1}A'D^{-1}[A\pi + \mathscr{E}(\xi)] = v$$

and

$$\mathscr{V}(\mathbf{u}) = T^{-1}A'D^{-1}\mathscr{V}(\mathbf{y})D^{-1}A(T^{-1})'$$
$$= T^{-1}A'D^{-1}DD^{-1}A(T^{-1})'$$
$$= T^{-1}TT'(T^{-1})'$$
$$= I$$

as required. (3) Finally, because T' is upper triangular, the last component of the vector of orthogonal parameters, υ, involves only the last component of π; similarly, the next to the last component of υ involves only the last two components of π; and so on, until the first component of υ involves all components of π. In other words, the jth orthogonal parameter,

$$\upsilon_j = \mathbf{t}'_j\pi,$$

is a linear combination of the original parameters in which the first $k - 1$ coefficients are zero and the last $n - k + 1$ are in general nonzero. This type of reparameterization makes for interesting tests of hypothesis because a subhypothesis concerning the last $n - j + 1$ parameters in the original model may be tested without regard to the previous k parameters. The practical value of such a test is that it aids the investigator in judging whether a subset of parameters accounts for an additional part of the variation in the observation that cannot be attributed merely to random error. In the context of the solution for the constant method, the subhypothesis of interest corresponds to a test of the slope parameter β without regard to the value of the intercept. It is with this subhypothesis in mind that we begin the reparameterization with α (or α_0) as the first component of π, and β as the second. This gives a test of variation due to β eliminating that due to α. If β is assumed to equal zero, a test of α is then possible in this reparameterization. That is, if the line is assumed horizontal, then it is possible to test in general whether it has intercept zero.

The triangular (Cholesky) factor of the matrix of coefficients required for this general form of analysis of variance can always be obtained and inverted in case 1 by the numerical methods in Computing Note A. However, in simple problems it is often convenient to express algebraically the results of the calculations described in Computing Note A. For example, the Cholesky factor of the matrix of coefficients in (D.9) is found in this way to be

$$T = \begin{bmatrix} \sqrt{\mathbf{1}'D^{-1}\mathbf{1}} & 0 \\ \mathbf{x}'D^{-1}\mathbf{1}/\sqrt{\mathbf{1}'D^{-1}\mathbf{1}} & \sqrt{\mathbf{x}'M\mathbf{x}} \end{bmatrix}.$$

And the inverse of this factor is

$$T^{-1} = \begin{bmatrix} 1/\sqrt{\mathbf{1}'D^{-1}\mathbf{1}} & 0 \\ \dfrac{-\mathbf{x}'D^{-1}\mathbf{1}}{\mathbf{1}'D^{-1}\mathbf{1}\sqrt{\mathbf{x}'M\mathbf{x}}} & 1/\sqrt{\mathbf{x}M\mathbf{x}} \end{bmatrix}.$$

Thus, the estimates of the orthogonal parameters computed from (D.10) are

$$\begin{bmatrix} u_1 \\ u_2 \end{bmatrix} = \begin{bmatrix} \mathbf{1}'D^{-1}\mathbf{y}/\sqrt{\mathbf{1}'D^{-1}\mathbf{1}} \\ \mathbf{x}'M\mathbf{y}/\sqrt{\mathbf{x}'M\mathbf{x}} \end{bmatrix}.$$

Note that the squares of these two estimates provide the sums of squares attributable to intercept and slope in Table D.1. We can also easily show that the remaining sum of squares due to error can also be expressed as a sum of squares of uncorrelated variates with unit variance. Let

$$\mathbf{c}' = \frac{1}{\sqrt{\mathbf{1}'D^{-1}\mathbf{1}}} \mathbf{1}'D^{-1}$$

and

$$\mathbf{m}' = \frac{1}{\sqrt{\mathbf{x}'M\mathbf{x}}} \mathbf{x}'M.$$

These are the $1 \times n$ vectors of coefficients of the linear forms which define u_1 and u_2, respectively.

Now let the $n \times (n-2)$ matrix E be a completion of $\mathbf{c}$ and $\mathbf{m}$ which is orthogonal in the metric D. That is, $\mathbf{c}$, $\mathbf{m}$, and E must satisfy the condition,

$$\begin{bmatrix} \mathbf{c}' \\ \mathbf{m}' \\ E' \end{bmatrix} D[\mathbf{c}, \mathbf{m}, E] = \begin{bmatrix} 1 & 0 & 0 & 1 \\ 0 & 1 & 0 & 1 \\ 0 & 0 & 1 & n-2 \\ & 1 & 1 & n-2 \end{bmatrix}. \tag{D.11}$$

Since $\mathscr{V}(\mathbf{y}) = D$, condition (D.11) implies that the n variates

$$u_1 = \mathbf{c}'\mathbf{y}, \qquad u_2 = \mathbf{m}'\mathbf{y}, \qquad \mathbf{w} = E'\mathbf{y}$$

are pairwise uncorrelated and have unit variances. Their expectations are

$$\mathscr{E}(u_1) = \frac{1}{\sqrt{\mathbf{1}'D^{-1}\mathbf{1}}} \mathbf{1}'D^{-1}\mathscr{E}(\mathbf{y}) = (\alpha + \beta\bar{x})\sqrt{\mathbf{1}'D^{-1}\mathbf{1}},$$

$$\mathscr{E}(u_2) = \frac{1}{\sqrt{\mathbf{x}'M\mathbf{x}}} \mathbf{x}'M\mathscr{E}(\mathbf{y}) = \beta\sqrt{\mathbf{x}'M\mathbf{x}},$$

and

$$\mathscr{E}(\mathbf{w}) = E'\xi(\mathbf{y}) = \alpha E'\mathbf{1} + \beta E'\mathbf{x} = 0.$$

That $\mathbf{w}$ has zero expectation follows from the fact that the columns of E are orthogonal to the vectors $\mathbf{1}$ and $\mathbf{x}$, as implied by (D.11):

$$\mathbf{c}'DE = \mathbf{1}'E/\sqrt{\mathbf{1}'D^{-1}\mathbf{1}} = 0,$$

and

$$\mathbf{m}'DE = \mathbf{x}'E - \mathbf{x}'\frac{D^{-1}\mathbf{1}\mathbf{1}'E}{\mathbf{1}'D^{-1}\mathbf{1}} = \mathbf{x}'E - 0 = 0.$$

We can readily show that the sum of squares of these variables is equal to the total sum of squares in Table D.1:

$$[u_1, u_2, \mathbf{w}'] \begin{bmatrix} u_1 \\ u_2 \\ \mathbf{w} \end{bmatrix} = \mathbf{y}'[\mathbf{c}, \mathbf{m}, E] \begin{bmatrix} \mathbf{c}' \\ \mathbf{m}' \\ E' \end{bmatrix} \mathbf{y} = \mathbf{y}'D^{-1}\mathbf{y}.$$

To verify this result we note that, by (D.11) the matrix $[\mathbf{c}, \mathbf{m}, E]$ is nonsingular, in which case

$$\begin{bmatrix} \mathbf{c}' \\ \mathbf{m}' \\ E' \end{bmatrix} D = [\mathbf{c}, \mathbf{m}, E]^{-1}$$

and

$$[\mathbf{c}, \mathbf{m}, E] \begin{bmatrix} \mathbf{c}' \\ \mathbf{m}' \\ E' \end{bmatrix} = D^{-1}$$

Because the variates u_1, u_2, and $\mathbf{w}$ are linear compounds of variables normally distributed in the limit, they have limiting normal distributions. From (D.11) they are also independent and the standard theorems for the sums of squares of independent normal variables apply (Cramér, 1951, p. 233). In particular, the error sum of squares in the analysis of variance is the sum of squares of $n - 2$ variates, normally and independently distributed in the limit, with unit variance and zero mean independent of the parameters of the model:

$$\text{SSE} = \mathbf{w}'\mathbf{w} = \mathbf{y}D^{-1}\mathbf{y} - u_1^2 - u_2^2 = \text{SST} - \text{SSM} - \text{SSR}.$$

It is therefore unconditionally distributed in the limit as a central χ^2 distribution with $n - 2$ degrees of freedom.

The regression sum of squares,

$$u_2^2 = \mathbf{y}'M\mathbf{x}\mathbf{x}'M\mathbf{y}/\mathbf{x}'M\mathbf{x},$$

is the square of a limiting normal variate with unit variance and mean $\beta\sqrt{\mathbf{x}'M\mathbf{x}}$ independent of the parameter α. It is therefore unconditionally distributed in the limit as a noncentral χ^2 on one degree of freedom with noncentrality parameter $\beta^2\mathbf{x}'M\mathbf{x}$. It is distributed as a central χ^2 on one degree of freedom on condition that $\beta = 0$.

Finally, the correction term for the sum of squares is the square of a limiting normal deviate with unit variance and mean $(\alpha + \beta\bar{x})\sqrt{\mathbf{1}'D^{-1}\mathbf{1}}$. It is therefore distributed in the limit as a noncentral χ^2 with one degree of freedom and noncentrality parameter $\alpha^2\mathbf{1}'D^{-1}\mathbf{1}$ on condition that $\beta = 0$. It is distributed in the limit as a central χ^2 on one degree of freedom on condition that $\beta = 0$ and $\alpha = 0$. These results justify the use of the χ^2 distribution for the statistical tests described in Section 2.7.

The least squares estimation and the associated analysis of variance have a simple interpretation in geometric terms (Corsten, 1958). Equation (D.1) is interpreted as a vector sum (resultant) of the vectors $\alpha\mathbf{1}$, $\beta\mathbf{x}$, and ξ in n-dimensional space. In this space length and angles are defined in terms of inner products of vectors with respect to the matrix D^{-1}. Thus $\xi' D^{-1}\xi$ is the square length of the error vector.

The vectors $\mathbf{1}$ and $\mathbf{x}$ are a basis of a subspace which contains all possible psychophysical models which could be constructed by arbitrary choice of α and β. This subspace is called the *estimation space*. The principle of least squares asserts that values should be chosen for α and β which place the resultant of $\alpha\mathbf{1}$ and $\beta\mathbf{x}$ in the estimation space as close as possible to the observational vector $\mathbf{y}$. According to a theorem of Euclid, the least distance between a point and a plane is on a line normal to the plane. Thus, the length of the residual, $\mathbf{y} - \alpha\mathbf{1} - B\mathbf{x}$, will be minimal when it is orthogonal to all vectors in the space span by the model, and in particular, to the vectors $\mathbf{1}$ and $\mathbf{x}$. Since two vectors are orthogonal to each other when their inner products vanish, the condition that the residual be orthogonal to $\mathbf{1}$ and $\mathbf{x}$ with respect to D^{-1} determines the normal equations,

$$(\mathbf{y} - \alpha\mathbf{1} + \beta\mathbf{x})' D^{-1}\mathbf{1} = 0,$$

and

$$(\mathbf{y} - \alpha\mathbf{1} + \beta\mathbf{x})' D^{-1}\mathbf{x} = 0.$$

These are precisely the equations obtained above by formal minimization of the quadratic form in the residuals.

The geometric interpretation of the partition of sum of squares in the analysis of variance is equally simple. The vector $\mathbf{y}$ is projected on a certain orthogonal basis (with respect to D^{-1}) of the n-dimensional space of the observation. By the generalized Pythagorean theorem, the square length of the vector $\mathbf{y}$ is equal to the sum of the square lengths of these projections. It is these square lengths of projections that provided the additive partition of the total sum of squares in the anlysis of variance.

By *projection* is meant a component in some subspace resulting from the decomposition of a vector spanning a larger space. The length of a projection is the length of the original vector times the cosine of the angle between this vector and its projection. From the law of cosines, the cosine of the angle between the vectors $\mathbf{u}$ and $\mathbf{v}$, in an inner product space with respect to D^{-1}, is

$$\frac{\mathbf{u}' D^{-1}\mathbf{v}}{(\mathbf{u}' D^{-1}\mathbf{u})^{1/2}(\mathbf{v}' D^{-1}\mathbf{v})^{1/2}}.$$

Thus the *square* length of the projection of $\mathbf{v}$ on $\mathbf{u}$ is

$$\frac{(\mathbf{u}' D^{-1}\mathbf{v})^2}{\mathbf{u}' D^{-1}\mathbf{u}\,\mathbf{v}' D^{-1}\mathbf{v}}\,\mathbf{v}' D^{-1}\mathbf{v} = \frac{\mathbf{v}' D^{-1}\mathbf{u}\mathbf{u}' D^{-1}\mathbf{v}}{\mathbf{u}' D^{-1}\mathbf{u}}. \tag{D.12}$$

If **v** is a vector of n coordinates with respect to some n-dimensional basis, it can be decomposed into n projections on other bases provided by, say, the columns of the matrix U. If U is orthogonal with respect to a metric matrix such as D^{-1}, that is, such that $U'D^{-1}U$ is a diagonal matrix, then the square lengths of the projections on this basis will sum to the square length of **v**.

In the simple least squares problem that we have been considering, two vectors of such a basis are provided by **1** and $\mathbf{x} - \mathbf{1}\bar{x}$. These vectors are orthogonal with respect to D^{-1}, since

$$\mathbf{1}'D^{-1}(\mathbf{x} - \mathbf{1}\bar{x}) = \mathbf{1}'D^{-1}\left(\mathbf{x} - \mathbf{1}\frac{\mathbf{1}'D^{-1}\mathbf{x}}{\mathbf{1}'D^{-1}\mathbf{1}}\right) = 0.$$

Using **y** as **v**, and **1** and $\mathbf{x} - \mathbf{1}\bar{x}$ as **u** in (D.12), we obtain the sum of squares, for intercept and slope respectively, of the analysis of variance shown in Table D.1. The balance of the square length of **y** makes up the sum of the square lengths of projections on the remaining $n - 2$ vectors of the basis orthogonal to **1** and $(\mathbf{x} - \mathbf{1}\bar{x})$. Thus the error sum of squares can always be obtained by subtraction, as in Table D.1. Note that the degrees of freedom in the analysis of variance represents the dimensionality of the subspaces on which the observational vector is projected.

In more general applications of analysis of variance the problem arises of how to construct a suitable orthogonal basis upon which to project the observational vector. Such a construction may be carried out routinely by a generalized Gram-Schmidt process (i.e. with inner products with respect to D^{-1}) applied to the columns of the model matrix A (Stoll, 1952, p. 222; Davis, 1962). This construction results in a basis for A which is *orthonormal* with respect to D^{-1}; that is, the vectors are not only orthogonal, but are of unit length, thus making the quantity in the numerator of (D.12) equal to unity and simplifying somewhat the calculation of the square lengths of the projections.

The Gram-Schmidt construction produces a basis which is unique except for the order in which the original vectors are entered in the orthogonalization. This order must be specified by the investigator, since it determines which parameters in the model may be tested in a subhypothesis. The columns of A which correspond to terms that are to be eliminated must enter the construction first, and those which correspond to parameters in the subhypothesis must follow. Note also that since the square length of the component of the observation in the error space may be obtained by subtraction, the basis for the error space never needs to be constructed explicitly.

The generalized Gram-Schmidt construction and the Cholesky factorization employed in the preceding matrix formulation of the analysis of variance are intimately related. The inverse of the Cholesky factor of $A'D^{-1}A$ is precisely the transformation which orthonormalizes the columns of A in the metric D^{-1}; that is, the matrix $T^{-1}A'$ is orthonormal with respect to D^{-1}:

$$T^{-1}A'D^{-1}A(T^{-1})' = I.$$

Thus the matrix of estimators of the orthogonal parameters, $T^{-1}A'D^{-1}$, is orthonormal with respect to $D = \mathscr{V}(\mathbf{y})$ as required.

Further development of the geometric treatment of least squares and analysis of variance may be found in Corsten (1958), Kruskal (1961), and Bock (1963).

Bibliography

Aitchison, J. and J. A. C. Brown, 1957. *The Lognormal Distribution*, Cambridge University Press, London.

Anderson, R. L. and T. A. Bancroft, 1952. *Statistical Theory in Research*, McGraw-Hill, New York.

Anderson, T. W., 1958. *An Introduction to Mathematical Statistical Analysis*, Wiley, New York.

Anscombe, F. J., 1948. "The transformation of Poisson, binomial, and negative binomial data," *Biometrika* **35**, 246–254.

Anscombe, F. J., 1954. "Comments on a paper by R. A. Fisher," *Biometrics* **10**, 141–144.

Anscombe, F. J., 1956. "On estimating binomial response relations," *Biometrika* **42**, 461–464.

Anscombe, F. J. and J. W. Tukey, "The examination and analysis of residuals," *Technometrics* **5**, 141–160.

Arrow, K. J., 1951. *Social Choice and Individual Values*, Wiley, New York.

Bargmann, R. E., 1965. "A statistician's instructions to the computer: a report on a statistical computer language," *Proceedings of the IBM scientific computing symposium on statistics, October 21–23, 1963*, IBM Data Processing Division, White Plains, N.Y.

Berkson, J., 1953. "A statistically precise and relatively simple method of estimating the bio-assay with quantal response, based on the logistic function," *J. Am. Stat. Assoc.* **48**, 565–599.

Berkson, J., 1955a. "Maximum likelihood and minimum chi-square estimates of the logistic function," *J. Am. Stat. Assoc.* **50**, 130–162.

Berkson, J., 1955b. "Estimates of the integrated normal curve by minimum normit chi-square with particular reference to bio-assay," *J. Am. Stat. Assoc.* **50**, 529–549.

354

Berkson, J., 1956. "Estimation by least squares and maximum likelihood," in J. Neyman (Ed.), *Proceedings of the Third Berkeley Symposium on Mathematical Statistics and Probability*, Vol. 1, University of California Press, Berkeley, pp. 1–11.

Berkson, J., 1957. "Tables for use in estimating the normal distribution function by normit analysis," *Biometrika* **44**, 411–435.

Bishop, R., 1940. "Points of neutrality in social attitudes of delinquents," *Psychometrika* **5**, 35–45.

Bliss, C. I., 1935. "The calculation of the dosage mortality curve" (Appendix by R. A. Fisher), *Ann. Appl. Biol.* **22**, 134–167.

Bock, R. D., 1958a. "Remarks on the test of significance for paired comparisons," *Psychometrika* **23**, 323–334.

Bock, R. D., 1958b. "Some sampling theory for successive intervals solutions," *University of North Carolina Psychometric Laboratory Report No. 18*, Chapel Hill.

Bock, R. D., 1963. "Programming univariate and multivariate analysis of variance," *Technometrics* **5**, 95–117.

Bock, R. D., 1968. "Estimating multinomial response relations," in R. C. Bose (Ed.), *Contributions to Statistics and Probability: Essays in Memory of Samarendra Nath Roy*, University of North Carolina Press, Chapel Hill.

Bock, R. D. and A. Peterson, 1967. *Matrix Operations Subroutines for statistical computation* (*FORTRAN. Coded Subroutines for the FORTRAN IV Compiler*), Department of Education Statistical Laboratory, Research Memo. No. 7, University of Chicago, Chicago, Ill.

Bock, R. D. and S. J. Zyzanski, 1963. "A matrix interpretative subroutine system for the General Precision LGP-30 computer," *University of North Carolina Psychometric Laboratory Report No. 38*, Chapel Hill.

Bodewig, E., 1959. *Matrix Calculus*, North-Holland Publishing Co., Amsterdam.

Boring, E. G., 1950. *A History of Experimental Psychology*, 2nd ed., Appleton-Century-Crofts, New York.

Bose, R. C., 1956. "Paired comparison designs for testing concordance between judges," *Biometrika* **43**, 113–121.

Bose, R. C., W. H. Clatworthy, and S. S. Shrikhande, 1954. "Tables of partially balanced designs with two associate classes," *North Carolina Agricultural Experiment Station, Technical Bulletin No. 107*, Raleigh.

Box, G. E. P., 1954. "The exploration and exploitation of response surfaces: some general consideration and examples," *Biometrics* **10**, 16–60.

Box, G. E. P. and J. S. Hunter, 1954. "A confidence region for the solution of a set of simultaneous equations with an application to experimental design," *Biometrika* **41**, 190–198.

Box, G. E. P. and K. P. Wilson, 1951. "On the experimental attainment of optimum conditions," *J. Royal Stat. Soc. Ser. B* **13**, 1–45.

Bradley, R. A., 1954. "Incomplete block rank analysis: on the appropriateness of the model for a method of paired comparison," *Biometrics* **10**, 375–390.

Bradley, R. A. and M. E. Terry, 1952. "Rank analysis of incomplete block designs. I. The method of paired comparisons," *Biometrika* **39**, 324–345.

Browne, E. T., 1958. *Introduction to the Theory of Determinants and Matrices*, University of North Carolina Press, Chapel Hill.

Brownlee, K. A., 1960. *Statistical Theory and Methodology in Science and Engineering*, Wiley, New York.

Buck, P. A., and K. G. Weckel, 1956. "Study of consumer preference of salt and sugar levels in canned green beans," *Food Technology* **10**, 421–423.

Cameron, A. T., 1947. "The taste sense and the relative sweetness of sugars and other sweet substances," *Scientific Report No. 9*, Sugar Research Foundation, New York.

Claringbold, D. J., J. D. Biggers, and C. W. Emmers, 1953. "The angular transformation in quantal analysis," *Biometrics* **9**, 467–484.

Cliff, N., 1959. "Adverbs as multipliers," *Psych. Rev.* **66**, 27–44.

Cochran, W. G. and G. M. Cox, 1957. *Experimental Designs*, Wiley, New York.

Cohn, J., 1948. "Experimentelle Untersuchungen über die Gefühlsbetonung der Farben, Helligkeiten, und ihrer Combinationen," *Philosophische Studien* **10**, 562–603.

Coombs, C. H., 1964. *A Theory of Data*, Wiley, New York.

Corsten, L. C. A., 1958. "Vectors, a tool in statistical regression theory," *Mededelingen van de Landbouwhogeschool Te Wageningen Nederland* **58**, 1–92.

Cramer, E. M., 1962. "A comparison of three methods of fitting the normal ogive," *Psychometrika* **27**, 183–192.

Cramer, E. M., 1964. "Some comparisons of methods of fitting the dosage response curve for small samples," *J. Am. Stat. Assoc.* **59**, 779–793.

Cramér, H., 1951. *Mathematical Methods of Statistics*, Princeton University Press, Princeton, N.J.

David, H. A., 1963. *The Method of Paired Comparisons*, Hafner, New York.

David, H. A., 1967. "Resolvable cyclic designs," *Sankhyā* **29**, 191–198.

Davis, P., 1962. "Orthonormalizing codes in numerical analysis," in J. Todd (Ed.), *A Survey of Numerical Analysis*, McGraw-Hill, New York.

Dwyer, P. S. and M. S. MacPhail, 1948. "Symbolic matrix derivatives," *Ann. Math. Stat.* **19**, 517–534.

Edwards, A. L. and L. L. Thurstone, 1952. "An internal consistency check for the method of successive intervals and the method of graded dichotomies," *Psychometrika* **17**, 169–180.

Eisenhart, C., 1947. "The assumptions underlying the analysis of variance," *Biometrics* **4**, 1–21.

Eisler, H., 1965. "The connection between magnitude and discrimination scales and direct and indirect scaling methods," *Physchometrika*, **30**, 271–289.

Ekman, G., 1956. "Discriminal sensitivity on the subjective continuum," *Acta Psychologia* **12**, 233–243.

Ekman, G., 1959. "Weber's law and related functions," *J. Psych.* **47**, 343–352.

Ekman, G., 1962. "Measurement of moral judgment: a comparison of scaling methods," *Perceptual and Motor Skills* **15**, 3–9.

Fechner, G. T., 1860. *Elemente der Psychophysik*, Breitkopf and Hartel, Leipzig.

Fechner, G. T., 1876. *Erinnerungen an die letzten Tage des Odlehre und ihres Urhebers*, C. von Reichenbach, Leipzig.

Finney, D. J., 1952. *Probit Analysis: A Statistical Treatment of the Sigmoid Response Curve*, 2nd ed., Cambridge University Press, London.

Fisher, R. A., 1935. "Appendix to Bliss, C. I. The calculation of the dosage-mortality curve," *Ann. Appl. Biol.* **22**, 134–167.

Fiske, D. W., 1966. "On the coordination of personality concepts and their measurement, *Human Development* **1**, 74–83.

Freeman, M. F. and J. W. Tukey, 1950. "Transformations related to the angular and the square root," *Ann. Math. Stat.* **21**, 607–611.

Fullerton, G. S. and J. McK. Cattell, 1892. *On the Perception of Small Differences*, University of Pennsylvania Philosophical Series, Philadelphia, p. 25.

Garwood, F., 1941. "The application of maximum likelihood to dosage-mortality curves," *Biometrika* **32**, 46–58.

Glenn, W. A. and H. A. David, 1960. "Ties in paired-comparison experiments using a modified Thurstone-Mosteller method, *"Biometrics* **16**, 86–109.

Graybill, F. A., 1961. *An Introduction to Linear Statistical Models*, Vol. 1, McGraw-Hill, New York.

Gridgeman, N. T., 1959. "Paired comparison, with and without ties," *Biometrics*, **15**, 382–388.

Gross, G. W., 1954. "A study of consumer preferences of creamed cottage cheese with different sugar and salt levels," unpublished doctoral dissertation, University of Georgia, Athens.

Guilford, J. P., 1954. *Psychometric Methods*, 2nd ed., McGraw-Hill, New York.

Gulliksen, H., 1956. "Measurement of subjective values," *Psychometrika* **21**, 229–244.

Gulliksen, H., 1958. "Comparatal dispersion, a measure of accuracy of judgment," *Psychometrika* **23**, 137–150.

Gulliksen, H. and S. Messick (Eds.), 1960. *Psychological Scaling: Theory and Applications*, Wiley, New York.

Gulliksen, H. and L. R Tucker, 1961. "A general procedure for obtaining paired comparisons from multiple rank orders," *Psychometrika* **26**, 173–183.

Gumbel, E. J., 1961. "Bivariate logistic distributions," *J. Am. Stat. Assoc.* **56**, 335–349.

Hastings, C., Jr., 1955. *Approximations for Digital Computers*, Princeton University Press, Princeton, N.J.

Hegelmayer, F., 1852. "Über das Gedächtnis für Linearan-schauungen," *Archiv Fur Physiologische Heilkunde* **11**, 844–853.

Henrici, P., 1964. *Elements of Numerical Analysis*, Wiley, New York.

Hicks, J. M., 1962. "Zero-point scaling of social objects as affected by scaling method and context," unpublished doctoral dissertation, Northwestern University, Evanston, Ill.

Hicks, J. M. and D. T. Campbell, 1965. "Zero-point scaling as affected by social object, scaling method, and context," *Journal of Personality and Social Personality* 2, 793–808.

Hotelling, H., 1941. "Experimental determination of the maximum of a function," *Ann. Math. Stat.* 12, 20–45.

Householder, A. S., 1953. *Principles of Numerical Analysis*, McGraw-Hill, New York.

Indow, T., K. Sano, M. Hiroshi, and H. Makita, 1962. "A mathematical model for interpretations in projective tests: an application to Seiken SCT," *Japan. Psych. Res.* 4, 163–172.

Jones, L. V., 1957. "A rational origin in paired comparison and successive intervals scaling," *P–1101, Report No. 3,* Quartermaster Food and Container Institute for the Armed Forces, Chicago, Ill.

Jones, L. V., 1959a. "Prediction of consumer purchase and the utility of money," *J. Appl. Psych.* 43, 334–337.

Jones, L. V., 1959b. "The problem of successive intervals scale origin," *P–1113, Report No. 4,* Quartermaster Research and Engineering Command, Natick, Mass.

Jones, L. V., 1959c. "Some invariant findings under the method of successive intervals," *Am. J. Psych.* 72, 210–220 (also in H. Gulliksen and S. Messick (Eds.), *Psychological Scaling: Theory and Applications*, Wiley, New York, 1960, pp.7–20).

Jones, L. V., 1967. "Invariance of zero-point scaling over changes in stimulus context," *Psych. Bull.* 67, 153–164.

Jones, L. V., and R. D. Bock, 1957. "Methodology of preference measurement," *P–1101, Report No. 4,* Quartermaster Food and Container Institute for the Armed Forces, Chicago, Ill.

Jones, L. V. and R. D. Bock, 1959. "Prediction of choice for food combinations," *P–1113, Report No. 5,* Quartermaster Research and Engineering Command, Natick, Mass.

Jones, L. V. and T. E. Jeffrey, 1964. "A quantitative analysis of expressed preferences for compensation plans," *J. Appl. Psych.* 48, 201–210.

Jones, L. V., D. R. Peryam, and L. L. Thurstone, 1955. "Development of a scale for measuring soldier's food preferences," *Food Res.* 20, 512–520.

Jones, L. V. and L. L. Thurstone, 1954. "Psychophysics and the normality assumption: an experimental report," in D. R. Peryam, F. J. Pilgrim, and M. Peterson (Eds.), *Food Acceptance Testing Methodology*. National Academy of Sciences, National Research Council, Washington, D.C., pp. 105–112.

Jones, L. V. and L. L. Thurstone, 1955. "The psychophysics of semantics: an experimental investigation," *J. Appl. Psych.* 39, 31–36.

Kalmus, H., 1959. "Genetical variation and sense perception," in G. E. W. Wolstenholme and C. M. O'Connor (Eds.), *Biochemistry of Human Genetics*, Little, Brown, Boston.

Kelton, J. D., 1956. "Determination of a ratio scale of preference," unpublished doctoral dissertation, University of North Carolina, Chapel Hill.

Kempthorne, O., 1952. *The Design and Analysis of Experiments*, Wiley, New York.

Kempthorne, O., 1957. *An Introduction to Genetic Statistics*, Wiley, New York.

Kendall, M. G. and A. Stuart, 1963. *Advanced Theory of Statistics*, Vol. 1, 2nd ed., Charles Griffin & Co., London.

Kendall, M. G. and A. Stuart, 1961. *Advanced Theory of Statistics*, Vol. 2, Charles Griffin & Co., London.

Kruskal, W., 1961. "The coordinate-free approach to Gauss-Markov estimation, and its application to missing and extra observations," in J. Neyman (Ed.), *Proceedings of the Fourth Berkeley Symposium on Mathematical Statistics and Probability*, Vol. 1, University of California Press, Berkeley, pp. 435–452.

Linhart, H., 1966. "Streuungszerlegung für Paar-Vergleiche," *Metrika* **10**, 16–38.

Lockhart, E. E., C. L. Tucker, and M. C. Merritt, 1955. "The effect of water impurities on the flavor of brewed coffee," *Food Res.* **20**, 598–605.

Lord, F. M., 1952. "A theory of test scores," *Psychometric Monograph*, No. 7, 1–84.

Lord, F. M. and M. R. Novick, 1968. *Statistical Theories of Mental Test Scores (with Contributions by A. Birnbaum)*, Addison-Wesley, Reading, Mass.

Luce, R. D., 1959. *Individual Choice Behavior*, Wiley, New York.

Luce, R. D., R. R. Bush, and E. Galanter (Eds.), 1963. *Handbook of Mathematical Psychology*, Vol. 1, Wiley, New York.

Luce, R. D. and E. Galanter, 1963. "Discrimination," in R. D. Luce, R. R. Bush, and E. Galanter (Eds.), *Handbook of Mathematical Psychology*, Wiley, New York, pp. 191–243.

Marschak, J., 1960. "Binary-choice constraints and random utility indicators," in K. Arrow, J. Korlin, and P. Suppes (Eds.), *Mathematical Models in Social Sciences*, Stanford University Press, Palo Alto, Calif.

McKeon, J. J., 1960. "Some cyclical incomplete paired comparison designs," *University of North Carolina Psychometric Laboratory Report No. 24*, Chapel Hill.

McKeon, J. J., 1961. "Measurement procedures based on comparative judgment," unpublished doctoral dissertation, University of North Carolina, Chapel Hill.

Mood, A. M. and F. A. Graybill, 1963. *Introduction to the Theory of Statistics*, McGraw-Hill, New York.

Morris, C., and L. V. Jones, 1955. "Value scales and dimensions," *J. Abnormal and Social Psych.* **51**, 523–535.

Mosteller, F., 1951. "Remarks on the method of paired comparisons. III. A test of significance for paired comparisons when equal standard deviation and equal correlations are assumed," *Psychometrika* **16**, 207–218.

Mosteller, R. and C. Youtz, 1961. "Tables of the Freeman-Tukey transformations for the binomial and Poisson distributions," *Biometrika* **48**, 433–440.

Müller, G. E., 1878. *Zur Grundlegung der Psychophysik*, Grieben, Berlin.

Neyman, J., 1949. "Contributions to the theory of the χ^2 test," *Proceedings of the Berkeley Symposium on Mathematical Statistics and Probability*, University of California Press, Berkeley, pp. 239–273.

Noel, J. T., 1964. "Fit of an order effect model for paired comparisons," *University of North Carolina Psychometric Laboratory Report No. 23*, Chapel Hill.

Olkin, I. and J. W. Pratt, 1958. "Unbiased estimation of certain correlation coefficients," *Ann. Math. Stat.* **29**, 210–211.

Peryam, D. R., 1958. "Sensory difference tests," *Flavor Research and Food Acceptance* (Arthur D. Little, Inc.), Reinhold, New York, pp. 47–64.

Plackett, R. L., 1954. "A reduction formula for normal multivariate integrals," *Biometrika* **41**, 351–360.

Rao, C. R., 1952. *Advanced Statistical Methods in Biometric Research*, Wiley, New York.

Rao, C. R., 1965. *Linear Statistical Inference and its Applications*, Wiley, New York.

Reiersøl, O., 1961. "Linear and non-linear comparisons in logit analysis," *Biometrika* **48**, 359–365.

Restle, F., 1961. *Psychology of Judgment and Choice: a Theoretical Essay*, Wiley, New York.

Rimoldi, H. J. A., 1956. "Prediction of scale values for combined stimuli," *Brit. J. Stat. Psych.* **9**, 29–40.

Roy, S. N. and R. Gnanadesiken, 1959. "Some contributions to anova in one or more dimensions. I," *Ann. Math. Stat.* **30**, 304–317.

Roy, S. N. and A. E. Sarhan, 1956. "On inverting a class of patterned matrices," *Biometrika* **43**, 227–231.

Sadacca, R., 1962. "Dimensions of response consistency in paired comparisons," *Research Bulletin 62–14*, Educational Testing Service, Princeton, N.J.

Saffir, M. A., 1937. "A comparative study of scales constructed by three psychophysical methods," *Psychometrika* **2**, 179–198.

Schlaifer, R., 1959. *Probability and Statistics for Business Decisions*, McGraw-Hill, New York.

Schutz, H. G. and F. J. Pilgrim, 1957. "Differential sensitivity in gustation," *J. Exptl. Psych.* **54**, 41–48.

Sheba, C., I. Ashkenazi, and A. Szeinberg, 1962. "Taste sensitivity to phenylthiourea among the Jewish population groups in Israel," *Am. J. Human Genetics* **14**, 44–51.

Shuford, E. H., L. V. Jones, and R. D. Bock, 1960. "A rational origin obtained by the method of contingent paired comparisons," *Psychometrika* **25**, 343–356.

Spearman, C., 1908. "The method of 'right and wrong cases' without Gauss' formulae," *Brit. J. Psych.* **2**, 227–242.

Stevens, S. S., 1951. *Handbook of Experimental Psychology*, Wiley, New York.

Stevens, S. S., 1957. "On the psychophysical law," *Psych. Rev.* **64**, 153–181.

Stevens, S. S., 1959. "Review of L. L. Thurstone, "The measurement of values," *Contemporary Psych.* **4**, 388–389.

Stevens, S. S., 1961. "To honor Fechner and repeal his law," *Science* **133**, 80–86.

Stevens, S. S., 1966. "A metric for the social consensus," *Science* **151**, 530–541.

Stoll, R. R., 1952. *Linear Algebra and Matrix Theory*, McGraw-Hill, New York.

Suppes, P. and J. L. Zinnes, 1963. "Basic measurement theory," in R. D. Luce, R. R. Bush, and E. Galanter (Eds.), *Handbook of Mathematical Psychology*, Vol. 1, Wiley, New York, pp. 1–76.

Thorndike, E. L., 1910. "Handwriting," *Teachers College Record* 11, 1–93.

Thurstone, L. L., 1927a. "A law of comparative judgment," *Psych Rev.* 34, 278–286 (also in Thurstone, 1959, pp. 39–49).

Thurstone, L. L., 1927b. "Psychophysical analysis," *Am. J. Psych.* 38, 368–389 (also in Thurstone, 1959, pp. 19–38).

Thurstone, L. L., 1928. "The phi-gamma hypothesis," *J. Exptl. Psych.* 11, 293–305 (also in Thurstone, 1959, pp. 82–91.)

Thurstone, L. L., 1931a. "Rank order as a psychophysical method," *J. Exptl. Psych.* 14, 182–201 (also in Thurstone, 1959, pp. 100–111).

Thurstone, L. L., 1931b. "The indifference function," *J. Soc. Psych.* 2, 139–167.

Thurstone, L. L., 1945. "The prediction of choice," *Psychometrika* 10, 236–253 (also in Thurstone, 1959, pp. 145–160).

Thurstone, L. L., 1952. "An experiment in the prediction of food preference and the prediction of choice," *Proceedings of the 4th Research Conference, Council on Research, American Meat Institute* (also in Thurstone, 1959, pp. 161–169).

Thurstone, L. L., 1959. *The Measurement of Values*, University of Chicago Press, Chicago, Ill.

Thurstone, L. L. and L. V. Jones, 1957. "The rational origin for measuring subjective values," *J. Am. Stat. Assoc.* 52, 458–471 (also in Thurstone, 1959, pp. 195–210).

Titchener, E. B., 1905. *Experimental Psychology*, Vol. II, Part ii, Macmillan, New York.

Torgerson, W. S., 1958. *Theory and Methods of Scaling*, Wiley, New York.

Uhrbrock, R. D. and M. W. Richardson, 1933. "Item analysis," *Personnel J.* 12, 141–154.

Urban, F. M., 1908. *The Application of Statistical Methods to the Problems of Psychophysics*, Psychological Clinic Press, Philadelphia, Pa.

Wallace, D. L., 1958. "Intersection region confidence procedures with an application to the location of the maximum in quadratic regression," *Ann. Math. Stat.* 29, 457–475.

Wilks, S. S., 1962. *Mathematical Statistics*, Wiley, New York.

Willers, F. A., 1948. *Practical Analysis*, Dover, New York.

Working, H. and H. Hotelling, 1929. "Applications of the theory of error to the interpretation of trends," *J. Am. Stat. Assoc.* 34, 73–85.

Woodworth, R. S., 1938. *Experimental Psychology*, Holt, New York.

Author Index

362

Subject Index

Absolute threshold, 85
  confidence bounds for, 90, 93, 94, 98, 102
  conventional definition, 89
  estimation of, two-sample procedure for, 85
    three-sample procedure for, 99
    minimum normit χ^2, 88, 100
    maximum likelihood, 94, 103
    standard error, 90, 102, 105
    working deviates—Table of 314, 95, 103
    weights—Table of 307, 88, 100
  examples of, 90, 96, 100, 103
  model of, 87, 100
    goodness-of-fit test of, 93, 98, 102, 103
Additivity index, 265, 268
Aesthetics, 116
Affective values, 4, 117
  additivity of, 264, 270
  confidence bounds for, 129, 132, 135
  contrasts of, 129, 135
  estimation of, in the correlated case, 151
    by paired comparisons, 120, 134
    in the presence of order effect, 140
    by rank order, 161

    by successive categories, 219, 220, 225, 232
  multifactor model for, 187
  rational origin for, 265, 270, 275, 277
  transformation of scale for, 133, 269
Angular (arc-sine) deviates, 72, 134
  estimation of, 72
    bias in, 73
    correction for bias, 72
    mean square error, 75
    variance of, 72
  table of, 303
  working deviate, 74
Angular response function, applications of, 134
Associates, first and second, 173
Association scheme, 173, 178

Basis of linear model, 245
  orthonormal, 352
Best Asymptotic Normal (BAN) estimators, 6
Bias, corrections for, 67, 70, 72
Bias in estimator, of angular deviates, 73
  of discriminal precision, 37
  of intercept of response function, 37
  of logistic deviates, 67
  of normal deviates, 21

365